D0909848

McGraw-Hill Series in Nuclear Engineering
Walter H. Zinn, *Consulting Editor*
J. D. Luntz, *Associate Consulting Editor*

---

# NUCLEAR RADIATION DETECTION

McGraw-Hill Series in Nuclear Engineering

Walter H. Zinn, *Consulting Editor*

J. D. Luntz, *Associate Consulting Editor*

---

*Benedict and Pigford* · Nuclear Chemical Engineering

*Bonilla* · Nuclear Engineering

*Etherington* · Nuclear Engineering Handbook

*Price* · Nuclear Radiation Detection

*Schultz* · Control of Nuclear Reactors and Power Plants

*Stephenson* · Nuclear Engineering

# Nuclear Radiation Detection

WILLIAM J. PRICE

*Professor of Physics*
*Air Force Institute of Technology*
*Wright-Patterson Air Force Base, Ohio*

McGRAW-HILL BOOK COMPANY, INC.
*New York Toronto London*
*1958*

NUCLEAR RADIATION DETECTION



Library of Congress Catalog Card Number 57–11865

# PREFACE

There has been a rapid growth in nuclear science and technology during the past decade. To bring this about, many scientists and engineers have pooled their various disciplines and experiences to develop what in many cases have been new and strange gadgets and techniques. Many more technical personnel will be joining this effort in the future.

The detection of nuclear radiation is involved to a certain extent in all nuclear science and technology. While only a few people are called upon to develop new detection methods and equipment, many are continually faced with the application of existing techniques to their own problems. Still a larger group are indirectly but still intimately connected with nuclear-radiation detection because their own responsibilities depend on the correct measurement of nuclear radiation by others.

In this book the attempt has been made to collect the basic information on all the important nuclear-radiation detectors in use today. Included with the description of the detectors is sufficient specific information on applications to enable the reader to select his own detection equipment and, in many cases, to apply it.



Practically all the detection equipment which is discussed in this book is available from commercial sources; the reader is referred to a very comprehensive buyers' guide published annually by *Nucleonics* magazine. Nevertheless, sufficient emphasis has been given to the principles on which the detection systems depend that the book should also prove useful to the reader who desires to design his own equipment.



This book was developed for use in the Nucleonics Instrumentation Course at the Air Force Institute of Technology. This course is given to Air Force officers enrolled in the Nuclear Engineering Curriculum at that Institute. It is hoped that this book will be useful to future students planning to enter the very fascinating field of nuclear science and technology as well as to many of the engineers and scientists presently engaged in these activities.

The author would like to express his thanks for the kind permission to use illustrations and data which has been given to him by many editors and scientists. The author would also like to express deep gratitude to his colleagues and students who have helped in various ways in the preparation of this book, to W. H. Jordan of Oak Ridge National Laboratory who read an earlier manuscript and offered many valuable criticisms and suggestions, to Miss Beulah McCray and others for their painstaking efforts in typing the manuscript, and to his wife, Betty N. Price, for her encouragement and able assistance.

*William J. Price*

## CONTENTS

CHAPTER 1

# PROPERTIES OF NUCLEAR RADIATION

The study of nuclear-radiation detection requires an understanding of the interaction of radiation with matter. This first chapter covers the essential aspects of that subject.

Nuclear radiation emanates from systems undergoing nuclear transformations, from particle accelerators, and as cosmic rays from outer space. This emanation includes subatomic and atomic particles as well as X and gamma rays. In Table 1–1 the common types of nuclear radiations are listed, along with several of their more important properties.

There are several obvious omissions from Table 1–1. One is the long list

TABLE 1–1. SOME CHARACTERISTICS OF NUCLEAR RADIATION

| Type of Particle | Symbol | Charge (relative) | Approximate rest mass (relative) | Rest mass, amu |
|---|---|---|---|---|
| Neutron | n | 0 | 1 | 1.008982 |
| Proton | p | 1 | 1 | 1.007593 |
| Deuteron | d | 1 | 2 | 2.014187 |
| Triton | t | 1 | 3 | 3.01645 |
| Alpha particle | $\alpha$ | 2 | 4 | 4.002777 |
| Positron* | $\beta^+$, $e^+$ | 1 | 1/1,840 | 0.000549 |
| Electrons or beta particles† | $\beta^-$, $e^-$ | −1 | 1/1,840 | 0.000549 |
| $\mu$ meson | $\mu$ | ±1 | 210/1,840 | 0.115 |
| $\pi$ meson | $\pi$ | ±1 | 276/1,840 | 0.152 |
| Gamma ray‡ | $\gamma$ | | | |
| X ray‡ | X | | | |
| Neutrino | $\eta$ | 0 | Small or zero | ? |
| Fission fragments, average light | ... | ~20 | ~95 | |
| Fission fragments, average heavy | ... | ~22 | ~139 | |

* The first symbol is used when the radiations are emitted from nuclei; this is sometimes referred to as beta-plus emission. The second symbol refers to the same particles when they occur in other connections.

† The term beta minus and the symbol $\beta^-$ refer to electrons emitted from nuclei; usually these are called simply beta ($\beta$) particles.

‡ Gamma and X rays differ only in their origins; the former originate in the nucleus while the latter do not.

of particles of a more transient nature, such as neutral $\pi$ mesons, $\tau$ mesons, $\kappa$ mesons, and $V$ particles. A discussion of the properties of these particles is beyond the scope of this book. However, the detection of this class of radiation is based on the principles covered in this text. Of the particles with atomic number greater than 2, only fission products are entered in Table 1–1. The omissions include those heavy particles which are given energy in modern particle accelerators and which are found as components of cosmic radiation.

The nature of the interactions with matter varies between the different types of nuclear radiation. In this discussion certain types are taken as prototypes and are discussed in detail. The properties of other types of radiation are then obtained from those of the prototype to which they are the most similar. The criteria for determining similarity are primarily charge and mass when the interest is in such properties as absorption. However, one should not overlook the fact that particles belonging to a given prototype may differ greatly in such important properties as spin and magnetic moment.

The radiations which have been selected here for the prototypes are alpha particles, fission fragments, electrons, gamma rays, and neutrons.

## PROPERTIES OF ALPHA PARTICLES

### 1–1. *Alpha Particles as a Prototype*

The rate of energy loss of charged particles in passing through matter is shown in the next section to depend on the mass and the charge of particles. In the group of particle types consisting of alphas, tritons, deuterons, and protons, the masses differ by no more than a factor of 4, and the charges differ only by a factor of 2. Consequently, the ranges of these several particles can be related accurately. In addition, mesons may be included in this group; however, the large mass differences decrease the accuracy of the relationships.

Over a period of many years, extensive measurements have been made of alpha-particle ranges. These particles are emitted by radioactive nuclei and were among the first radiation types available. The energy with which these particles are emitted is dependent on the radioactive species, ranging up to about 10 Mev. In addition, alpha particles can be accelerated in several types of particle accelerators and are available with energies up to several hundred Mev.

### 1–2. *Absorption of Alpha Particles*

When alpha particles pass through absorbers, they lose energy by excitation and ionization of the absorber atoms. The mechanism which is mainly responsible for this energy loss is the interaction of the Coulomb fields of the particle with those of the bound electrons of the absorber. Because of the relative masses of the particles involved, the deflections of the alpha particles are negligible.

Two other processes occur by which alpha particles can be absorbed or removed from a beam of collimated alpha particles. These are nuclear transmutation and scattering by atomic nuclei. However, the contribution of these processes to the attenuation of a beam of alpha particles is negligible compared with that of the excitation and ionization processes.

Calculations of the charged-particle energy loss due to ionization and excitation have been made by Livingston and Bethe [1]. The energy loss per unit path, $dE/dx$, is known as the stopping power of the material. It can be expressed as

$$-\frac{dE}{dx} = \frac{4\pi e^4 z^2 ZNB}{mv^2} \qquad (1\text{–}1)$$

where $E$, $ze$, and $v$ = kinetic energy, charge, velocity, respectively, of primary particle
$N$ = no. of absorber atoms per $cm^3$
$Z$ = atomic no. of absorber
$B$ = stopping number

The symbols $e$ and $m$ have the usual meanings of the electronic charge and the electronic mass, respectively.

The stopping number $B$ is a logarithmic function of $v$ and $Z$ in the nonrelativistic energy range. Therefore, in this range, $dE/dx$ depends on the particle velocity primarily through the $1/v^2$ term. The increase in the rate of energy loss with the decrease in velocity is to be expected because of the increase in the time required for the alpha particle to pass the bound electrons; this results in a larger impulse on the electrons and a larger probability for excitation and ionization.

Equation (1–1) breaks down for alpha particles when energies as low as 0.1 Mev are reached. This breakdown occurs because the velocity of the particles becomes so low that their charges fluctuate, owing to the alternate capture and loss of electrons. There is no theoretical expression for $dE/dx$ in this region.

The dependence of the rate of energy loss on the atomic number of the absorber is primarily through the term outside the logarithmic function $B$. Thus, for a constant velocity, $dE/dx$ is nearly proportional to $NZ$, the electron density in the absorber.

In the relativistic range of particle energy, $dE/dx$ passes through a minimum which is followed by a slow increase with increasing particle energy. This is illustrated in Fig. 1–1, where the energy loss per centimeter of path in air is plotted for several particle types over a wide range of energy.

The status of the investigations of the stopping power of various materials has been reviewed by Allison and Warshaw [2]. The review contains values of $dE/dx$ in several solids and gases; data for alpha particles and a number of similar particles are included.

The absorption of alpha particles may be studied experimentally by measuring the number of ion pairs produced per unit path length; this quantity is known as the specific ionization. The energy loss is related to the ionization through the quantity $w$ which is the ratio of the energy lost by a charged particle to the total ionization produced by it. Values of $w$

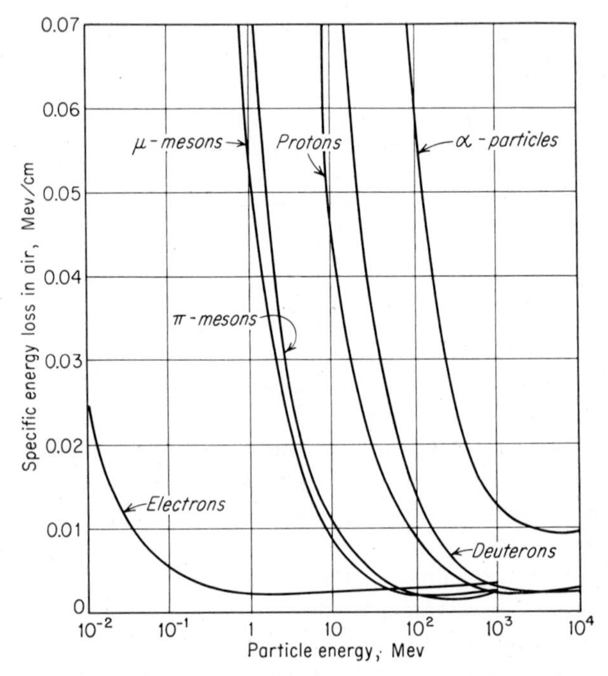


FIG. 1–1. Specific energy loss of various particles in air as a function of energy. [*From A. Beiser, Revs. Mod. Phys.*, **24**:273 (1952).]

have been found to depend on a number of factors, including the absorber material, particle type, and particle energy. This dependence has been reviewed by Uehling [3]. However, all values for gases appear to lie in a range from about 25 to 50 ev per ion pair. A number of different values of $w$ for various conditions are collected in Table 1–2. An additional compilation of values of $w$ appears in the review article by Bethe and Ashkin [4]. For condensed media, $w$ is about 5 ev per ion pair.

The energy loss by a particle in the production of an ion pair in a gas is considerably in excess of that required only to ionize the atom. The addi-

TABLE 1–2. ENERGY LOSS PER ION PAIR*

| Gas | $w$, ev | Particle | Energy, Mev |
|---|---|---|---|
| Air | 32.0† | Electron | >0.3 |
| Air | 36.0 | Proton | 2.5–7.5 |
| Air | 35.1 | Alpha | 7.8 |
| Air | 35.6 | Alpha | 5.3 |
| Hydrogen | 36.0 | Alpha | 5.3 |
| Helium | 31.0 | Alpha | 5.3 |

* From L. H. Gray, *Proc. Cambridge Phil. Soc.*, **40**:72 (1944).

† The recommendation that $w$ be taken as 34 ev is made in the publication Report of the International Commission on Radiological Units and Measurements (ICRU) 1956, *Natl. Bur. Standards (U.S.) Handbook* 62, 1957.

tional energy goes into the dissociation of the gas molecules and the excitation of the atoms and molecules.

**Example 1–1.** Compute the charge of either sign which is released in an air ionization chamber by a 5-Mev alpha particle if it dissipates its entire energy in the air of the chamber.

*Solution.* The total number of ion pairs produced is

$$\frac{E}{w} = \frac{5 \times 10^6}{35.6} = (1.41 \times 10^5) \text{ ion pairs}$$

The value of $w$ given in Table 1–2 for 5.3-Mev alpha particles has been used. The charge which is released is

$$\frac{Ee}{w} = (1.41 \times 10^5)(1.60 \times 10^{-19}) = (2.25 \times 10^{-14}) \text{ coulomb}$$

A plot of the specific ionization versus the particle energy is known as the Bragg curve. Figure 1–2 is a Bragg curve for alpha particles. In this

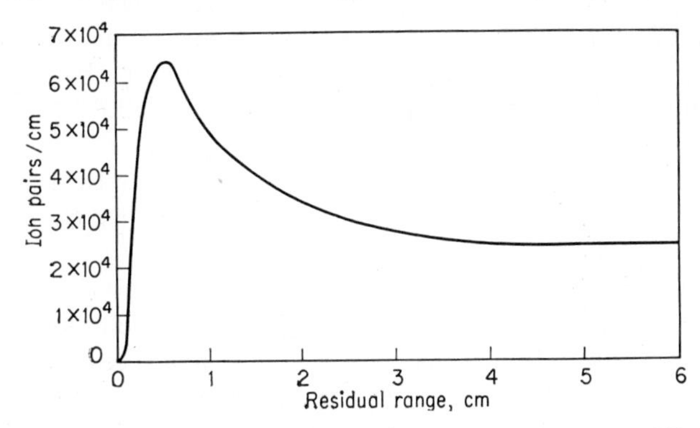


FIG. 1–2. Bragg curve for specific ionization in air at 15°C and 760 mm Hg.

curve the residual range of the particles in air is used as a measure of the particle energy.

## 1–3. *Range of Alpha Particles*

Alpha particles which are initially monoenergetic all are found to travel nearly the same distance in a given medium before coming to rest. This can be studied experimentally through the use of a collimated beam of alpha particles from a thin radioactive source. A thin source is one in which the loss of energy within the source is negligible. Measurements of the number of particles reaching a given distance versus the distance result in curves similar to those in Fig. 1–3. The ordinate of the integral curve is the

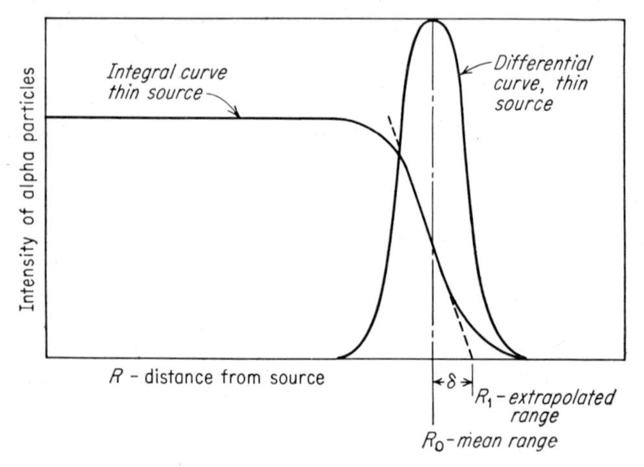


FIG. 1–3. Integral and differential range-distribution curves for alpha particles.

number of alpha particles per unit time which travel the distance $R$ from the source or farther. The ordinate of the differential curve multiplied by $dR$ is the number per unit time which have paths ending between the distances $R$ and $R + dR$ from the source. The differential curve is Gaussian in form, with its maximum occurring at the mean range $R_0$ of the particles. The range $R_1$, which is obtained from the integral curve by a straight-line extrapolation from the point on the curve determined by $R_0$, is known as the extrapolated range.

The variation in the ranges of monoenergetic particles arises because of the statistical nature of the process by which the particles lose their energies. The energy loss occurs in a large but finite number of events. There are fluctuations in both the energy lost per event and the number of events per unit path length. Consequently there is a statistical fluctuation in the range of the particles.

The difference between the extrapolated and the mean ranges is referred to as the straggling and is designated as $\delta$. The straggling amounts to about 1 per cent of the total range for 5-Mev alpha particles [3].

Extensive measurements have been made of the range-energy relationship of alpha particles in air. These results are commonly expressed with the normal conditions of temperature and pressure taken as 15°C and 760 mm Hg, respectively. Figures 1–4 and 1–5 show these relationships for the energy ranges of 0 to 8 Mev and 8 to 15 Mev, respectively.

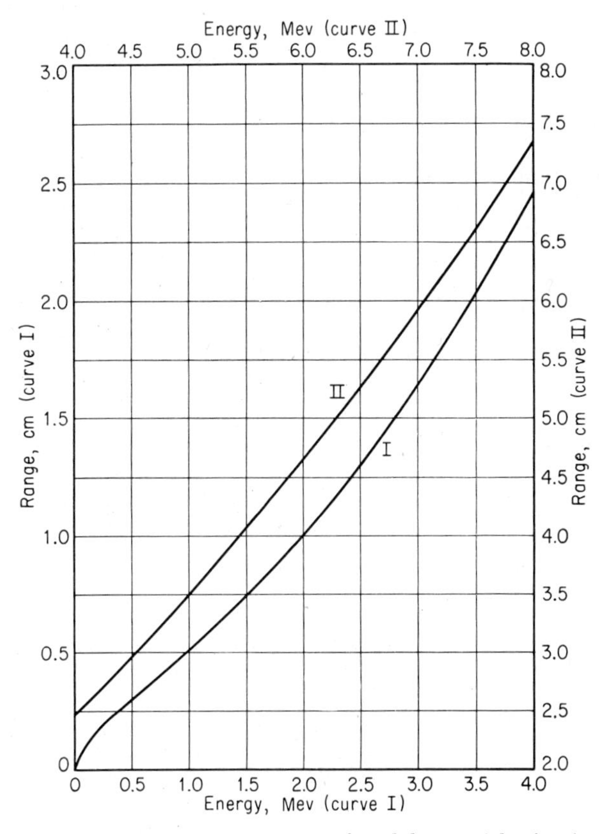


FIG. 1–4. Range-energy curves for alpha particles in air (15°C, 760 mm); energy range, 0 to 8 Mev. (*From H. A. Bethe, U.S. Atomic Energy Comm. Document BNL-T-7, 1949.*)

Empirical equations have been developed to relate the range in air and the energy of alpha particles. One such equation which fits with fair accuracy in the range from 4 to 7 Mev is

$$R = 0.309E^{3/2} \tag{1-2}$$

where $R$ is the mean range in centimeters at normal conditions and $E$ is the alpha-particle energy in Mev. At lower energies the dependence on energy is more nearly proportional to $E^{3/4}$, while at higher energies an $E^2$ dependence fits better.

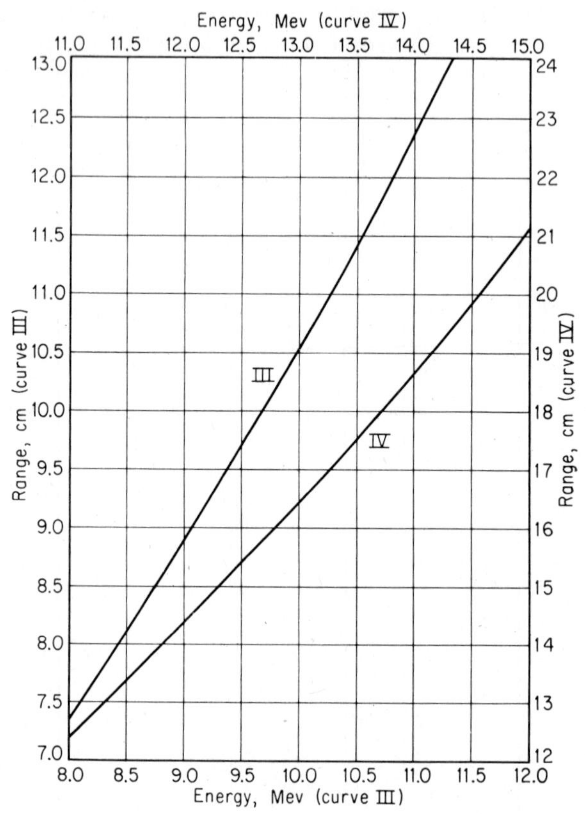


FIG. 1–5. Range-energy curves for alpha particles in air (15°C, 760 mm); energy range, 8 to 15 Mev. (*From H. A. Bethe, U.S. Atomic Energy Comm. Document BNL-T-7, 1949.*)

## 1–4. *Absorption in Substances Other Than Air*

Extensive studies, both experimental and theoretical, have been made of the range-energy relationships of heavy particles in a variety of substances. Taylor [6] has reviewed the status of these investigations.

The range of heavy particles in materials other than air can be calculated through the use of the theoretical formula of Livingston and Bethe [1]. An extensive compilation of such curves has been made by Aron, Hoffman, and Williams [7]. More recently, Rich and Madey [8] have extended this work.

An empirical formula which allows the calculation of the range $R_A$ of alpha particles in a material of atomic weight $A$ is

$$R_A(\mathrm{mg/cm^2}) = 0.56R(\mathrm{cm})A^{1/3} \tag{1-3}$$

where $R$ is the range, expressed in centimeters, of the alpha particle in air at 15°C and 760 mm Hg. The range in the material, expressed in centimeters, is obtained by dividing $R_A$ by $10^3\rho$, where $\rho$ is the density of the material in grams per cubic centimeter. Table 1–3 contains a comparison of the values of Aron, Hoffman, and Williams and those calculated from Eq. (1–3). It is seen that the agreement is reasonably good, particularly below 10 Mev.

TABLE 1–3. RANGE OF ALPHA PARTICLES IN VARIOUS SUBSTANCES

| Range in air, cm | Energy in Mev | Range in Al, mg/cm² | | Range in Cu, mg/cm² | | Range in Ag, mg/cm² | | Range in Pb, mg/cm² | |
|---|---|---|---|---|---|---|---|---|---|
| | | Eq. (1–3) | Ref. 7 | Eq. (1–3) | Ref. 7 | Eq. (1–3) | Ref. 7 | Eq. (1–3) | Ref. 7 |
| 1 | 2 | 1.7 | 1.5 | 2.2 | ..... | 2.7 | ..... | 3.3 | 3.7 |
| 2 | 3.5 | 3.4 | 3.1 | 4.4 | ..... | 5.4 | ..... | 6.6 | 6.7 |
| 5 | 6.3 | 8.4 | 7.6 | 11.2 | 10.4 | 13.4 | 11.5 | 16.6 | 18.0 |
| 10 | 9.7 | 17 | 14.8 | 22 | 20.2 | 27 | 24.3 | 33 | 34.5 |
| 100 | 37 | 168 | 140 | 224 | 185 | 268 | 220 | 332 | 303 |
| 1,000 | 132 | 1,680 | 1,400 | 2,240 | 1,700 | 2,680 | 2,000 | 3,320 | 2,500 |

**Example 1–2.** Calculate the minimum energy which an alpha particle can have and still be counted with a Geiger-Müller tube if the tube window is stainless steel with 2-mg/cm² thickness.

*Solution.* To be counted, the particle must pass through the tube window. Substituting 56 as the effective atomic weight of steel into Eq. (1–3), the range of the alpha particle in air at standard temperature and pressure is

$$R(\mathrm{cm}) = \frac{R_A}{0.56A^{1/3}} = \frac{2}{(0.56)(56)^{1/3}} = 0.94 \text{ cm}$$

This range is seen by Fig. 1–4 to be that of a 1.9-Mev alpha particle.

The ranges of particles in various materials can be related to those in air through the concept of relative stopping power. The relative stopping power $S$ of a material is the ratio of its stopping power to that of air. The stopping power may be expressed either as the energy loss per unit path length or as the energy loss per unit of thickness expressed in mass per unit area. The corresponding relative stopping powers are designated as the relative linear stopping power $S_L$ and the relative mass stopping power $S_m$, respectively. The average values of $S_L$ and $S_m$ are listed in Table 1–4 for several metals at different alpha-particle energies. Again the range data on which this table is based are those of Aron, Hoffman, and Williams [7].

It is seen that these quantities are dependent on energy and consequently can yield only a very approximate answer unless this energy dependence is taken into account.

It is seen from the values of relative mass stopping power presented in

TABLE 1-4. RELATIVE STOPPING POWERS OF VARIOUS SUBSTANCES FOR ALPHA PARTICLES

| Particle energy, Mev | Range in air, cm | Aluminum $\rho = 2.7$ g/cm³ | | Copper $\rho = 8.9$ g/cm³ | | Lead $\rho = 11.0$ g/cm³ | |
|---|---|---|---|---|---|---|---|
| | | $S_L$ | $S_m$ | $S_L$ | $S_m$ | $S_L$ | $S_m$ |
| 2.0 | 1 | 1,800 | 0.80 | ..... | ..... | 2,900 | 0.32 |
| 6.3 | 5 | 1,780 | 0.79 | 4,300 | 0.58 | 3,050 | 0.33 |
| 9.7 | 10 | 1,820 | 0.81 | 4,400 | 0.59 | 3,200 | 0.35 |
| 37 | 100 | 1,940 | 0.86 | 4,800 | 0.65 | 3,600 | 0.39 |

Table 1-4 that the energy loss per unit of thickness expressed in mass per unit area decreases with an increase in the atomic number of the absorber. This decrease in the absorption is due largely to the increase in the average binding energy of the orbital electrons and shows up as a decrease in $B$ in Eq. (1-1). An additional factor is the decrease in the number of orbital electrons per unit mass of the absorber.

**Example 1-3.** Compute the range of a 6-Mev alpha particle in lead.

*Solution.* By Fig. 1-4, a 6-Mev alpha particle has a range of 4.66 cm in air. By Table 1-4, the value of $S_L$ for a 6.3-Mev alpha in lead is 3,050. Therefore, the range of the particle in lead is

$$R_{\text{Pb}} = \frac{R_{\text{air}}}{S_L} = \frac{4.66}{3{,}050} = (1.5 \times 10^{-3}) \text{ cm}$$

## 1-5. *Scaling Laws for Ranges of Similar Particles*

When the range-energy relationship is known for one type of particle in a given substance, it is possible to calculate the corresponding relationship for a different type of particle in the same substance. This calculation is made possible by the form of Eq. (1-1). The distance $R_{zM}(E_1 \rightarrow E_2)$ which a particle of mass $M$ and charge $ze$ travels while its energy decreases from $E_1$ to $E_2$ is

$$R_{zM}(E_1 \rightarrow E_2) = -\int_{E_2}^{E_1} \frac{dE}{dE/dx} = \frac{Mm}{4\pi e^4 z^2 ZN} \int_{v_2}^{v_1} \frac{v^3\, dv}{B(v)} \qquad (1\text{-}4)$$

where Eq. (1-1) has been used along with the relationship $E = Mv^2/2$. If the final velocity $v_2$ is taken as zero, one can write

$$R_{zM}(v) = Mz^{-2}F(v) \qquad (1\text{-}5)$$

where $F(v)$ is essentially the integral in Eq. (1–4) evaluated between the limits 0 to $v$. Equation (1–5) states that for different types of fast particles in a given absorber the range depends only upon the particle speed, its mass $M$, and its charge $z$.

By using Eq. (1–5), one can relate $R_p(v)$, the range of a proton of velocity $v$, to $R_\alpha(v)$, the range of an alpha particle of the same velocity; that is,

$$R_p(v) = \frac{M_p z_\alpha^2}{M_\alpha z_p^2} R_\alpha(v) - C \tag{1–6}$$

where the constant $C$ must be used to take account of the capture and loss of electrons at low energy. Although the constant $C$ is small, it is not zero, because alpha particles are affected differently from protons. For air at normal temperature and pressure, $C$ has been found experimentally to be 0.20 cm when the energy is greater than about 500 kev. It gradually decreases to 0.02 cm at 6.7 kev [9]. Thus, for air at energies above 500 kev,

$$R_p(v) = 1.007R_\alpha(v) - 0.20 \text{ cm} \tag{1–7}$$

Since for equal velocities the energies are related in the nonrelativistic case by $E_p = E_\alpha M_p/M_\alpha$, one can write

$$R_p(E) = 1.007R_\alpha(3.972E) - 0.20 \text{ cm} \tag{1–8}$$

where $R_\alpha(3.972E)$ means the range of the alpha particle evaluated at $3.972E$.

The range-energy relationship for a particle of a given $z$ can be obtained readily from that of a particle of different type but the same $z$. Since the capture and loss of electrons near the end of the range are the same for both types of particles, the correction term $C$ disappears. Therefore the range of a particle of mass $M$ can be calculated from that of mass $M_0$ when the charge is the same by the relationship

$$R_{zM}(E) = \frac{M}{M_0} R_{zM_0}(E') \tag{1–9}$$

where $E' = EM_0/M$.

The range of deuterons in air is shown in Fig. 1–6 for a large energy range. Through the use of Figs. 1–4 to 1–6 along with the scaling laws and the information in Sec. 1–4, it is possible to calculate the range-energy relationships for a number of different particle types in a large variety of substances.

**Example 1–4.** Use the information contained in the preceding sections to find the range of 10-Mev protons in air at standard conditions and in lead.

*Solution.* By Eq. (1–9) the range of a 10-Mev proton is obtained from that of a 19.9-Mev deuteron. Values of the latter for air appear in Fig. 1–6. Accordingly,

$$R_p(10 \text{ Mev}) = \frac{M_p}{M_d} R_d\left(\frac{M_d}{M_p} 10 \text{ Mev}\right) = \frac{1.008}{2.014} R_d(19.9 \text{ Mev})$$
$$= 115 \text{ cm of air}$$

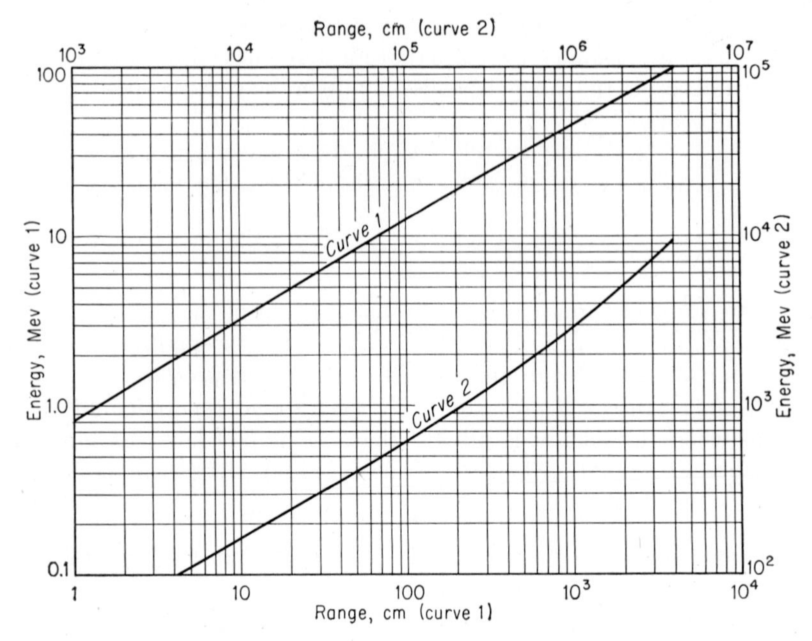


FIG. 1–6. Range-energy curves for deuterons in air (15°C, 760 mm); energy range, 1 to $10^5$ Mev. (*From W. A. Aron, B. G. Hoffman, and F. C. Williams, U.S. Atomic Energy Comm. Document AECU*-663, 1949.)

The range of deuterons in lead is not available. However, the range of alphas in lead can be computed from Eq. (1–3), and the range of the protons can be obtained from that of the alphas by Eq. (1–6). The range in air of an alpha with the same velocity as a 10-Mev proton is, by Eq. (1–7),

$$R_\alpha(v) = \frac{R_p(v) + C}{1.007} = \frac{115 + 0.2}{1.007} = 114 \text{ cm}$$

By Eq. (1–3), the range of the same-energy alpha in lead is

$$R_\alpha \text{ (mg/cm}^2) = (0.56)\ (114)\ (207)^{1/3} = 378 \text{ mg/cm}^2$$

Applying Eq. (1–6) again and neglecting $C$ lead to

$$\text{Range of 10-Mev proton in lead} = (378)\ (1.007) = 380 \text{ mg/cm}^2$$

(NOTE. A more accurate value is 340 mg/cm².)

## FISSION FRAGMENTS

### 1–6. *Penetration of Fission Products through Matter*

Fission fragments contain elements of mass numbers from approximately 72 to 160. However, the yield curve is found to have two predominant maxima. The group around the maximum of lowest mass number is referred to as the "light fragment," while the other group is known as the "heavy fragment."

In Table 1–5 some of the properties of the fission products of $U^{235}$ are given. These properties apply to the average fission product of each of the two fragments.

TABLE 1–5. AVERAGE PROPERTIES OF $U^{235}$ FISSION PRODUCTS

| Property | Light group | Heavy group |
|---|---|---|
| Mass number | ~95 | ~139 |
| Atomic number | ~38 | ~54 |
| Initial net charge | ~+20$e$ | ~+22$e$ |
| Initial energy, Mev | 97 | 65 |
| Range in air at NTP*, mm | 27 | 21 |

* NTP is an abbreviation for normal temperature and pressure, that is, 15°C and 760 mm Hg, respectively.

The net charge of a fission product decreases continually during the slowing-down process. In this respect, its properties are different from those of an alpha particle. Another factor that distinguishes the absorption of fission products from alpha particles is the relative importance of energy loss by nuclear collisions and that by collisions with electrons of the absorber. In the absorption of alpha particles, the contribution of the nuclear collisions is negligible. However, for the absorption of fission products, the nuclear collisions become important because of the increased nuclear charge.

Calculation of the range of fission products is complicated by the decrease of the net charge of the particles and by the nuclear collisions. Some calculations which have been carried out have been reviewed by Bethe and Ashkin [4]. Experimental measurements of the range of fission products in air versus their mass numbers are shown in Fig. 1–7.

## ABSORPTION OF ELECTRONS

### 1–7. *Penetration of Electrons through Matter*

Electrons which are emitted from nuclei in radioactive decay are known as beta-minus, or simply beta, particles. Beams of energetic electrons may be produced by accelerating electrons in various particle accelerators. When other types of radiations, such as gamma rays, pass through matter, energetic electrons are released; these particles are referred to as secondary electrons.

The interactions of positrons and electrons with matter will be discussed jointly because of their similarity. Positrons may be emitted in radioactive-decay processes; these particles are known sometimes as beta-plus particles. The other primary source of positrons is in the pair-production process. In this reaction a high-energy gamma ray disappears, and in its place two particles, a positron and an electron, appear.

Upon coming to rest, a positron combines with an electron, and the pair is annihilated; the mass energy of the particles is converted into two photons. These photons, which are referred to as annihilation radiation, have 0.51 Mev of energy each and travel in opposite directions.

The usual fate of electrons is not annihilation, because the number of positrons available for sharing in the process is usually quite small compared with the number of electrons. Rather, the electron, upon coming to rest, generally becomes a part of the total electron population in the material.

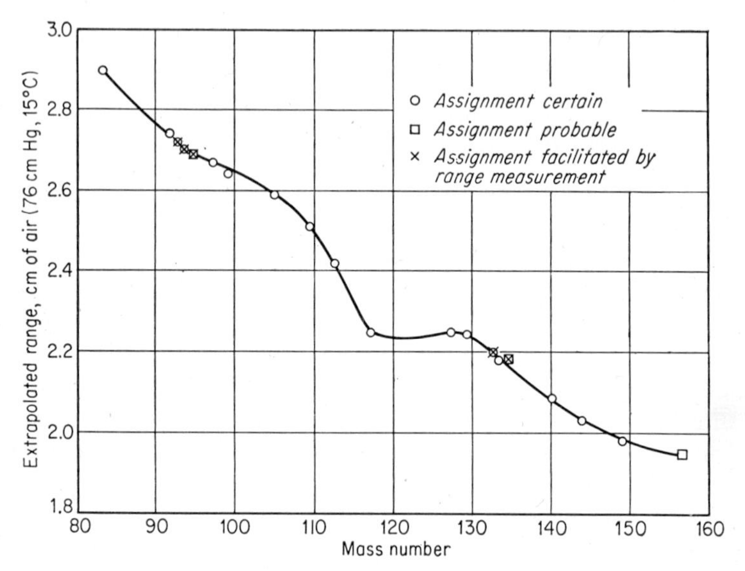


FIG. 1-7. Range versus mass number for fission fragments from $Pu^{239}$. [*From S. Kateoff, J. A. Miskel, and C. W. Stanley, Phys. Rev.,* **74**:631 (1948).]

Electrons differ from alpha particles and other heavy particles in that they are not characterized by straight-line paths and definite ranges. Rather, the electron paths are quite tortuous, and the ranges of monoenergetic electrons vary greatly. The crooked paths are due to the multiple scattering with atoms along the paths. Scattering may take place in collisions with the orbital electrons or with the nuclei of the absorbing material.

The variation in the ranges of monoenergetic electrons is due primarily to the crooked paths followed by the particles. In this regard, the range of the particle is considered to be the thickness of the absorber through which it can just penetrate. In addition, the total path length, as might be measured along a cloud-chamber picture, is found to have 10 to 15 per cent straggling. The reason for this is that individual electrons may lose up to one-half of their energies in a single collision with another electron. This is to be contrasted with the maximum fractional energy loss per collision of $4m/M$ for heavy particles of mass $M$. In the case of the electron-electron collision, the one retaining the largest energy is the electron which is followed farther through the material.

Electrons lose energy to the absorbers by excitation and ionization of the bound electrons in the absorber just as do heavy particles. However, for electrons there is another important mechanism for the loss of energy; this is through the emission of electromagnetic radiation. This radiation is often referred to as *bremsstrahlung*.

### 1–8. *Energy Loss of Electrons through Inelastic Collisions*

The absorption of electrons, through the inelastic collisions leading to excitation and ionization, follows Eq. (1–1); however, the term $B$ differs somewhat from that for heavy particles. For energies up to nearly 0.5 Mev, $B$ is approximately constant, so that $(dE/dx)_c$, the rate of energy loss due to collision, is given by

$$\left(\frac{dE}{dx}\right)_c \sim \frac{1}{v^2} \tag{1–10}$$

where $v$ is the particle velocity. The rate of energy loss passes through a minimum at about 1 Mev; above approximately 3 Mev it rises slowly as the logarithm of $E$. The rate of energy loss, $(dE/dx)_c$, is proportional to the specific ionization $I_m$; that is,

$$\left(\frac{dE}{dx}\right)_c = wI_m \tag{1–11}$$

where $w$ is the energy loss per ion pair formed, or about 32.5 ev for electrons in air.

Measurements of the specific ionization at various energies have been made by cloud-chamber techniques. These experiments confirm the general predictions of the theory for the rate of energy loss by collisions. Data on the specific ionization in air are presented in Fig. 1–8. In the primary-ionization process, the electrons which are released are often given large energies and therefore produce additional, or secondary, ionization while dissipating this energy. The paths of the secondary electrons are known as delta tracks. The total ionization is the sum of the primary and the secondary ionization.

The specific ionizations presented in Fig. 1–8 for the primary and total ionizations pass through minima of 21 and 42 ion pairs per centimeter, respectively. These values are 10 to 20 per cent lower than the ones which are often quoted. However, these low values appear to have the best experimental confirmation.

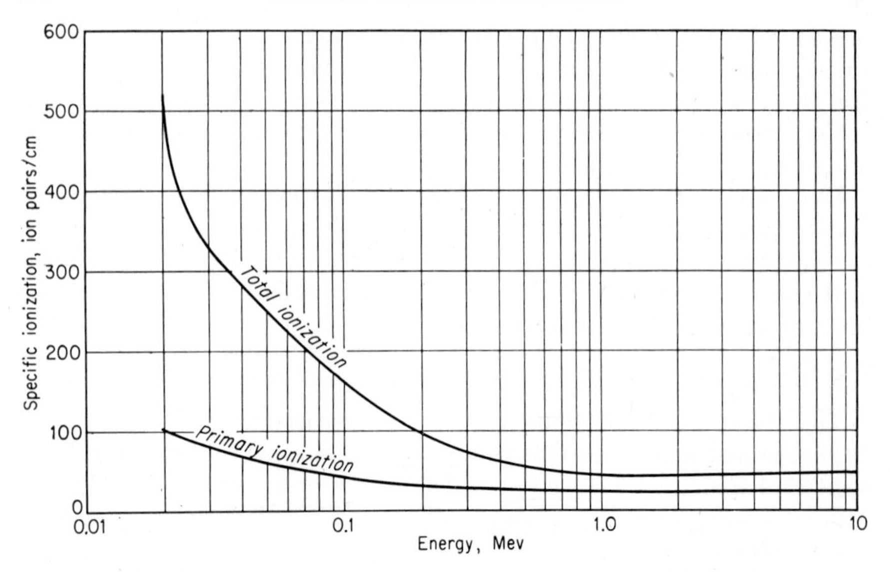


FIG. 1–8. Specific ionization versus energy for electrons in air (15°C, 760 mm). (*Data from D. H. Wilkinson, "Ionization Chambers and Counters," Cambridge University Press, London,* 1950.)

## 1–9. *Radiative Losses for Electrons*

According to the classical electromagnetic theory, a charge which undergoes an acceleration $a$ emits radiant energy at a rate $2e^2a^2/3c^3$. An electron in the Coulomb field of a nucleus can experience a large acceleration by virtue of its small mass, the acceleration being proportional to the nuclear charge $Z$ divided by the electron mass.

Theory predicts [10] that $(dE/dx)_r$, the rate of energy loss due to radiation, should follow the relationship

$$\left(\frac{dE}{dx}\right)_r \sim Z^2EN \tag{1–12}$$

where $Z$ and $N$ are the atomic number and the atomic density, respectively, of the absorber and $E$ is the electron energy. The ratio of radiative and collision losses is

$$\frac{(dE/dx)_r}{(dE/dx)_c} = \frac{EZ}{800} \tag{1–13}$$

where $E$ is expressed in Mev. Thus, in lead at 10 Mev, the two mechanisms contribute equally to the loss of energy, and above 10 Mev the radiative loss rapidly becomes the predominant factor.

The acceleration of a particle is inversely proportional to its mass. Therefore *bremsstrahlung* does not become important in the energy loss of heavy particles until the Bev energy range is reached. At these energies the particles can approach the scattering nuclei more closely and thereby experience larger forces which compensate for the increased mass.

## 1–10. *Ranges of Electrons*

The range of particles through absorbers may be investigated by the determination of absorption curves. Figure 1–3 is an example of such a curve for alpha particles. It is seen that it is possible to assign a rather definite range to a heavy particle of a given energy.

Figure 1–9 illustrates absorption curves for collimated beams of monoenergetic electrons and of beta particles with a continuous energy distribution.

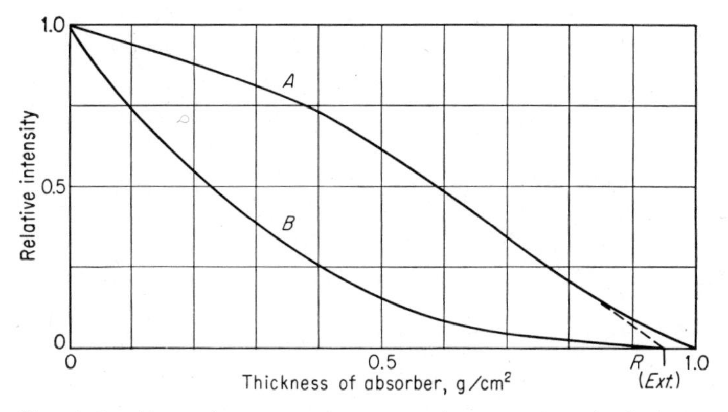


FIG. 1–9. Absorption curves for, curve $A$, monoenergetic electrons (1.9 Mev) and, curve $B$, beta particles with continuous energy spectrum ($E_{\max} = 1.9$ Mev).

The majority of the particles are scattered from the beam. The electrons travel the maximum perpendicular distance through the absorber in only the most favorable cases.

An absorption curve for monoenergetic electrons is found to have a linear portion. If this linear portion is extrapolated to zero, as is done in Fig. 1–9, this extrapolated range is found to be characteristic of a given energy particle and is usually taken as the range of the electrons.

For continuous spectra of electrons, the range is quite indeterminant from plots such as Fig. 1–9. However, methods have been devised by which range values can be calculated from the absorption data. In one such method, known as Feather's comparison method [11], the range in the unknown substance is determined by comparing its absorption curve with that of a substance with known range.

Numerous measurements of range versus energy of electrons have been made. In Fig. 1–10 the results of Glendenin [12] are presented. Empirical equations expressing these results are

$$\begin{aligned} R &= 0.542E - 0.133 \qquad 0.8 < E < 3 \text{ Mev} \\ R &= 0.407E^{1.38} \qquad 0.15 < E < 0.8 \text{ Mev} \end{aligned} \tag{1–14}$$

where $R$ is the range in grams per square centimeter and $E$ is the electron energy in Mev.

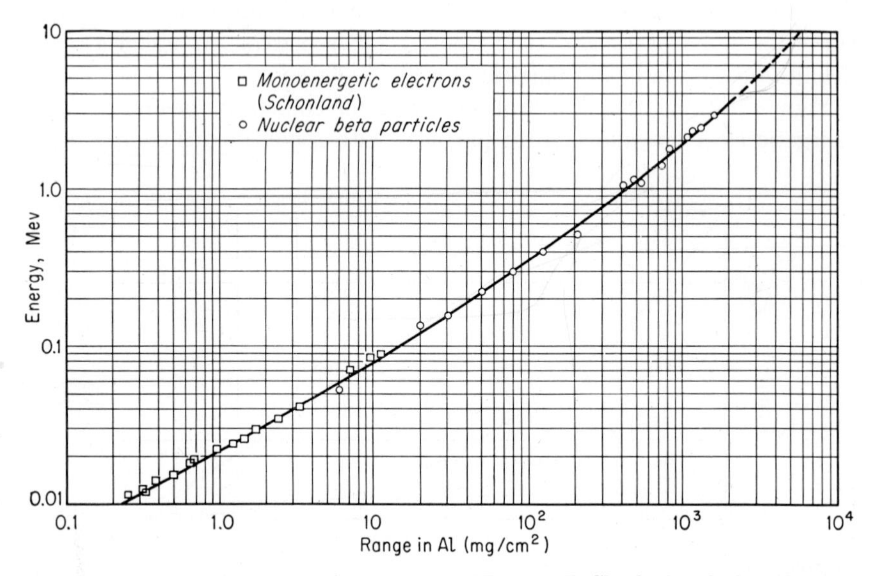


FIG. 1–10. Range-energy curve for electrons. [*From L. E. Glendenin, Nucleonics,* 2:12 (*January,* 1948).]

A large portion of the absorption curve for a specific beta-particle source can be represented by an exponential curve of the form

$$\text{Relative intensity} = e^{-\mu_m d} \tag{1–15}$$

where $\mu_m$ is the mass absorption coefficient in square centimeters per gram and $d$ is the absorber thickness in grams per square centimeter. An empirical relation which gives approximate values for the mass absorption coefficient is

$$\mu_m = \frac{22}{{E_m}^{1.33}} \tag{1–16}$$

where $E_m$ is the maximum energy of the beta emitter in Mev. This expression fails at the lower energies ($E_m < 0.5$ Mev) and at the very high energies ($E_m > 6$ Mev).

The fact that the absorption curve of a beta emitter follows an exponential curve is apparently fortuitous. The distribution in energy of the beta emitter combined with the absorption characteristic for each energy leads to the exponential function.

**Example 1–5.** The beta particles from a $P^{32}$ source are counted by means of a Geiger-Müller tube having a wall thickness of 30 mg/cm². Estimate the fraction of the particles which is absorbed while passing into the tube.

*Solution.* The fraction which is absorbed is obtained from Eq. (1–15) as

$$\text{Fraction absorbed} = 1 - e^{-\mu_m d} = 1 - e^{-(10.7)(30 \times 10^{-3})} = 0.27$$

where

$$\mu_m = \frac{22}{E_m^{1.33}} = \frac{22}{(1.71)^{1.33}} = 10.7 \text{ cm}^2/\text{g}$$

The range of electrons expressed in terms of the mass per unit area is independent of the atomic number of the absorber, to a good approximation. This can be expressed as

$$R(\text{g/cm}^2)_{Z_1} \simeq R(\text{g/cm}^2)_{Z_2} \tag{1–17}$$

Equation (1–17) should not be applied in cases where *bremsstrahlung* accounts for a significant part of the energy loss. Equation (1–13) can be used to check this condition.

**Example 1–6.** Compare the ranges of $P^{32}$ beta particles in lucite and in lead.

*Solution.* The radioisotope $P^{32}$ is a beta emitter with a maximum energy of 1.7 Mev. The range of these betas in aluminum is found from Fig. 1–10 to be 880 mg/cm². By Eq. (1–13), the radiative loss in lead is

$$\left(\frac{dE}{dx}\right)_r = \frac{EZ}{800}\left(\frac{dE}{dx}\right)_c = \frac{(1.7)(82)}{800}\left(\frac{dE}{dx}\right)_c = 0.17\left(\frac{dE}{dx}\right)_c$$

which is a large fraction of the loss by inelastic collision. However, in lucite the radiative loss would be negligible, as it also is in aluminum. Therefore, the maximum range of these particles is 880 mg/cm² in lucite and somewhat less than this in lead.

## 1–11. *Scattering of Electrons*

Since the electronic mass is small compared with that of a nucleus, large deflections can occur in single collisions, particularly when electrons of low energies are scattered by high-atomic-number elements. The effects of these scattering processes on the range of electrons have already been discussed.

When the scattering material is sufficiently thick and multiple scattering occurs, a large fraction of the electrons may be scattering through more than 90°. This phenomenon is called backscattering, since it scatters the particles back in the direction from which they came. This effect is quite important in radioactive measurements. The backing material on which the sample is mounted affects the counting rate by scattering electrons back to the detector. This can result in an increase of over 50 per cent in the counting rate if the backing material is of high atomic weight.

## PROPERTIES OF GAMMA AND X RAYS

### 1-12. *Absorption of Gamma and X Rays*

Gamma rays and X rays are two forms of electromagnetic radiation differing only in their origins. Gamma rays are produced in nuclear reactions, whereas X rays are caused by the excitation or removal of orbital electrons or by the deceleration of electrons. The gamma and X rays consist of photons, each with energy $E_p$ given by the expression

$$E_p = h\nu = \frac{hc}{\lambda} \tag{1-18}$$

where $h$ = Planck's constant
$c$ = velocity of light
$\nu$ and $\lambda$ = frequency and wavelength, respectively, which are associated with the wave nature of the radiation

The emission of gamma rays is a mechanism by which the energy of excitation of a nucleus can be removed. Such excited states may accompany the decay of radioisotopes, or they may result from induced nuclear transmutations. The gamma rays accompanying a particular type of nuclear reaction are composed of photons with either a single energy or a group of discrete energies. Typical energies of gamma rays range from a few kev to several Mev.

The excitation or removal of orbital electrons, which precedes the production of X rays, may be accomplished in many ways, including the inelastic scattering of other electrons, the internal-conversion phenomenon, and the electron-capture process. The energy released upon the return of the orbital electrons to the ground state appears as X-ray photons, known as fluorescent radiation. The energy of the photons is characteristic of the element, varying from a few electron volts for the lighter elements to about 0.1 Mev for the transuranium elements.

The X-ray production which accompanies the deceleration of electrons is the *bremsstrahlung* which was discussed in connection with the absorption of electrons. These X rays occur whenever high-energy electrons bombard targets, particularly those targets of high atomic number. The spectrum of the photons ranges from zero to the maximum energy of the bombarding electrons. Therefore these radiations can contain very-high-energy photons, even in the Bev region, with the high-energy particle accelerators.

The interaction of X and gamma rays with matter is primarily through three mechanisms, namely, the photoelectric effect, Compton scattering, and pair production. An additional mechanism is the production of nuclear reactions. However, this occurs so seldom compared with the other three mechanisms that it may be neglected in a discussion of the absorption of gamma and X rays.

In the photoelectric effect a photon of energy $h\nu$ interacts with the atom as a whole. Its energy is transferred to an electron, usually one in the innermost shell. The electron is ejected with a kinetic energy $E_{\text{kin}}$ given by

$$E_{\text{kin}} = h\nu - E_b \tag{1-19}$$

where $E_b$ is the binding energy of the orbital electron. Of course, when the electron shell is refilled, one or more characteristic X rays with total energy $E_b$ are emitted.

In Compton scattering the primary photon may interact with any one of the orbital electrons. The electrons are considered essentially as free electrons under the condition that the primary-photon energy is large compared with the electron binding energy. The interaction may be analyzed as an elastic collision between the primary photon and the electron. The energy is shared between the recoil electron and the secondary photon. This secondary photon travels in a direction differing from that of the primary photon, and it is referred to as the scattered photon.

At low energies where the photon energy is nearly equal to or less than the electron binding energy, the primary photon may be reradiated or scattered with the entire energy. In this process, known as coherent scattering, the entire atom absorbs the recoil momentum; since its mass is large, it receives negligible energy from the photon.

In pair production the primary photon disappears, and its energy goes into the rest-mass energy and the kinetic energy of the positron and electron pair which is produced.

The absorption of X and gamma rays may be studied through the measurement of their transmission through absorbers. If one uses an arrangement similar to Fig. 1–11 to measure the intensity of the beam which reaches the detector, one obtains the relationship

$$\frac{I}{I_o} = e^{-\mu d} \tag{1-20}$$

where $I/I_o$ is the fraction of the photons remaining in the beam after passage through an absorber of thickness $d$. In the processes which remove photons from the beam, each absorbed photon is eliminated individually in a single event. Since the number of photons eliminated from the beam in traversing a distance $dx$ of the absorber is proportional to $dx$ and to the number of incident photons, the exponential function results.

The quantity $\mu$ is known as the total linear absorption coefficient. The coefficient measured by the arrangement in Fig. 1–11 includes both the true absorption of photons and the scattering from the collimated beam. This coefficient is referred to as the "narrow beam" coefficient. Its value is greater than that which would be measured by an arrangement in which scattered photons can reach the detector.

The total coefficient $\mu$ can be expressed as

$$\mu = \tau + \sigma + \kappa \tag{1-21}$$

where $\tau$, $\sigma$, and $\kappa$ represent the partial absorption coefficients due to the photoelectric effect, Compton effect, and pair production, respectively.

In the absorption of X and gamma rays, the concept of range has a different meaning from that for charged particles. One cannot say with certainty that a particle will travel no farther than a certain range $R$. Instead, one can only specify the probability that it will travel no farther than $R$. This probability is given by Eq. (1–20) as $1 - e^{-\mu R}$.

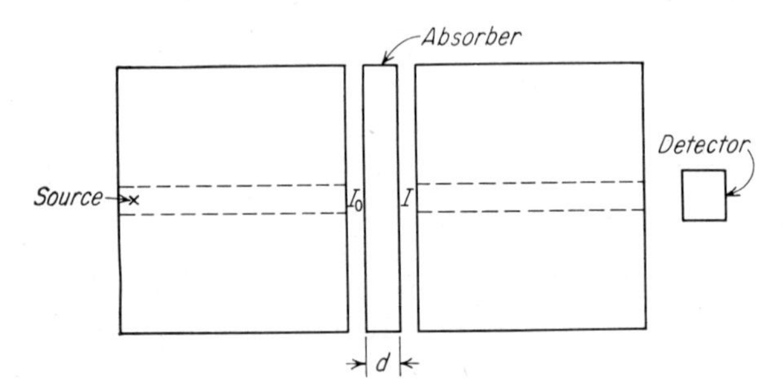


FIG. 1–11. Experimental arrangement for the measurement of the total linear absorption coefficient for gamma rays.

The concepts of half-thickness $x_{1/2}$ and mean range $\bar{R}$ are useful in regard to the absorption of X and gamma rays. The half-thickness $x_{1/2}$, defined as the absorber thickness required to absorb half of the photons, is given by

$$x_{1/2} = \frac{\ln 2}{\mu} = \frac{0.693}{\mu} \tag{1-22}$$

The mean range $\bar{R}$ is the average distance traveled by a photon before it is absorbed; $\bar{R}$ is calculated as follows:

$$\bar{R} = \frac{\int_0^\infty xe^{-\mu x}\mu\, dx}{\int_0^\infty e^{-\mu x}\mu\, dx} = \frac{1}{\mu} \tag{1-23}$$

An alternative form of Eq. (1–20) is

$$\frac{I}{I_0} = e^{-\mu_m d_m} \tag{1-24}$$

where $\mu_m$ = total mass absorption coefficient, that is, $\mu/\rho$
$d_m$ = mass thickness, or $\rho d$
$\rho$ = mass density of absorber

The mass absorption coefficients are functions of both the energy of the photons and the atomic number of the absorber. In Figs. 1–12 and 1–13 the dependence of $\mu_m$ on energies in the range from 0.01 to 100 Mev is shown for a group of elements from carbon to lead. The calculations for these figures were made by G. R. White [13]. Additional data on X- and

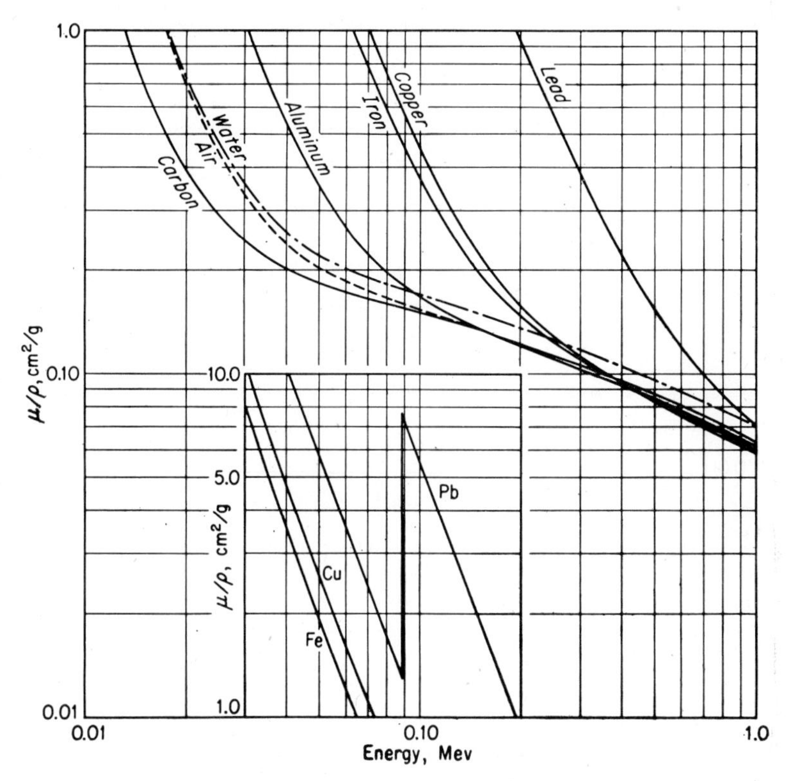


FIG. 1–12. Total mass absorption coefficient versus photon energy (0.01 to 1 Mev) for various materials. [*Reprinted from S. Kinsman (ed.), "Radiological Health Handbook," U.S. Department of Commerce, Office of Technical Services,* 1957; *data from G. R. White, Natl. Bur. Standards (U.S.) Circ.* 583, 1957.]

gamma-ray absorption can be found in a review article by Davisson and Evans [14]. It is seen that the absorption coefficients decrease with increasing energy until broad minima are reached. As the atomic number of the absorber increases, the energy of the minimum absorption decreases.

## 1–13. *Photoelectric Absorption*

Photons cannot interact with free electrons by the photoelectric effect. Therefore it is understandable that the interaction between photons and electrons is strongest with the most strongly bound electrons, i.e., the $K$-shell electrons. Further, for a given shell, the interaction is largest for photon energies just above the ionization potential for the shell, and it falls off rapidly with increasing energies.

Calculations of the dependence of $\tau$ on $Z$ and $h\nu$ have been made by

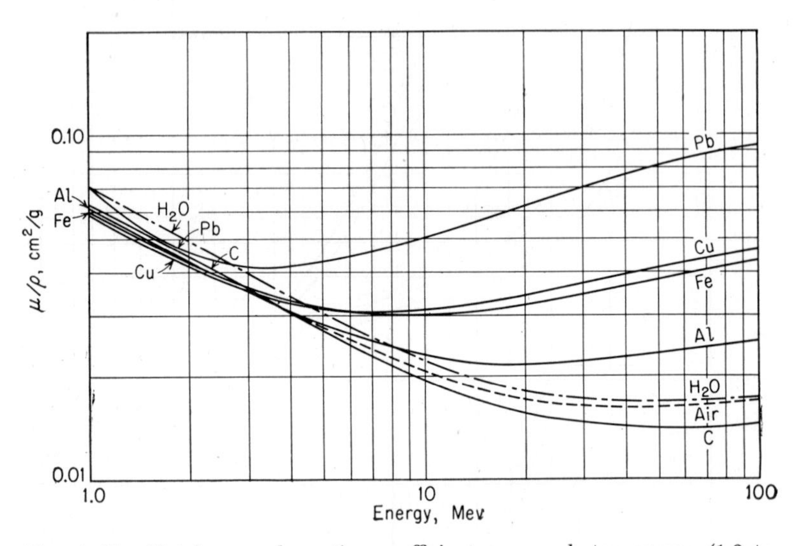


FIG. 1–13. Total mass absorption coefficient versus photon energy (1.0 to 100 Mev) for various materials. [*Reprinted from S. Kinsman (ed.), "Radiological Health Handbook," U.S. Department of Commerce, Office of Technical Services,* 1957; *data from G. R. White, Natl. Bur. Standards (U.S.) Circ.* 583, 1957.]

Heitler [10] and others [4]. One special case of the theoretical expression, which holds for $E_b \ll h\nu \ll mc^2$ (0.51 Mev), is

$$\tau \sim NZ^5(h\nu)^{-3.5} \tag{1–25}$$

Here $N$ is the number of atoms per unit volume and $E_b$ is the binding energy of the orbital electrons. In Figs. 1–14 and 1–15 the contributions of the individual absorption processes to the total absorption are shown for lead and aluminum, respectively. The photoelectric effect is seen to predominate below 600 kev for lead and below 60 kev for aluminum.

## 1–14. *Compton Effect*

The application of the laws of conservation of energy and momentum to the collision of a primary photon with a free electron leads to the expression

$$h\nu' = \frac{h\nu}{1 + (1 - \cos\theta)h\nu/mc^2} \tag{1–26}$$

where $h\nu'$ is the energy of the scattered photon and $\theta$ is the angle between its direction and that of the primary photon. The kinetic energy $E_{\text{kin}}$ of the recoil electron is

$$E_{\text{kin}} = h\nu - h\nu' = \frac{h\nu}{1 + mc^2/[h\nu(1 - \cos\theta)]} \tag{1-27}$$

From Eq. (1–27) it is seen that for $h\nu \ll mc^2$ (0.51 Mev) the energy given to the recoil electron is negligible, while for $h\nu \gg mc^2$, $E_{\text{kin}}$ approaches $h\nu$.

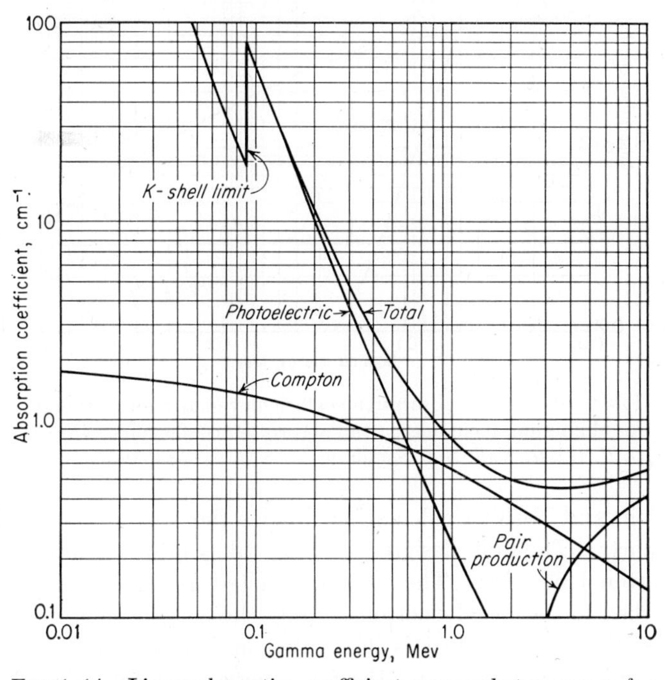


FIG. 1–14. Linear absorption coefficient versus photon energy for lead, including partial absorption coefficients. [*From G. R. White, Natl. Bur. Standards (U.S.) Circ.* 583, 1957.]

Since each electron enters individually into the scattering process, the partial absorption coefficient $\sigma$ is proportional to $Z$. The dependence of $\sigma$ on photon energy has been calculated quantum-mechanically by Klein and Nishina [15]. For $h\nu \gg mc^2$ the expression for $\sigma$ is

$$\sigma \sim \frac{NZ}{h\nu}\left(\ln\frac{2h\nu}{mc^2} + \frac{1}{2}\right) \tag{1-28}$$

which is essentially an inverse dependence on $h\nu$.

The Compton effect is the principal mechanism for photon absorption throughout a large energy range. In lead it is the chief effect from 0.6 to 5 Mev, while in aluminum it predominates the absorption from 0.05 to 15 Mev.

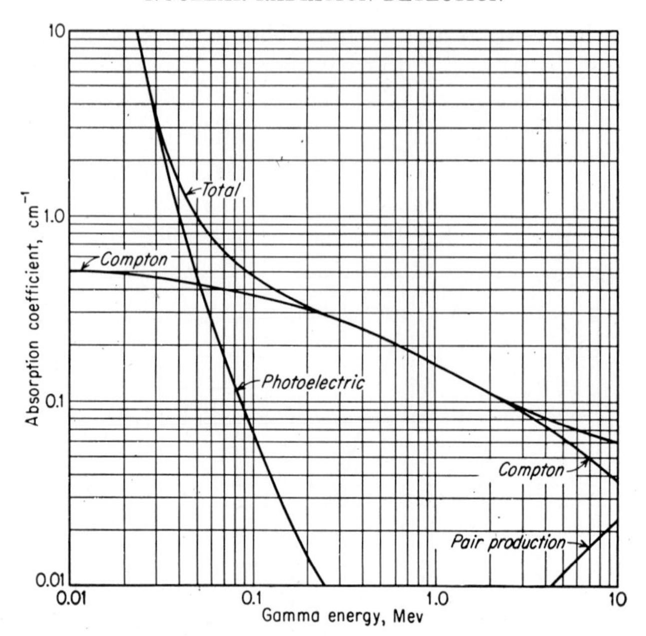


FIG. 1–15. Linear absorption coefficient versus photon energy for aluminum, including partial absorption coefficients. [*From G. R. White, Natl. Bur. Standards (U.S.) Circ.* 583, 1957.]

The Klein and Nishina calculation divides the absorption coefficient $\sigma$ into two parts. The first, designated as $\sigma_s$, takes into account the energy in the scattered photons. The second, denoted as $\sigma_a$, represents the energy absorbed in the recoil electrons. Only the latter represents a true energy absorption. This effect is illustrated in Fig. 1–16 where both the total absorption coefficient and the true-energy absorption coefficient of air are plotted.

**Example 1–7.** A collimated beam of gamma rays from $I^{135}$ impinges perpendicularly on the surface of a parallel-plate ionization chamber. If the gas in the chamber is air at standard conditions and the plates are 10 cm apart, compute the fractional decrease in the intensity of the beam due to the absorption in the air. What proportion of this absorption is true-energy absorption?

*Solution.* The gamma rays emitted by $I^{135}$ have an energy of 1.6 Mev. By Fig. 1–16, the total absorption coefficient in air is $6 \times 10^{-4}$ cm$^{-1}$, while the true energy absorption coefficient is $3 \times 10^{-4}$ cm$^{-1}$. Therefore the fractional decrease in the intensity of the collimated beam is $\mu d = 6 \times 10^{-4} \times 10 = 0.006$. The proportion of this decrease which results in true-energy absorption is $3 \times 10^{-4}/6 \times 10^{-4}$, or $\frac{1}{2}$.

## 1–15. *Absorption by Pair Production*

In the pair-production process, the gamma ray disappears, and a positron and an electron are produced. For the event to occur, the gamma-ray

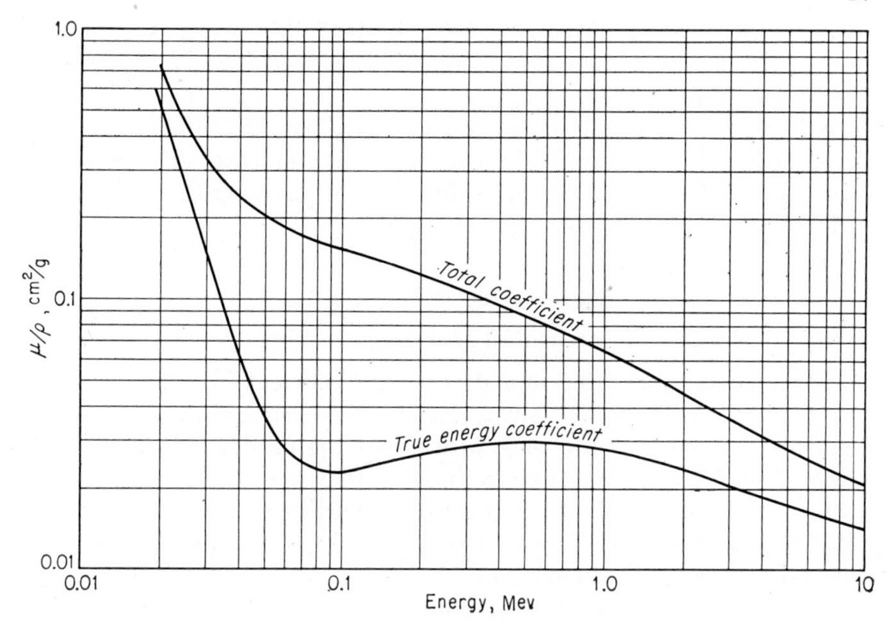


FIG. 1–16. Total mass absorption coefficient and true-energy absorption coefficient for air. [*Data for energy absorption from Report of the International Commission on Radiological Units and Measurements*, 1956, *National Bureau of Standards* (*U.S.*) *Handbook*.]

energy must be larger than the total rest-mass energy of the pair, that is, $2mc^2 = 1.02$ Mev. In addition, the event must occur in the Coulomb field of a nucleus. The energy in excess of that required to supply the rest-mass energy goes in the kinetic energy $E_{\text{kin}}$ of the pair; that is,

$$E_{\text{kin}} = h\nu - 2mc^2 = h\nu - 1.02 \text{ Mev} \tag{1–29}$$

Somewhat more than one-half of the energy goes to the positron, since the positively charged particle is repelled by the nucleus, while the electron is attracted.

The presence of the nucleus is necessary for the pair production. Its principal function is to allow conservation of momentum when the photon transfers its entire energy to the recoil particles. The probability for the process increases with the square of the nuclear charge.

The partial absorption coefficient $\kappa$ starts at zero for $h\nu \leq 1.02$ Mev, increases linearly at the lower energies, and ultimately rises as ln $E$ at the higher energies. Thus one can write

$$\kappa \sim NZ^2(h\nu - 2mc^2) \tag{1–30}$$

in the vicinity of 1 Mev and

$$\kappa \sim NZ^2 \ln h\nu \tag{1–31}$$

at very high energies. From Figs. 1–14 and 1–15, it is seen that absorption by pair production is the predominant factor in lead above 5 Mev and in aluminum above 15 Mev.

As in the case of Compton scattering, only a part of the photon energy becomes absorbed energy in the pair-production process. The rest-mass energy $2mc^2$ reappears as two 0.51-Mev photons following the annihilation of the positron-electron pair.

## PROPERTIES OF NEUTRONS

### 1–16. *Interaction of Neutrons with Matter*

The behavior of neutrons in matter is quite different from that of either charged particles or gamma rays. Since the neutrons are uncharged, no Coulomb forces come into play with either the orbital electrons or the nuclei. Thus, for neutrons to affect matter, they must either enter the nucleus or come sufficiently close to it for the nuclear forces to act. On the other hand, nuclear reactions play only a minor role in the absorption of charged particles and gamma rays.

The reaction of a neutron with a nucleus ${}_ZX^A$ can be represented as

$${}_ZX^A + {}_0n^1 \rightarrow ({}_ZY^{A+1})^*$$

where $({}_ZY^{A+1})^*$ represents the compound nucleus in an excited state. The excitation energy, including both the binding energy and the kinetic energy of the neutron, is distributed among the many constituents of the nucleus. The compound nucleus remains in the excited state only a short time, from $10^{-12}$ to $10^{-20}$ sec. The excess energy may be removed by the emission of one or more particles. If, for example, an alpha particle is emitted, the reaction is designated as a (n,$\alpha$) reaction.

Processes in which the neutrons are reemitted are referred to as scattering processes. The scattering is inelastic or elastic, depending on whether the nucleus is left in an excited or an unexcited state after the neutron reemission. In either case the neutron energy is degraded, the amount of degradation being larger for the inelastic scattering.

For any given compound nucleus in an excited state, several different types of nuclear reactions may be energetically possible. The probabilities for the various reactions depend on the amount of the excitation energy and the location of the energy levels in the compound and product nuclei. Consequently, the probability for each type of absorption process depends on the energy of the incident neutron and the composition of the absorber. These probabilities often vary greatly even between different isotopes of the same element, since each type of nuclide has its own characteristic nuclear properties.

The importance of the neutron energy in the interaction of neutrons with matter makes necessary a classification of neutrons according to their energies. The terms thermal, epithermal, and fast each represent a broad, rather indefinite range of neutron energies. Thermal neutrons are those which have reached thermal equilibrium with their surroundings. At 20°C the thermal neutrons have an average kinetic energy of 0.038 ev in a non-absorbing medium; most of these neutrons have energies less than 1 ev. Epithermal neutrons are the group between thermal and fast. The lower boundary on the fast-neutron group is quite arbitrary. Perhaps about 100 kev is a convenient value.

A list of the various mechanisms by which neutrons interact with matter follows:

1. Elastic scattering, (n,n). The initial kinetic energy of the neutron is shared with the nucleus. The nucleus is not left in an excited state. The smaller the mass of the nucleus, the greater the fraction of the kinetic energy taken by the nucleus.

2. Inelastic scattering, (n,n), (n,n$\gamma$), or (n,2n). This process is energetically possible only for fast neutrons. In the (n,n$\gamma$) reaction the excitation energy is removed by a gamma ray. In the (n,n) process the nucleus remains in a metastable state. For incident-neutron energies of 10 Mev or higher, the (n,2n) processes can occur.

3. Simple capture, (n,$\gamma$). This reaction is probably the most common of all reactions, since thermal neutrons induce this reaction in nearly all nuclides. It also occurs with a very high probability for a number of nuclides at particular energies in the epithermal range. This latter phenomenon is known as resonance capture. The gamma rays which are emitted in the (n,$\gamma$) reaction usually have energies of several Mev.

4. Ejection of charged particles, (n,p), (n,d), (n,$\alpha$), (n,t), (n,$\alpha$p), etc. Since the charged particles must overcome the Coulomb barrier before escaping the nucleus, this type of reaction is most probable for light nuclides and fast neutrons. Important exceptions are those (n,$\alpha$) reactions which are sufficiently exothermic to allow the escape from the Coulomb barrier even with thermal neutrons. Examples of these thermal reactions are the $Li^6$(n,$\alpha$) and the $B^{10}$(n,$\alpha$) reactions.

5. Fission, (n,f). The compound nucleus splits into two fission fragments and one or more neutrons. Fission occurs with thermal neutrons in $U^{235}$, $Pu^{239}$, and $U^{233}$ and with fast neutrons in many heavy nuclides.

6. High-energy processes. The capture in a nucleus of neutrons with energies around 100 Mev or higher may cause the emission of a shower of many different types of particles.

### 1–17. *Nuclear Cross Sections*

A quantitative description of the interaction of neutrons with nuclei can be made through the use of the concept of nuclear cross sections. The rate at which a particular reaction proceeds in a given material depends on the number and energy of the neutrons and on the quantity and type of the nuclei in the material. The dependence on the neutron energy and target type is included in the nuclear cross section.

Consider a hypothetical slab of material one atom thick containing $N_a$ nuclei of one type per square centimeter. Let a collimated beam of neutrons with intensity $I$ neutrons per square centimeter per second impinge perpendicularly on the surface. The microscopic cross section $\sigma$ for a particular reaction is defined as

$$\sigma = \frac{C}{N_a I} \qquad \text{cm}^2 \tag{1-32}$$

where $C$ is the number of reactions of the type in question which occur per square centimeter per second. Since nuclear cross sections often have values of the order of $10^{-24}$ cm$^2$, this quantity has been chosen as the cross-section unit; this unit is called a barn.

The physical significance of cross section can be seen by rewriting Eq. (1–32) as

$$N_a\sigma = \frac{C}{I}$$

The quantity $C/I$ is the fraction of the incident neutrons which cause the nuclear reaction. Also, it is the probability that a given neutron in the beam will take part in the reaction. The quantity $N_a\sigma$ may be regarded as the portion of the 1-cm$^2$ surface area which, if struck, undergoes the nuclear reaction. This leads to the concept that the slab consists of $N_a$ nuclei per square centimeter, each having an effective cross-sectional area, or, for short, cross section $\sigma$. However, this cross section is related to the geometrical cross section only in certain special cases.

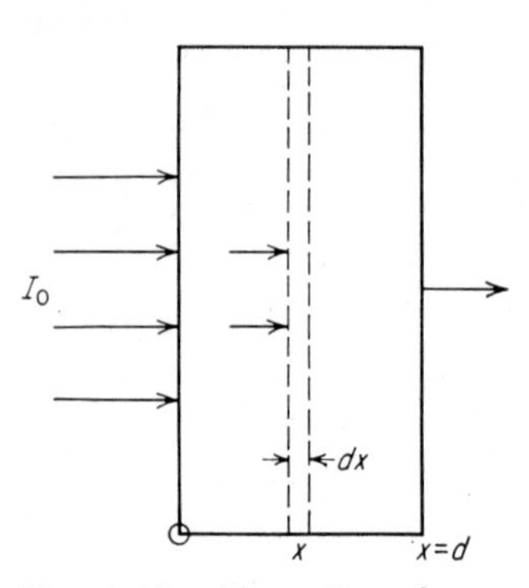

FIG. 1–17. Absorption of neutrons in a finite absorber.

In the preceding paragraphs, $\sigma$ was defined in terms of a monoatomic layer. In many applications of the concept, a finite thickness of material must be used. Consider a collimated beam of neutrons with intensity $I_0$ neutrons per square centimeter per second incident normally on a slab of thickness $d$, as shown in Fig. 1–17. If $N$ indicates the number of target nuclei per cubic centimeter, a square centimeter of the surface of a differential slab contains $N\,dx$ targets. The differential slab produces a fractional change in the beam intensity of $N\sigma\,dx$; that is,

$$-\frac{dI}{I} = N\sigma\, dx \tag{1-33}$$

Therefore, integration over the thickness $d$ leads to

$$I = I_0 e^{-N\sigma d} \tag{1-34}$$

The fraction of the neutrons absorbed in a thickness $d$ is $1 - e^{-N\sigma d}$. For $N\sigma d \ll 1$, this fraction reduces to that given by Eq. (1–32). When Eq. (1–34) is applied to the scattering processes, the quantity $I$ must be interpreted as the number of neutrons arriving at $d$ without having been scattered.

The cross section $\sigma$ is known as the microscopic cross section since it refers to a single nucleus. The macroscopic cross section $\Sigma$ is defined as

$$\Sigma \equiv N\sigma \qquad \text{cm}^{-1} \tag{1-35}$$

Thus $\Sigma$ is seen to be the total cross section of all the nuclei in 1 $\text{cm}^3$ of the material. Equation (1–33) becomes

$$-\frac{dI}{I} = \Sigma\, dx \tag{1-36}$$

From this it is seen that $\Sigma$ is the probability of absorption per unit path length. In addition, $\Sigma$ is the reciprocal of $\lambda$, the average distance which a neutron will travel before the process occurs. This, of course, is identical to the relationship between $\mu$ and $\bar{R}$ for photons, as discussed in Sec. 1–12.

The preceding discussion has been restricted to a collimated beam of neutrons. It can be extended to fields of neutrons with random directions through the following considerations. If the neutron travels with an average velocity $v$, then $v/\lambda$ is the probability that a given neutron will undergo a reaction per second. If $n$ is the number of neutrons per cubic centimeter, then $R$, the reaction rate per cubic centimeter, is

$$R = \frac{nv}{\lambda} = nv\Sigma = \Phi\Sigma \tag{1-37}$$

where the quantity $nv$ is known as the neutron flux and is given the symbol $\Phi$. This relationship is independent of the direction in which the neutrons are moving.

**Example 1–8.** Calculate the rate at which the (n,$\alpha$) reaction occurs in a neutron-counter tube of a volume of 100 $\text{cm}^3$, containing $BF_3$ gas at normal temperature and pressure, if the tube is placed in a neutron field of energy of 0.025 ev and flux magnitude of $10^{12}$ neutrons/($\text{cm}^2$) (sec).

*Solution.* The cross section for the (n,$\alpha$) reaction is given by Fig. 1–21 as 755 barns at 0.025 ev. Since the number of boron atoms per cubic centimeter is $6.02 \times 10^{23}/2.24 \times 10^4$, or $2.68 \times 10^{19}$ $\text{cm}^{-3}$ under the condition of the problem, Eq. (1–37) yields a total reaction rate of

$$\text{Reaction rate} = VN\sigma\Phi = (100)(2.68 \times 10^{19})(755 \times 10^{-24})(10^{12}) = 2.06 \times 10^{12}/\text{sec}$$

In general, the neutrons involved in a given situation have a range of energies. Since neutron cross sections are often energy-dependent, it is necessary to adopt a notation which specifies the neutron energy. For this purpose, $\phi(E)$, the neutron flux per unit energy interval, is introduced so that the flux in the energy interval from $E$ to $E + dE$ is $\phi(E)\,dE$. The quantity $\phi(E)$ is related to $n(E)$, the neutron density per unit energy interval, by the expression

$$\Phi(E) = n(E)\,v \tag{1–38}$$

The total flux of all energies is

$$\Phi = \int_0^\infty \phi(E)\,dE = \int_0^\infty n(E)\,v\,dE \tag{1–39}$$

where $v = (2E/M_n)^{1/2}$, $M_n$ being the neutron mass. The reaction rate $R$ becomes

$$R = \int_0^\infty \Sigma(E)\,\phi(E)\,dE \tag{1–40}$$

where the macroscopic cross section $\Sigma(E)$ is a function of energy. The reaction rate can be expressed in terms of the total flux $\Phi$ and an average cross section $\bar{\Sigma}$ as

$$R = \Phi\bar{\Sigma} \tag{1–41}$$

where $\bar{\Sigma}$ is defined as

$$\bar{\Sigma} = \frac{\int_0^\infty \Sigma(E)\,\phi(E)\,dE}{\int_0^\infty \phi(E)\,dE} \tag{1–42}$$

The number of atoms per cubic centimeter of the material can be calculated by

$$N = \frac{\rho N_o}{\mathrm{W}} \tag{1–43}$$

where $\rho$ = density, g/cm$^3$
$W$ = atomic weight
$N_o$ = Avogadro's number

In terms of these quantities,

$$\Sigma(\mathrm{cm}^{-1}) = \frac{0.602\sigma\rho}{W} \tag{1–44}$$

where $\sigma$ is expressed in barns.

As was discussed previously, several different types of nuclear reactions can occur with neutrons. For each process there will be a certain cross section. Since the probabilities for the different processes are additive, one can define a total cross section $\sigma_t$ as the sum of the individual cross sections. If $\sigma_i$ refers to the cross section for the $i$th process, then

$$\sigma_t = \sum_i \sigma_i \tag{1-45}$$

**Example 1-9.** Calculate the mean free path of 0.025-ev neutrons in cadmium of a density of 8.6 g/cm³.

*Solution.* The mean free path $\lambda$ or $1/\Sigma$ is obtained by Eq. (1-44) as

$$\lambda = \frac{W}{0.602\sigma\rho} = \frac{113}{(0.602)(2{,}600)(8.6)} = 0.0084 \text{ cm}$$

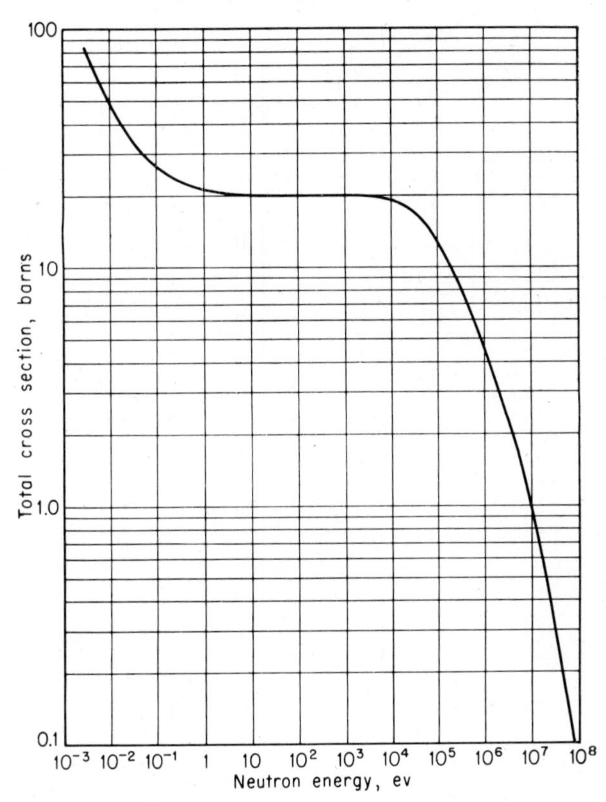


FIG. 1-18. Total cross section versus energy for neutrons in hydrogen; energy range, $10^{-3}$ ev to $10^2$ Mev. (*From D. J. Hughes and J. A. Harvey, "Neutron Cross Sections," U.S. Atomic Energy Commission Document, McGraw-Hill Book Company, Inc., New York,* 1955.)

## 1-18. *Variation of Cross Sections with Neutron Energy*

The complete determination of cross sections for the several possible nuclear reactions is a complex problem. In most cases, these cross sections vary greatly with energy. Also, the variations between different elements and between different isotopes of the same element may be quite large. For the determination of cross sections, actual measurements must be employed, as in most cases theory is not sufficiently advanced to allow their computa-

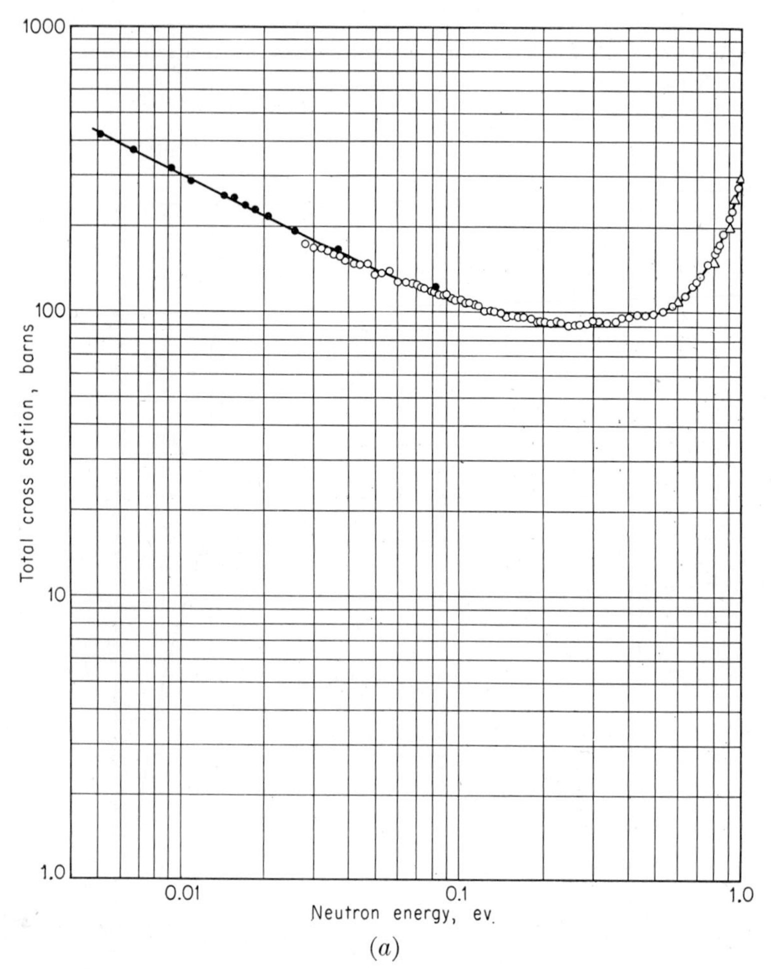


(*a*)

FIG. 1–19*a*. Total cross section versus energy for neutrons in indium; energy range, 0.01 to 1 ev. (*From D. J. Hughes and J. A. Harvey, "Neutron Cross Sections," U.S. Atomic Energy Commission Document, McGraw-Hill Book Company, Inc., New York,* 1955.)

tion. A comprehensive compilation of thermal-neutron cross sections as well as of curves of neutron cross sections versus energy for a large energy range are included in an Atomic Energy Commission publication [16]. Figures 1–18 to 1–21 are examples of curves taken from that publication. These figures give the neutron cross sections of several materials of interest in nuclear-radiation detection.

Figure 1–18 is the total cross section for hydrogen. This cross section is due primarily to the elastic scattering by protons, the nuclei of the $H^1$ atoms. This phenomenon is important in the detection of fast neutrons.

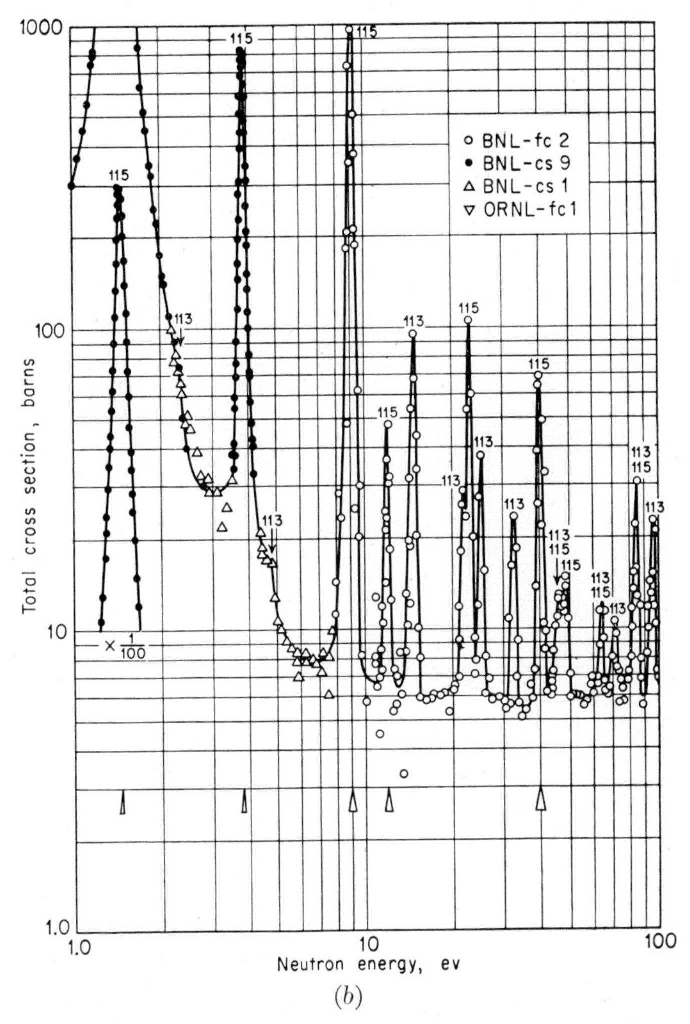


(b)

FIG. 1–19b. Total cross section versus energy for neutrons in indium; energy range, 1.0 to 100 ev. (*From D. J. Hughes and J. A. Harvey, "Neutron Cross Sections," U.S. Atomic Energy Commission Document, McGraw-Hill Book Company, Inc., New York,* 1955.)

Figure 1–19 is the total cross section for the element indium with its natural abundance of isotopes. This cross section is due primarily to the (n,$\gamma$) reaction in $In^{115}$. The high resonance peak at 1.4 ev is particularly

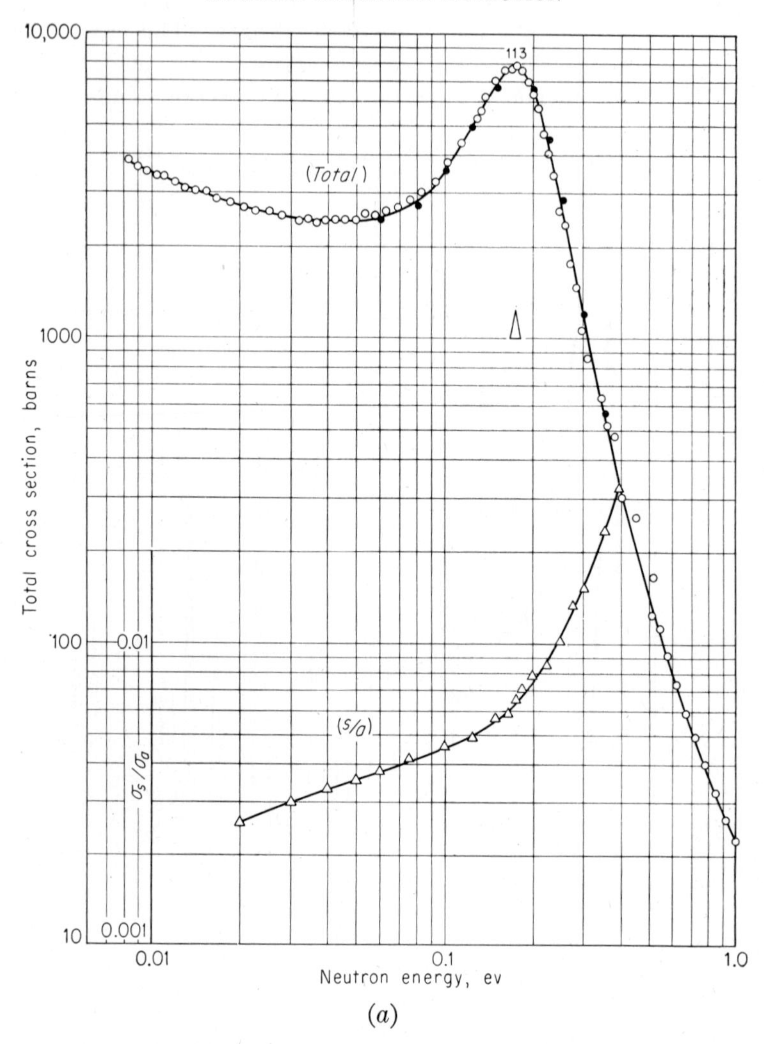


(*a*)

FIG. 1–20*a*. Total cross section versus energy for neutrons in cadmium; energy range, 0.01 to 1.0 ev; also, the ratio of scattering to absorption cross sections. (*From D. J. Hughes and J. A. Harvey, "Neutron Cross Sections," U.S. Atomic Energy Commission Document, McGraw-Hill Book Company, Inc., New York,* 1955.)

useful. The $In^{116}$ which is formed is radioactive and can be used as a measure of the neutron flux at 1.4 ev.

Figure 1–20 is the total cross section of the element cadmium. This cross section is due almost entirely to the (n,$\gamma$) reaction in $Cd^{113}$. This reaction is particularly useful because of its sharp rise at the upper energy limit of the thermal neutrons.

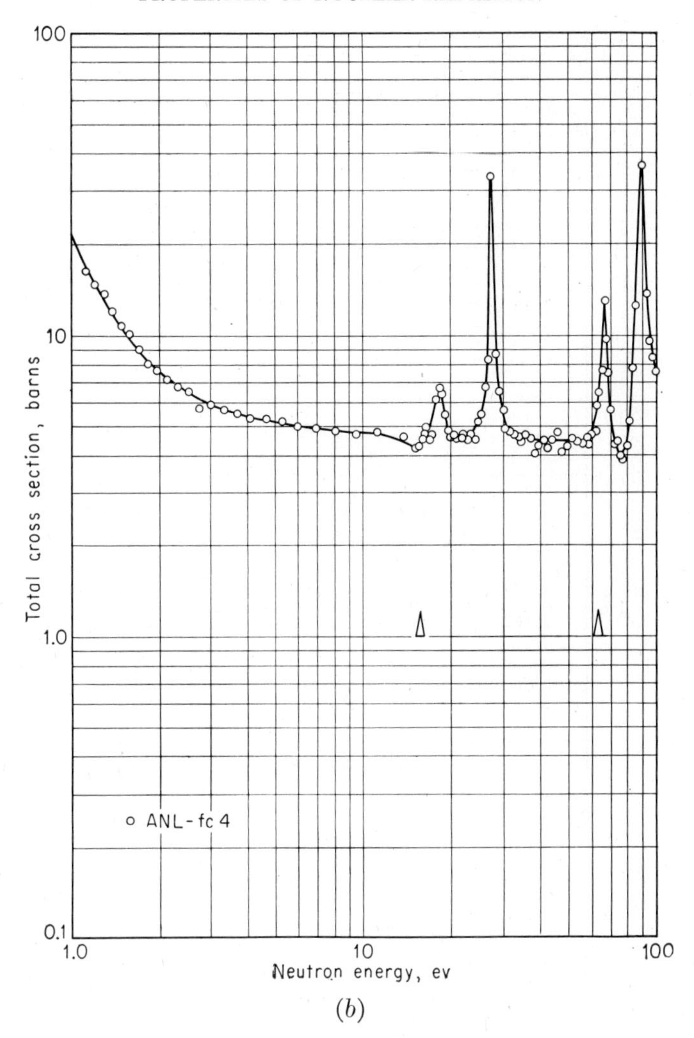


(*b*)

FIG. 1–20*b*. Total cross section versus energy for neutrons in cadmium; energy range, 1.0 to 100 ev. (*From D. J. Hughes and J. A. Harvey, "Neutron Cross Sections," U.S. Atomic Energy Commission Document, McGraw-Hill Book Company, Inc., New York,* 1955.)

Figure 1–21 shows the cross section for the (n,$\alpha$) reaction in boron. This reaction occurs primarily in $B^{10}$ and is represented by the equation

$$_5B^{10} + {_0n^1} \rightarrow {_3Li^7} + {_2He^4} + Q$$

where $Q = 2.78$ Mev. The $Li^7$ and the $He^4$ products make possible the detection of the neutrons.

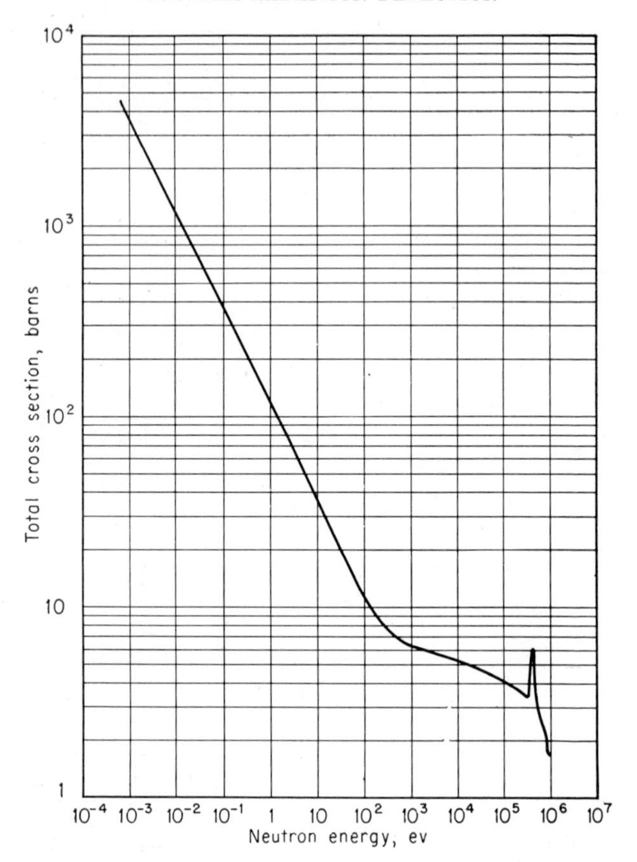


FIG. 1–21. Total cross section versus energy for neutrons in boron; energy range, 0.01 ev to 1 Mev. (*From D. J. Hughes and J. A. Harvey, "Neutron Cross Sections," U.S. Atomic Energy Commission Document, McGraw-Hill Book Company, Inc., New York,* 1955.)

## 1–19. *Slowing Down of Neutrons*

When neutrons are epithermal or fast, there is a tendency for them to be slowed down or thermalized by scattering processes. These scattering processes may be either the elastic or inelastic type.

In a large system in which the cross sections for the scattering processes are large compared with those for absorption processes, a large fraction of the neutrons are slowed down to thermal equilibrium with the system before eventual absorption. A medium which is employed for slowing down neutrons is called a moderator. For moderation by elastic collision, materials with small mass numbers are most effective, since these can absorb the largest fraction of the neutron energy per collision. Materials which contain a large amount of hydrogen make good moderators; water and paraffin are noteworthy examples. In addition, heavy water, beryllium, and carbon are very good moderators since they have reasonably low mass numbers and very low absorption cross sections.

Inelastic scattering is an important mechanism in the degradation of the energy of fast neutrons. The cross section for this process increases with the neutron energy and with the atomic number of the material in which the scattering occurs. This is an important mechanism in the shielding against fast neutrons [17].

A particular thermal neutron undergoing collisions with the nuclei of the medium may gain or lose energy in any one collision. However, if a large number of neutrons diffusing in a nonabsorbing medium are considered, there is no net energy change for all the neutrons. The kinetic energy of the neutrons will then be distributed according to the Maxwell-Boltzmann distribution law, as derived from the kinetic theory of gases; thus,

$$\frac{n(E)}{n_{th}} = \frac{2\pi}{(\pi kT)^{3/2}} e^{-E/kT} E^{1/2} \tag{1-46}$$

where $n(E)$ = no. of neutrons of energy $E$ per unit energy interval
$n_{th}$ = total no. of thermal neutrons
$k$ = Boltzmann constant
$T$ = temperature, °K

With this distribution law, a neutron with energy $kT$ has the most probable velocity while the average kinetic energy is $\frac{3}{2}kT$. If a thermal neutron is designated as one having the most probable velocity for a Maxwell-Boltzmann distribution at the temperature in question, the following relationships hold:

$$\begin{aligned} &\text{Kinetic energy} = 8.61 \times 10^{-5} T \quad &&\text{ev} \\ &\text{Velocity} = 13.8 \times 10^{5} E^{1/2} \quad &&\text{cm/sec} \\ &\text{Velocity} = 1.28 \times 10^{4} T^{1/2} \quad &&\text{cm/sec} \end{aligned} \tag{1-47}$$

where $E$ is the kinetic energy in electron volts and $T$ is the temperature in degrees Kelvin. At 293°K the energy is 0.025 ev, and the velocity is $2.2 \times 10^5$ cm/sec.

It is customary [18] to replace the expressions for the reaction rate that are given by Eqs. (1–40) and (1–41) by

$$R = n \times 2.2 \times 10^5 \times \Sigma(0.025\,\text{ev}) \tag{1-48}$$

when the neutron field is primarily thermal neutrons. Here $n$ is the number of neutrons per cubic centimeter and $\Sigma(0.025\text{ ev})$ is the macroscopic cross section for the process, evaluated at 0.025 ev. This expression is accurate when the cross section has a $1/v$ dependence on the neutron velocity and only neutrons with velocity in the range for which the $1/v$ dependence holds are present. The quantity $n \times 2.2 \times 10^5$ is the so-called "thermal flux" and is often used rather than the actual flux that would be calculated from Eq. (1–39).

## PROBLEMS

**1–1.** In certain methods of operation of an electron pulse-type ionization chamber, the conditions are such that the entire electronic charge which is released in the chamber is collected. What is the maximum electronic charge that is collected per particle when a uranium source is placed within the chamber and the chamber gas is helium?

**1–2.** Find the maximum range in air and in aluminum of the following particles if each has an energy of 3 Mev: alphas, protons, deuterons, and electrons.

**1–3.** Construct two range-energy curves for protons in air, one based on Fig. 1–4 and the other on Fig. 1–6.

**1–4.** Use Eq. (1–5) to develop a relationship between the ranges of alpha particles and deuterons in air. Use this relationship to obtain a range-energy curve for deuterons in air from Fig. 1–4. Compare the result with Fig. 1–6.

**1–5.** The alpha emitter $Po^{210}$ is plated on the surface of a thick nickel planchet. At what plating thickness is the condition reached for which the addition of more $Po^{210}$ makes no increase in the number of alpha particles escaping from the surface?

**1–6.** An experiment was run in which counting-rate measurements were made for various thicknesses of aluminum absorbers between a radioactive source, emitting beta particles, and the counter. The following data were obtained:

| Absorber thickness, mg/cm² | Counting rate, counts/sec | Absorber thickness, mg/cm² | Counting rate, counts/sec |
|---|---|---|---|
| 9.60 | 52.5 | 39.4 | 30.4 |
| 16.6 | 45.5 | 68.5 | 19.8 |
| 23.6 | 40.0 | 88.0 | 12.2 |
| 31.4 | 35.5 | 127 | 7.90 |

Estimate the maximum range of the beta particles and the maximum energy with which they are emitted. Determine the mass absorption coefficient for use in Eq. (1–15), and check this value with the one predicted by Eq. (1–16).

**1–7.** What pressure of air would be required in a spherical ionization chamber of 15-cm radius if all the electrons emitted by a $P^{32}$ source placed at the center of the chamber were to give up their entire energies to ionization within the chamber gas?

**1–8.** Determine the mean free paths for the following processes:

| Process | Material | Particle | Particle energy, Mev |
|---|---|---|---|
| Pair production | Lead | Gamma | 10 |
| Any process | Aluminum | Gamma | 2 |
| Neutron capture | Cadmium | Neutron | $10^{-7}$ |
| (n,α) | Boron | Neutron | $10^{-6}$ |

**1-9.** When gamma rays of 1.25 Mev passed through various thicknesses of iron, it was found that the intensity varied with the thicknesses, as shown in the following table. Find the absorption coefficient and compare with the value obtained from Fig. 1-13.

| Thickness of iron, cm | Intensity | Thickness of iron, cm | Intensity |
|---|---|---|---|
| 0 | 100 | 8.50 | 3.05 |
| 1.80 | 47.5 | 9.60 | 1.92 |
| 3.20 | 27.0 | 10.60 | 1.26 |
| 5.00 | 12.5 | | |

**1-10.** Derive an analytical expression for the probability that a gamma photon will pass through a thickness $d$ of a material without undergoing any interaction.

**1-11.** Calculate the rate of energy evolution due to the (n,$\alpha$) reaction that is produced by 100-kev neutrons in boron if the flux at this energy is $10^{12}$ neutrons/(cm$^2$)(sec).

**1-12.** Show that $\bar{\Sigma} = \sqrt{\pi}\, \Sigma(kT)/2$, where $\Sigma(kT)$ is the value of the cross section at the energy $kT$, provided that $n(E)$ is the Maxwell-Boltzmann distribution and $\Sigma(E) = \Sigma(kT)\, \sqrt{kT}/\sqrt{E}$.

## REFERENCES


1. Livingston, S., and H. Bethe: *Revs. Mod. Phys.*, **9**:263 (1937).
2. Allison, S. K., and S. D. Warshaw: *Revs. Mod. Phys.*, **25**:779 (1953).
3. Uehling, E. A.: *Ann. Rev. Nuclear Sci.*, **4**:315 (1954).
4. Bethe, H., and J. Ashkin: Article in E. Segrè (ed.), "Experimental Nuclear Physics," vol. 1, John Wiley & Sons, Inc., New York, 1953.
5. Gray, L. H.: *Proc. Cambridge Phil. Soc.*, **40**:72 (1944).
6. Taylor, A. E.: *Repts. Progr. in Phys.*, **15**:49 (1952).
7. Aron, W. A., B. G. Hoffman, and F. C. Williams: *U.S. Atomic Energy Comm. Document* AECU-663, 1949.
8. Rich, M., and R. Madey: *U.S. Atomic Energy Comm. Document* UCRL-2301, 1954.
9. Cook, C. J., E. Jones, Jr., and T. Jorgensen: *Phys. Rev.*, **91**:1417 (1953).
10. Heitler, W.: "The Quantum Theory of Radiation," chap. 3, Oxford University Press, London, 1944.
11. Feather, N.: *Proc. Cambridge Phil. Soc.*, **34**:599 (1938).
12. Glendenin, L. E.: *Nucleonics*, **2**:12 (January, 1948).
13. White, G. R.: *Natl. Bur. Standards (U.S.) Circ.* 583, 1957.
14. Davisson, C. M., and R. D. Evans: *Revs. Mod. Phys.*, **24**:79 (1952).
15. Klein, O., and Y. Nishina: *Z. Physik*, **52**:853 (1929).
16. Hughes, D. J., and J. A. Harvey: "Neutron Cross Sections," U.S. Atomic Energy Commission Document, McGraw-Hill Book Company, Inc., New York, 1955.
17. Stephenson, R.: "Introduction to Nuclear Engineering," chap. 5, McGraw-Hill Book Company, Inc., New York, 1954.
18. Hughes, D. J.: "Pile Neutron Research," chap. 7, Addison-Wesley Publishing Company, Reading, Mass., 1953.

CHAPTER 2

# SURVEY OF DETECTION METHODS

The term detection is used in this text to include not only the indication of the presence of nuclear radiation but also the measurement of the amount, energy, and related properties. A detection system can be considered to consist of two parts, a detector and a measuring apparatus. The interaction of the radiation with the system takes place in the detector. The measuring apparatus takes the output of the detector and performs the functions required to accomplish the measurements.

The different types of detectors can be characterized by the nature of the interaction of the radiation with the detector. Several types operate by virtue of the ionization which is produced in them by the passage of charged particles. These detectors include ionization chambers, proportional counters, Geiger-Müller counters, crystal counters, and cloud chambers. In the event that the primary radiation consists of charged particles, this ionization is produced directly. For example, a 5-Mev alpha particle can release $2.25 \times 10^{-14}$ coulomb of charge in a detector containing air, as was computed in Example 1–1. For uncharged particles such as neutrons and gamma rays, the charged particles which are required for the production of ionization originate by secondary processes, as described in Chap. 1.

In certain detectors, excitation and sometimes molecular dissociation also play important roles. These phenomena, in combination with ionization, produce the luminescence involved in scintillation detectors and the latent images in photographic emulsions. Molecular dissociation is particularly important in chemical detection systems, i.e., those systems which function through the occurrence of certain chemical reactions.

Other important primary processes involved in the interaction of radiation with the detectors include the emission of Cerenkov radiation in Cerenkov detectors and secondary-electron emission in electron multipliers. Each of these several processes will be discussed in later chapters on the specific detectors.

Nuclear-radiation-detection systems can be classified as to whether their operation is of the pulse type or not. In the pulse type of operation, the output of the detector is a series of signals separated or resolved in time. Each signal represents the interaction of a nuclear particle with the detector. A Geiger-Müller tube is an example of a pulse-type detector. If the pulse character of the output of the detector is used, such as in the case of counting by an electronic counter, the detection system is of the pulse type.

In the nonpulse type of operation of a detection system, the quantity measured directly is the average effect due to many interactions of the radiation with the detector. No attempt is made to resolve the individual particles. In fact, this is often impossible because of the high rate at which they occur. Such an arrangement may be referred to as a mean-level detection system.

The current-type ionization chamber is a good example of a mean-level detection system. The current output is proportional to the number of particles incident upon the detector per unit time.

## SURVEY OF DETECTOR TYPES

### 2–1. *Gas-filled Detectors*

Three of the oldest but still very useful nuclear-radiation-detector types are the ionization chambers, the proportional counter, and the Geiger-Müller (G-M) tube. Each of these detector types employs gas-filled chambers. The difference in the three systems can be explained through the use of Fig. 2–1. The system shown consists of a gas-filled chamber with a central electrode well insulated from the chamber walls. A voltage $V$ is applied between the wall and the central electrode through the resistor $R$ shunted by the capacitor $C_2$.

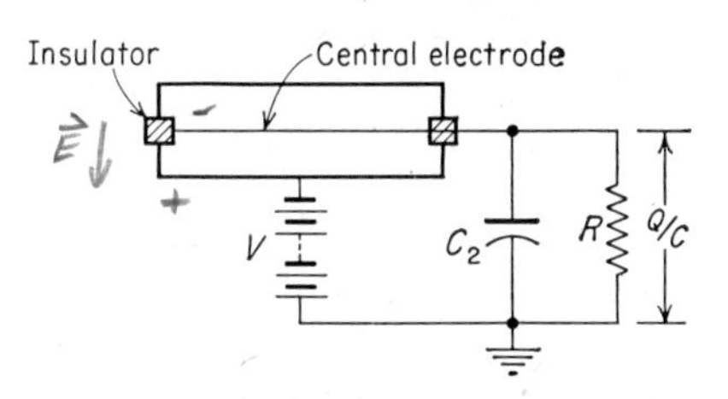


FIG. 2–1. Schematic diagram for pulse operation of a gas-filled chamber.

Assume that the passage of a nuclear particle releases $N_1$ ion pairs within the chamber. The positive and negative charges within the chamber move toward the chamber wall and central electrode, respectively, because of the direction of the electric field. Under the condition that the time constant $RC_2$ is much greater than the time required for the collection of the charge, the charge $Q$ appearing on the capacitor per particle as a function of $V$ is given by curve 1 in Fig. 2–2. For a particle producing a larger number of ion pairs $N_2$, curve 2 is obtained.

These curves can be divided into four main regions. In region I there is a competition between the loss of ion pairs by recombination and the removal charge by collection on the electrodes. With increasing field the drift velocity of the ions increases; therefore the time available for recombination decreases, and the fraction of the charge which is collected becomes larger.

In region II the recombination loss is negligible, and the charge collected is

$$Q_1 = N_1 e \qquad \text{and} \qquad Q_2 = N_2 e \tag{2-1}$$

The change in voltage across the capacitor $C_2$ is

$$\Delta V_1 = \frac{N_1 e}{C} \qquad \text{and} \qquad \Delta V_2 = \frac{N_2 e}{C} \tag{2-2}$$

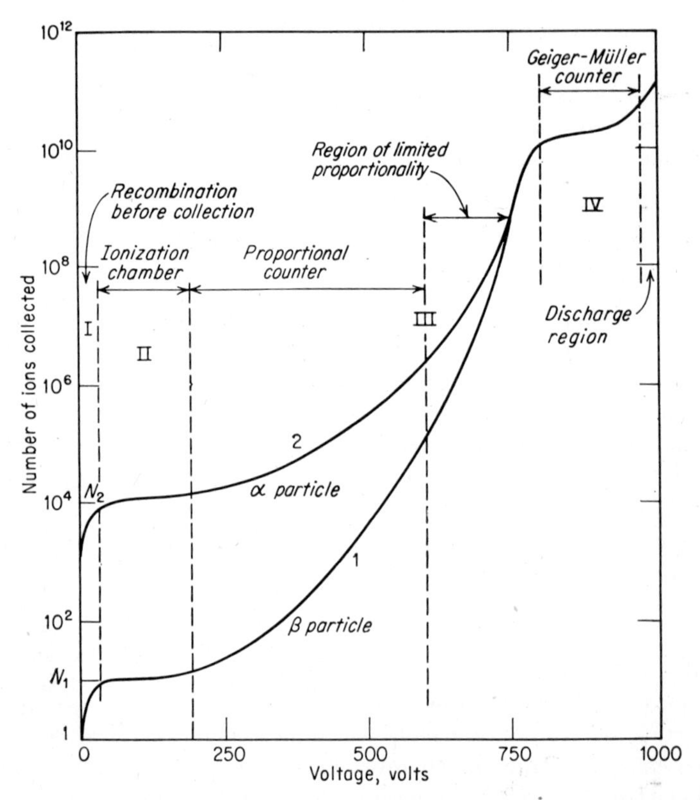


FIG. 2–2. Pulse-height versus applied-voltage curves to illustrate ionization, proportional, and Geiger-Müller regions of operation. [*From C. G. Montgomery and D. D. Montgomery, J. Franklin Inst.,* **231**:447 (1941).]

where $C$ is the sum of the ionization-chamber capacity and $C_2$, as discussed in Sec. 4–23. This region is referred to as the saturation region or the ionization-chamber region.

In region III the collected charge is increased by a factor $M$ through the phenomenon of gas multiplication. The electrons which are released in the primary ionization are accelerated sufficiently to produce additional ionization and thus add to the collected charge. At the onset of region III, the multiplication $M$ for a given applied voltage is independent of the initial ionization, thus preserving the proportionality of pulse sizes. This strict proportionality breaks down with increase in applied voltage until, at the upper limit of region III, the pulse size is independent of the initial ionization. This region, in which gas multiplication is employed while at the same time a dependence of the collected charge on the initial ionization remains, is known commonly as the proportional region. The upper end of it is designated as the region of limited proportionality.

In region IV the charge collected is independent of the ionization initiating it. Rather, gas multiplication increases the charge to a value that is limited by the characteristics of the chamber and the external circuit. This region is known as the G-M region.

## 2–2. *Ionization-chamber Detectors*

An ionization-chamber detector can take many forms, as discussed in Chap. 4. However, a typical form consists of a cylindrical, conducting chamber containing a central conducting electrode located on the axis of the chamber and insulated from it, as in Fig. 2–1. The proper voltage is maintained between the wall of the chamber and the central electrode to operate it in region II of Fig. 2–2. The gas contained in the chamber is often dry air at atmospheric pressure but it may be other gases chosen for particular properties.

Ionization chambers are used to some extent for detection of all types of particles producing either primary or secondary ionization. An example of pulse-type operation is the measurement of the specific ionization and energy of highly ionizing particles such as alpha particles. In this application the ionization-chamber detector is used in conjunction with electronic equipment for pulse-height analysis. In mean-level operation either the current is measured, yielding a quantity proportional to the rate of arrival of nuclear radiation, or the charge released in the chamber over a time is determined, yielding a quantity related to the total radiation incident on the chamber during the period of the measurement. Applications of the latter types are used widely in the monitoring of nuclear radiation for personnel protection.

## 2–3. *Proportional Counters*

In proportional counters the voltage applied between the collector electrode and the chamber wall is such that the detector is operated in region III of Fig. 2–2. Gas-multiplication factors as high as $10^5$ or $10^6$ are sometimes employed.

The most common applications of proportional counters employ pulse-type operation. Use is made of the fact that a gain in pulse size is achieved while the dependence of pulse size on the primary ionization is preserved.

The gas multiplication makes possible the counting of a given type of nuclear particle with less amplification in the associated electronic equipment than is needed with pulse-type ionization chambers. This simplifies the electronic equipment which is required. In addition, the proportional counter can be extended to lower-energy particles than can the pulse-type ionization chamber before the limitation set by the noise level of the electronic amplifier is reached.

The preservation of the dependence of pulse size on the primary ionization makes possible the discrimination between radiation types which differ in the primary ionization that is produced. For example, alpha particles can be counted easily in the presence of beta particles by making use of the large difference in the specific ionization of the two particle types; the smaller pulses produced by the beta particles can be rejected by the counting system.

## 2–4. *Geiger-Müller Tubes*

Gas-type detectors operating in region IV of Fig. 2–2 are known as Geiger-Müller (G-M) tubes. These detectors can be used for counting any type of nuclear particles which will produce ionization within the tube, no matter how small the amount of ionization. The G-M tube is widely used for counting electrons, beta particles, gamma rays, and X rays. It is ideally suited for these radiations since their small specific ionization makes them hard to detect otherwise. Alpha particles and highly ionizing particles are sometimes detected by G-M tubes. However, because of the short range of these particles, either tubes with thin windows are required or the source of radiation must be placed inside the tube.

Because the pulse sizes in the G-M tube are independent of the primary ionization, this factor cannot be used as a measure of particle energy, nor is it possible to discriminate between different types of particles by means of the sensitivity of the electronic circuit.

## 2–5. *Scintillation Detectors*

When ionizing particles pass through certain crystals, flashes of light, or scintillations, are emitted. In the modern scintillation detector, this light is picked up by a photomultiplier tube, and the resulting pulse of current out of the photomultiplier indicates the passage of the ionizing particles through the scintillator. Under proper conditions, the resulting charge is proportional to the energy lost by the ionizing particle in the crystals. Thus, as in the cases of the proportional counter and the pulse ionization chamber, this detector can be used to measure the energy distribution of particles in addition to counting them.

The scintillation detector has found use with all types of particles. At the present time it is the most versatile type of nuclear-radiation detector.

### 2–6. *Other Detectors*

Several other types of detectors are in use and are quite important for specialized detection problems. These methods will only be listed here and will be discussed in some detail in Chaps. 8 and 9. These detectors are cloud chambers, nuclear-track plates, crystal counters, Cerenkov counters, chemical detectors, calorimetric methods, and various types of neutron detectors.

## SURVEY OF RADIATION-DETECTION SYSTEMS

### 2–7. *Particle Counting*

The commonest type of measurement performed with nuclear-radiation detectors is that of particle counting. The number of detector output pulses is the number of particles striking the detector multiplied by the

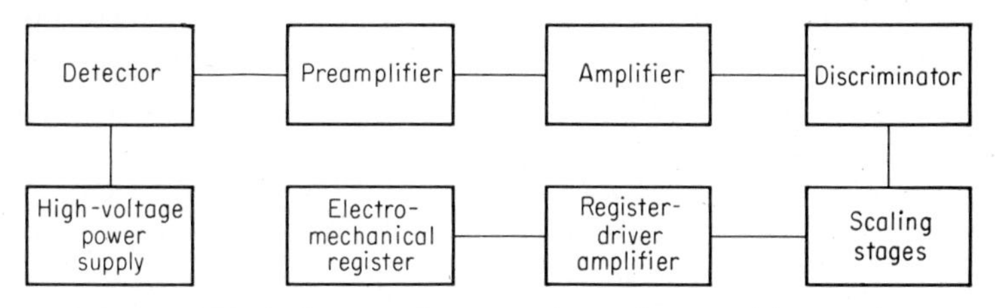


FIG. 2–3. Block diagram of a system for nuclear-particle counting.

efficiency of the detector. In some applications the number of counts occurring in a measured time is determined. Such a detection system is referred to as a counter. These measurements can be converted to an average counting rate by dividing the total counts by the time. In other systems the counting rate is obtained directly by a determination, through an electronic means, of the rate of arrival of the pulses. Such a system is called a counting-rate meter.

Figure 2–3 is a block diagram of a nuclear-radiation-detection system for particle counting. The detector may be any of the preceding types which are capable of pulse-type operation. The output of the detector appears as a pulse of current at the input of the preamplifier.

The preamplifier is located physically close to the detector. Often it only serves the purpose of impedance transformation; that is, it transforms the voltage which is developed across the small capacity at the input of the preamplifier into an approximately equal voltage across the high capacity of an output cable. The output cable may be quite long and may have a total capacity of several hundred micromicrofarads. In systems requiring high total gain, the preamplifier provides a gain up to as much as 100 in addition to impedance matching.

The over-all gain of the system, preamplifier and amplifier combined, depends on the size of the detector output pulses. Gains which are employed vary from about 10 for a Geiger-Müller tube to 10,000 or more for an ionization-chamber instrument.

The discriminator passes only those pulses with a height exceeding a certain minimum. The action of the discriminator makes it possible to reject the smaller noise pulses while counting larger pulses from nuclear radiation. The discriminator also allows the counting of a given radiation type in the presence of other radiation-producing smaller pulses. The use of a proportional counter in this manner was discussed in Sec. 2–3.

The output pulses from the discriminator are of a standard height and usually of a constant width. These go into the scaling stages. The function of these stages is to divide the rate of occurrence of the pulses down to one which can be followed by an electromechanical register. These registers have maximum counting rates varying from about 10 to 60 counts/sec, depending on the type. Since many counting applications require rates of several thousands or even tens of thousands counts per second, electronic scaling is employed.

The most common scaling circuit makes use of scale-of-2 stages (see Sec. 10–12). For each scale-of-2 unit one output pulse appears for two input pulses. Thus a series of $n$ of these circuits gives a dividing factor of $2^n$.

An important characteristic of a counting system is its ability to count accurately at high rates. This property is expressed as the resolving power of the system. The resolving time, which is inversely proportional to the resolving power, is defined as the minimum time which can elapse between the interactions of two successive particles within the detector if they are to produce two counts. In the case of a Geiger-Müller tube, the minimum resolving time is limited by the characteristics of the detector. On the other hand, scintillation detectors, particularly those employing organic scintillators, are fast-acting, and the resolving time for these systems may be limited by the measuring apparatus. In proportional-counter and ionization-chamber instruments, the detectors and measuring apparatus present similar limitations on the resolving time.

If the resolving time $\tau$ is comparable with the average period between counts, an appreciable number of counts are lost. If $\dot{m}$ is the observed counting rate, then the fraction of the time which the counter system is insensitive is $\dot{m}\tau$. Consequently, the number of counts lost per unit time is $\dot{n}\dot{m}\tau$, where $\dot{n}$ is the counting rate which would be observed if the resolving time were negligibly small. Therefore,

$$\dot{n} - \dot{m} = \dot{n}\dot{m}\tau \tag{2-3}$$

or

$$\dot{n} = \frac{\dot{m}}{1 - \dot{m}\tau} \tag{2-4}$$

The correction given by Eq. (2-3) is often referred to as the dead-time correction.

In particle-counting systems, the attempt is made to operate under conditions such that the counting rate for a fixed source is insensitive to changes in such factors as the high voltage applied to the detector. Curves of counting rate versus detector high voltage which exhibit such a region are said to have plateaus. A plateau may be described by its slope expressed in percentage change of counting rate per unit voltage increase and by its length measured in volts.

### 2-8. *Pulse-height Analysis*

Pulse-type detectors in which there is a proportionality between the height of the output pulse and the energy dissipated by the nuclear radiation within the detector make possible the measurements of the energy of nuclear particles. Measurements of this type are usually presented as energy-distribution curves; these may be either integral or differential curves. The latter curve is the type usually required.

The integral energy-distribution curves are plots of $N(E)$, the rate of occurrence of particles with energy equal to or greater than $E$, versus the energy $E$. The differential curves are plots of $dN/dE$ versus $E$. Energy-distribution curves are commonly referred to as spectra, and the equipment for obtaining the curves is known as spectrometers.

The energy-distribution curves may be obtained by measuring the pulse-height distribution of the detector output. The measuring apparatus for obtaining the pulse-height-distribution curves is known as a pulse-height analyzer. Integral pulse-height-distribution curves can be taken with counting apparatus such as that shown in Fig. 2-3, provided that the gain of the amplifier is independent of the pulse height and the discrimination level is adjustable over the range of pulse heights of interest. The first requirement, known as amplifier linearity, is necessary to maintain the proportionality between the height of the input and output pulses. Actually, the requirements of the amplifier and discriminator are considerably more severe for pulse-height analysis than for counting, so that the two types of apparatus are usually not employed in common. The integral pulse-height-distribution curves are obtained from counting rates for various discriminator settings, along with the knowledge of the pulse heights represented by the various discriminator settings.

The differential curves might be obtained by differentiating the integral curves. However, in many spectra the slopes change rapidly, and consequently accurate differential curves cannot be obtained in this manner. Accurate work requires the use of instruments which measure the slope directly; these devices are known as differential pulse-height analyzers. The block diagram of one type of pulse-height analyzer is given in Fig. 2–4. By this analyzer the rate of occurrence of pulses having heights between $H$ and $H + \Delta H$ is determined. The discriminator levels may be varied simultaneously, holding the difference $\Delta H$, which is known as the window, fixed. Thus the differential curve of $\Delta N/\Delta H$ versus $H$ is determined directly. As $\Delta H$ is decreased, this curve approaches the required differential pulse-height curve.

The anticoincidence circuit of Fig. 2–4 passes to the counter only those pulses with heights between $H$ and $H + \Delta H$. This is accomplished by passing only those portions of the pulses from discriminator 1 which do *not*

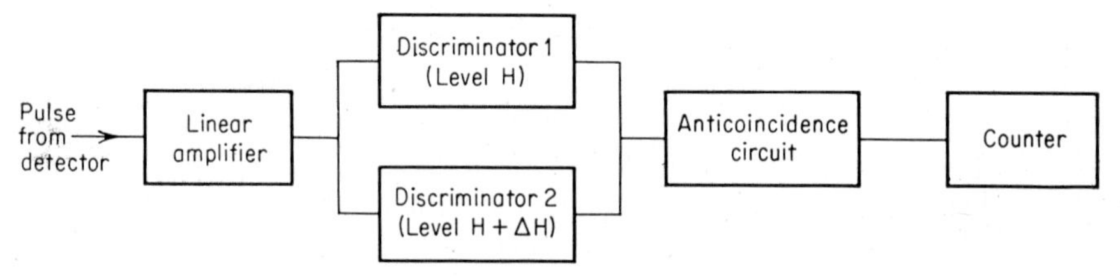


FIG. 2–4. Block diagram of a differential pulse-height analyzer.

arrive at the anticoincidence circuit in time coincidence with pulses from discriminator 2.

## 2–9. *Coincidence Measurements*

In many phases of nuclear-radiation detection, it is necessary to investigate time coincidence between nuclear events. In radioactivity measurements the study of coincidences between beta rays, gamma rays, X rays, etc., gives information on the decay schemes. In cosmic-ray physics, coincidence measurements make possible the study of the direction of incidence of the particles as well as the investigation of the simultaneous production of many particles. Delayed coincidences make possible the measurement of half-lives of the order of 1 $\mu$sec or less. Other applications, too numerous to list here, have been made.

A coincidence circuit is one in which an output pulse occurs only when suitable input signals appear at each of several inputs. In one simple coincidence circuit only two inputs are used. Two pulses, one in each input, will produce an output pulse if they appear in time coincidence. The condition for time coincidence requires that the time between corresponding points on the two pulses be less than $\tau$, the resolving time of the coincidence circuit. With a fast-acting detector, such as the scintillation detector, and an electronic amplifier with small rise times (see Chap. 10), resolving times as low as $10^{-9}$ sec can be obtained.

Because of the finite resolving time, two independent signals may give rise to an output signal due to chance coincidences. These chance coincidences need to be minimized relative to the true coincidences. If $\dot{n}_1$ and $\dot{n}_2$ are the rates at which the pulses arrive at two respective inputs of the coincidence circuits, the rate of occurrence $c$ of chance coincidences is

$$c = 2\tau\dot{n}_1\dot{n}_2 \tag{2-5}$$

where $\tau$ is the resolving time. This expression follows since the probability that a signal at the first input be accompanied by one at the second input within a time $\pm\tau$ is $\dot{n}_2 2\tau$.

## 2–10. *Mean-level Detection Systems*

In several detection systems, the process of averaging the effects produced by many nuclear particles is done within the detector; that is, the

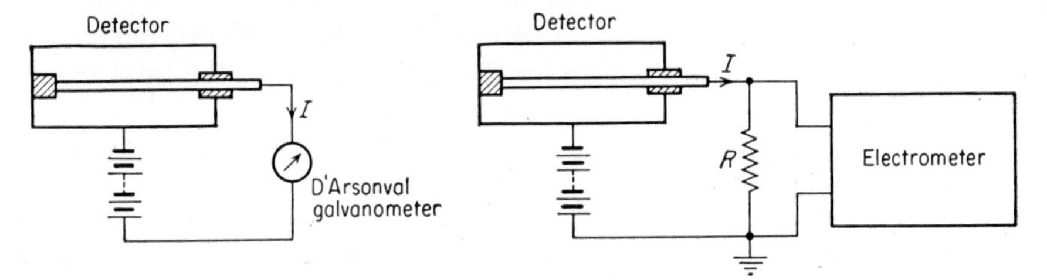


FIG. 2–5. Method for measuring the current flow in an ionization chamber.

individual interactions of the radiation with the detector are not resolved. A detector is employed in which each interaction makes a contribution to the output that is characteristic of the particle causing it. Such a system gives information concerning the amount of radiation striking the detector.

Mean-level detection systems can be divided into those which measure a rate and those which determine a total over a time, i.e., perform an integration. Systems employing ionization-chamber detectors serve as a good example of both methods of operation.

Figure 2–5 illustrates an ionization chamber in a circuit for measuring the current released within the ionization chamber. The current is proportional to the intensity of the radiation striking the detector. For large-intensity radiation fields such as that found within a reactor shield or other high-level facility, the currents can be sufficiently large (perhaps a microampere) to be measured directly by a conventional sensitive ammeter of the D'Arsonval type. However, in many applications the current is around $10^{-12}$ amp or less. For these cases the current flow may be determined by measuring the voltage drop across a known resistor. The electrometer employed is essentially a voltmeter with an input resistance high compared with the resistor $R$.

For the measurement of the total radiation striking the detector over a time, a condenser-type ionization chamber may be employed. Figure 2–6 is a schematic diagram of this system, including an ionization-chamber detector, a battery for charging it, and a voltmeter for reading the residual charge. Placing the switch in position 1 charges the chamber. If the switch is then placed in position 2 and the chamber is exposed to radiation, the reduction in stored charge will be equal to the total ionization produced within the chamber.

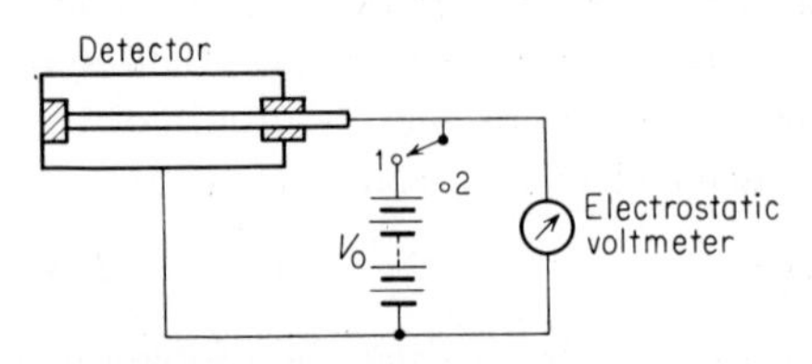


FIG. 2–6. Schematic diagram of a condenser-type ionization-chamber instrument.

In addition to ionization chambers, proportional counters, scintillation detectors, and crystal counters also can be used for rate measurements in a similar manner. Also, chemical detectors, calorimetric methods, and photographic films are used extensively for the measurement of the total radiation over a period of time.

## 2–11. *Other Detection Systems*

In addition to the detection systems discussed above, there are a number of other methods applicable to specific detector types. These include such methods as nuclear-emulsion and cloud-chamber techniques. Discussion of these and other specialized techniques is included in the chapters dealing with the specific detectors.

# CHAPTER 3

# STATISTICS OF DETECTION SYSTEMS

The measurements of nuclear radiation which are carried out by the methods described in this textbook involve phenomena which are statistical in nature. The understanding of these statistical effects is important both from the standpoint of the design of the experiments and in the interpretation of the results. The statistical nature of detection systems is discussed first for pulse-type counters and then is extended to mean-level detection systems.

## STATISTICS OF COUNTING

### 3–1. *Introduction*

The statistical nature of counting experiments can be introduced by considering a pulse-type detector, such as a Geiger-Müller type, subjected to the gamma radiation emitted from a radioactive source. An experiment of this type involves statistical processes in both the emission of the radiation and the interaction of the radiation with the tube.

Table 3–1 gives the background count taken in a typical radiochemistry laboratory by a Geiger-Müller counter. The data are 30 separate measurements, each taken for a 1-min interval. The source of the radiation was "steady"; that is, during the 30 min while the measurements were being made, the source of the radiation did not change in its nature. Nevertheless, the number of counts recorded per minute is clearly not uniform. This is the statistical nature of the phenomenon.

One cannot speak of a *true* rate of occurrence of counts in a nuclear-radiation detector but rather only of a true *average* rate. By the true average rate one means the value approached as the total number of counts employed for the determination of the average is increased. For the data in Table 3–1, the value most nearly equal to the true average for the 1-min interval is the arithmetic mean $\bar{n}$ of all the determinations. This is given by

$$\bar{n} = \frac{1}{N}\sum_{i=1}^{N} n_i \qquad (3\text{–}1)$$

where $n_i$ is the number of counts in the $i$th interval and $N$ is the total number of intervals. For the example given, $\bar{n}$ is 28.2 counts.

TABLE 3-1. STATISTICAL FLUCTUATIONS IN RADIATION COUNTING

| Number of counts in 1-min interval, $n_i$ | $\lvert \bar{n} - n_i \rvert$ | $(\bar{n} - n_i)^2$ |
|---|---|---|
| 29 | 0.8 | 0.64 |
| 36 | 7.8 | 60.84 |
| 19 | 9.2 | 84.64 |
| 26 | 2.2 | 4.84 |
| 24 | 4.2 | 22.48 |
| 37 | 8.8 | 77.44 |
| 35 | 6.8 | 46.24 |
| 29 | 0.8 | 0.64 |
| 30 | 1.8 | 3.24 |
| 34 | 5.8 | 33.64 |
| 27 | 1.2 | 1.44 |
| 24 | 4.2 | 17.64 |
| 32 | 3.8 | 14.44 |
| 21 | 7.2 | 51.84 |
| 14 | 14.2 | 201.64 |
| 33 | 4.8 | 23.04 |
| 30 | 1.8 | 3.24 |
| 27 | 1.2 | 1.44 |
| 28 | 0.2 | 0.04 |
| 30 | 1.8 | 3.24 |
| 35 | 6.8 | 46.24 |
| 30 | 1.8 | 3.24 |
| 27 | 1.2 | 1.44 |
| 25 | 3.2 | 10.24 |
| 24 | 4.2 | 17.64 |
| 32 | 3.8 | 14.44 |
| 23 | 5.2 | 27.04 |
| 27 | 1.2 | 1.44 |
| 33 | 4.8 | 23.04 |
| 24 | 4.2 | 17.64 |
| Sum 845 | | 815.04 |

$$\bar{n} = \frac{\Sigma n_i}{N} = \frac{845}{30} = 28.2 \text{ counts}$$

By the use of statistical analysis, estimates can be made of the accuracy of counting determinations, and counting procedures can be devised which will minimize errors due to the random nature of the process. In addition, the apparatus can be tested for fluctuations due to causes other than statistical by comparing the actual distribution in counts with that predicted by the statistical law.

### 3–2. *Binomial Distribution*

The binomial distribution is the statistical law which is followed. Consider a very large set of objects consisting of two classes, say $A$ and $B$. Let $p$ represent the probability that any object selected at random will be of class $A$; then $1 - p$ is the probability that it will be of class $B$. The probability $W(n)$ that exactly $n$ of $N_o$ objects selected from the set will be of class $A$ can be shown to be

$$W(n) = \frac{N_o!}{(N_o - n)!n!} p^n (1 - p)^{N_o - n} \tag{3–2}$$

This equation is known as the binomial distribution because the term $N_o!/(N_o - n)!n!$ is the coefficient of the $n$th term in the binomial expansion of $(1 + x)^{N_o}$.

The average value $\bar{n}$ is given by $pN_o$. The deviation from the average may be expressed as the root-mean-square deviation called the standard deviation $\sigma$. The standard deviation is given by

$$\sigma^2 = \overline{(\bar{n} - n)^2} = \sum_{n=0}^{n=N_o} (\bar{n} - n)^2 W(n) \tag{3–3}$$

Expanding this,

$$\sigma^2 = \sum_{n=0}^{n=N_o} \bar{n}^2 W(n) - \sum_{n=0}^{n=N_o} 2\bar{n}nW(n) + \sum_{n=0}^{n=N_o} n^2 W(n) = \overline{n^2} - \bar{n}^2 \tag{3–4}$$

where

$$\overline{n^2} = \sum_{n=0}^{n=N_o} n^2 W(n) \tag{3–5}$$

In this calculation,

$$\sum_{n=0}^{n=N_o} W(n) = 1 \tag{3–6}$$

When Eq. (3–5) is evaluated [1], using the binomial distribution, and is substituted into Eq. (3–4) along with the value $\bar{n} = pN_o$, the standard deviation becomes

$$\sigma = [N_o p(1 - p)]^{1/2} \tag{3–7}$$

### 3-3. *Binomial Distribution for Radioactive Decay*

Consider the radioactive decay in the time $t$ of a system containing $N_o$ radioactive atoms. These $N_o$ atoms can be divided into two groups, those that decay in time $t$ and those that do not decay. The probability that a given atom does not decay is simply $e^{-\lambda t}$, where $\lambda$ is the decay constant for the species in question. It follows also that the probability $p$ for decay is

$$p = 1 - e^{-\lambda t} \tag{3-8}$$

Using Eq. (3-2), one has for the probability $W(n)$ that $n$ atoms will decay in time $t$

$$W(n) = \frac{N_o!}{(N_o - n)!n!}(1 - e^{-\lambda t})^n(e^{-\lambda t})^{N_o - n} \tag{3-9}$$

The true average number decaying in time $t$ is

$$\bar{n} = N_o(1 - e^{-\lambda t}) \tag{3-10}$$

Therefore the standard deviation is

$$\sigma = [N_o(1 - e^{-\lambda t})e^{-\lambda t}]^{1/2} = (\bar{n}e^{-\lambda t})^{1/2} \tag{3-11}$$

For $\lambda t \ll 1$, that is, for observation times short compared with the half-life, the standard deviation is simply

$$\sigma = (\bar{n})^{1/2} \tag{3-12}$$

If $c$ denotes the probability that a disintegration results in a count, then $p$, the probability of an atom producing a count in time $t$, is

$$p = (1 - e^{-\lambda t})c \tag{3-13}$$

Again for the condition $\lambda t \ll 1$, Eq. (3-12) holds, with $\bar{n}$ representing the average number of counts.

### 3-4. *Poisson and Gaussian Distributions*

Under the restrictions $\lambda t \ll 1$, $N_o \gg 1$ and $n \ll N_o$, the binomial-distribution law for radioactive decay can be put into a more convenient form. To accomplish this, the following mathematical approximations are used:

$$e^{\lambda t} \simeq 1 + \lambda t \tag{3-14}$$

$$x! \simeq (2\pi x)^{1/2}\, e^{-x}\, x^x \tag{3-15}$$

$$\left(1 - \frac{n}{N_o}\right)^{N_o} \simeq \lim_{N_o \to \infty}\left(1 - \frac{n}{N_o}\right)^{N_o} = e^{-n} \tag{3-16}$$

Upon making these substitutions, Eq. (3-9) becomes

$$W(n) = \frac{\bar{n}^n e^{-\bar{n}}}{n!} \tag{3-17}$$

This distribution law is known as Poisson's distribution. It is a good approximation for $N_0$ as small as 100 and $\lambda t$ as large as 0.01.

Equation (3–17) is defined only for integral values of $n$. However, a smooth curve can be drawn through these points. This leads to an unsymmetrical curve for small values of $\bar{n}$. Figure 3–1 shows the Poisson distribution for $\bar{n} = 20$. As the value of $\bar{n}$ increases, this curve becomes more symmetrical.

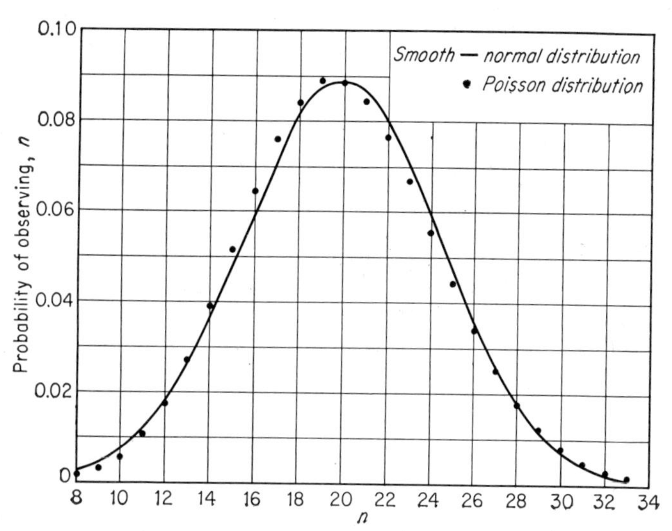


FIG. 3–1. The Gaussian or normal distribution as an approximation of the Poisson distribution at an average value of 20.

Under the approximations that $n$ is large (say $> 100$) and that $|\bar{n} - n| \ll \bar{n}$, Eq. (3–9) can be approximated by [2]

$$W(n) = (2\pi\bar{n})^{-1/2} \exp\left[\frac{-(\bar{n} - n)^2}{2\bar{n}}\right] \tag{3–18}$$

which is the Gaussian, or normal, distribution law. This distribution is also presented in Fig. 3–1 for $\bar{n} = 20$, an average considerably lower than that for which the approximation is good.

If the absolute deviation from the mean $|\bar{n} - n|$ is given the symbol $\epsilon$, Eq. (3–18) becomes

$$W(\epsilon) = \frac{(2/\pi)^{1/2}}{\sigma} e^{-\epsilon^2/2\sigma^2} \tag{3–19}$$

The probability $P(k\sigma)$ of obtaining an absolute deviation greater than $k\sigma$ is obtained by evaluating the expression

$$P(k\sigma) = \int_{k\sigma}^{\infty} W(\epsilon)\, d\epsilon \tag{3–20}$$

Numerical values of this integral are found in probability tables [3]. Some values which are referred to in the succeeding sections appear in Table 3–2.

TABLE 3–2. PROBABILITY OF EXCEEDING GIVEN DEVIATION

| $\frac{\|\bar{n} - n\|}{\sigma} = k$ | 0 | 0.6745 | 1.000 | 1.6449 | 1.9600 |
|---|---|---|---|---|---|
| $P(k\sigma)$ | 1.000 | 0.5000 | 0.3173 | 0.1000 | 0.0500 |
| Terminology | ..... | Probable error | Standard error | Nine-tenths error | Ninety-five-hundredths error |

**Example 3–1.** If the true average for a given time interval is 100 counts, determine the probability of obtaining 105 counts for the same time interval and that for obtaining an absolute deviation from this true average of greater than 5.

*Solution.* The standard deviation $\sigma$ is $(100)^{1/2} = 10$; therefore $k$ is $5/10$. By tables of the normal-error curve, the value of the ordinate $(2/\pi)^{1/2}e^{-k^2/2}$ is 0.3521. Therefore the probability is $0.3521/\sigma = 0.03521$ of obtaining 105. By the same tables, the area under the probability curve from $k$ equals 0 to 0.5 is 0.1915. Therefore the probability of exceeding a deviation of 5 is $1 - 2(0.1915) = 0.617$.

## 3–5. *Accuracy of Counting Measurements*

In most counting equipment the errors introduced by the processes of totalizing the counts and measuring the elapsed time are negligible compared with the statistical error. Based on this assumption, the accuracy of the counting determinations can be estimated. The standard deviation will be used for the precision index in the following discussion. Of course, this can be changed readily to other types of errors by multiplying by the appropriate values of $k$ listed in Table 3–2.

The case of greatest applicability is that in which $\lambda t$ is much less than 1. For this condition, $\sigma^2$ was found to be the true average number of counts for the time interval in question. In the usual case the true average is not known. Rather, a single determination of $n$ counts is made. This value is reported as $n \pm n^{1/2}$. The meaning of the precision index is that there are only about 32 chances out of 100 that the true average number of counts for this time interval differs from $n$ by more than $n^{1/2}$. Here it is assumed that

$$n \simeq \bar{n} = \sigma^2 \tag{3–21}$$

As an example, consider the data in Table 3–1. The value of $\bar{n}$ is 28.2 counts. For the first interval counted, $n \pm (n)^{1/2}$ is $29 \pm (29)^{1/2}$; these limits include $\bar{n}$. The results for the next two intervals, being $36 \pm (36)^{1/2}$ and $19 \pm (19)^{1/2}$, do not include $\bar{n}$. Ten of the thirty intervals, or 33 per cent, do not contain $\bar{n}$ in the interval defined by these standard-deviation calculations. This is exceptionally good agreement with the theory.

If $n$ is the number of counts totalized over a time interval $t$, the counting rate $r$ is

$$r = \frac{n}{t} \tag{3-22}$$

This value with its standard deviation may be stated as

$$r \pm \sigma_r = \frac{n}{t} \pm \frac{n^{1/2}}{t} = r \pm \left(\frac{r}{t}\right)^{1/2} \tag{3-23}$$

Stated in terms of percentage error, this is

$$r \pm \frac{100}{(rt)^{1/2}}\% = r \pm \frac{100}{n^{1/2}}\% \tag{3-24}$$

Table 3-3 gives the percentage errors for several values of $n$.

TABLE 3-3. TOTAL COUNTS REQUIRED FOR GIVEN ERROR

| Error, % | Counts | | |
|---|---|---|---|
| | Standard error | Probable error | Nine-tenths error |
| 0.1 | $10^6$ | $4.5 \times 10^5$ | $2.7 \times 10^6$ |
| 0.3 | $1.1 \times 10^5$ | $5.1 \times 10^4$ | $3.0 \times 10^5$ |
| 1 | $10^4$ | $4.5 \times 10^3$ | $2.7 \times 10^4$ |
| 3 | $1.1 \times 10^3$ | 506 | $3.0 \times 10^3$ |
| 10 | 100 | 45 | 271 |

When several quantities having standard deviations $\sigma_1, \sigma_2, \cdots, \sigma_n$ are combined by either addition or subtraction, the standard deviation $\sigma_s$ of the result is

$$\sigma_s = (\sigma_1^2 + \sigma_2^2 + \cdots + \sigma_n^2)^{1/2} \tag{3-25}$$

The absolute values rather than the fractional or percentage values of the errors must be used in Eq. (3-25).

As an example, consider a background counting rate of $r_b \pm \sigma_b$ and a total counting rate, due to both the source and the background, of $r_T \pm \sigma_T$. The counting rate $r_s$ due to the source only is

$$r_s \pm \sigma_s = (r_T - r_b) \pm (\sigma_b^2 + \sigma_T^2)^{1/2} \tag{3-26}$$

### 3-6. *Design of Counting Experiments*

The application of the previous results makes possible the calculation of the number of counts required for a given accuracy. The judicious use of these results can often save time in counting experiments by eliminating useless counts.

When a single count determination is to be made, the results in Table 3–3 can be applied directly. A more common measurement consists of the determination of $r_s$, the net counting rate due to a source, from a total counting rate $r_T$ and a background counting rate $r_b$. The optimum division of time between the determination of $r_T$ and $r_b$ to obtain the highest accuracy in a fixed time can be calculated. Two types of situations should be considered in this regard.

If it is required to make a series of counts on different samples and if during the counting period there is no reason to suspect a change in the background counting rate, it will usually be advantageous to make relatively accurate background measurements so that $\sigma_b$ is negligible, say an order of magnitude smaller than $\sigma_T$. It is advisable to take several such measurements to check the constancy of the background. As an example, one determination can be made at the beginning and another at the end of each day's measurements.

The other situation is that in which a fixed time is available for making both a total-counting-rate and a background-rate determination. If $t_b$ and $t_T$ are the times taken for the background and total activity counts, respectively, then $\sigma_s$, the standard deviation of the net counting rate, is, from Eqs. (3–26) and (3–23),

$$\sigma_s = \left(\frac{r_b}{t_b} + \frac{r_T}{t_T}\right)^{1/2} \tag{3–27}$$

By differentiation,

$$2\sigma_s\, d\sigma_s = -\frac{r_b}{t_b^2}\, dt_b - \frac{r_T}{t_T^2}\, dt_T$$

Setting $d\sigma_s = 0$, the condition for minimum error, and $dt_b + dt_T = 0$, the condition for constant time, the result

$$\frac{t_b}{t_T} = \left(\frac{r_b}{r_T}\right)^{1/2} \tag{3–28}$$

is obtained for the optimum use of the counting time. To determine this ratio at the start of the experiment, approximate values of the two rates as determined by short counting times are adequate.

**Example 3–2.** One hour is available for a counting-rate determination including the background measurement. What is the optimum division of time between sample and background counting if the accuracy is to be the largest possible in the allowed time? Case 1: approximate total and background rates of 1,000 and 20 counts/min, respectively; case 2: 60 and 20 counts/min, respectively. Calculate also the percentage accuracy obtained in each case.

*Solution.* By Eq. (3–28),

$$\frac{t_b}{t_T} = \left(\frac{r_b}{r_T}\right)^{1/2} = \left(\frac{20}{1{,}000}\right)^{1/2} = 0.14 \text{ for case 1}$$

and 0.575 for case 2. Since $t_b + t_T = 60$ min, $t_T$ and $t_b$ are 53 and 7 min, respectively, for case 1, while their values are 38 and 22 min for case 2.

The percentage accuracy is obtained from Eq. (3–28) and the meaning of per cent as

$$\frac{(r_T/t_T + r_b/t_b)^{1/2}}{r_T - r_b}\,100\% = \frac{(1{,}000/53 + 20/7)^{1/2}}{1{,}000 - 20}\,100\% = 0.3\%$$

for case 1 and

$$\frac{(60/38 + 20/22)^{1/2}}{60 - 20}\,100\% = 4\%$$

for case 2.

The question as to when a counting rate represents a change greater than statistical fluctuations from a previously determined rate can be investigated by use of the statisticians' concept of level of significance [4]. The ninety-five-hundredths error, referred to as the 0.05 level, is often used for this purpose. As an example, if measurements of a counting rate exceed an accurately determined background rate by more than the 0.05 level of significance, the increase is said to be significant, since it is greater than that expected due to statistical fluctuations.

An additional application of statistics to counting comes through the guidance it provides in the rejection of data. Chauvenet's criterion [2] is frequently used for this purpose. The criterion states that any one in a series of $m$ readings will be rejected when its deviation from the mean of the series is such that the probability of the occurrence of all deviations from the mean that are as large or larger is less than $1/2m$. Table 3–4 gives the magnitude of this deviation in terms of multiples $k$ of $\sigma$ for several values of $m$.

TABLE 3–4. MAXIMUM ACCEPTABLE DEVIATIONS IN ACCORDANCE WITH CHAUVENET'S CRITERION

| No. of readings, $m$ | 2 | 3 | 4 | 5 | 7 | 10 | 15 | 25 |
|---|---|---|---|---|---|---|---|---|
| $k$, ratio of deviation to standard deviation | 1.15 | 1.38 | 1.54 | 1.65 | 1.80 | 1.96 | 2.13 | 2.33 |

## 3–7. *Test of Counting Equipment*

When counting equipment is suspected of recording spurious counts arising from factors other than the nuclear radiation, this can be checked by comparing the deviations in the results for successive measurements. One method [5] consists of calculating the standard error of the difference between two counting-rate determinations on the same source and comparing this with the observed difference between the two determinations. The standard error of the difference of two counting rates $r_1$ and $r_2$ taken in time intervals $t_1$ and $t_2$, respectively, is, by Eqs. (3–23) and (3–25),

$$\sigma = \left(\frac{r_1}{t_1} + \frac{r_2}{t_2}\right)^{1/2} \qquad (3\text{–}29)$$

The probability of observing an absolute difference $|r_1 - r_2|$ in counting rates equal to or greater than $k\sigma$ is given in Table 3–5 for several values

TABLE 3–5. PROBABILITY $P$ OF OBTAINING $|r_1 - r_2| \geq k\sigma$

| $k$ | 1.0 | 1.2 | 1.4 | 1.6 | 2.0 | 2.5 | 3.0 | 4.0 |
|---|---|---|---|---|---|---|---|---|
| $P$ | 0.159 | 0.115 | 0.081 | 0.055 | 0.023 | 0.006 | 0.001 | 0.00003 |

of $k$. If the probability of the observed deviation is less than 0.05, it is likely that the deviations are due to causes other than the statistical nature of the disintegration process.

**Example 3–3.** Two counting rates of 1,010 and 1,069 counts/min are obtained by two 10-min counts of a source with long half-life. Does the counting equipment appear to be operating normally?

*Solution.* By Eq. (3–29),

$$\sigma = \left(\frac{r_1}{t_1} + \frac{r_2}{t_2}\right)^{1/2} = 14 \text{ counts/min}$$

Therefore $k = 59/14 = 4.2$. From Table 3–5, the probability of obtaining this difference because of statistical fluctuations is less than 3 in 100,000. Therefore it is quite certain that the counter is receiving erratic counts.

One further useful technique in this regard is the so-called "chi-squared test" [6]. This test allows the evaluation of the probability that a given set of data follows the Gaussian distribution. To make this test, the quantity $\chi^2$, defined as

$$\chi^2 = \frac{\sum_{i=1}^{N} (\bar{n} - n_i)^2}{\bar{n}} \qquad (3\text{–}30)$$

is calculated. Here $N$ is the number of times that a given counting determination is made, $n_i$ is the value obtained in the $i$th measurement, and $\bar{n}$ is the average value. Tables which give the probability $P$ of obtaining given values of $\chi^2$ for various values of $N$ are available in Ref. 6.

**Example 3–4.** What is the probability that the data in Table 3–1 follow the Gaussian distribution?

*Solution.* The quantity $\chi^2$ is

$$\chi^2 = \frac{\sum_{i=1}^{30} (\bar{n} - n_i)^2}{\bar{n}} = \frac{815}{28.2} = 29$$

and the probability that the distribution is Gaussian is given by Ref. 6 as 0.5.

## MEAN-LEVEL SYSTEMS

### 3–8. *Statistical Considerations in Mean-level Detection Systems*

The previous considerations can also be applied to estimate the statistical variations in detection systems other than counters. The example considered is the mean-level ionization chamber, of both the integrating and the rate type.

In the integrating-type chamber a measurement is made of the charge which is released by the ionization in a fixed time interval. If $Q$ is the total charge released and $q$ is the total charge released per nuclear particle which interacts with the chamber, then $n$, the number of particles interacting, is

$$n = \frac{Q}{q} \tag{3–31}$$

The fractional value of the standard deviation in $n$ due to the statistical nature of the decay process is $(Q/q)^{-1/2}$, and one can write

$$\sigma_Q = \left(\frac{q}{Q}\right)^{1/2}(100\%) = (Qq)^{1/2} \tag{3–32}$$

This consideration neglects the fluctuations in the value of $q$, the charge produced per particle. Therefore the actual statistical variations will be at least as great as that given by Eq. (3–32).

**Example 3–5.** Compute the standard deviation in the charge collected in an ionization chamber if the magnitude of the charge is $10^{-12}$ coulomb and it is known to be produced by beta particles dissipating an average of 20 kev/particle in the chamber.

*Solution.* Taking the energy to produce an ion pair as 32.5 ev, $q$ is

$$q = \frac{(20 \times 10^{3})(1.6 \times 10^{-19})}{32.5} = 9.84 \times 10^{-17} \text{ coulomb}$$

Therefore $\sigma_Q$ is

$$\sigma_Q = \left(\frac{9.84 \times 10^{-17}}{10^{-12}}\right)^{1/2} (100\%) = 0.94\%$$

In the rate-type ionization-chamber instruments such as that shown in Fig. 2–5, the instantaneous value of the meter output fluctuates even though the source of radiation has a constant average value. These variations are contributed to by the exponential discharge-charge characteristic of the input circuit, as well as by the statistical variations in the rate of arrival of the radiation. The amount of fluctuation changes with the time constant of the circuit. The time constant is the product of the input resistance $R$ of the electrometer which follows the chamber and the total input capacity $C$ of the circuit, as discussed in Sec. 4–11. Increasing the time constant tends to smooth out the current fluctuations. The standard deviation $\sigma_I$

of an instantaneous value taken at random, under equilibrium conditions, is

$$\sigma_I = \left(\frac{q\bar{I}}{2RC}\right)^{1/2} \tag{3-33}$$

where $\bar{I}$ is the average current. This is obtained as follows: The charge on the capacitor at time $t_o$ is that remaining from the charge contributed over the preceding period of operation. Thus, of the average charge $rq\,dt$ which is produced between $t$ and $t + dt$, the quantity $rq \exp[-(t_o - t)/RC]\,dt$ remains, where $r$ is the average rate of occurrence of the particles. The standard deviation of the charge produced between $t$ and $t + dt$ is given by Eq. (3–12) as $q(r\,dt)^{1/2}$. The contribution of this deviation to that at $t_o$ is $q(r\,dt)^{1/2} \exp[-(t_o - t)/RC]$. Since the individual contributions are independent, the square of their deviations can be added to obtain the mean-deviation square $\sigma_Q^2$ of the net charge. Therefore,

$$\sigma_Q^2 = \int_{-\infty}^{t_o} q^2 r \exp\left[\frac{-2(t_o - t)}{RC}\right] dt = \frac{q^2 rRC}{2} \tag{3-34}$$

Using the relationships $rq = \bar{I}$ and $I = Q/CR$ in Eq. (3–34) leads to Eq. (3–33). Expressed as a relative value, the standard deviation is

$$\sigma_I = \left(\frac{q}{2\bar{I}RC}\right)^{1/2} 100\% = \left(\frac{1}{2rRC}\right)^{1/2} 100\% \tag{3-35}$$

**Example 3–6.** Consider a current-type ionization-chamber instrument used to measure the current from an alpha source. What is the expected standard deviation in a single reading when the average current is $10^{-12}$ amp, if the input time constant is 2 sec and each alpha particle produces $10^5$ ion pairs?

*Solution.* By Eq. (3–33),

$$\sigma_I = \left(\frac{q\bar{I}}{2RC}\right)^{1/2} = \left[\frac{(10^5)(1.6 \times 10^{-19})(10^{-12})}{(2)(2)}\right]^{1/2} = 6 \times 10^{-14} \text{ amp, or } 6\%$$

The accuracy can be improved by taking the average of several instantaneous readings or, better, by taking the time average of the recorded output. This latter average is the line on the recorder trace drawn in such a manner that the first moment vanishes. The ratio of the standard deviation $\sigma_T$ of the time average over a time $T$ to $\sigma_1$, that of a single reading, has been shown [7] to be

$$\frac{\sigma_T}{\sigma_1} = \frac{2RC}{T}\left(1 - \frac{RC}{T} + \frac{RC}{T} e^{-T/RC}\right) \tag{3-36}$$

The results given above are also applicable to counting-rate meters of the type discussed in Chap. 10. For this application the time constant is that of the integrating circuit of the counting-rate meter.

## PROBLEMS

**3-1.** The disintegrations from a radioactive sample are being counted. The true average counting rate is determined to be 12 counts/sec. Using Poisson's formula, determine the probability that the number of counts in any one second will lie between 19 and 21, inclusive.

**3-2.** Consider 1,000 measurements of a radioactive-decay phenomenon, each made in a fixed time interval. Assume that the time required to make these measurements is small compared with the half-life of the radioisotope.

*a.* If the average number of counts per interval is 10, how many of the 1,000 trials should yield exactly 10? Exactly 5?

*b.* What is the standard deviation on the average 10, and what is the meaning of this $\sigma$?

*c.* What is the standard deviation of a single one of the thousand measurements, and what is the meaning of this deviation?

**3-3.** Living or once-living matter contains a small $C^{14}$ activity. This activity is believed to arise from bombardment of atmospheric nitrogen by cosmic-ray neutrons, chiefly in the upper atmosphere. This radiocarbon enters living systems by exchange processes and reaches an equilibrium concentration. After death, exchange stops, and the amount of radiocarbon decreases with the half-life of $C^{14}$. By comparing the specific activity in the dead material with that in the atmosphere, the time since death can be computed. In a particular experiment of this sort, the total counting rate was about 14.0 counts/min, and the background was 9.5 counts/min. How long would it take to measure the activity due to $C^{14}$ to a precision of 4 per cent? How long would it take if the background were twice as great?

**3-4.** Prove that the accuracy that can be obtained in a fixed counting time increases as the square root of the counter efficiency, provided that the efficiency for counting the sample activity and the background both increase by the same amount.

**3-5.** The background counting rate and the total counting rate are $500 \pm 20$ and $750 \pm 25$ counts/min, respectively, where the error quoted is the standard deviation. Compute the absolute value and the percentage value of the standard deviation for the net counting rate.

**3-6.** A sample was counted for 8 min, and the average counting rate was 25.0 counts/min. The background was counted for 4 min and averaged 18.0 counts/min. What is the probable error for this determination of the sample activity?

**3-7.** Show that the probability of obtaining an error of $1.96\sigma$ is 0.05. (NOTE. This error is referred to as the 0.95 error.)

**3-8.** It is desired to make a measurement of the counting rate due to a radioactive sample to the largest possible accuracy in a time of 10 min. The counting rate due to the sample is the difference between the counting rate due to the sample plus background and that due to background only. A 1-min count with and without the sample resulted in 980 and 42 counts, respectively. What would be the optimum counting schedule with and without the sample, and what would be the accuracy of the result?

**3-9.** Two successive measurements on a single source, each for the same duration of time, yield 4,012 and 4,067 counts, respectively. Is this amount of deviation normal?

**3-10.** Five successive readings of a given phenomenon yield counts of 1,010, 1,018, 1,002, 950, 1,060. If it is desired to compute the most significant average from this data, should any of these counts be rejected?

**3-11.** Apply the "chi-squared" test to determine the probability that the spread in the data given in Prob. 3-10 is due to statistical variations.

**3-12.** A condenser-type ionization chamber is used to integrate the gamma-ray dose accumulated in a region. If the mean distance which the secondary electrons travel through the air of the chamber is 1 cm, estimate the standard deviation of the accumulated dose when the total charge that is released is $10^{-13}$ coulomb.

**3–13.** A rate meter employing an ionization chamber is equipped with a recorder. The average current is $10^{-11}$ amp in a certain gamma-ray field. The time constant of the input circuit is 2 sec, and the average energy loss per secondary electron passing through the chamber is 500 ev. Compute the standard deviation of an instantaneous reading of the recorder and of the average of the recorder trace over a 1-min interval.

## REFERENCES

1. Friedlander, G., and J. W. Kennedy: "Introduction to Nuclear Chemistry," chap. 9, John Wiley & Sons, Inc., New York, 1949.
2. Beers, Y.: "Theory of Errors," chap. 7, Addison-Wesley Publishing Company, Reading, Mass., 1953.
3. "Handbook of Chemistry and Physics," p. 200, Chemical Rubber Publishing Company, Cleveland, 1949.
4. Weatherburn, C. E.: "Mathematical Statistics," p. 171, Cambridge University Press, London, 1946.
5. Jarrett, A. A.: *U.S. Atomic Energy Comm. Document* AECU-262, 1946.
6. Fisher, R. A.: "Statistical Methods for Research Workers," p. 112, Hafner Publishing Company, New York, 1950.
7. Schiff, L. I., and R. D. Evans: *Rev. Sci. Instr.*, **7**:456 (1936).

CHAPTER 4

# IONIZATION CHAMBERS

An ionization chamber operates by collecting ionization that is produced within it. If this detector is to be used for quantitative measurements, it must furnish an output having a definite relationship to this ionization. This requires that a known fraction of the charge that is produced in the chamber be collected. In pulse-type chambers the time dependence of the charge collection is another important consideration, as it affects the pulse shape. As a background for these discussions, the motion of electrons and ions in gases will be treated briefly.

## MOTION OF ELECTRONS AND IONS IN GASES

### 4–1. *Introduction*

The ionization of a gas by nuclear radiation consists of the removal of one or more electrons from a number of gas molecules; thus positive ions and free electrons are formed. The behavior of these charged particles after formation depends on the conditions within the chamber, including the type of gas and the electric field.

The free electrons make many collisions with the gas molecules as they move about. The average distance traveled between collisions, i.e., the mean free path, in a given type of gas is inversely proportional to the number of molecules per unit volume. For most common gases the mean free path at normal temperature and pressure lies in the range from $5 \times 10^{-5}$ to $3 \times 10^{-4}$ cm. Precise values have been tabulated by Staub [1].

The direction of the electron motion is random. However, there is a net drift in the direction opposite to that of the electric field. The average drift velocity $w$ is given in terms of the quantity $\mu$, known as the mobility, by the expression

$$w = \mu \frac{E}{p} \tag{4–1}$$

where $E$ is the electric-field strength and $p$ is the gas pressure. The quantity $\mu$ varies with the type of gas; in addition, it depends strongly on both the electric-field strength and the gas pressure. Tabulations valid over limited ranges of pressure and electric-field strength are available [1] for several gases. For most gases the order of magnitude of $\mu$ for electrons is $10^6$ (cm/sec)(volts/cm)$^{-1}$ (mm Hg) for low values of $E/p$. However, for $E/p$ greater than about 1 to 10 (volt/cm)(mm Hg)$^{-1}$, the electron drift velocity approaches a constant value of about $10^6$ to $10^7$ cm/sec.

**Example 4–1.** Estimate the drift velocity of electrons in a parallel-plate ionization chamber containing argon at atmospheric pressure, if the applied voltage is 1,000 volts and the plate spacing is 2 cm.

*Solution.* By use of Eq. (4–1),

$$w = \mu \frac{E}{p} = \frac{\mu 1{,}000/2}{760} = 0.66 \times 10^6 \text{ cm/sec}$$

where $\mu$ is approximated by $10^6$.

There is a tendency for the electrons to attach themselves to the neutral atoms or molecules with which they collide, thus forming negative ions. The electron attachment coefficient $h$ is defined as the probability of attachment per collision of an electron with neutral molecules (or atoms). Values [2] of the attachment coefficient vary widely with the gas type. In addition, $h$ depends strongly on the electron energy and therefore on the electric-field strength. The halogen gases form negative ions quite easily, having values of $h$ around $10^{-3}$. Oxygen and water vapor also have large electron affinities, the value of $h$ being about $10^{-4}$. On the other hand, a number of gases, including argon, hydrogen, nitrogen, carbon monoxide, methane, and ammonia, have coefficients of $10^{-6}$ or smaller. The prevention of the formation of negative ions requires that $1/h$, the number of collisions required per attachment, be large compared with the number of collisions undergone by the electron in passing to the collector electrode. The latter depends on the gas pressure, electric-field strength, and dimensions of the chamber. To prevent negative-ion formation, the halogen gases, oxygen, and water vapor must be avoided. For example, in precise energy measurements by means of an electron pulse chamber (see Sec. 4–28), the oxygen content in the filling gas must be less than 50 parts per million.

When positive ions and negative ions (or electrons) exist in the same region, there is a tendency for them to recombine to form neutral molecules. The number of recombinations per unit volume per unit time is

$$\frac{dn_+}{dt} = \frac{dn_-}{dt} = -\alpha n_+ n_- \qquad (4\text{–}2)$$

where $n_+$ and $n_-$ are the density of positive and negative charges, respectively, and $\alpha$ is the recombination coefficient. In air, $\alpha$ is $10^{-6}$ to $2 \times 10^{-6}$ cm$^3$/sec when the negative charge exists as negative ions and from $10^{-7}$ to $10^{-10}$ cm$^3$/sec for electrons. This relationship assumes that the ionization is uniformly distributed throughout the region. When high local densities of ion pairs are present, such as along the tracks of alpha particles, the local recombination rate is correspondingly much higher.

**Example 4–2.** Compute the equilibrium density of positive and negative ions in a region of air at which the ionization is being produced at the rate of 1 esu/(hr)(cm³) and the only loss of charge is by recombination.

*Solution.* Since the net charge is zero, $n_+ = n_-$. Therefore,

$$\frac{dn_+}{dt} = \frac{dn_-}{dt} = -\alpha n_+^2 = -\alpha n_-^2$$

or

$$n_+ = n_- = \left(\frac{dn_+/dt}{\alpha}\right)^{1/2} = \left[\frac{1}{(4.8 \times 10^{-10})(3{,}600)(2 \times 10^{-6})}\right]^{1/2}$$

$$= 5.4 \times 10^5 \text{ ions/cm}^3$$

The mobilities of positive and negative ions are much smaller than those of electrons. Also, in contrast with electrons, the mobility for ions is quite insensitive to changes in the electric-field strength and the gas pressure. Table 4–1 lists $\mu_+$ and $\mu_-$, the mobilities of positive and negative ions, respectively, in several gases of interest in ionization chambers.

## 4–2. *Electron and Ion Current in a Gas*

The motion of electrons and ions through the gas may result in the net transfer of charge. This net transfer can be expressed as a current density **j** given by

$$\mathbf{j} = \mathbf{j}_+ + \mathbf{j}_- \tag{4–3}$$

TABLE 4–1. MOBILITIES OF POSITIVE AND NEGATIVE IONS IN UNITS OF (CM/SEC)(VOLT/CM)$^{-1}$(MM HG)*

| Gas | Air | Argon | Hydrogen | Nitrogen | Carbon dioxide |
|---|---|---|---|---|---|
| $\mu_+$ | 1,070 | 1,040 | 4,300 | 980 | 600 |
| $\mu_-$ | 1,350 | 1,290 | 6,500 | 1,380 | 720 |

* From "International Critical Tables," vol. VI, McGraw-Hill Book Company, Inc., New York, 1929.

where $\mathbf{j}_+$ and $\mathbf{j}_-$ refer to the current density due to the positive and negative charges, respectively.

A current may occur, even in the absence of an electric field, because of the nonuniformity of the charge distribution. The positive and negative components of this current, that is, $\mathbf{j}_{D+}$ and $\mathbf{j}_{D-}$, can be expressed in terms of the diffusion coefficients $D_+$ and $D_-$ and the gradient of the charge density as

$$\mathbf{j}_{D+} = -eD_+ \operatorname{grad} n_+ \tag{4–4}$$

and

$$\mathbf{j}_{D-} = eD_- \operatorname{grad} n_- \tag{4–5}$$

For positive and negative ions, the diffusion coefficient can be approximated from the mobility by the expression

$$D(\text{cm}^2/\text{sec}) = 3.3 \times 10^{-5}\mu \tag{4-6}$$

When an electric field is present, there will be a net drift of the charged particles in a direction parallel to the field. The currents $\mathbf{j}_{E_+}$ and $\mathbf{j}_{E_-}$ due to this cause will be

$$\mathbf{j}_{E_+} = n_+ e \mathbf{w}_+ \tag{4-7}$$

$$\mathbf{j}_{E_-} = -\, n_- e \mathbf{w}_- \tag{4-8}$$

where $\mathbf{w}_+$ and $\mathbf{w}_-$ are the drift velocities of the positive and negative charges, respectively. Equation (4–3) becomes

$$\mathbf{j} = e(n_+\mathbf{w}_+ - n_-\mathbf{w}_- - D_+ \operatorname{grad} n_+ + D_- \operatorname{grad} n_-) \tag{4-9}$$

and is known as the diffusion equation.

In a region where charges are present and several processes including current flow, charge production, and recombination are taking place, the rate of change of charge density $dn/dt$ can be expressed by application of the principle of conservation of charge. The contribution $(dn/dt)_j$ due to current flow is $-\operatorname{div}(\mathbf{j}/e)$. This follows from consideration of a bounded region and equating the rate of flow of particles from it to the rate of change of the number in the region. Thus,

$$\frac{1}{e}\int_A \mathbf{j}\cdot\mathbf{k}\, dA = -\int_V \left(\frac{dn}{dt}\right)_j dV \tag{4-10}$$

where $\mathbf{k}$ is the unit vector normal to the surface. Applying the divergence theorem,

$$\frac{1}{e}\int_V \operatorname{div}\mathbf{j}\, dV = -\int_V \left(\frac{dn}{dt}\right)_j dV \tag{4-11}$$

Consequently,

$$\operatorname{div}\frac{\mathbf{j}_+}{e} = \operatorname{div}(n_+\mathbf{w}_+) - D_+\nabla^2 n_+ = -\left(\frac{dn_+}{dt}\right)_j \tag{4-12}$$

and

$$\operatorname{div}\frac{\mathbf{j}_-}{e} = \operatorname{div}(n_-\mathbf{w}_-) - D_-\nabla^2 n_- = -\left(\frac{dn_-}{dt}\right)_j \tag{4-13}$$

Letting $N_o$ represent the time rate of production of ion pairs per unit volume and $\alpha n_+ n_-$ the rate of recombination per unit volume, the total time rate of change of positive- and negative-ion density becomes

$$\frac{dn_+}{dt} = D_+\nabla^2 n_+ - \operatorname{div}(n_+\mathbf{w}_+) - \alpha n_+ n_- + N_o \tag{4-14}$$

and
$$\frac{dn_-}{dt} = D_-\nabla^2 n_- - \text{div}\,(n_-\mathbf{w}_-) - \alpha n_+ n_- + N_o \qquad (4\text{–}15)$$

respectively.

## 4–3. *Current Flow in Ionization Chamber with Constant Ionization*

Figure 4–1 is a schematic diagram of a parallel-plate ionization chamber incorporated in a circuit which measures the current flow. The electrode to which the measuring instrument is attached is referred to as the collecting electrode. Its potential varies with the current flowing through the chamber. The other electrode is held at a potential $V$ above ground by means of the battery. This electrode is sometimes called the high-voltage electrode.

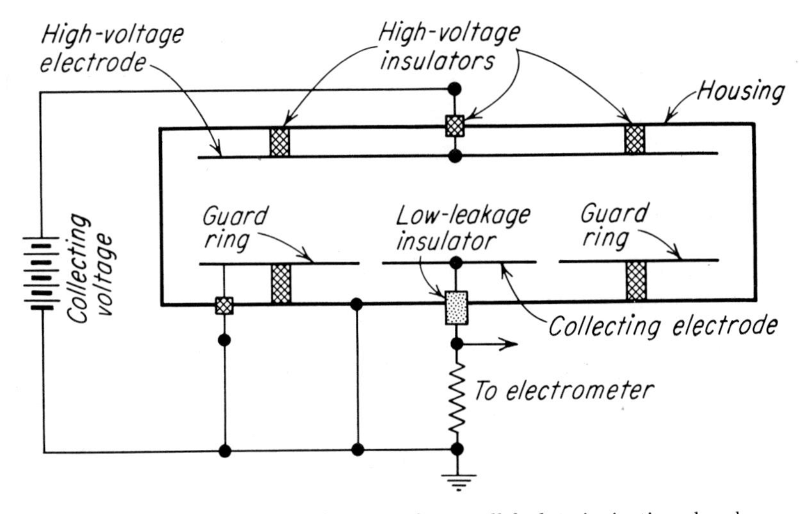


FIG. 4–1. Schematic diagram of a parallel-plate ionization chamber.

The collecting electrode is supported by an insulator from the instrument housing as is also another electrode known as the guard electrode or guard ring. The guard electrode is maintained at a potential near that of the collector, in this case the circuit ground. One of the functions of the guard ring is to shape the electric field near the extremities of the collecting electrode, thus defining accurately the volume from which ionization is collected. This volume is known as the sensitive or active volume of the chamber. Provided that both diffusion and recombination are neglected, the equilibrium current flow $I_s$ to the collecting electrode is

$$I_s = e\int_{V_a} N_o(x,y,z)\,dx\,dy\,dz \qquad (4\text{–}16)$$

where $N_o(x,y,z)$ is the number of ion pairs produced per unit volume per unit time at the point $x,y,z$ and the integral is taken over $V_a$, the active volume of the chamber. The rate of production $N_o$ is considered to be constant with time. Equation (4–16) simply states that the charge is collected at the electrodes at the same rate it is formed in the active volume. This current $I_s$ is referred to as the saturation current.

The approximations of neglecting diffusion and recombination in Eq. (4–16) have been discussed by Rossi and Staub [3]. The correction for recombination is significant only for gases containing negative ions rather than free electrons, and in these cases only for very high rates of ion production and moderate field strengths. The fractional loss in the saturation current due to recombination, designated as $(\delta I_s/I_s)_{rec}$, is calculated as

$$-\left(\frac{\delta I_s}{I_s}\right)_{rec} = \frac{\int_{V_a} \alpha n_+ n_- \, dx\, dy\, dz}{\int_{V_a} N_o(x,y,z)\, dx\, dy\, dz} \tag{4–17}$$

For a parallel-plate ionization chamber with plate spacing $d$, the charge densities $n_-(x)$ and $n_+(x)$ between the plates at a distance $x$ from the negative plate are given by the expressions

$$n_-(x) = \frac{N_o x}{w_-} \qquad \text{and} \qquad n_+(x) = \frac{N_o(d - x)}{w_+} \tag{4–18}$$

where, as a first approximation, recombination and diffusion are neglected. Taking $N_o$ as independent of position, the substitution of Eq. (4–18) into Eq. (4–17) leads to

$$-\left(\frac{\delta I_s}{I_s}\right)_{rec} = \frac{\alpha N_o d^2}{6 w_+ w_-} \tag{4–19}$$

**Example 4–3.** Calculate the maximum fractional loss of saturation current by recombination in a parallel-plate ionization chamber with a plate spacing of 2 cm and an applied voltage of 200 volts, provided that the gas in the chamber is air at atmospheric pressure. Assume that the chamber is irradiated uniformly throughout with gamma rays so that the rate of production of ionization is 1 esu/(cm³)(sec).

*Solution.* For the worst case, assume that all the negative charges exist in the air as negative ions, for which the recombination coefficient with positive ions is $2 \times 10^{-6}$ cm³/sec. By Eq. (4–1), the drift velocities of the ions are

$$w_+ = \frac{\mu_+ E}{p} = \frac{(1{,}070)(200)}{(760)(2)} = 140 \text{ cm/sec}$$

using the mobilities in Table 4–1. Similarly, $w_- = 177$ cm/sec. By Eq. (4–19), the fractional loss by recombination is

$$-\left(\frac{\delta I_s}{I_s}\right)_{rec} = \frac{(2 \times 10^{-6})(2.08 \times 10^9)(2)^2}{(6)(140)(177)} = 0.11$$

where $2.08 \times 10^9$ is the number of ion pairs corresponding to 1 esu of charge.

Diffusion causes charges to move in directions not necessarily parallel to the electric field. The net flow due to diffusion is in the direction of the gradient in the ion density. Thus, if such a gradient exists, the charge may flow in or out of the active volume, depending on the sign of the gradient. Further, even if the rate of production of ionization is constant throughout the system, there will still be a gradient in charge due to the current flow. The drift of ions toward the collecting electrodes tends to make the density of positive ions a minimum at the positive electrodes, increasing to a maximum at the negative electrodes, and vice versa for the negative charges. The ion gradient causes a diffusion current to flow in a direction opposite to that produced by the action of the electric field. The fractional loss in saturation current due to this latter diffusion phenomenon is given by theory [3] for a parallel-plate ionization chamber as

$$-\left(\frac{\delta I_s}{I_s}\right)_{dif} = \frac{\epsilon k T}{eV} \tag{4-20}$$

where $\epsilon$ = ratio of mean energy of ions with and without electric field present
$k$ = Boltzmann's constant
$T$ = absolute temperature
$V$ = voltage between plates

When Eq. (4–20) is evaluated at room temperature, it becomes

$$-\left(\frac{\delta I_s}{I_s}\right)_{dif} = \frac{\epsilon 2.5 \times 10^{-2}}{V(\text{volts})} \tag{4-21}$$

Thus, since $\epsilon$ may be of the order of several hundred for electrons but is around 1 for negative ions, the diffusion loss is important only for gases having largely electronic current. For this case, however, Eq. (4–21) indicates that the diffusion loss can be quite significant.

The current-voltage characteristic of an ionization chamber depends on the chamber construction, its filling gas, and the intensity and type of the radiation to which it is exposed. As an example, Fig. 4–2 is a diagram of a cylindrical ionization chamber [4], and Fig. 4–3 shows its current-voltage

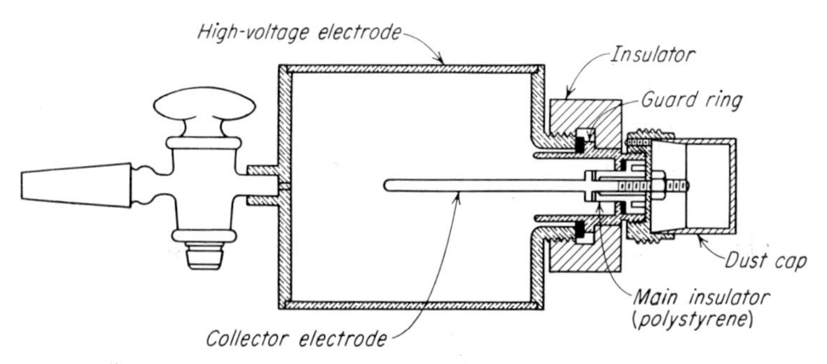


FIG. 4–2. Schematic diagram of a cylindrical ionization chamber for measurements on gaseous $C^{14}$. *(From C. J. Borkowski, U.S. Atomic Energy Comm. Document MDDC-1099, 1947.)*

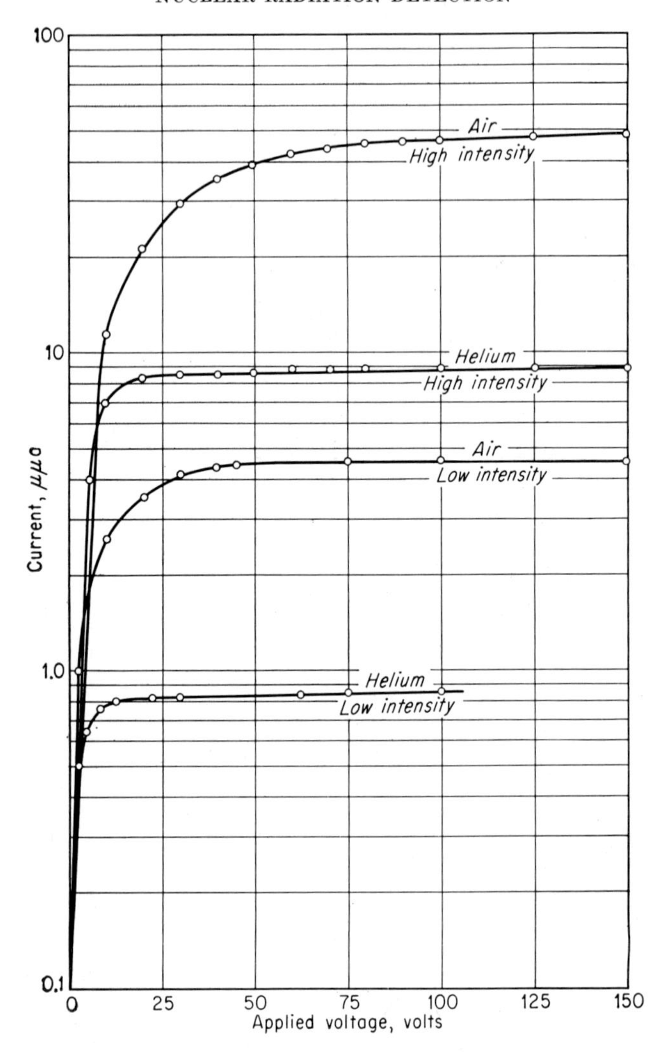


Fig. 4–3. Current versus voltage characteristic of a cylindrical ionization chamber of the type shown in Fig. 4–2, for both air and helium filling gas at two different intensities of gamma radiation.

characteristics for two different intensities of gamma radiation and two types of gases.

When the specific ionization is high, as with alpha particles and protons, columnar recombination takes place. The fractional loss in saturation current is larger, and the current-voltage characteristic of the chamber subjected to radiation of these types has a larger slope.

## DESIGN CONSIDERATIONS

### 4–4. *General Aspects*

Because of its simplicity of operation, the ionization chamber is a very versatile instrument. It can be designed in many sizes and shapes and can be employed to measure all types of radiation that produce either primary or secondary ionization. Further, it can be used in either pulse- or mean-level-type operation.

The filling gas in many cases is only air at atmospheric pressure, although nearly any gas or pressure may be used as required in the application. For electron pulse-type operation, a gas with a small electron affinity must be used for most operations.

The radiation source may be either internal or external to the chamber. Often the source is introduced directly as a gas mixed with the chamber filling gas. The chamber shown in Fig. 4–2 was designed [4] for use with gaseous $C^{14}$.

### 4–5. *Insulators*

One of the most important design considerations for ionization chambers involves the insulators. The main insulator is the one which supports the collecting electrode either from the high-voltage electrode, as shown in Fig. 4–4, or from the housing and guard ring, as in Figs. 4–1 and 4–2, respectively.

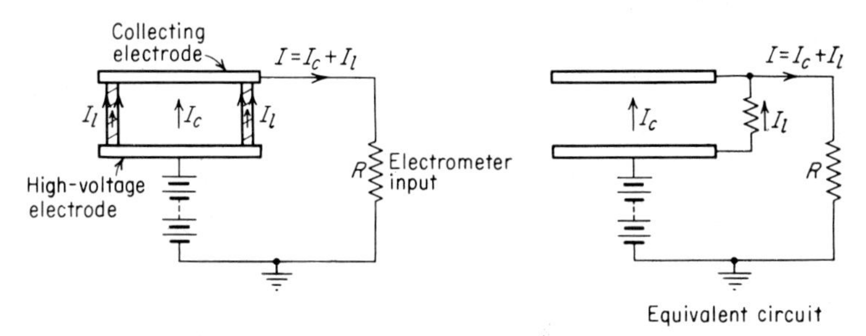


FIG. 4–4. Illustration of leakage through the insulator of an ionization chamber.

The first requirement of an insulating material for use with an ionization chamber is that it have extremely high leakage resistance. The importance of this can be seen readily by reference to Fig. 4–4. The current flow in the external circuit is the sum of $I_c$, the ionization current in the chamber, and $I_l$, the leakage current in the insulator. The latter can easily become a large portion of the total if sufficient care is not taken with the insulators.

The volume resistivity of most insulating materials is sufficiently high, but surface leakage makes certain materials unusable. Surface leakage is mainly dependent on the ability of the insulating material to absorb water vapor. The insulator should be kept dry by use of desiccants or hermetical seals. In addition, the leakage surfaces of an insulator should be clean and free of scratches and other surface imperfections; otherwise the absorption of water is enhanced. Ceresin wax and the fluoroethylenes (e.g., Teflon) are best with respect to minimum water absorption. Aluminum oxide, polystyrene, and quartz are also satisfactory if they are highly polished to reduce surface imperfections. The General Electric Company has developed a silicone compound called Dri-Film 9987 which forms a good water-repellent coating. When it is used on the above materials, the polishing problems are greatly reduced.

The resistivity of insulators is, in general, reduced by ionizing radiation. With regard to permanent changes, Teflon appears to be one of the most sensitive materials [5], showing reduction in resistivity at doses of $2 \times 10^8$ r of gamma radiation, while polystyrene does not show appreciable changes at $10^{10}$ r. Concerning rate-dependent processes, relatively low dose rates have been reported to make large reductions in resistivity while the radiation is in progress. Armstead, Pennock, and Mead [6] have reported a reduction in the resistivity of polystyrene by a factor of 2,000 during exposure at a rate of 100 r/min. Other investigators [7–9] have reported similar effects.

Because of the susceptibility of plastics to radiation-induced changes in mechanical properties [5] as well as in electrical properties, these materials should be avoided for the high-dose and dose-rate applications. Rather, inorganic materials such as quartz and aluminum oxide should be adopted.

An important criterion of insulators is the extent to which they are free from stress currents. These stress currents appear across an insulator after it has received either electrical or mechanical stress. Apparently they are due to the transfer of charge through the insulator as the stress in the insulator is relieved. In "soft" materials such as polystyrene, these currents may start at values from $10^{-14}$ to $10^{-15}$ amp and drop off exponentially with a time constant in the range from 10 to 30 min. Stress currents may be minimized by making the insulator volume as small as is consistent with the requirements for high surface leakage and by avoiding undue mechanical stress. "Hard" materials such as aluminum oxide and quartz have very low stress currents and therefore are particularly attractive for measurements of currents less than $10^{-14}$ amp.

### 4–6. *Guard Rings*

The use of guard rings in a parallel-plate design of an ionization chamber is illustrated in Fig. 4–1. In addition to defining accurately the active volume of the chamber, this design also ensures that ions will not collect on the insulators, thereby causing a distortion of the electric field in the active volume of the chamber.

The use of guard rings also serves a major function in the reduction of leakage current through the insulators. This improvement is illustrated in Fig. 4–5, which is the equivalent circuit of Fig. 4–1. The resistors $R_1$ and $R_2$ represent the insulation resistance between the guard ring and the high-voltage electrode and between the guard ring and the collector electrode, respectively. In this case, as in the one without the guard ring, the error due to leakage is $I - I_c = I_l$. However, $I_l$ is much less with the guard ring than without, because the potential difference across the insulation is nearly zero instead of the order of several hundred volts, as it may be without a guard ring.

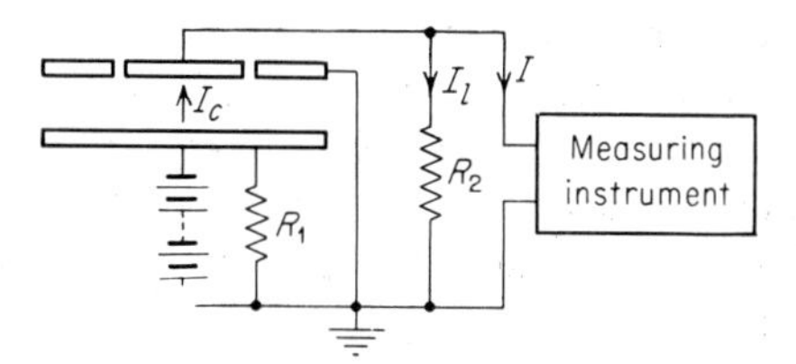


FIG. 4–5. Equivalent circuit of an ionization chamber with the guard ring connected as in Fig. 4–1.

An arrangement of a guard ring for a cylindrical ionization chamber is illustrated in Fig. 4–2. This application of the guard-ring technique, together with the insulator design, achieves [4] leakage currents which are small compared with $1.5 \times 10^{-16}$ amp, the cosmic-ray background current for a 300-cm³ chamber. However, in this design the active volume of the chamber is not well defined because of the variation in the electric field as the insulator region is approached. Cockroft and Curran [10] have studied the elimination of this type of "end effect" for cylindrical chambers. They have found that small field-adjusting tubes, fitted over the usual grounded guard tubes and maintained at potentials appropriate to their diameters, reduce the end effects to negligible proportions. Their arrangement is shown schematically in Fig. 4–6. The potential of the field tube is adjusted to the potential of the same radial position in the gas near the center of the chamber. Provided that the length of the field tube is at least equal to the radius of the high-voltage electrode, the resulting electric-field lines are radial along the whole length of the chamber up to the end of the field tubes.

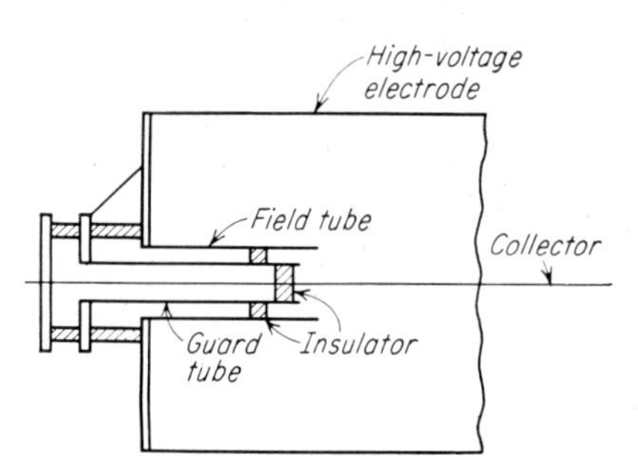


FIG. 4–6. Electrode assembly illustrating the use of a field tube for eliminating end effects. [*From A. L. Cockroft and S. C. Curran, Rev. Sci. Instr.*, **22**:37 (1951).]

### 4–7. *Background Sources in Ionization Chambers*

All materials which are used to construct ion chambers exhibit a small amount of alpha activity. Bearden [11] has found, for example, alpha activities ranging from 3 alphas/(100 $cm^2$)(hr) for steel to 2,800 alphas/(100 $cm^2$) (hr) for solder.

One alpha particle per hour results in an average current of $10^{-17}$ amp. Therefore the alpha contamination can be very objectionable for low-current measurements. Fortunately, by using the rate-of-drift method (see Sec. 4–11), the alpha-particle background can be rejected, provided that the output is recorded, since the alpha particles appear as discontinuities in the output.

Cosmic-ray background produces about 2.7 ion pairs/($cm^3$)(sec) or $4.3 \times 10^{-19}$ amp/$cm^3$ inside a shield of 4 in. of lead at sea level. If the lead is removed, the radiation that is emitted by the contamination in the earth and in the building materials raises the background current two to four times.

## MEASURING INSTRUMENTS FOR MEAN-LEVEL IONIZATION CHAMBERS

### 4–8. *Measurement of Small Currents*

The range of ionization currents of interest in ionization chambers is from as large as $10^{-6}$ amp in such applications as reactor control systems to as small as $10^{-16}$ amp in tracer applications of radioisotopes. The larger currents can be measured by standard sensitive D'Arsonval-type meters. Below about $10^{-8}$ amp these instruments are not sufficiently sensitive. Consequently less direct means of current measurement must be employed. The method discussed in Sec. 2–10 and illustrated by Fig. 2–5 is quite useful for this purpose. This technique involves the use of an electrometer to measure the voltage drop across a high resistance.

The ionization current $I$ can be computed from the voltage drop $V$ by the relationship

$$I = \frac{V}{R_p} \tag{4–22}$$

where $R_p$ is the combined resistance of the calibrated resistor $R$ in parallel with the electrometer input resistance $R_e$. Usually $R_e \gg R$ so that $R_p \simeq R$. This condition requires the use of special electrical insulators in the construction of the electrometers.

Dependable current measurements require that the resistance $R_p$ remain constant. Since this value may be as high as $10^{14}$ or $10^{15}$ ohms, which is of the same order as that of insulating material, the control of $R_p$ presents a formidable problem.

Because of the very high input resistances involved and the high stability that is required, special techniques are necessary in the manufacture and use of input resistors. To avoid a variation in resistance due to surface leakage, resistors must be kept clean and dry. In some cases this is accomplished by placing them in evacuated chambers. Polarization, or the tendency of materials composing the resistors to have induced dipoles and thus act as voltage sources, places limitations on the materials that can be used. In some resistors it may be several seconds or even minutes before the polarization will come to an equilibrium value.

Burmaster [12] has studied the stability, polarization, and temperature effects in several commercial types of resistors. At present the carbon-compounded resistors in evacuated envelopes, such as those manufactured by Victoreen Instrument Company, appear to be the most satisfactory for precision work.

### 4–9. *Electrostatic Electrometers*

Several electrostatic-type electrometers have been devised. The operation of these instruments depends on electrostatic forces; consequently the steady-state input current is very low, and the input resistance is correspondingly high. Each of these instruments contains a very fine, light, movable electrode which is well insulated from the remainder of the instrument. A local electric field is produced in the space occupied by the movable electrode. This is accomplished through the use of other pairs of electrodes between which a constant potential difference is maintained. The voltage to be measured is applied between the movable electrode and the case of the instrument. The equilibrium position of the movable electrode is determined by a balance between the electrostatic forces and the mechanical restoring forces.

The Lindemann electrometer [13] is a compact, portable instrument of the electrostatic type. This electrometer is shown schematically in Fig. 4–7. A silvered quartz needle is supported from a silvered quartz fiber mounted on good insulators. The voltages applied between the quadrants $A$, $B$, $C$, and $D$ produce electric fields which cause the needle to be deflected when a voltage is applied between this needle and ground. The deflection is observed by means of a microscope containing an eyepiece scale.

The Lindemann-type electrometer is quite stable for sensitivities up to 1-volt full-scale deflection and can be used satisfactorily up to 0.1-volt full-scale deflection. The input resistance can easily be kept greater than $10^{15}$ ohms. Its input capacity is quite low, being around 1 $\mu\mu$f. The speed with which it reaches a new deflection is limited by the inertia and the viscous damping. This speed drops off with increased sensitivity, but the time required is never greater than a few seconds.

Other types of electrostatic electrometers include the string electrometer, the Wulf electrometer, and the Dolezalek quadrant electrometer.

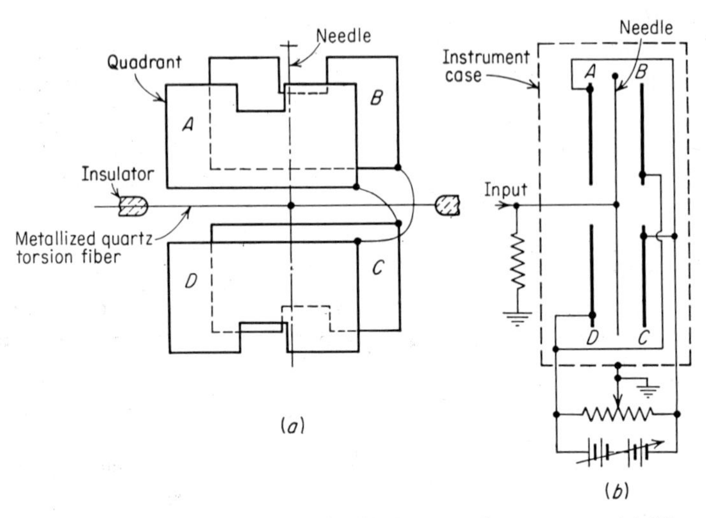


FIG. 4-7. Schematic diagram of a Lindemann electrometer. (*a*) Mechanical arrangement of the needle and quadrants; (*b*) the electrical circuit.

## 4-10. *Vacuum-tube Electrometers*

Vacuum-tube electrometers are in wide-scale use for ionization-current measurements. These vacuum-tube circuits employ specially designed tubes known as electrometer tubes [14]. The outstanding feature of these devices is their low grid currents. Maximum grid currents as small as $10^{-14}$ amp can be obtained, giving input resistances of $10^{14}$ ohms or higher for a 1-volt input.

Figure 4-8 is a typical schematic diagram illustrating the use of a vacuum-tube electrometer with an ionization chamber. This is a balanced circuit in which the voltage drop from the plate to the cathode of the type

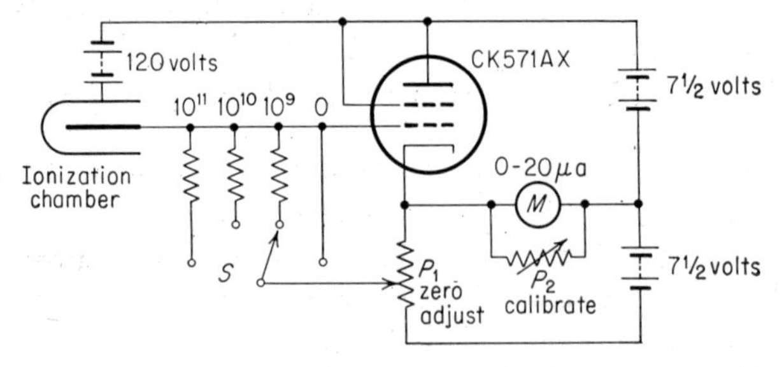


FIG. 4-8. Vacuum-tube electrometer circuit connected with an ionization chamber.

CK571AX electrometer tube is compared with that across the potentiometer $P_1$. Any unbalance is indicated by the microammeter $M$. To "zero" the instrument, the input signal is shorted out by placing the switch $S$ in position 0, and the potentiometer $P_1$ is adjusted so that the meter reads zero. The current sensitivity of the electrometer is controlled by selection of one of the resistors of $10^9$ to $10^{11}$ ohms. A voltage drop across the input resistor due to the flow of ionization current causes an unbalance of the circuit and a resulting deflection of the meter $M$. Full-scale deflection of the meter requires 0.25 volt so that the current range which is covered is $2.5 \times 10^{-10}$ to $2.5 \times 10^{-12}$ amp.

Many other vacuum-tube electrometer circuits have been developed. Some of these have been discussed by Elmore and Sands [15]. Notable among these circuits are the feedback amplifiers (see Chap. 10). Inverse feedback is employed so that not only the gain is stabilized but also the speed of response is improved.

The sensitivity and stability of the vacuum-tube electrometers are seriously limited by the basic difficulties inherent in multistage dc amplifiers. These difficulties are circumvented by a recent development, the vibrating-reed electrometer [16,17]. In this instrument the direct current is first converted into an alternating current of fixed frequency, and the required amplification is accomplished at this frequency by a narrow-band feedback amplifier which is inherently quite stable. The operation of the vibrating-reed electrometer is covered in Chap. 10 of this text. These instruments work satisfactorily down to input voltages as low as 1 mv full scale. The input resistance can be as high as $10^{15}$ to $10^{16}$ ohms and the input capacity as low as 10 $\mu\mu$f. The output of the electrometer can operate a recorder.

### 4–11. *Dynamic Response of Current-type Ionization Chamber*

In order to study the dynamic response of ionization-chamber instruments to changes in ionization current, both the capacitance and resistance of the ionization chamber and the electrometer input must be taken into account. This circuit is shown in Fig. 4–9*a*. The equivalent circuit is shown in Fig. 4–9*b* where resistances and capacitances have been combined in parallel with $C = C_e + C_c$ and $R = R_eR_c/(R_e + R_c)$.

The relationship between the ionization-chamber current $I$ and the voltage $v$ at the input of the electrometer is, by Kirchhoff's law,

$$RC\frac{dv}{dt} + v = RI \tag{4–23}$$

If the ionization-chamber current is suddenly changed from $I_1$ to $I_2$, the time dependence of $v$ is

$$v = RI_2 + R(I_1 - I_2)e^{-t/RC} \tag{4–24}$$

The change is seen to occur exponentially. The quantity $RC$ is known as the time constant for the circuit. In Fig. 4–9$c$ the voltage is plotted as a function of the time measured in time constants.

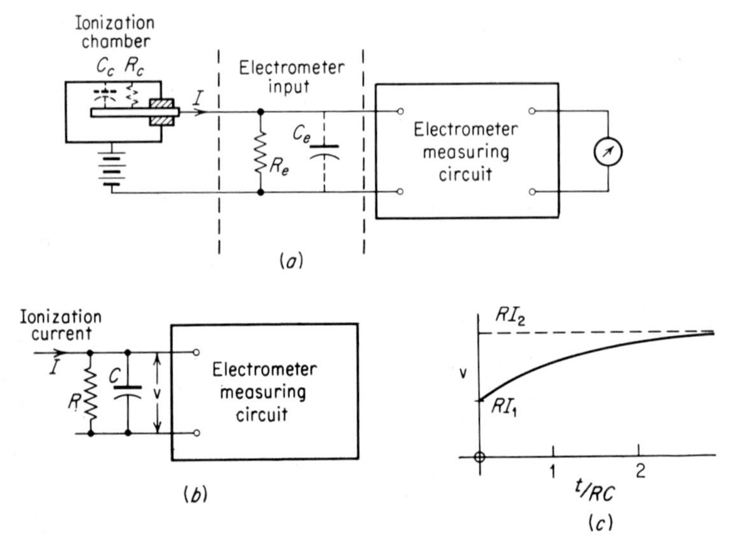


FIG. 4–9. Response of an electrometer to a change in ionization current from $I_1$ to $I_2$. (*a*) Electrometer circuit; (*b*) equivalent circuit of the electrometer input $[R = R_eR_c/(R_e + R_c)$ and $C = C_e + C_c]$; (*c*) time dependence of the electrometer input voltage following a step change in current.

**Example 4–4.** Consider the use of a vibrating-reed electrometer for the measurement of $10^{-15}$ amp through determining the voltage drop across a $10^{12}$-ohm resistor. Compute the time required for the indicated voltage to reach 99 per cent of its final value after the current is suddenly changed from zero to some finite value.

*Solution.* By Eq. (4–24), the fractional change remaining after a time $t$ is $e^{-t/RC}$. Therefore,

$$e^{-t/RC} = 0.01 \qquad \text{or} \qquad \frac{t}{RC} = \ln 100 = 4.6$$

and

$$t = 4.6RC = (4.6)(10^{12})(10 \times 10^{-12}) = 46 \text{ sec}$$

where the input capacity of the electrometer and chamber combined has been taken as 10 $\mu\mu$f and the ionization-chamber leakage resistance is assumed to be large compared with $10^{12}$ ohms.

When the electrometer which is used is a vacuum-tube type, its input capacity and therefore its response time can be reduced through the use of feedback, as described in Sec. 10–22.

In addition to the time constant of the electrometer input circuit, the polarization of the resistors, as discussed in Sec. 4–8, and the speed of response of the electrometer may place limitations on how rapidly changes in ionization can be followed.

To avoid the long time constants and to obtain the maximum sensitivity for small current measurements, the rate-of-drift method can be used. For this purpose the input resistor is omitted, and the rate of change of voltage is observed as the current flows into the input capacity of the electrometer. The current $I$ is calculated as

$$I = C\frac{dv}{dt} \tag{4-25}$$

To employ this method, the electrometer is originally shorted out. Upon removing the short, the voltage registered by the electrometer varies according to Eq. (4–25). Through the use of this method, currents as low as $10^{-16}$ amp can be measured by the vibrating-reed electrometer. This current results in a rate of change of 1 mv/100 sec if $C$ is taken as 10 $\mu\mu$f. By recording the electrometer output, the rate of change can be obtained quickly and easily. The lower limit on the current measurable by this method is set by the drift in the indicated voltage with no input current.

### 4–12. *Integrating-type Ionization Chambers*

A schematic diagram of a condenser-type ionization chamber is given in Fig. 2–6. If the voltage source $V_o$ is connected between the two electrodes and then removed, a charge $Q = C_1V_o$ is stored on the electrodes of the chamber, where $C_1$ is the capacitance of the chamber. If a mechanism for the transfer of charge between the electrodes exists, a change $\Delta v$ in the potential difference occurs by a charge transfer $\Delta q$, where

$$\Delta q = C_1\Delta v \tag{4-26}$$

The charge will be transferred primarily by ionization in the sensitive volume of the chamber and by leakage through the insulator. If $\Delta q_c$ represents the former and $\Delta q_i$ the latter, then

$$\Delta q_c + \Delta q_i = \Delta v\, C_1 \tag{4-27}$$

When the voltage between the electrodes is large enough for operation in the ionization-chamber region, $\Delta q_c$ is the total ionization produced in the sensitive volume of the chamber during the period of the measurement. If $\Delta q_i$ is not negligible, it may be measured while subjecting the chamber to negligible radiation. In practice, the background will consist of both leakage and ionization due to background radiation.

It is clear from the preceding discussions that the method of measuring the voltage remaining on the ionization chamber should draw negligible current. In addition, if the voltmeter is to be removed from the ionization chamber during the irradiation of the chamber and connected to it at the end to measure the remaining voltage, the voltmeter capacity must be small compared with that of the chamber. The voltage range of the instrument should be a few hundred volts in order to ensure that saturation current is drawn. The electroscope satisfies all these conditions.

Gold-leaf electroscopes have been used widely for studying ionizing radiations. In fact, the first measurements of the ionizing properties of nuclear radiations were made with these instruments. In these measurements the gold leaf is observed by a microscope containing a graduated scale in the eyepiece. The gold leaf may be carried by the central electrode inside the ionization chamber, or the electroscope may be external to the ionization chamber.

Lauritsen [18] has developed a quartz-fiber electroscope that has many advantages over the gold-leaf type. It is more compact, less dependent on

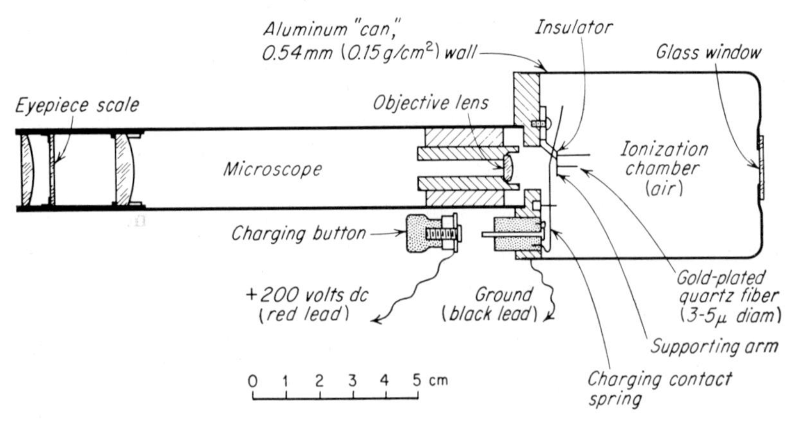


FIG. 4–10. Schematic diagram of the Lauritsen electroscope. [*From C. S. Garner, J. Chem. Educ.,* **26**:542 (1949).]

position, and more portable. As a result of its lower electrical capacity and fine fiber, it is more sensitive. Its capacity is about 0.2 $\mu\mu$f and its voltage sensitivity about 1 volt/division. The sensitive element consists of a fine metallized quartz fiber, mounted from a parallel metal support, as shown in Fig. 4–10. The metal support is mounted on a small insulator. It may be charged by a battery through pressing the charging key. A small piece of quartz fiber mounted across the end of the metallized fiber serves as an index that is viewed through a microscope equipped with an eyepiece scale. Upon being charged, the metallized fiber is deflected from the support; it returns toward the position of zero charge when the gas in the chamber is ionized. A window is provided for illuminating the fiber. Approximately 200 volts are required to produce full-scale deflection of the fiber. A typical background rate of discharge is of the order of 4 divisions/hr, and the sensitivity is such that about 2 divisions/min discharge occurs when 1 mg of radium is placed 1 m from the chamber. This corresponds to a dosage rate (see Sec. 4–14) of only 0.84 mr/hr. Because of its dependability, simplicity, sensitivity, and accuracy, the Lauritsen electroscope is applied quite widely in the measurement of gamma radiation.

A simple string electrometer of the type shown in Fig. 4–11 is often used for measurement of the voltage remaining on a condenser-type ionization chamber. A potential difference between the highly insulated brass rod and the grounded platinum wire causes the latter to be deflected toward the rod. Thus the deflection of the wire gives a measurement of the potential difference while drawing only negligible currents.

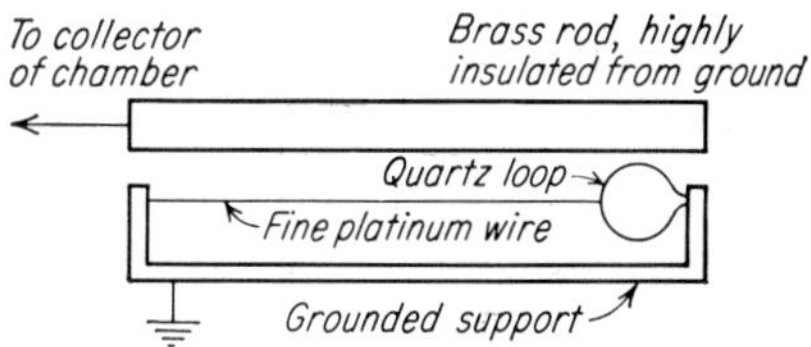


Fig. 4–11. Schematic diagram of a string electrometer for a condenser-type ionization chamber.

## IONIZATION CHAMBERS FOR DOSE MEASUREMENTS

### 4–13. *General Considerations*

In most fields of endeavor involving nuclear radiation, it becomes important to have measurements of the amount of interaction of radiation and matter and of the effects of this radiation on matter. This is particularly true in evaluating the possible effect of radiation on personnel. It also is of considerable importance in studies of radiation effects on inanimate materials. These latter studies arise in assessing possible radiation damage to materials, in fundamental measurements, in applications of radiation chemistry, and related fields.

The principal quantity of interest is $dE/dm$, the energy absorption per unit mass. Since the mechanism for transfer of energy from radiation to matter involves the ionizing processes caused by the primary radiation, ionization-chamber instruments play a central role in these investigations.

These measurements of the energy dissipated by ionizing radiation in a material rest on the Bragg-Gray principle [19–21] that the amount of ionization produced in a gas cavity serves as a measure of the energy dissipated in the surrounding material. This procedure relies on the assumption that the gas cavity is traversed by the same flow of corpuscular radiation as exists in the material under consideration. For this condition,

$$\frac{dE}{dm} = S_m w J \tag{4–28}$$

where $S_m$ = relative mass stopping power of medium with respect to gas
$w$ = average energy dissipated in gas per ion pair formed in it
$J$ = no. of ion pairs formed per unit mass in gas

The gas cavity must be small with respect to the range of the ionizing particles, and $w$ and $S_m$ must be independent of the energy of the radiation. In the application of Eq. (4–28), the gas-filled cavity may be an ionization chamber in which $J$ is determined by measurement of the saturation current.

**Example 4–5.** Compute the energy absorbed per gram in a large tissue-equivalent phantom if a charge of $2.58 \times 10^{-7}$ coulomb/g is produced in a small air-filled cavity within the phantom. Assume that the relative mass stopping power of tissue is 1.11.

*Solution.* By the Bragg-Gray principle,

$$\frac{dE}{dm} = S_m wJ = \frac{(1.11)(32.5)(2.58 \times 10^{-7})(1.60 \times 10^{-12})}{1.60 \times 10^{-19}} = 93 \text{ ergs/g}$$

Here $w$ is taken as 32.5 ev per ion pair* or $32.5/(1.6 \times 10^{-19})$ ev/coulomb, and 1 ev = $1.60 \times 10^{-12}$ erg.

The size limitation on the cavity is often too restrictive [21]. Therefore the actual applications of the Bragg-Gray principle often rest on another basis [22], that the flow of corpuscular radiation will remain undisturbed by the cavity, provided only that the chemical compositions of the gas and the surrounding material are equal, irrespective of the cavity size. This latter principle is, however, subject to the restriction that the primary flux (such as X ray or neutrons) be uniform throughout the media. Further, it does neglect a small dependence on density because of a variation in electron stopping power [23].

### 4–14. *Dose Units*

The unit of absorbed dose known as the rad was introduced recently [24] by the International Commission on Radiological Units. The rad is defined as an absorbed dose of 100 ergs/g. This unit depends on neither the type of radiation nor the material in which the energy is absorbed. The dose in rads can be measured through the use of an ionization chamber by means of Eq. (4–28) or by means of calorimeters, as discussed in Chap. 8. This unit is finding wide acceptance and utility.

The most widely used unit for specifying the interaction of X and gamma radiation with matter is the roentgen (r). This unit is defined by the International Commission [24] as follows:

> The roentgen shall be the quantity of X or gamma radiation such that the associated corpuscular emission per 0.001293 gram of air produces, in air, ions carrying 1 electrostatic unit of quantity of electricity of either sign. (NOTE. The mass given is that of 1 cm³ of dry atmospheric air at 0°C and 760 mm Hg.)

Thus the roentgen is a unit of radiation exposure based on the effect of X or gamma radiations on the air through which they pass. It is important to

* The International Commission on Radiological Units and Measurements (ICRU) recommended that $w$ be assigned the value 34 ev; see *Natl. Bur. Standards (U.S.) Handbook* 62, 1957.

notice that it applies only to X and gamma radiations in air. Any attempt to use the unit for other radiations or for media other than air implies an extension of this definition. These extensions are possible.

To avoid the reference to the type of radiation, the roentgen-equivalent-physical (rep) unit has been introduced. The rep is defined as that amount of *any* type of radiation from which *tissue* will absorb energy to the extent of 93 ergs/g. This quantity was chosen since it is the energy absorbed per gram of tissue placed at a location such that 1 r of X or gamma dosage is received. The energy absorbed per gram of air is calculated as

$$\frac{1 \text{ esu}}{1.293 \times 10^{-3} \text{ g}} \; \frac{1 \text{ ion pair}}{4.80 \times 10^{-10} \text{ esu}} \; \frac{32.5 \text{ ev}}{1 \text{ ion pair}} \; \frac{1.60 \times 10^{-12} \text{ erg}}{1 \text{ ev}} = 83.8 \text{ ergs/g}$$

Experiments have shown that when 1 r of X or gamma rays is absorbed in soft body tissue, the amount of energy absorbed is larger than in air, actually about 93 ergs/g at 1 Mev, and that this amount does not differ by more than 10 per cent from 2 kev to greater than 1 Mev [25]. Consequently, for the absorption of photon radiation, 1 rep is roughly equivalent to 1 r in soft tissue. However, it should be understood that this correspondence is only approximate; it depends on the wavelength of the radiation and also on the nature of the medium. In bone, for example, the energy gain from the absorption of 1 r of X rays is considerably in excess of 93 ergs/g, and so 1 r and 1 rep would not be identical. However, for many purposes it is convenient to regard these quantities as equivalent.

### 4–15. *Air-wall Ionization Chamber*

It is clear from the definition of the roentgen that the measurement of the ionization in air is basic in the determination of radiation exposure. The largest application of ionization chambers is in this area.

An examination of the definition of a roentgen shows that the ionization which is produced by all the secondary electrons ejected from a known mass of air is considered. These electrons produce some ionization outside the region in which they receive their energy. In order to apply the definition to obtain the dosage in roentgens, it is necessary either that this ionization be collected wherever it is produced or that it be compensated for by an equal amount of ionization which enters the region in question.

For absolute measurements based on the roentgen unit, the free-air standard chamber [26] may be used. Such a chamber is shown in Fig. 4–12. This chamber provides compensation for the corpuscular emission which leaves the sensitive volume of the chamber before producing all its ionization. This compensation is made possible by establishing artificial boundaries of the chamber by means of guard rings. Thus the "walls" of the chamber are composed of air, and any loss of corpuscular emission from the active volume of the chamber is compensated by gain from the air "walls" of the chamber as long as the secondary electrons from the small central volume are completely absorbed within the air of the chamber.

If the voltage which is applied to a free-air standard ionization chamber

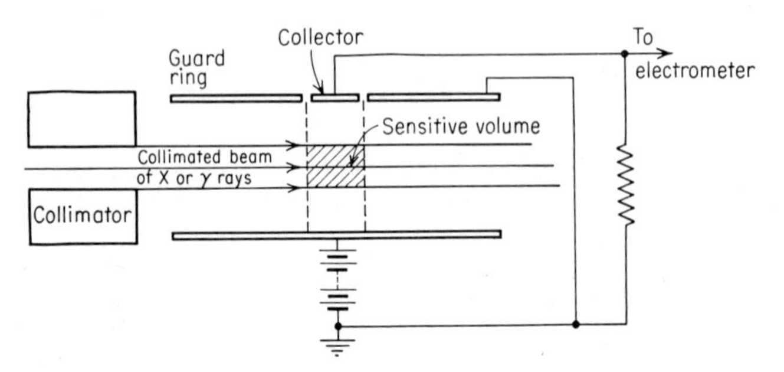


FIG. 4–12. Schematic diagram of a standard air-wall ionization chamber.

is such that all the charge released in the active volume is collected, this collected charge $Q$ due to a dose of $D$ is given by

$$Q(\text{coulombs}) = \frac{D(\text{r})\ V(\text{cm}^3)\ 273p(\text{mm Hg})}{3 \times 10^9\ T(°\text{K})\ 760} \tag{4-29}$$

where $D$ = dose
$V$ = active volume
$T$ = absolute temperature
$p$ = pressure in chamber

The current flow $i$ for a dosage rate of $R$ is obtained from Eq. (4–29) as

$$\begin{aligned} i(\text{amp}) &= \frac{R(\text{r/hr})V(\text{cm}^3)\ 273p(\text{mm Hg})}{3 \times 10^9 \times 3600T(°\text{K})\ 760} \\ &= 0.926RV\frac{273}{T}\frac{p}{760}10^{-13} \end{aligned} \tag{4-30}$$

As the energy of the X- or gamma-ray photon increases, so does the size of the standard ionization chamber. This condition arises since the air "wall" surrounding the sensitive volume of the chamber must have a thickness greater than the range of the secondary electrons. By the Bragg-Gray principle, this difficulty could be circumvented through the use of an actual wall of solid material with the same chemical composition as the air. Such a wall is referred to as an air-equivalent wall. Small air-equivalent chambers are known as thimble chambers.

An air-equivalent wall is approximated by using a material with a mean atomic number near that of air. Bakelite, lucite, and other plastics are suitable materials for this purpose. The surface of the plastic is ordinarily coated with colloidal carbon to give it the conductive properties necessary for electrodes of ionization chambers.

For other wall materials, both the magnitude of the ionization in the air volume and its energy dependence will differ from those with an air-wall chamber. This effect has been treated by Marinelli [26] and Whyte [23].

## 4–16. *Instruments for Gamma- and X-ray-dose Measurements*

It can be seen by reference to Eqs. (4–27) and (4–29) that the change in voltage on the condenser chamber can be related to the dose received after correction has been made for the charge leaking through the insulator. This leakage can be neglected except when the accumulated dose is small com-

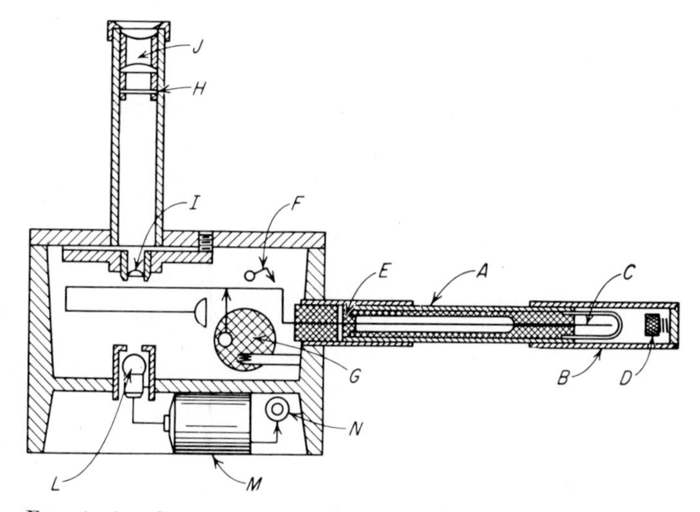


FIG. 4–13. Condenser roentgen meter (Glasser-Seitz type). *A*, chamber tube containing the capacitor and chamber; *B*, chamber tube cap (for the end opposite the chamber); *C*, ionization chamber; *D*, insulating button to cover the insulation at *E; F*, discharge switch; *G*, static charger wheel; *H*, scale; *I*, objective; *J*, ocular; *L*, lamp; *M*, battery; *N*, light switch. [*From J. A. Victoreen, article in O. Glasser (ed.), "Medical Physics," Year Book Publishers, Inc., Chicago,* 1944.]

pared with the full range of the instrument or when the time required to accumulate the dose is large. In any case, the conditions under which leakage can be neglected need to be investigated for each type of chamber.

Several types of condenser chambers for dose measurements are available commercially. Certain of these instruments require a separate electrometer for reading the charge, while others contain an integral charge-reading mechanism.

One of the earliest instruments for measuring dose is the condenser roentgen meter developed by Victoreen [27]. The condenser chamber along with the charger–charge-reader unit is shown schematically in Fig. 4–13.

The condenser chamber consists of a thimble chamber of about 1 $cm^3$ connected across a capacitor. Since the capacitor has a solid dielectric, the unit is sealed against all ionization except that which occurs in the chamber. The charge reader is an electrostatic-type electrometer. This unit has a full-scale reading of 25 r.

The term pocket chamber is used to designate a fountain-pen-size condenser-type ionization chamber which is used with a separate charge reader. Figure 4–14 is a photograph of an instrument which includes a pocket chamber, both assembled and unassembled, and a charger–charge reader.

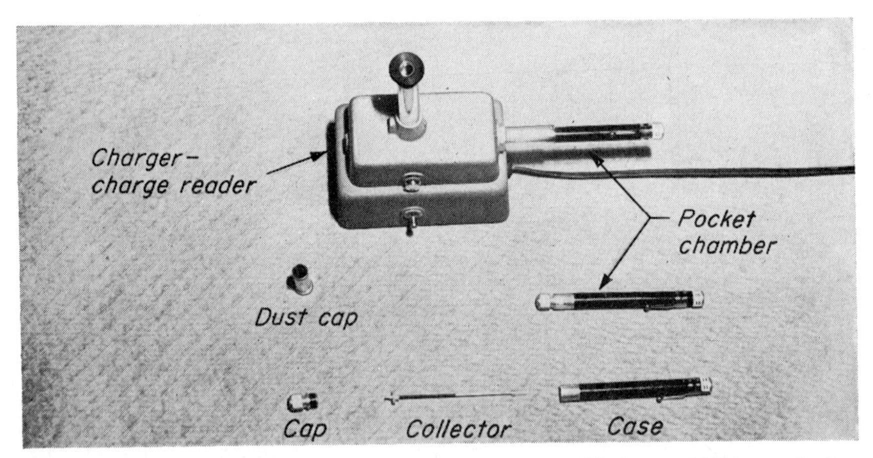


FIG. 4–14. Pocket chamber and charger–charge reader. (*Courtesy of Victoreen Instrument Company.*)

The chamber is charged by inserting it in the charger and pressing the button which connects an internal power supply across the chamber. The charge reader, a string electrometer, serves to indicate the charge. Following the charging process, the chamber is removed from the charging unit and exposed to the nuclear radiation which it is required to monitor. Normally two chambers are worn by each individual. At the end of the working period, the amount of radiation which has been received is determined. In case of a discrepancy between the two chambers, the lower reading is considered to be more nearly correct since any difference may usually be attributed to leakage.

After the exposure, the chamber is reinserted into the electrometer, the latter having been first fully charged. The charge which remains on the chamber is measured by the electrometer, the deflection of the string being observed by means of a built-in microscope. The ocular scale of the microscope is calibrated in roentgens.

Day [28] has studied several types of radiation-monitoring equipment to determine the dependence of their responses on the X- and gamma-ray energy. Included in these instruments were several commercial pocket chambers having a full-scale range of 200 mr. Typical of these was the Victoreen model. The wall of the chamber consisted of an 8-cm-long Tenite II (cellulose acetate butyrate) tube with an outside diameter of 0.6 in. and a wall thickness of 0.087 in. The wall was lined by a 0.017-in. cardboard insert which was coated on the inside surface with 0.0005 in. of graphite. The collector was a 0.062-in.-diameter aluminum wire, coated

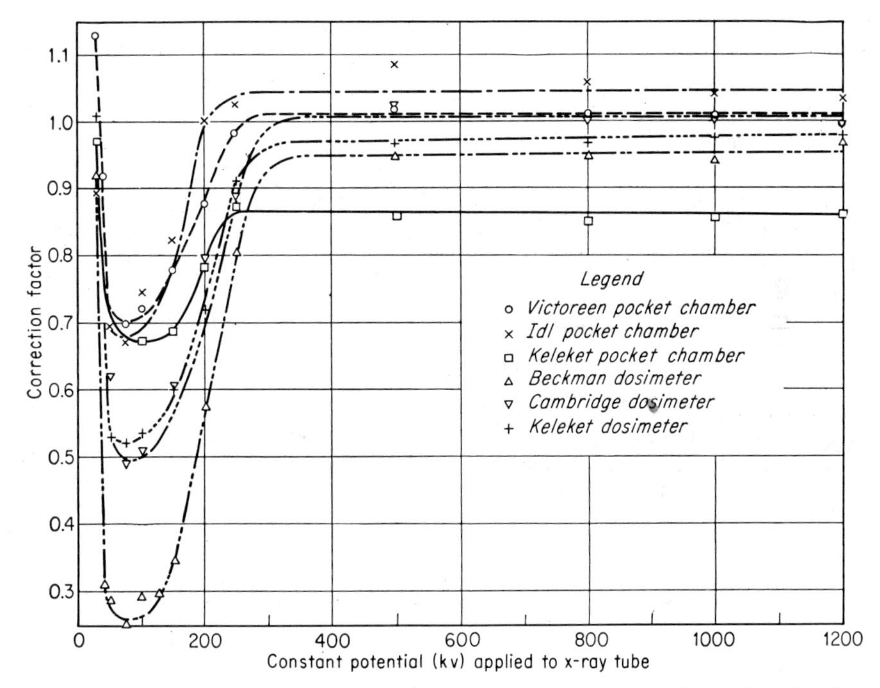


Fig. 4–15. Correction factor versus peak X-ray energy for various ionization-chamber instruments. [*From F. H. Day, Natl. Bur. Standards (U.S.) Circ.* 507, 1951.]

with 0.0005 in. of graphite. The insulators were polystyrene, and the filling gas was air at atmospheric pressure. The chamber [28] was found to be sufficiently air-equivalent that its response, shown in Fig. 4–15, was independent of energy from 1.2 to 0.3 Mev. Below this energy the response rose, passing through a maximum of 140 per cent of normal at about 0.1 Mev. This rise was attributed to the secondary electrons which were emitted from the aluminum portion of the chamber by the photoelectric absorption process. In this energy region the photoelectric absorption process is quite important. Since this process depends on $Z^5$ (see Sec. 1–13), the aluminum is much more effective than air. As the energy was lowered below 0.1 Mev, the response dropped rapidly because the radiation suffered appreciable attenuation in the wall before reaching the interior of the chamber. The readings indicated by the pocket chamber were much less than the actual doses at energies below about 40 kev.

The Lauritsen electroscope (see Sec. 4–12) serves as a very sensitive dosimeter with a self-contained charge-reading mechanism. With this instrument it is possible to totalize doses occurring at a rate of less than 1 mr/hr.

The term pocket dosimeter designates a condenser ionization chamber of fountain-pen size with a self-contained charge-reading mechanism. Figure 4–16 is a self-explanatory diagram of a 200-mr pocket dosimeter in which the charge reading is made possible by a very compact, rugged electroscope.

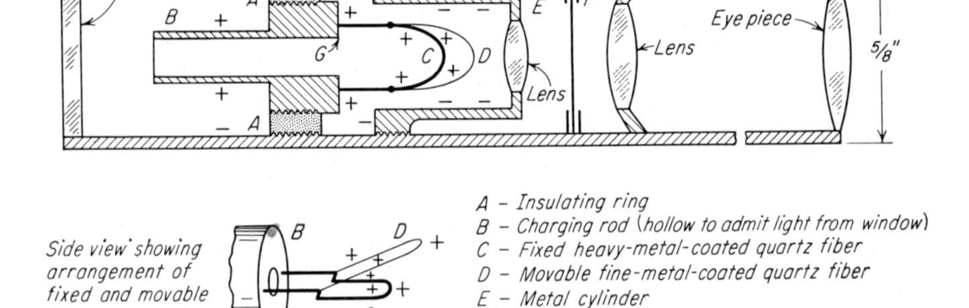


Side view showing arrangement of fixed and movable fibers

A – Insulating ring
B – Charging rod (hollow to admit light from window)
C – Fixed heavy-metal-coated quartz fiber
D – Movable fine-metal-coated quartz fiber
E – Metal cylinder
F – Transparent scale
G – Metal support for fibers

FIG. 4–16. Self-reading-type pocket dosimeter. (*From Ralph E. Lapp and Howard L. Andrews, "Nuclear Radiation Physics," p. 199, Copyright, 1948, by Prentice-Hall, Inc., Englewood Cliffs, N.J. Reproduced by permission of the publisher.*)

Current-type ionization chambers equipped with current-measuring devices of the type discussed in Sec. 4–8 are used widely for dose-rate meters. These instruments are normally calibrated in milliroentgens per hour or roentgens per hour.

Portable dose-rate meters often contain vacuum-tube electrometers as the current-measuring devices. For stationary chambers other electrometers, such as the Lindemann and the vibrating-reed, may be used to provide more sensitivity.

Figure 4–17 is a schematic diagram of a beta-gamma survey instrument. This device is one version of the instrument commonly known as the "Cutie Pie." The chamber is made of bakelite coated on the inside with graphite. The energy dependence of the response of this instrument has been studied [29]. Its response has been found to be within 10 per cent of that of the ideal air-equivalent chamber down to about 20-kev X rays.

Below this energy the response drops rapidly, being less than one-half at 10 kev. The drop in the response is due primarily to the attenuation of the chamber wall for the primary gammas.

Another version of the ionization-chamber dose-rate meter which has been developed recently is known as the Neher-White ionization chamber.

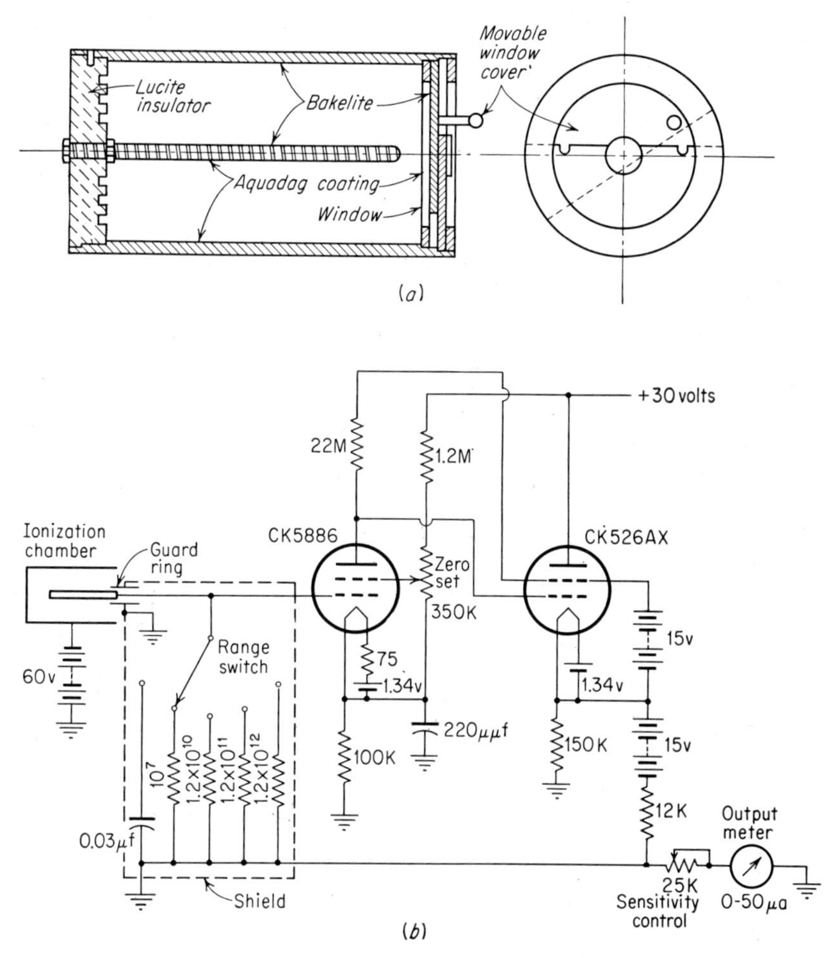


FIG. 4–17. Beta-gamma survey instrument. (*a*) Ionization chamber; (*b*) circuit schematic diagram. (*Courtesy of Tracerlab, Inc.*)

This instrument is essentially a steel shell with an electrometer tube sealed inside it. The chamber contains pure argon at a pressure of 10 atm. The grid of the electrometer tube is connected only to the collector electrode. Figure 4–18 is the basic-circuit diagram. Positive ions are attracted to this collector, and the floating-grid circuit assumes a voltage determined by a balance between the positive-ion current and the electron current from the tube filament. The plate current is found to be a logarithmic function of the ionization current. The plate-current change is 10 to 15 μamp per decade change in radiation.

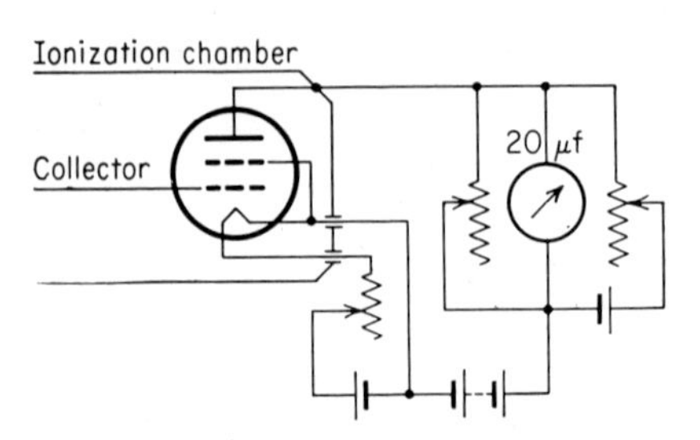


Fig. 4–18. Basic circuit for the Neher-White ionization chamber. (*Courtesy of Jordan Electronic Mfg. Co., Inc.*)

The use of the high-pressure filling gas gives the chamber proportionately larger ionization current and therefore more sensitivity. The steel shell of the chamber gives it the required strength. However, to make its response insensitive to changes in the gamma-ray energy, a lead absorber is placed on the outside of the steel and an aluminum secondary-electron emitter on the inside. This makes the spectral response essentially flat from 75 kev to 1.3 Mev.

Mounting the electrometer tube inside the chamber and eliminating the high resistance effectively eliminate insulation trouble and give the instrument high stability. The high sensitivity combined with the good stability allows the measurement of radiation rates as small as 0.002 mr/hr above background. At the same time, the logarithmic response makes it possible to go to high ranges on the same instrument.

## 4–17. *Calibration of Instruments for Gamma- and X-ray-dose Measurements*

In many cases it is not feasible to calculate dose or dose rate from the relationships discussed in Sec. 4–15. Such factors as inaccuracies in resistors, uncertainties as to the sensitive volume, and errors due to the influence of wall materials make it advisable that calibration sources be available.

Radium, in equilibrium with its decay products, is used as a standard for dose measurements. For this purpose the radium is enclosed in a thin platinum filter, usually of either ½- or 1-mm thickness. The purpose of the platinum is to remove the beta radiation. The dosage rate $R$ in roentgens per hour at $d$ cm from a radium source of activity $A$ millicuries (mc) encased in platinum of thickness $t$ mm is

$$R = \frac{8.98(1 - 0.13t)A}{d^2} \tag{4–31}$$

For a 0.5-mm filter,

$$R(\text{r/hr}) = \frac{8.4A(\text{mc of Ra})}{d^2(\text{cm}^2)} \tag{4–32}$$

It is enlightening to develop Eq. (4–31) from the definition of the roentgen and the nature of the absorption process. For this purpose it is convenient to express the roentgen in terms of the energy given to the secondary electrons per cubic centimeter of air at 0°C and 760 mm Hg. Since 32.5 ev of energy is required per ion pair of charge produced, the release of 1 esu of charge, or $2.085 \times 10^9$ ion pairs, by secondary electrons represents an energy absorption of $(32.5)(2.085 \times 10^9) = 6.77 \times 10^{10}$ ev/cm³. Therefore $6.77 \times 10^4$ Mev of energy absorbed per cubic centimeter of air at normal conditions is equivalent to 1 r of X or gamma radiation.

The energy flux $I$ at a distance of $d$ cm from a point source emitting $S$ gammas/sec of energy $E$ Mev is

$$I[\text{Mev}/(\text{cm}^2)(\text{sec})] = \frac{SE}{4\pi d^2} \tag{4-33}$$

The distribution in direction is assumed to be uniform. The fraction of the energy absorbed per centimeter of distance in the radial direction from the source is $\mu_a$ cm$^{-1}$, where $\mu_a$ is known as the true-energy absorption coefficient in air. Thus the rate of energy absorption at a distance $d$ from a point source is $\mu_a SE/4\pi d^2$ Mev/(sec)(cm³), where it is assumed that the fraction of the gammas absorbed in going a distance $d$ from the source is negligible. Converting to energy absorption per hour and expressing 1 r as $6.77 \times 10^4$ Mev/cm³ of air, one obtains the dosage rate $R$ as

$$\begin{aligned} R(\text{r/hr}) &= \frac{(3{,}600)\mu_a SE}{(6.77 \times 10^4)(4\pi)d^2} \\ &= \frac{(4.24 \times 10^{-3})\mu_a(\text{cm}^{-1})S(\text{gammas/sec})E(\text{Mev})}{d^2(\text{cm}^2)} \end{aligned} \tag{4-34}$$

The true-energy absorption coefficient $\mu_a$ is

$$\mu_a = \sigma_a + \tau + \left(1 - \frac{2m_oc^2}{E}\right)\kappa \tag{4-35}$$

The coefficient $\mu_a$ is nearly equal to $\sigma_a$ up to about 2 Mev where pair production becomes significant.

The dosage rate can be expressed as

$$R(\text{r/hr}) = \frac{I_\gamma S(\text{mc})}{d^2(\text{cm}^2)} \tag{4-36}$$

where $S$ is the gamma-source strength expressed in millicuries and

$$I_\gamma[\text{r}/(\text{hr})(\text{mc})(\text{cm}^{-2})] = \mu_a E(3.7 \times 10^7)(4.24 \times 10^{-3}) \tag{4-37}$$

or the dosage rate at 1 cm from a source emitting $3.7 \times 10^7$ gammas of energy $E$ per second. The gamma-source strength is the activity of the radioisotope multiplied by the fraction of the disintegrations resulting in the emission of gammas with the energy in question. Values of $I_\gamma$ as a function of energy as calculated by Marinelli et al. [30] are shown in Fig. 4–19.

The gamma-ray spectrum of radium and its equilibrium products is given in Table 4–2. The average number $P_j$ of photons of energy $E_j$ per disintegration of $Ra^{226}$ is given, along with $E_j$ and the corresponding value of $(I_\gamma)_j$. The dosage rate from $A$ millicuries of radium is therefore

$$R(\text{r/hr}) = \frac{A(\text{mc of Ra}^{226})}{d^2} \sum_j P_j(I_\gamma)_j = \frac{9.79A}{d^2}$$

which is in reasonable agreement with the empirical value computed from Eq. (4–31) with $t = 0$.

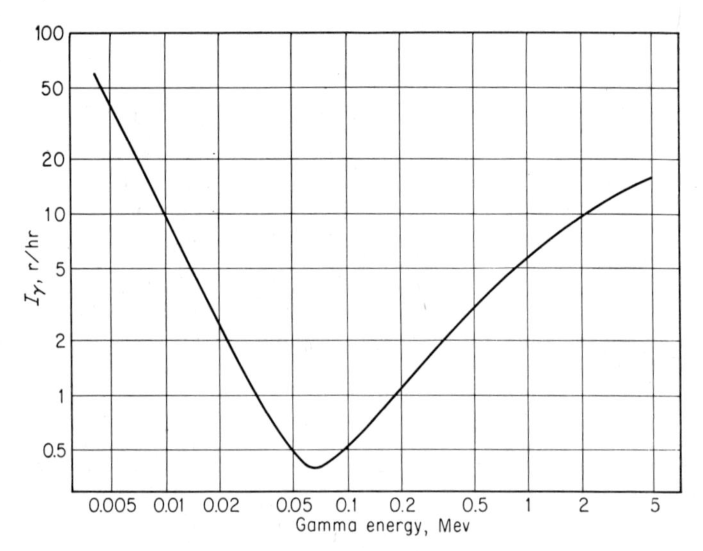


FIG. 4–19. Dosage rate versus energy. Dosage rate is in roentgens per hour at 1 cm from a point source emitting $3.7 \times 10^7$ gammas/sec. [*From L. D. Marinelli et al., Dosage Determination with Radioactive Isotopes, Am. J. Roentgenol. Radium Therapy,* **59**:273 (1948); *Charles C Thomas, Publisher, Springfield, Ill.*]

For a $Co^{60}$ source, another material used for standardization, the dosage rate is

$$R(\text{r/hr}) = \frac{14A(\text{mc of Co}^{60})}{d^2(\text{cm}^2)} \qquad (4\text{–}38)$$

It is important to correct the certified activity of a $Co^{60}$ source for decay since it has a half-life of only 5.3 years.

## 4–18. *Beta-dose Measurements and the Extrapolation Chamber*

The Bragg-Gray principle (see Sec. 4–13) is applicable to the measurements of the dose produced by beta radiation as well as by other types of radiation. However, since the energy spectrum of beta-radiation fields covers a large range down to zero, the condition that the cavity be small compared with the electron ranges requires special precautions. The

TABLE 4–2. GAMMA-RAY SPECTRUM OF RADIUM AND ITS EQUILIBRIUM PRODUCTS

| $E_j$† gamma energy, Mev | $P_j$† yields, gammas/$Ra^{226}\alpha$ | $(I\gamma)_j$‡ | $P_j(I\gamma)_j$ [r/(hr)(mc of $Ra^{226}$)($cm^{-2}$)] |
|---|---|---|---|
| 0.184 | 0.012 | 1.00 | 0.012 |
| 0.241 | 0.115 | 1.35 | 0.155 |
| 0.294 | 0.258 | 1.69 | 0.436 |
| 0.350 | 0.450 | 2.05 | 0.923 |
| 0.607 | 0.658 | 3.65 | 2.402 |
| 0.766 | 0.065 | 4.50 | 0.293 |
| 0.933 | 0.067 | 5.40 | 0.362 |
| 1.120 | 0.206 | 6.30 | 1.298 |
| 1.238 | 0.063 | 6.80 | 0.428 |
| 1.379 | 0.064 | 7.40 | 0.474 |
| 1.761 | 0.258 | 8.80 | 2.270 |
| 2.198 | 0.074 | 10.03 | 0.742 |
| Total. . . . . . . . . . . . . . . . . . | . . . . | . . . . | 9.79 |

† From R. D. Evans, *Nucleonics*, **1**:40 (October, 1947).
‡ From L. D. Marinelli, E. H. Quimby, and G. J. Hine, *Am. J. Roentgenol. Radium Therapy*, **59**:260 (1948).

extrapolation chamber [31,32], introduced by Failla [31], is particularly suitable for measurements of this type.

Figure 4–20 shows a cross-sectional view of an extrapolation chamber. For the application of this instrument to the measurement of beta-energy absorption in a material, the high-voltage electrode, collector electrode, and guard ring would all be made of the material in question. Measurements are made of the saturation value of the ionization current $i$ versus the electrode spacing. By making the appropriate changes in units, Eq. (4–28) can be written as

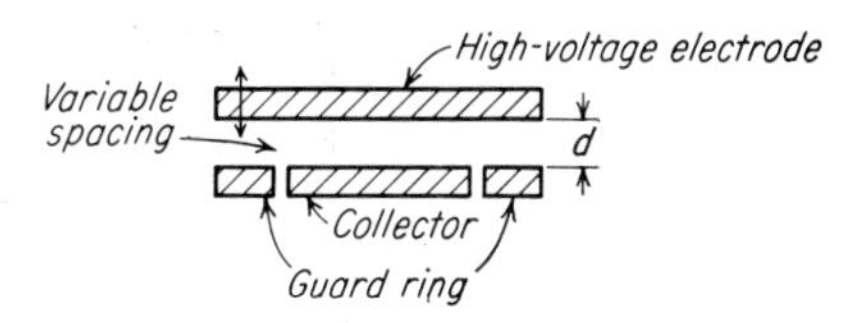


FIG. 4–20. Cross-sectional view of an extrapolation chamber.

$$R(\text{rads/hr}) = 7.8 \times 10^{11} \frac{iwS_mT}{Vp} \qquad (4\text{–}39)$$

where $R$ = dose rate in material
$i$ = saturation ionization current (amp)
$V$ = active volume ($cm^3$) as determined by guard ring and plate spacing
$w$ = average energy (ev) required per ion pair formed in gas
$S_m$ = relative mass stopping power of absorbing medium to gas
$T$ and $p$ = temperature (°K) and pressure (mm Hg) respectively, of gas in the cavity

From the slope of the ionization-current versus plate-spacing curve taken at the zero extrapolation, one obtains the limiting value of the ratio $i/V$ as the cavity in the medium becomes vanishingly small and thereby satisfies the conditions for the applicability of the Bragg-Gray principle.

The values of $w$ and $S_m$ in Eq. (4–39) must be averages which are suitable for the media and beta spectrum involved. Since $w$ is essentially energy-independent, the value 32.5 ev per ion pair can be used. However, $S_m$ does change with energy. Values of $S_m$ relative to air are given in Table 4–3

TABLE 4–3. MASS STOPPING POWER OF VARIOUS MATERIALS RELATIVE TO AIR FOR FAST ELECTRONS*

| $E$, Mev | Be | $(CH_2)_n$ | C | Poly-styrene | Lucite | Mg | Al |
|---|---|---|---|---|---|---|---|
| 0.5 | 1.036 | 1.051 | 1.007 | 1.038 | 1.031 | 0.950 | 0.946 |
| 0.75 | 1.023 | 1.038 | 1.000 | 1.030 | 1.022 | 0.952 | 0.950 |
| 1.0 | 1.012 | 1.028 | 0.992 | 1.020 | 1.014 | 0.951 | 0.949 |
| 1.5 | 0.997 | 1.009 | 0.977 | 1.003 | 0.997 | 0.947 | 0.944 |
| 2.0 | 0.985 | 0.995 | 0.963 | 0.988 | 0.982 | 0.942 | 0.936 |
| 3 | 0.968 | 0.976 | 0.944 | 0.969 | 0.963 | 0.932 | 0.926 |
| 5 | 0.937 | 0.948 | 0.919 | 0.942 | 0.937 | 0.911 | 0.903 |
| 10 | 0.897 | 0.911 | 0.884 | 0.907 | 0.901 | 0.879 | 0.866 |
| 20 | 0.856 | 0.879 | 0.848 | 0.870 | 0.865 | 0.850 | 0.835 |
| 50 | 0.816 | 0.830 | 0.804 | 0.826 | 0.821 | 0.811 | 0.799 |
| 100 | 0.802 | 0.815 | 0.791 | 0.813 | 0.808 | 0.799 | 0.789 |

* From L. D. Marinelli, *Ann. Rev. Nuclear Sci.*, **3**:249 (1953).

over a range of electron energies for a number of materials. Ideally, $S_m$ should be obtained experimentally for a situation simulating as nearly as possible the actual measurement to which Eq. (4–39) is to be applied. Failla [34] has discussed such determinations of $S_m$. It has been estimated [35] that its value for tissue relative to air is 1.13 within 6 per cent for beta energies from 0.01 to 2 Mev.

**Example 4–6.** An extrapolation chamber with tissue-equivalent walls has an extrapolated current value of $10^{-14}$ amp/$cm^3$ when placed in a uniform beam of beta radiation.

Calculate the dosage rate which would occur in tissue at a depth equal to the upper-electrode (window) thickness of the extrapolation chamber.

*Solution.* By Eq. (4–39),

$$R(\text{rads/hr}) = 7.8 \times 10^{11} \frac{iwS_mT}{Vp}$$

$$= \frac{(7.8 \times 10^{11})(10^{-14})(32.5)(1.13)(273)}{760} = 0.10 \text{ rad/hr}$$

where standard temperature and pressure have been assumed.

An ionization-chamber instrument calibrated to read in roentgens for X and gamma rays will give a rough approximation of the dose in rep or rads due to beta rays, provided that the window of the chamber is sufficiently thin to allow the entry of the beta particles. Actually, there are a number of practical difficulties which cause the true tissue dose in rep due to beta particles to be quite different from that indicated by an ionization-chamber instrument calibrated in roentgens for gamma radiation. Failla [36] has shown, by comparison with an extrapolation chamber, that the readings on a commercial-type "Cutie Pie" monitoring instrument indicate a reading too low by a factor of 3 or more when the scale calibration in roentgens per hour is interpreted as expressing the beta-dosage rate in rep per hour. His measurements were made with the open beta window of the chamber held quite near large flat sources of beta particles of various energies. One of the principal reasons for this discrepancy is the fact that the thick side walls of the ionization chamber prevent the entry into the chamber of a large fraction of the particles whose contribution to the dosage should be included.

Roesch and Donaldson [37] have described the development of portable instruments for accurate beta-ray dosimetry. Among other instruments, they have described a modified "Cutie Pie" survey instrument consisting of a shallow cylindrical chamber 20 cm in diameter and 2.5 cm deep.

### 4–19. *Tissue-equivalent Ionization Chambers*

Because of the importance of absorption of nuclear radiation in tissues, extensive work has been carried out [38] on the development of tissue-equivalent ionization chambers. Chambers have been developed which contain, in both the wall and the gas, the significant elements of the tissue in the correct proportions. A good typical approximation for soft tissue is furnished by the formula $(C_5H_{40}O_{18}N)_n$.

It has been established [38] that a satisfactory tissue-equivalent gas consists of the mixture 38.1 per cent hydrogen, 22.2 per cent methane, 37.6 per cent oxygen, and 2.1 per cent nitrogen. For wall material, a resilient gel of 66.2 per cent water, 20.2 per cent gelatin, 5.2 per cent glycerol, and 8.4 per cent sucrose has been used. In addition, tissue-equivalent plastics are available which, after standardization by means of the gel chamber, have satisfactory properties.

## OTHER APPLICATIONS OF MEAN-LEVEL IONIZATION CHAMBERS

### 4–20. *Alpha Monitoring*

Because of their large specific ionization, relatively small intensities of alpha radiation can be measured by a mean-level ionization chamber. One 4-Mev alpha per minute in a chamber produces an average current of about $3 \times 10^{-16}$ amp. This high sensitivity makes possible the use of mean-level chambers in such applications as the checking for alpha contamination on table tops.

The typical instrument consists of an ionization chamber having a large thin window (less than 1 $mg/cm^2$) together with a sensitive electrometer, usually of the electrometer-tube type. The thin window is very important because of the short range of alpha particles.

**Example 4–7.** A commercial ionization-chamber instrument has a lowest range of 500 alphas/min full scale. What current flows in the chamber for full-scale deflection?

*Solution*

$$i = 500\ (\alpha/\text{min})\ \frac{(4 \times 10^{6}\ \text{ev}/\alpha)(1.6 \times 10^{-19}\ \text{coulomb/ion pair})}{(35\ \text{ev/ion pair})(60\ \text{sec/min})}$$
$$= 1.7 \times 10^{-13}\ \text{amp}$$

where it is assumed that the alpha particles have 4 Mev of energy remaining upon entering the chamber.

### 4–21. *Ionization Chambers Containing Radioactive Gases*

When the radioactivity to be observed can be incorporated as part of the chamber filling gas, high sensitivity can be obtained. The chamber shown in Fig. 4–2 was devised [4] for use in this way with $C^{14}$. The output of this type of chamber with a volume of 250 $cm^3$ is about $10^{-14}$ amp per microcurie of $C^{14}$ when the chamber contains carbon dioxide at normal temperature and pressure.

Chambers similar to that shown in Fig. 4–2 are useful in the monitoring for airborne contamination by radioisotopes emitting alpha or beta particles. For this application, both an entrance and exit are provided in the chamber, and the air is continually drawn through it. Unless special provisions are made, the ionization which is produced outside the chamber will contribute to the current flow in the chamber, and there will be a dependence on the air-flow rate through the chamber. One straightforward way to avoid this is to draw the air through two ionization chambers in series. The first one serves to collect the ionization from the air before its entry into the second chamber. In the latter chamber the only ionization which is measured is that produced by the radioactive decay while the air is in the chamber. This current is directly proportional to the concentration of the radioisotopes in the air and is independent of the flow rate.

### 4–22. *The Ohmart Cell*

The Ohmart cell [39], a modification of ionization-chamber instruments, employs the contact-potential differences between the electrodes of the chamber to produce the current flow. In this way, the use of an external battery is avoided, and some simplicity is achieved. The cell, manufactured by The Ohmart Corporation, is available in a number of sizes and shapes for different applications. Typical uses include the monitoring of the flow of radioactive liquids by an Ohmart cell wrapped around the pipe and general area monitoring of gamma radiation.

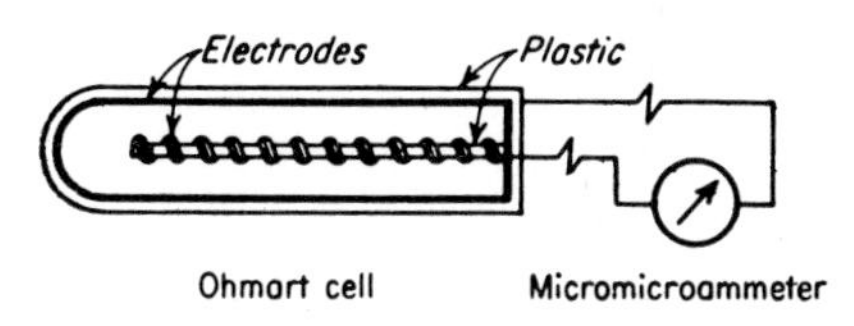


FIG. 4–21. Schematic diagram of an Ohmart cell in a circuit with a micro-microammeter. (*Courtesy of The Ohmart Corporation.*)

Figure 4–21 is the schematic diagram of an Ohmart cell designed for measuring the internal dose of X-ray radiation in the human body. The current flow in this chamber as a function of the gamma intensity, as determined by Dowell [40], is shown in Fig. 4–22. It is interesting to note that, even though the contact-potential difference between the electrodes is much less than the voltage required to draw saturation current, the actual current flow varies approximately linearly with the radiation intensity.

## PULSE-TYPE IONIZATION CHAMBERS

### 4–23. *Pulse Shape in an Ionization Chamber*

The operation of both pulse and mean-level ionization chambers depends on collection of the ion pairs which are produced by the passage of ionizing radiation through the chambers. However, the details of the collection process take on importance in the pulse chamber that they do not have in the other type. The development of Wilkinson [41] is followed here.

The pulse chambers are used for studies of single particles of nuclear radiation. If the information desired is the number of ionizing particles, the requirements for the pulses are relatively simple. They are that the resulting voltage pulse at the input of the pulse amplifier be greater than the lower level set by the amplifier discriminator and that the duration of the voltage pulses at the input of the amplifier be sufficiently short to allow successive pulses to be distinguished. If time relationships are being studied, the time required for the development of the pulse is important. If energy measurements are being made, the relationship between the pulse amplitude and the amount of ionization is the primary design consideration.

Consider an ionization chamber connected to the input of an amplifier as represented schematically in Fig. 4–23. For the quiescent condition

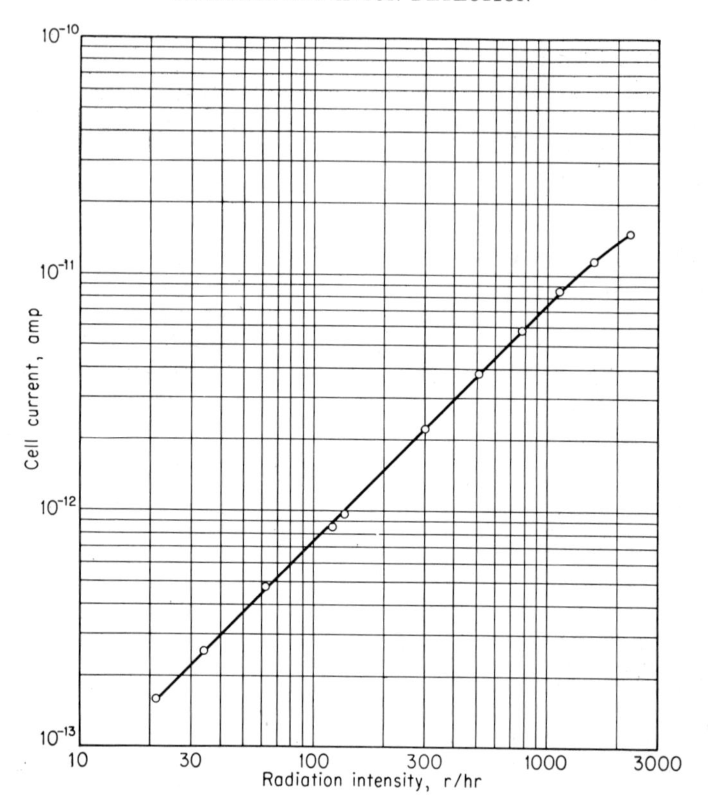


FIG. 4-22. Ohmart-cell current versus gamma intensity. (*From D. C. Dowell, Testing and Evaluation of the Ohmart Cell, Thesis, Air Force Institute of Technology, Wright-Patterson Air Force Base, Ohio,* 1956.)

between pulses, $v$, the potential of the collecting electrode relative to ground, is zero. This corresponds to the equilibrium condition in which a charge $Q$ is stored on the electrodes of the chamber. If $N$ ion pairs with charge $+Ne$ and $-Ne$ are produced in the chamber, say at point 1, the negative charge will be attracted toward the collector electrode and the positive charge toward the high-voltage electrode. Upon arrival at the respective electrodes, these charges will be collected. This results in a change in the charge stored on the electrodes. Ultimately, after sufficient time elapses for the charge to flow through the external resistance $R$, the previous equilibrium condition is reached, with $v = 0$.

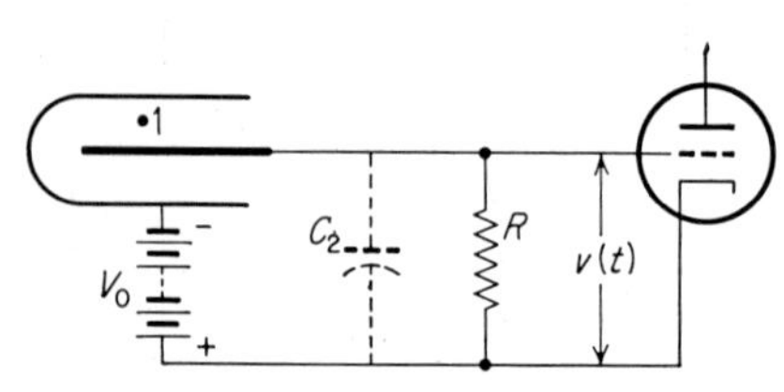


FIG. 4-23. Schematic diagram showing the input circuit for a pulse-type ionization chamber.

During the sequence of these events, $v$ varies with time; it is this quantity, $v(t)$, which we wish to predict.

Let $t_+$ and $t_-$ be the times required to collect the positive and negative ions, respectively. These times depend primarily on the ion mobilities, the electric-field strengths, and the distances traveled. If the negative portion of the ion pair is a negative ion, $t_-$ is of the same order of magnitude as $t_+$; however, if the negative portion is a free electron, $t_- \ll t_+$. Consider $v(t)$ for the case where the circuit time constant $RC \gg t_+$. Here $C = C_1 + C_2$, where $C_1$ is the capacity of the ionization chamber measured between the collector electrode and the high-voltage electrodes. This condition makes it possible to neglect the current flow through $R$ during the time required to collect the ions. Consequently, one can write $v(t) = q(t)/C$, where $q(t)$ is the net charge produced in the input circuit by the positive and negative ions. These ions can affect the net charge through the induced charge which they produce before collection as well as by being collected. If $-q_+(t)$ and $-q_-(t)$ are the charges induced on the collecting electrodes by the positive and negative charges, respectively, equal charges of opposite signs appear in the input circuit, and the potential is

$$v(t) = \frac{q_+(t) + q_-(t)}{C} \qquad (4\text{–}40)$$

When the negative charge reaches the collecting electrode, $q_-(t)$ becomes $-Ne$, and

$$v(t) = \frac{q_+(t) - Ne}{C}$$

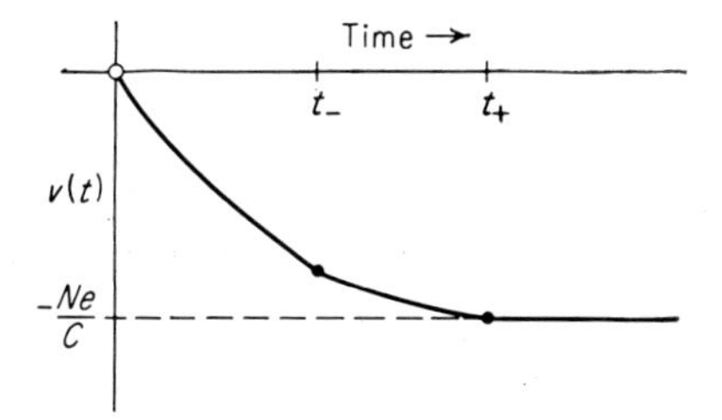


FIG. 4–24. Voltage appearing at the input of a circuit such as that shown in Fig. 4–23 as the charge $Ne$ is collected, for the condition $RC \gg t_+$.

Here it is assumed that $t_+ > t_-$. When the positive ion is collected, $q_+(t) = 0$, and

$$v(t) = -\frac{Ne}{C} \qquad (4\text{–}41)$$

It is important to notice that the potential change of $-Ne/C$ is reached only after all the charge is collected.

Figure 4–24 shows the form which $v(t)$ takes as the charge $Ne$ is collected, provided that it all originates at a point. When the ionization is spread initially over a region, the discontinuities at $t_-$ and $t_+$ tend to get lost since these times vary between various ion pairs.

## 4–24. *Calculation of Induced Charges*

The discussion in the preceding section shows that determination of $v(t)$ depends on the calculation of the induced charges $q_+(t)$ and $q_-(t)$.

These charges can be calculated through the use of Green's reciprocation theorem in electrostatics [42]. This theorem states that, if one has a system of conductors, 1, 2, 3, . . . , $n$, and, upon placing upon them charges $q_1$, $q_2$, $q_3$, . . . , $q_n$, one finds potentials $v_1$, $v_2$, $v_3$, . . . , $v_n$, the use of charges $q'_1$, $q'_2$, $q'_3$, . . . , $q'_n$ will result in potentials $v'_1$, $v'_2$, $v'_3$, . . . , $v'_n$ such that

$$\sum_{i=1}^{n} q_i v'_i = \sum_{i=1}^{n} q'_i v_i \qquad (4\text{–}42)$$

Consider an ionization chamber having two electrodes, denoted as 1 and 2, with a charge $q$ at point $P$ between them. Let $q_1$ and $q_2$ denote the charges induced on the respective electrodes. Under the condition that one electrode completely encloses the other,

$$-q = q_1 + q_2 \qquad (4\text{–}43)$$

since all the lines of force from $q$ end on either electrode 1 or 2. Let $v'_1$, $v'_2$, and $v'_p$ be the potentials in the absence of a charge at $P$, that is, with $q' = 0$. When the electrodes are grounded so that $v_1 = v_2 = 0$, Eq. (4–42) becomes

$$q_1 v'_1 + q_2 v'_2 + q v'_p = 0 \qquad (4\text{–}44)$$

Solving Eqs. (4–43) and (4–44) for $q_1$ and $q_2$, one obtains

$$q_1 = \frac{v'_2 - v'_p}{v'_1 - v'_2} q \qquad (4\text{–}45)$$

and

$$q_2 = \frac{v'_1 - v'_p}{v'_2 - v'_1} q \qquad (4\text{–}46)$$

For a parallel-plate ionization chamber with the charge located as shown in Fig. 4–25,

$$q_1 = \frac{-b}{a+b} q \qquad \text{and} \qquad q_2 = \frac{-a}{a+b} q \qquad (4\text{–}47)$$

since $v'_p - v'_1 = (v'_2 - v'_1)a/(a+b)$. For a coaxial chamber as shown in Fig. 4–26,

$$q_1 = \frac{-\ln (r_2/r)}{\ln (r_2/r_1)} q \qquad \text{and} \qquad q_2 = \frac{-\ln (r_1/r)}{\ln (r_1/r_2)} q \qquad (4\text{–}48)$$

since

$$v'_p - v'_1 = \frac{(v'_2 - v'_1) \ln (r/r_1)}{\ln (r_2/r_1)}$$

4–25. *Calculation of Pulse Shape in Parallel-plate Chambers*

Consider a parallel-plate chamber with dimensions large compared with the spacing $d$ between them so that Eq. (4–43) holds. If, in this chamber,

$N$ ion pairs are formed at a distance $x_o$ from the collecting electrode, the voltage on the collecting electrode is, from Eqs. (4–40) and (4–47),

$$v(t) = \frac{Ne}{C}\left(\frac{d - x_+}{d} - \frac{d - x_-}{d}\right) \tag{4–49}$$

where $x_+$ and $x_-$ are the positions of the positive and negative ions, respectively.

The application of Eq. (4–47) to this problem needs justification, since it was derived under the conditions that $v_1 = v_2 = 0$. The collector electrode changes from zero potential by $v(t)$ but, because of the magnitude of $C$, $v(t)$ is small and the approximation of zero is good. The high-voltage electrode is held at a fixed potential, $-V$. Since this is a constant, the charges due to it can be considered separately from those due to induction, and the results obtained by holding the electrode at zero will be superimposed on the steady charge due to $-V$.

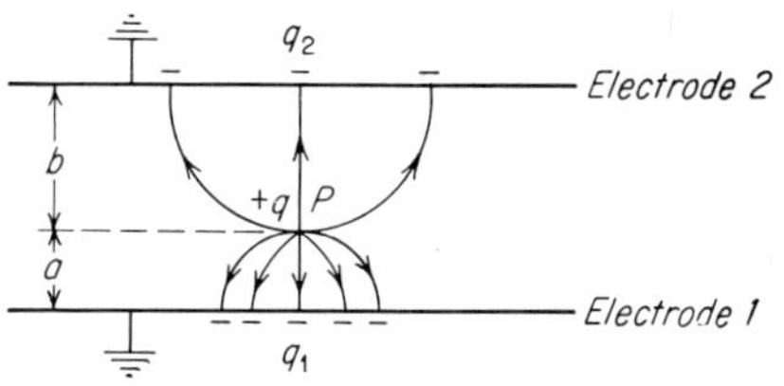

FIG. 4–25. Induced charges in a parallel-plate ionization chamber.

The positions $x_+$ and $x_-$ will be

$$x_+ = x_o + w_+t \qquad \text{and} \qquad x_- = x_o - w_-t \tag{4–50}$$

where $w_+$ and $w_-$ are the velocities of the ions. Consequently the velocities of the ions determine the duration of the voltage pulse. The velocities are obtained from Eq. (4–1). For ordinary conditions of ionization-chamber operation, the velocities are several hundred centimeters per second for the positive and negative ions but are $10^5$ cm/sec or greater for free electrons.

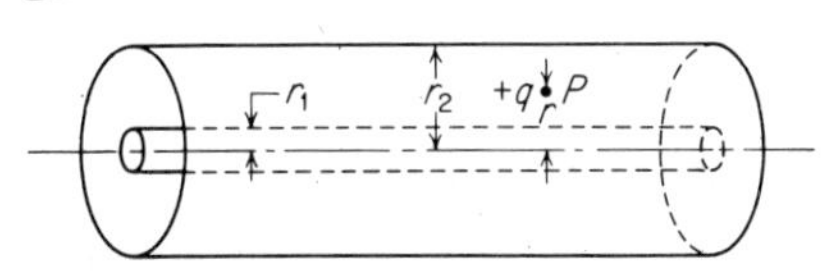

FIG. 4–26. Arrangement for calculating the induced charge produced in a cylindrical chamber by a charge $+q$ at point $P$.

Pulse chambers which depend on the collection of both the positive and negative charges for the pulse formation are known as ion pulse chambers. The collection time for the positive ions is several milliseconds in chambers of ordinary dimensions and pressures; therefore the circuit time constant $RC$ must be at least 10 msec, if the full pulse height is to be reached. This arrangement is limited to counting rates considerably less than 100 counts/sec. In addition, a wide-band amplifier (see Chap. 10) is required to utilize the slow pulses; such an amplifier is often unsatisfactory since it is subject to microphonics and a-c pickup. Ion pulse chambers have the advantage of giving a pulse height proportional to the ionization, independent of the position of the primary ionization in the chamber.

Because of the preceding considerations, the gases for pulse ionization chambers are selected to have small electron attachment coefficients so that the negative charge moves as free electrons. The circuit time constant is made much less than $t_+$ but somewhat larger than $t_-$. Ten to twenty microseconds is a typical value. In this arrangement the pulses depend only on the motion of the electrons. Such chambers are known as electron pulse chambers. The remaining discussion will be restricted to this latter type of detector.

Introducing Eq. (4–50) into Eq. (4–49), there results

$$v(t) = \frac{Ne}{C}\left(1 - \frac{x_o}{d} - 1 + \frac{x_o}{d} - \frac{w_-t}{d}\right) = \frac{-New_-t}{Cd} \tag{4–51}$$

when the motion of the positive ions is neglected and $RC$ is still much greater than $t_+$. This equation holds until $t_- = x_o/w_-$. After this time, $v(t)$ rises extremely slowly, reaching $-Ne/C$ at $t_+$ which is of the order of $1{,}000t_-$.

If the slow rise following $t_-$ is neglected, the pulse height is $-Nex_o/Cd$; that is, the pulse height depends on the position at which the ionization occurs in the chamber. In Fig. 4–27 the solid curves represent the voltage pulses resulting for three ion tracks, each containing $N$ ions but originating at different positions in the chamber.

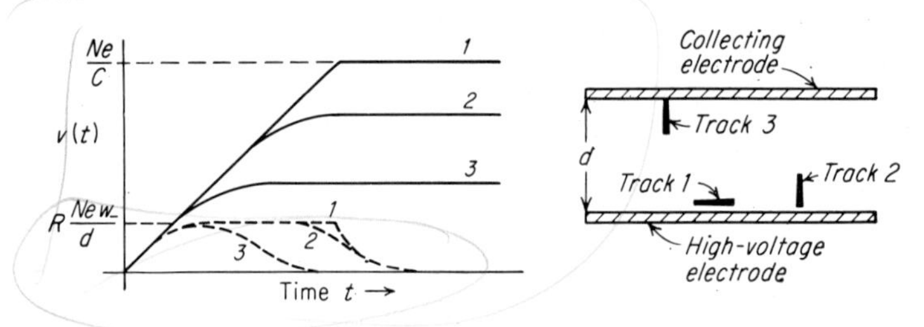


FIG. 4–27. Dependence of pulse size on the position of the primary ionization: solid curves, time constant much greater than electron-collection time $t_-$; dotted curves, time constant = 0.2 maximum electron-collection time.

From this analysis it is clear that the height of the electron pulse cannot be used as a measure of the number of ion pairs formed in a parallel-plate ionization chamber. It is to be noticed, however, that each of the curves of $v(t)$ starts with the same slope $(dv/dt)_o$ and that

$$\left(\frac{dv}{dt}\right)_o = \frac{-New_-}{Cd} \tag{4–52}$$

is proportional to $N$, the number of ion pairs. This means that the initial current which flows because of the induced charge is $-New_-/d$. Consequently, if an output voltage pulse can be obtained that is proportional to the current flow, its height can be used as a measure of $N$. This condition results for a time constant $RC \ll t_-$, since the differential equation

$$R\frac{dq}{dt} = RC\frac{dv}{dt} + v \tag{4–53}$$

which describes the system reduces to

$$v = R\frac{dq}{dt} \tag{4–54}$$

for $CR\, dv/dt \ll v$. The dotted curves in Fig. 4–27 represent the voltage for the three tracks with $RC = 0.2d/w_-$, where $d/w_-$ is the maximum transit time. It is to be noticed that this uniformity in pulse height is obtained at a considerable loss in amplitude.

**Example 4–8.** Compute the pulse height produced by a 5-Mev alpha particle in a parallel-plate ionization chamber if the capacity of the system is 20 $\mu\mu$f and the time constant $RC = 0.2d/w_-$, where $d/w_-$ is the maximum transit time.

*Solution.* By Eqs. (4–52) and (4–54),

$$v_{\max} = \frac{RNew_-}{d} = \frac{(0.2)(5 \times 10^6)(1.6 \times 10^{-19})}{(35)(20 \times 10^{-12})} = 230 \times 10^{-6} \text{ volt}$$

where the energy required to produce an ion pair is taken as 35 ev.

### 4–26. *Gridded Ionization Chambers*

The above discussion has shown the desirability of having an electron pulse ionization chamber in which the output pulse does not depend on the position or orientation of the track. This can be done by means of a gridded chamber of parallel-plate construction, sometimes known as the Frisch grid chamber [43].

Figure 4–28 is a schematic diagram of a Frisch grid chamber. A grid is placed between the two electrodes and held at an appropriate intermediate potential; the collecting electrode is positive relative to the other electrodes. The sample, emitting either alpha particles or other short-range radiation, is placed on the grounded electrode. Thus the ionization is produced between the grounded electrode and the grid.

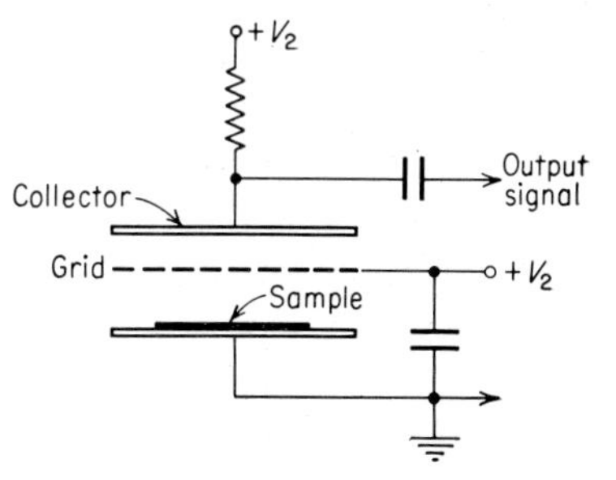


FIG. 4–28. Schematic diagram of a Frisch grid chamber.

The grid shields the collecting electrode from the charged particles as long as these are between the grid and the grounded electrodes. Since the positive ions remain in this region, they induce no charge on the collecting electrode. By optimizing the design, including the spacing of the grid wires, and the distances and voltages between the electrodes, it is possible, in theory [43] at least, to achieve the condition that no electron will be captured by the positive grid. Thus the charge appearing at the collector, following electron collection, is equal to the total ionization produced by the particle.

### 4–27. *Pulse Shape in a Cylindrical Chamber*

Another useful geometry for an ionization chamber is that of a coaxial cylinder. Consider such a chamber with a central collector electrode of radius $r_1$ and an outer negative electrode of inner radius $r_2$. The voltage pulse induced on the center electrode by the production of $N$ ion pairs at a distance $r_o$ from the center is calculated, by use of Eqs. (4–40) and (4–48), to be

$$v(t) = \frac{Ne}{C}\left[\frac{-\ln(r_2/r_-)}{\ln(r_2/r_1)} + \frac{\ln(r_2/r_+)}{\ln(r_2/r_1)}\right] \qquad (4\text{–}55)$$

where $r_+$ and $r_-$ are the positions of the positive and negative ions, respectively. Again assuming that the current is carried entirely by free electrons, so that the motion of the positive ion can be neglected, Eq. (4–55) becomes

$$v(t) = \frac{-Ne\ln(r_o/r_-)}{C\ln(r_2/r_1)}$$

where $r_+$ is replaced by $r_o$. When the ionization is produced at the outer electrode, that is, $r_o = r_2$, the pulse height reaches the maximum value of $-Ne/C$ when the electrons are collected, i.e., when $r_- = r_1$.

The maximum pulse heights versus $r_o/r_2$ for several values of $r_2/r_1$ are plotted in Fig. 4–29. These curves show that for large values of $r_2/r_1$ the height of a pulse is quite insensitive to its place of origin in the chamber.

### 4–28. *Miscellaneous Applications of Pulse Ionization Chambers* [1, 3, 41, 44]

Pulse ionization chambers are used primarily with alpha particles and other similar radiation which produce a large specific ionization. For these applications the source of the radiation is usually placed in the chamber. Measurements include energy distribution, absolute activity, range, and specific ionization.

For energy measurements the gridded ionization chamber has proved to be highly successful. An example of this type of chamber as designed by Coon and Barschall is shown in Fig. 4–30. Equipped with the paraffin radiator as illustrated, the chamber was used for fast-neutron detection (see Sec. 9–12). With the paraffin radiator replaced by a thin deposit of normal uranium, the alpha-energy spectrum shown in Fig. 4–31 was obtained. The peaks have a width of 150 kev at the half-maximum values corresponding to a resolution of 3 per cent. The gridded electrode consisted of 0.003-in. Cu wires spaced at 1.5-mm intervals. The chamber gas was argon at 7.5-atm pressure. The potentials of the high-voltage and gridded electrodes were 2,500 and 1,250 volts, respectively, below the collector.

Range measurements and specific-ionization measurements can be made through the use of a very shallow pulse-type ionization chamber. An ap-

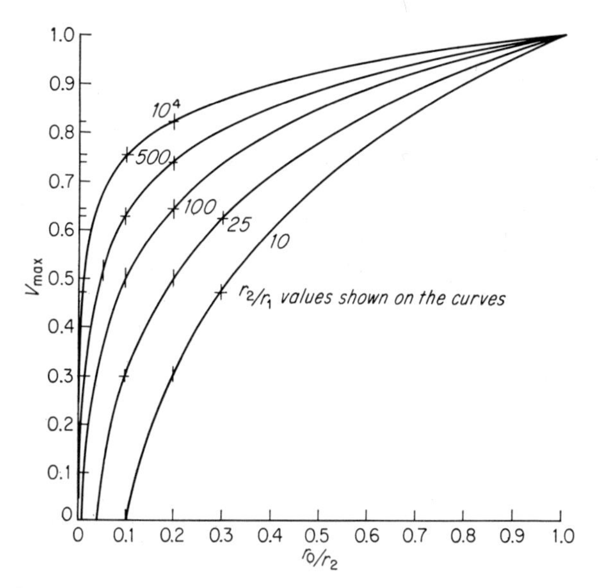


FIG. 4–29. Dependence of pulse size on the position of primary ionization in a cylindrical ionization chamber. (*From D. H. Wilkinson, "Ionization Chambers and Counters," Cambridge University Press, London,* 1950.)

paratus suitable for these measurements is shown schematically in Fig. 4–32. The chamber is around 1 mm deep. The range determinations are made through measurements of counting rate versus either source-to-counter distance or pressure. Specific-ionization measurements consist of pulse-height determinations at various source-to-counter distances.

For counting and coincidence measurements, the relationship between pulse height and energy is not important. Rather, the principal requirement is that fast counting be possible. In addition, for coincidence measurements the time of appearance should be well coordinated with the occurrence of the ionizing event. The ungridded parallel-plate chambers are particularly well suited for these applications. According to Eq. (4–51),

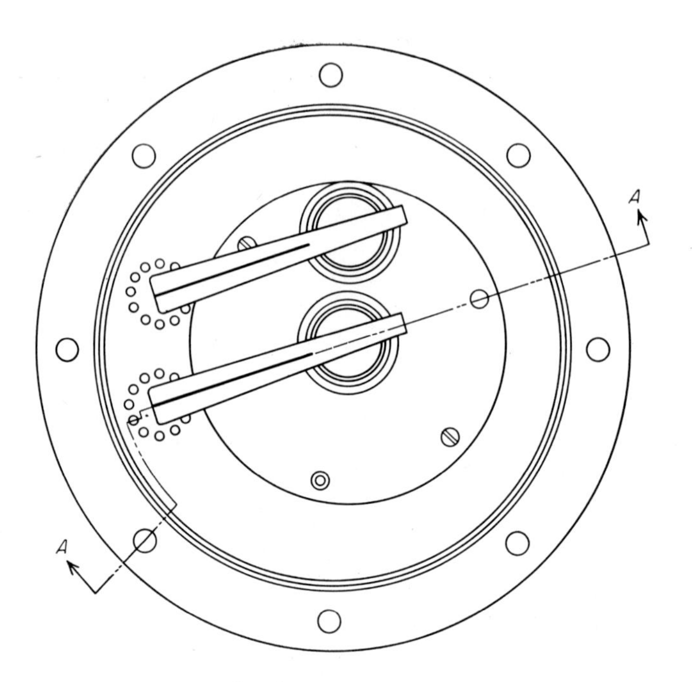


Top view cover removed

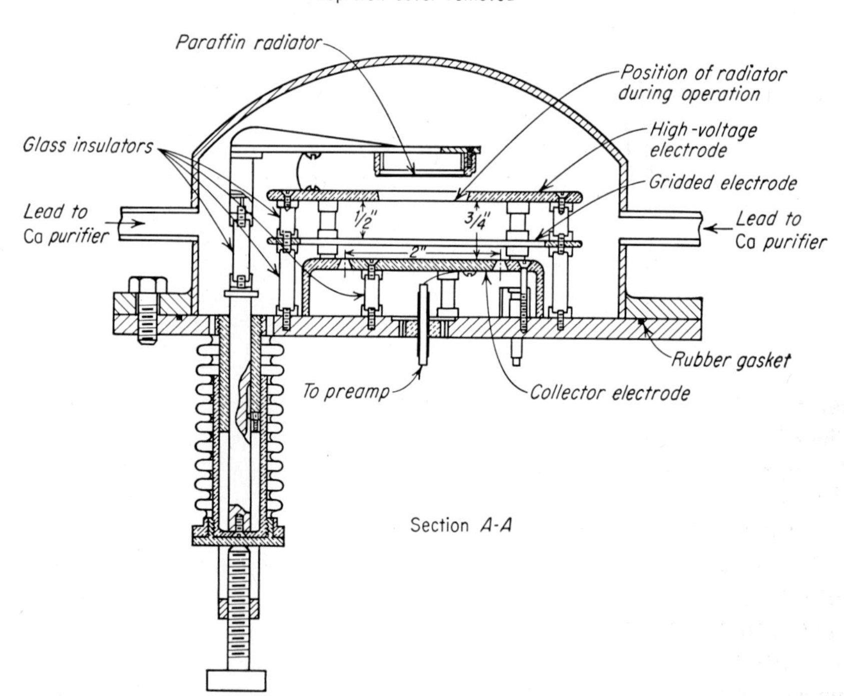


Section A-A

FIG. 4–30. Parallel-plate gridded ionization chamber for energy-distribution measurements. [*From J. H. Coon and H. H. Barschall, Phys. Rev.,* **70**:592 (1946).]

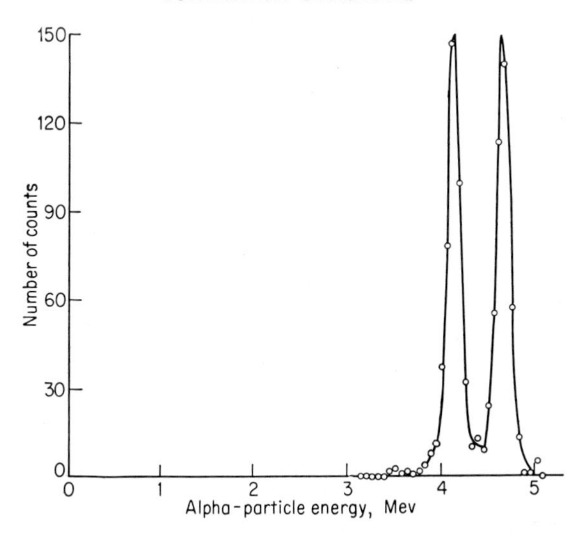


FIG. 4–31. Alpha-energy spectrum of normal uranium obtained by a gridded ionization chamber. [*From J. H. Coon and H. H. Barschall, Phys. Rev.,* **70**:592 (1946).]

the voltage pulse rises at a rate proportional to $w_-/d$, where $w_-$ is the electron velocity and $d$ the spacing between plates. The fraction of the total rise required to pass the discriminator depends on the sensitivity of the amplifier. The lower limit is set by the noise inherent in an amplifier (see Chap. 10). The maximum time required for the collection of the electrons is $d/w_-$ which is of the order of $10^{-6}$ sec. Amplifier sensitivities such that

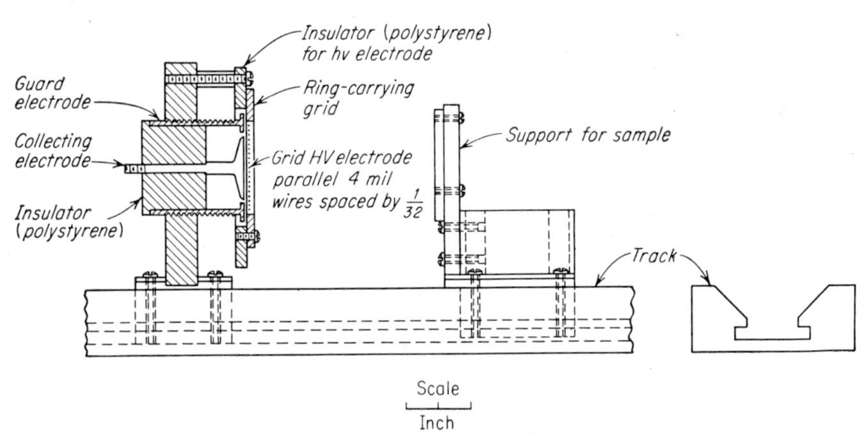


FIG. 4–32. Arrangement for specific-ionization and range measurements. (*From B. B. Rossi and H. H. Staub, "Ionization Chambers and Counters," chap. 2, National Nuclear Energy Series, div. V, vol. 2, McGraw-Hill Book Company, Inc., New York,* 1953.)

only one-tenth or less of this rise time is required are reasonable for alpha particles and other similar particles.

Applications of ionization chambers to neutron measurements are covered in Chap. 9. Both pulse- and nonpulse-type chambers are included.

## PROBLEMS

**4–1.** Consider a cylindrical ionization chamber with an applied voltage of 750 volts and a filling gas of argon at 1 atm and 20°C. Compute the time required for a positive argon ion to travel from the outer wall of a cylindrical ion chamber to the inner collector electrode, if the outer wall has a radius of 5 cm, the inner electrode has a radius of 1 cm, the argon-gas pressure is 760 mm Hg, and the temperature is 20°C.

**4–2.** Consider a cylindrical ionization chamber having field-adjusting tubes for guard rings, with the radii of the collector, field tube, and wall of the chamber being 0.005 cm, 1 cm, and 5 cm, respectively. Compute the proper protential for the field tube if the potentials of the collector and high-voltage electrode are +1,000 volts and 0, respectively.

**4–3.** A vibrating-reed electrometer, having an input capacity of 10 $\mu\mu$f, is used to make a current measurement by the rate-of-drift method. What is the current which produces a linear voltage change of 0.1 volt/min?

**4–4.** A certain commercial pocket chamber-type dosimeter with air-equivalent walls has the following dimensions: length, 8.0 cm; outside diameter of inner electrode, 0.15 cm; inside diameter of outer electrode, 1.06 cm. The filling gas is air. To charge the chamber, 200 volts are placed across the electrodes. Find the voltage between the electrodes following the exposure to 50 mr of gamma radiation.

**4–5.** An ionization-chamber-type rate meter employing a vacuum-tube electrometer is to be designed for monitoring the rate of exposure to X rays. Dependability is required down to 1 mr/hr. The chamber volume is fixed at 500 cm$^3$. If dependable operation requires that the grid current of the electrometer tube be less than one-tenth of the ionization-chamber current, what is the upper limit on the electrometer-tube currents? Can commercial tubes be obtained which meet this requirement?

**4–6.** A collimated beam of gamma rays with intensity 1 Mev/(cm$^2$)(sec) passes through air at 20°C and 760 mm Hg pressure. What is the rate of energy absorption in the air?

**4–7.** Consider a 1-millicurie source of Co$^{60}$ at the center of a sphere 1 m in radius. Compute in esu the ionization produced by all the secondary electrons created in the 1-m sphere, if the sphere contains air at normal temperature and pressure.

**4–8.** Show that the dose rate expressed in roentgens per hour at 1 ft from a point source is $6CE$ for gamma rays from about 0.2 to 2 Mev, where $C$ is the gamma-source activity in curies and $E$ is the gamma energy in Mev.

**4–9.** Derive Eq. (4–38), making use of Fig. 4–19.

**4–10.** Estimate the current flow which would be present in an extrapolation chamber having parallel lucite electrodes of an area of 10 cm$^2$ and 1-mm spacing if the dose rate in the lucite is 1 rad/hr. Assume that the gas is air at 20°C and 760 mm Hg.

**4–11.** Discuss the limitations on the use of a gas with a high negative-ion attachment coefficient for making energy measurements of alpha particles in a pulse-type ionization chamber.

**4–12.** A 4-Mev alpha particle produces a track parallel to the axis of a cylindrical ionization chamber at a distance of 2 cm from its axis. The radii of the collector and high-voltage electrodes are 0.5 cm and 2 cm, respectively. The total capacity of the collector-electrode circuit is 20 $\mu\mu$f. Compute the induced charge on the collector electrode at the instant that the electrons released by the alpha particles have just been collected; in addition, calculate the voltage rise that occurs between the time that the alpha particle passes through the chamber and the electrons are collected.

## REFERENCES

1. Staub, H. H.: Article in E. Segrè (ed.), "Experimental Nuclear Physics," vol. 1, John Wiley & Sons, Inc., New York, 1953.
2. Massey, H. S. W.: "Negative Ions," chap. 5, Cambridge University Press, London, 1950.
3. Rossi, B. B., and H. H. Staub: "Ionization Chambers and Counters," chap. 2, National Nuclear Energy Series, div. V, vol. 2, McGraw-Hill Book Company, Inc., New York, 1949.
4. Borkowski, C. J.: *U.S. Atomic Energy Comm. Document* MDDC-1099, 1947.
5. Sisman, O., and C. D. Bopp: *U.S. Atomic Energy Comm. Document* ORNL-928, 1951.
6. Armstead, F. C., J. C. Pennock, and L. W. Mead: *Phys. Rev.*, **76**:860 (1949).
7. Fowler, J. F., and F. T. Farmer: *Nature*, **173**:317 (1954).
8. Mayburg, S., and W. L. Lawrence: *J. Appl. Phys.*, **23**:1006 (1952).
9. Coleman, J. H., and D. Bohm: *J. Appl. Phys.*, **24**:497 (1953).
10. Cockroft, A. L., and S. C. Curran: *Rev. Sci. Instr.*, **22**:37 (1951).
11. Bearden, J. A.: *Rev. Sci. Instr.*, **4**:271 (1933).
12. Burmaster, K. E.: *U.S. Atomic Energy Comm. Document* AECU-618, 1949.
13. Lindemann, A. F., and T. C. Keely: *Phil. Mag.*, **47**:577 (1924).
14. Victoreen, J. A.: *Proc. IRE*, **37**:432 (1949).
15. Elmore, W. C., and M. Sands: "Electronics," chap. 3, National Nuclear Energy Series, div. V, vol. 1, McGraw-Hill Book Company, Inc., New York, 1949.
16. LeCain, H., and J. H. Waghoren: *Can. J. Research*, **19**:21 (1941).
17. Palevsky, H., R. K. Swank, and R. Grenchik: *Rev. Sci. Instr.*, **18**:298 (1947).
18. Lauritsen, C. C.: *Rev. Sci. Instr.*, **8**:438 (1937).
19. Gray, L. H.: *Proc. Roy. Soc. (London): A*, **122**:674 (1929).
20. Gray, L. H.: *Proc. Cambridge Phil. Soc.*, **40**:72 (1944).
21. Wang, T. J.: *Nucleonics*, **7**:55 (August, 1950).
22. Fano, U.: *Radiation Research*, **1**:237 (1954).
23. Whyte, G. N.: *Nucleonics*, **12**:18 (February, 1954).
24. Recommendations of the International Commission on Radiological Protection and of the International Commission on Radiological Units, *Nat. Bur. Standards (U.S.) Handbook* 47, 1950.
25. Marinelli, L. D.: *Radiation Research*, **1**:25 (1954).
26. Marinelli, L. D.: *Nucleonics*, **8**:S-20 (June, 1951).
27. Victoreen, J. A.: Article in O. Glasser (ed.), "Medical Physics," Year Book Publishers, Inc., Chicago, 1944.
28. Day, F. H.: *Nat. Bur. Standards (U.S.) Circ.* 507, 1951.
29. Brinkerhoff, J. M.: *Tracerlog*, no. 54, p. 10 (September, 1953).
30. Marinelli, L. D., E. H. Quimby, and G. J. Hine: *Am. J. Roentgenol. Radium Therapy*, **59**:260 (1948).
31. Failla, G.: *Radiology*, **20**:202 (1937).
32. Bortner, T. E.: *Nucleonics*, **9**:40 (September, 1951).
33. Marinelli, L. D.: *Ann. Rev. Nuclear Sci.*, **3**:249 (1953).

34. Failla, G.: "Proceedings of the International Conference on the Peaceful Uses of Atomic Energy," vol. 14, p. 239, United Nations, New York, 1956.
35. Morgan, Karl Z.: Personal communication.
36. Failla, G.: Paper at First Annual Meeting, American Nuclear Society, 1955.
37. Roesch, W. C., and E. E. Donaldson: "Proceedings of the International Conference on the Peaceful Uses of Atomic Energy," vol. 14, p. 172, United Nations, New York, 1956.
38. Rossi, H. H., and G. Failla: *Nucleonics*, **14**:32 (February, 1956).
39. Ohmart, P. E.: *J. Appl. Phys.*, **22**:1504 (1951).
40. Dowell, D. C.: Testing and Evaluation of the Ohmart Cell, Thesis, Air Force Institute of Technology, Wright-Patterson Air Force Base, Ohio, 1956.
41. Wilkinson, D. H.: "Ionization Chambers and Counters," chap. 4, Cambridge University Press, London, 1950.
42. Smythe, W. R.: "Static and Dynamic Electricity," 2d ed., p. 34, McGraw-Hill Book Company, Inc., New York, 1950.
43. Frisch, O. R.: *British Atomic Energy Rept.* BR-49, 1944.
44. Jordan, W. H.: *Ann. Rev. Nuclear Sci.*, **1**:207 (1952).

CHAPTER 5

# THE GEIGER-MÜLLER COUNTER

The Geiger-Müller (G-M) counter tube has been the most widely used detector of nuclear radiation during recent years. It will undoubtedly continue to be quite important in spite of its replacement by the scintillation counter in many applications.

The great utility of the G-M tube is a result of several of its characteristics. Some of the more important of these are high sensitivity, versatility for use with different types of radiation, wide variety of shapes and windows, large size of the output signal, and reasonable cost.

The large sensitivity of these devices arises from the characteristic that the nuclear radiation serves only to trigger a discharge. Any particle that produces ionization in the tube will produce a discharge, even though the ionization may consist of only one ion pair. Thus any types of particles which can release charge within G-M tubes can be counted by them. This includes X and gamma rays, which produce ionization by secondary processes, as well as all types of charged particles.

The principle of operation of the G-M tube is such that these devices can be made in a variety of types. Tubes have been built and operated successfully with diameters from around 2 mm to several centimeters and with lengths from about 1 cm to several feet. Further, there appears to be no apparent limitation at either extreme. Figure 5–1 shows several of the shapes and forms in which G-M tubes are made.

The voltage pulse at the input of the electronic circuits for counting G-M-tube pulses is typically of the order of a volt. Consequently, at the most, one stage of amplification is needed to precede the discriminator and pulse-shaping circuits in the electronic counters.

The simplicity of the G-M tube is such that its cost is usually only a small fraction of the total cost of its associated detection system. The costs of G-M tubes range from a few dollars for small cylindrical tubes to around one hundred dollars for special-purpose tubes such as high-speed and high-efficiency counters.

In Sec. 2–1 the G-M counter was characterized by the independence of its output-pulse size from the primary ionization which initiates it. This property leads to the high sensitivity of the counter which was mentioned above. On the other hand, this same property places limitations on the applications of G-M tubes; these same limitations are not encountered with scintillation detectors, proportional counters, or other detectors which have outputs that are characteristic of the radiations which cause them.

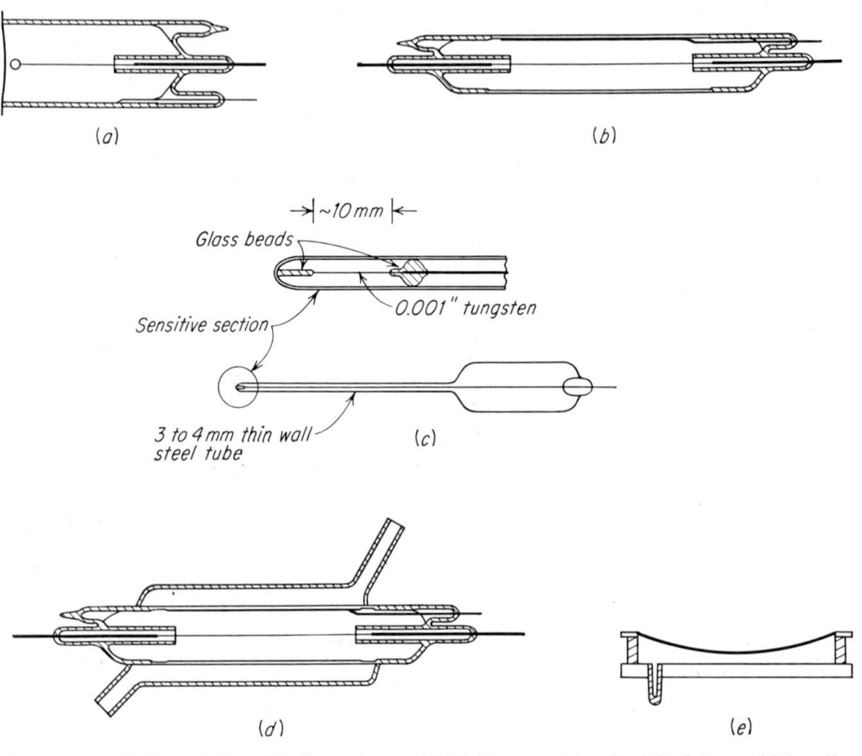


FIG. 5-1. Various Geiger-Müller tubes. (*a*) Bell type; (*b*) cylindrical type; (*c*) needle counter; (*d*) jacketed tube; (*e*) parallel-plate type.

## PRINCIPLES OF OPERATION

### 5-1. *Introductory Considerations*

The G-M counter tube consists of an envelope in which is incorporated two electrodes and the proper filling gas. A few typical arrangements are illustrated in Fig. 5-1. The techniques of constructing G-M tubes have been reviewed by Mandeville [1].

The internal or collector electrode is a fine wire around three- or four-thousandths of an inch in diameter. It is often made of tungsten because of the strength and uniformity of small-diameter wires of this material. The collector is usually a straight wire fastened from insulators at both ends. Sometimes, however, the collector is supported by one end only, and the free end is covered by a glass bead. The configuration of the G-M tube is usually cylindrical, with the collector mounted coaxially. However, other arrangements, such as small loops, have been used for the collector.

The other electrode, often referred to as the cathode, is generally part of the envelope of the tube. If the envelope is metal, it may serve directly as the cathode. If the envelope is glass, its inside surface may be covered with a conductive coating to form the cathode. Stainless steel, nickel, or other high-work-function materials make suitable cathode surfaces.

The most common filling gases are the noble gases, particularly argon and neon. Usually small percentages of additional gases are included for quenching purposes, as discussed in Sec. 5–4. Other gases which have been used successfully for G-M tubes include hydrogen and nitrogen. One principal requirement for satisfactory operation is that the electron attachment coefficient of the gas be sufficiently small that the negative-charge transfer in the tube is by free electrons. G-M tubes will work with gases,

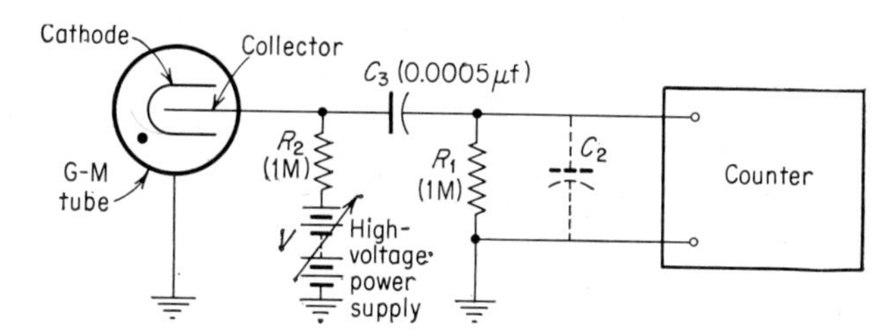


FIG. 5–2. Counter input circuit with a G-M tube detector.

such as air, in which negative ions are formed. However, such gases produce a large spread in the time required to form the pulses.

A large range of gas pressures can be used. Most tube types have operating pressures in the range from 7 to 20 cm Hg, although pressures up to 1 atm are used sometimes. The choice of pressure affects the operating voltage primarily.

A common circuit incorporating a G-M tube is shown in Fig. 5–2. The counter indicated may be the type discussed in Sec. 2–7 and shown in a block diagram in Fig. 2–3. It has the property of registering a count each time a pulse of voltage at its input exceeds a minimum value established by the discriminator of the counter. The capacitor $C_2$ represents the counter input capacity.

The high-voltage power supply furnishes the voltage between the collector electrode and the cathode. This particular input circuit has the advantage of maintaining the cathode at ground potential, a condition which is particularly desirable when the metal envelope of the tube is the cathode. The collector electrode is at a high positive potential above ground. The d-c potential is blocked off from the counter input by the capacitor $C_3$. The resistor $R_2$, in series with the power supply, isolates the power supply from the collector electrode, thus allowing the voltage at this point to drop upon the collection of electrons following a discharge in the G-M tube. The resistance $R_2$ in conjunction with $R_1$ allows the equilibrium values of voltages to be established again after the occurrence of a discharge.

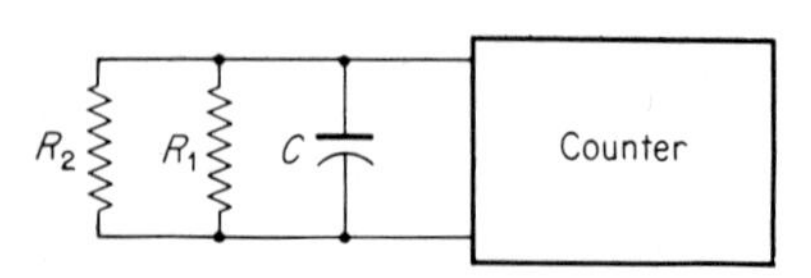


FIG. 5–3. Equivalent circuit of the counter input shown in Fig. 5–2.

Figure 5–3 is an equivalent circuit of Fig. 5–2 which eliminates from consideration the steady or d-c voltages. The coupling capacitor $C_3$ has been replaced by a short circuit since its capacity is large compared with $C_2$. The capacity $C$ is the sum of $C_2$ and the capacity of the G-M tube as well as the distributed capacity of the capacitor $C_3$ to ground. The resistances $R_1$ and $R_2$ can be combined into a single resistance $R = R_1R_2/(R_1 + R_2)$.

The primary ionization in the G-M tube initiates a series of events within the tube which result in a sheath of ion pairs encompassing the collector wire. The free electrons are collected very quickly because of their high mobility as well as their nearness to the positive collector wire. This leaves a positive-ion sheath around the wire which terminates the buildup of the discharge by the reduction in the electric-field strength near the wire.

Initially, the collection of the electrons from the ion sheath produces very little net charge on the collector. At this point in the production of the pulse, the net charge on the collector is estimated by Wilkinson [2] to be about 3 per cent of the total electron charge. Some work by Bell, Jordan, and Kelley indicates an initial rise much greater than 3 per cent [3]. As the positive-ion sheath moves away from the collector, the net charge which remains rises, as discussed in Sec. 4–23.

If the assumption is made that the space charge in the G-M tube does not affect its field and if the small initial effect due to the electron collection is neglected, the time dependence of the voltage produced at the G-M counter input can be calculated by the methods of Chap. 4. For the case in which the time constant of the input circuit is much greater than the collection time for positive ions, this voltage, $v(t)$, is given by Eq. (4–55). By use of Eq. (4–1), the velocity, $dr_+/dt$, of the positive ions is

$$\frac{dr_+}{dt} = \frac{\mu E}{p} = \frac{\mu V}{pr_+ \ln (r_2/r_1)} \tag{5–1}$$

where $\mu$ is the mobility of the positive ions and $V$ is the voltage between the electrodes. Upon integrating Eq. (5–1), one obtains

$$r_+ = \left[\frac{2V\mu t}{p \ln (r_2/r_1)} + r_1^2\right]^{1/2} \tag{5–2}$$

where the approximation has been made that all positive ions start at $r_1$ when $t = 0$. Combining Eqs. (5–2) and (4–55) leads to the expression

$$v(t) = -\frac{Ne \ln \{2V\mu t/[r_1^2 p \ln (r_2/r_1)] + 1\}}{2C \ln (r_2/r_1)} \qquad (5\text{–}3)$$

The solid curve in Fig. 5–4 is a plot of this equation for the case $r_2/r_1 = 100$.

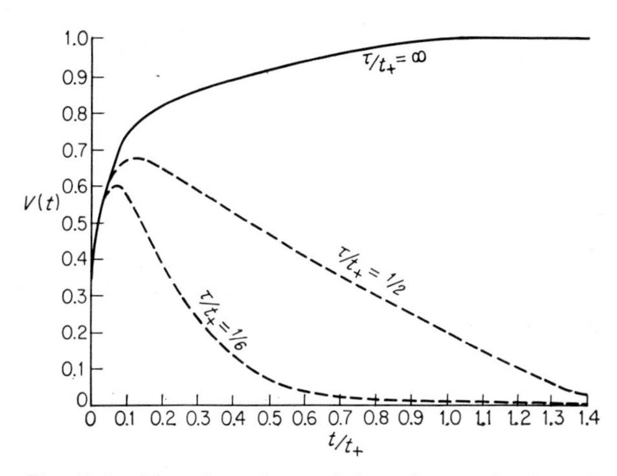


FIG. 5–4. Time dependence of the voltage pulse formed by a G-M tube for various input circuit time constants $\tau$; $r_2/r_1 = 100$.

Letting $r_+ = r_2$, one obtains the collection time $t_+$ for positive ions, from Eq. (5–2), as

$$t_+ = \frac{(r_2^2 - r_1^2)p \ln (r_2/r_1)}{2V\mu} \qquad (5\text{–}4)$$

**Example 5–1.** Compute the time required for the positive ions in a G-M tube to travel from the region of formation near the collector wire to the cathode in a tube having collector-wire and cathode radii of $5 \times 10^{-3}$ and 1 cm, respectively, argon filling gas to a pressure of 10 cm Hg, and an applied voltage of 1,000 volts.

*Solution.* By Eq. (5–4), one obtains

$$t_+ = \frac{(r_2^2 - r_1^2)p}{2V\mu} \ln \frac{r_2}{r_1}$$

$$= \frac{[1^2 - (5 \times 10^{-3})^2]\, 100}{2(10^3)(1.04 \times 10^3)} \ln 200 = 265 \times 10^{-6} \text{ sec}$$

where the value of $\mu$ is taken from Table 4–1.

Commonly, the time constants $\tau$ of the input circuits are chosen to be smaller than the collection time $t_+$. The resulting voltage pulses for three different values of $\tau/t_+$ are shown in Fig. 5–4.

## 5-2. *Counting-rate Versus Voltage Plateau*

The dependence of the pulse size on applied voltage in a gas-filled detector was introduced in Sec. 2-1. Figure 5-5 shows the results of measurements of this type on a bell-type thin-window G-M tube. This tube contained a mixture of helium and alcohol at a total pressure of 72 cm Hg. The cathode and collector had 0.63- and 0.005-in. radii, respectively. The input circuit was that shown in Fig. 5-2. The alpha source was $Po^{210}$ while the beta source was $P^{32}$. In all cases the pulse heights which are plotted were the largest observed.

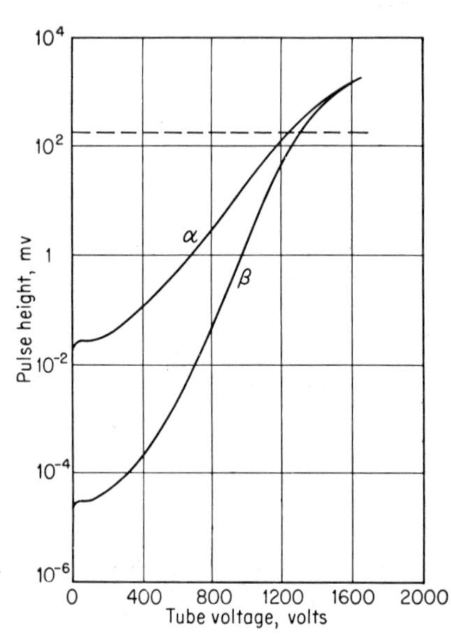


FIG. 5-5. Pulse height versus tube voltage for a bell-type G-M tube (Tracerlab TGC 1) for both alpha and beta particles; dotted line indicates discriminator setting.

A curve of counting rate versus the voltage applied to the G-M tube, when taken with the radioactive source as well as the discriminator setting (i.e., the sensitivity of the counting system) held fixed, is referred to as the characteristic curve. Under the correct operating conditions, this curve has a plateau (see Sec. 2-7) with a small slope and a length of several hundred volts. Figure 5-6 presents counting-rate characteristics taken for the G-M tube whose pulse-height versus voltage curves appear in Fig. 5-5. The data for Fig. 5-6 were taken with the discriminator set to pass all pulses with a height greater than the dotted line in Fig. 5-5.

The counting-rate characteristics are readily understood by reference to Fig. 5-5. The starting voltage $V_s$ is the voltage at which the pulse-height curve intersects the line indicating the minimum pulse height passed by the discriminator. The starting voltage is seen to depend on the particle type; it occurs at a lower voltage for alpha particles than for the less ionizing beta particles if the discriminator sensitivity is great enough, as in Fig. 5-5. The knee of the curve represents the condition under which all particles, no matter how small their primary ionization, produce voltage pulses larger than the discriminator setting. It also coincides approximately with the voltage in Fig. 5-5 at which alpha and beta particles produce pulses of the same size. This condition is sometimes referred to as the G-M threshold.

The rather indefinite knee in the counting-rate characteristic for alpha particles is typical for these particles in thin-end window tubes. The knee is spread out even more for higher fluxes of alpha particles. A large proportion of the particles succeed in just passing through the window, producing ionization only near its inside surface. The presence of the resulting positive-ion space charge prevents some of the alpha particles from initiating counts, which they would otherwise do. As the voltage is increased, this effect is reduced, and the plateau is reached.

The finite slope in the plateau of the counting-rate versus voltage curve is due partially to the extension of the sensitive volume of the counter as the voltage increases; in addition, the production of occasional spurious pulses (i.e., pulses occurring without the arrival of an ionizing particle)

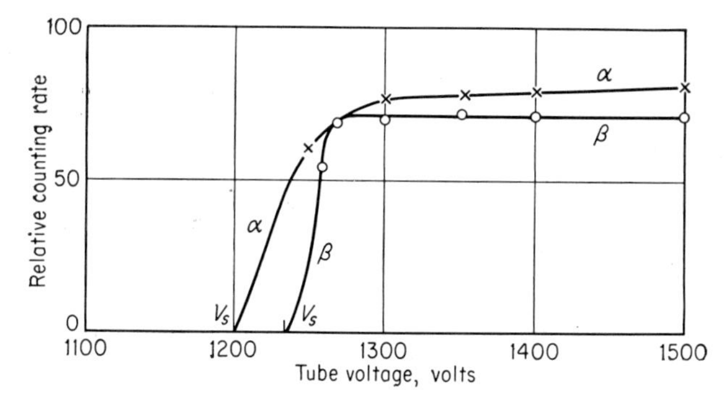


FIG. 5–6. Relative counting rate versus tube voltage for the same G-M tube as that used for Fig. 5–5; discriminator set at 125 mv.

happens more often at high potentials. The multiple discharges that occur because of the failure of the quenching mechanism (see Sec. 5–4) fall in the latter category. Slopes of less than 5 per cent per 100 volts are desirable, although up to 10 per cent per 100 volts are usable in many applications.

If the detector voltage is continually raised through the plateau, ultimately the region will be reached where the counting rate rises sharply. This rise results from multiple counts, as described in Sec. 5–4. This region is not included in Fig. 5–6.

5–3. *Production of the Discharge*

The detailed description of the production of the discharge in a G-M tube has been treated by Wilkinson [2] as well as by others. Briefly, the mechanism is as follows: The electrons produced in the G-M tube by the primary-ionizing events drift toward the collector electrode, making many collisions along their paths. These electrons gain energy while traveling toward the collector but lose energy when scattered away from it. They do not gain enough energy between collisions to produce ionization until they arrive within the last few mean free paths of the collector.

**Example 5–2.** Consider a G-M tube with a cathode and collector of 0.75- and 0.005-in. radii, respectively, filled with argon gas to 10 cm Hg pressure. If the tube has 1,000 volts applied across it, estimate the distance from the collector at which the electron gains just enough energy in one mean free path to ionize argon.

*Solution.* The distance in question is that at which the electric-field strength $E$ is such that the energy gained by the electron in one mean free path is equal to the minimum energy required to ionize argon, that is, 15.7 ev. Taking the mean free path $L$ in argon from Sec. 4–1 as approximately $2 \times 10^{-4}$ cm at room temperature and 76 cm Hg pressure, the required value of $E$ is

$$E = \frac{15.7 \text{ volts}}{L(\text{cm})} = \frac{15.7}{(2 \times 10^{-4})(76/10)} = 1 \times 10^4 \text{ volts/cm}$$

The electric-field strength as a function of the distance $r$ from the center is

$$E = \frac{V}{r \ln (r_2/r_1)}$$

and so one has

$$r = \frac{1{,}000}{(1 \times 10^4) \ln (0.75/0.005)} = 2 \times 10^{-2} \text{ cm} = 0.008 \text{ in.}$$

When the ionization does start, it builds up rapidly, since the secondary-ionizing events can also produce more ionization. The buildup of ionization is referred to as a Townsend avalanche. The initial Townsend avalanche terminates when all the electrons associated with it have reached the center wire. However, the initial avalanche is followed by a succession of avalanches, each triggered by the one preceding it. The propagation of the avalanches from one to another is believed to be through photon emission; the excited atoms, molecules, or ions of one avalanche release photoelectrons which initiate further avalanches [2]. In tubes containing pure gases and requiring external quenching (see Sec. 5–4), the photoelectrons are emitted primarily from the wall. In self-quenching counters containing mixed gases, the photoelectrons come principally from the gas.

For an initial discharge to be propagated to further avalanches, the condition $N_1\epsilon > 1$ must hold, where $\epsilon$ is the probability that an ion pair will initiate an additional avalanche and $N_1$ is the number of ion pairs produced in the first avalanche. A typical value [2] for $\epsilon$ is $10^{-5}$. The termination of the discharge comes about with the $n$th avalanche when the collection of positive ions around the center wire reduces the electric-field strength and therefore the gas multiplication to the point that $N_n\epsilon \leq 1$.

The entire production of the discharge occurs in a fraction of a microsecond. Also in this short interval of time the electrons are collected. During this period the positive-ion sheath is essentially stationary because of its low mobility. The next stage in the process is the migration of the positive ions to the cathode, as discussed in Sec. 5–1.

### 5–4. *Quenching the Discharge*

In counters containing pure gases, the positive ions migrate all the way to the cathode before being neutralized; upon reaching the cathode, they combine with electrons from the metal. There are two mechanisms by which an additional electron can be emitted as a result of this neutralization: the energy difference between the ionization potential of the ion and the work function of the cathode may be radiated as a photon which may release a photoelectron; or the energy difference may be used directly in a radiationless liberation of an electron from the cathode. This additional electron will result in another discharge unless provision is made to prevent, or quench, it.

Multiple discharge may be prevented by the circuit external to the G-M tube. The circuit shown in Fig. 5–2 will cause quenching, provided that the resistance $R_2$ is increased to about $10^8$ ohms or greater. With this arrangement the discharge proceeds until the cathode-to-collector voltage drops, because of electron collection on the collector, below the value required to maintain the discharge. This is made possible by the fact that the time constant of the input circuit is long compared with the collection time for positive ions. This circuit has the great disadvantage of long resolving times, these being of the order of $10^{-3}$ sec or greater. Various types of faster external quenching circuits have been designed; those devised by Neher and Pickering [4] are examples.

At the present time, because of the availability of good self-quenched tubes, nonquenched tubes are seldom used. The self-quenched tubes [5] contain a small percentage of a quenching gas in addition to the major constituent of the filling gas. There are two types of self-quenched tubes in use, namely, the organic-quenched and the halogen-quenched tubes.

A typical filling of an organic-quenched tube is 90 mm Hg of argon and 10 mm Hg of ethyl alcohol. More recently, ethyl formate has been preferred to ethyl alcohol because of its smaller temperature coefficient.

During the migration of the positive ions to the cathode, the argon ions with an ionization potential of 15.7 volts collide with alcohol molecules having an ionization potential of 11.3 volts. Because of the difference in the ionization potentials, the charge is transferred to the alcohol molecules. Therefore only the alcohol ions reach the cathode to be neutralized. The energy released when this occurs goes into dissociating alcohol molecules rather than producing further ionization. In this way multiple discharges are prevented.

It has been found [6] that organic-quenched tubes have a life of about $10^{10}$ counts if used near the G-M threshold; this indicates a dissociation of about $10^9$ molecules per discharge. When the organic gas is depleted to a sufficient extent, the operation of the tube is characterized by multiple discharges. This causes the plateau in the counting-rate versus tube-voltage curve to be shorter and to have a larger slope.

In the halogen-quenched G-M tube [7], a very small quantity of halogen gas, such as bromine or chlorine, is added to a noble gas such as argon or neon. A typical filling is about 0.1 per cent of chlorine in neon. The quenching mechanism is similar to that in the organic tubes. However, there is one important difference that affects the life of the tube. In the halogen-quenched tube, the quenching gas is apparently not consumed in the quenching process. It appears that the diatomic halogen-gas molecules are dissociated in the quenching but that there is a recombination mechanism present to replenish the supply of quenching gas. This not only extends greatly the life of the tube for normal use but also makes it possible to run the tubes at higher voltages without sacrificing the life of the tube. This latter feature means that output voltage pulses of 10 volts or more can be obtained from the tube in normal operation.

**Example 5–3.** Halogen-quenched tubes have been operated for more than $10^{13}$ counts without any deterioration in the quenching action. Show that a mechanism must exist for the recombination of the halogen molecules.

*Solution.* Assuming that the tube volume is 100 cm³ and that the filling gas is 10 cm Hg of neon with 0.1 per cent of chlorine by volume, one computes the number of chlorine molecules to be

$$\frac{(6.02 \times 10^{23})(100)(10)(10^{-3})}{(2.24 \times 10^{4})(76)} = 3.5 \times 10^{17}$$

If $10^{10}$ ion pairs are produced per discharge, only $3.5 \times 10^7$ counts would be required to use all the quenching gas if no recombination occurred.

In the manufacture of halogen-quenched tubes special precautions are necessary to prevent the small quantity of quenching gas that is present from being absorbed to the tube walls or in any other fashion depleted to a large extent. The halogen vapors cannot be used with some cathode materials because of chemical action, but cathodes of stainless steel have proved satisfactory.

The halogen-quenched tubes are characterized by short plateaus with rather large slopes. Typical values of plateau lengths and slopes are 150 volts and 10 per cent per 100 volts, respectively. The slope in the plateau of this type of tube is due primarily to the increase in the sensitive volume of the tube with increased tube voltage. The sensitive volume of the tube is defined as that volume in which a primary-ionizing event will result in a discharge. This variation in the sensitive volume is due to the dependence of the amount of negative-ion formation on the length of time which the electrons spend in the gas. The negative-ion formation occurs primarily near the cathode where the electric field is the smallest.

Until recently the normal operating voltage of a G-M tube has been around 1,000 volts. In many cases it is desirable that the voltage be lower, particularly to simplify the power supply. By the use of about 0.1 per cent of an admixture of argon and a halogen gas in neon, it has been found [7] possible to operate G-M tubes at 250 volts with good success.

## PARTICLE COUNTING BY G-M TUBES

### 5–5. *Requirements of the Counting System*

A general description of electronic systems for particle counting was given in Sec. 2–7. A typical input circuit for use with a G-M tube was described in Sec. 5–1. Detailed descriptions of suitable electronic circuits are given in Chap. 10.

The height of the pulse which appears at the input of the electronic counter is a certain fraction of the quantity $Ne/C$, where $N$ is the number of ion pairs formed per discharge in the tube and $C$ is the total input capacity. The fraction, which depends on the circuit time constant, as discussed in Sec. 5–1, is usually around one-half. The quantity $N$ depends on the voltage applied to the tube and on the tube type and construction; typical values are from $10^8$ to $10^{10}$, the lower values being appropriate for the organic-quenched tubes and the higher ones for the halogen-quenched tubes. Consequently, the typical pulse heights are from $8/C$ to $800/C$, where $C$ is in micromicrofarads. For a G-M tube connected directly to the input of an amplifier, $C$ is about 20 $\mu\mu$f; therefore the pulse heights are in the range from about 0.4 volt to 40 volts.

The high-voltage power supply for use with a G-M tube should be capable of variation and should have reasonably good regulation. A range of voltages from 400 to 1,600 volts would be satisfactory for most tubes. Of course, if a single-tube type is to be used, the range of voltage which is required is much less. The degree to which the power supply must be regulated is determined by the slope of the plateau in the counting-rate versus voltage characteristic.

The requirements of the electronic counter for use with the G-M tube are met rather easily. It was seen above that the input sensitivities can be quite low. In addition, the requirements for the resolving time are not stringent since the G-M tube itself limits the resolving time of the system to a few hundred microseconds, as is discussed in the next section. The principal considerations in the counter design are that it be insensitive to spurious signals and that the electronic scaling factor be sufficiently large that the mechanical register will follow satisfactorily.

### 5–6. *Resolving Times of G-M Tubes*

During the period immediately following the discharge, the electric field in the G-M tube is below normal because of the presence of the positive-ion sheath. The pulses which are produced by additional ionizing events during this time are modified accordingly. This is illustrated in Fig. 5–7, taken from the work of Stever [8]. Additional particles which enter the tube during the initial stages of the first pulse will not trigger a discharge. This interval is known as the dead time $t_d$ of the tube. The time required for the complete recovery of the pulse size after the end of the dead-time interval is known as the recovery time $t_r$.

This dead time for the tube sets a lower limit on the time interval between the arrival of nuclear particles, if they are to be resolved. For a system using a sensitive voltage amplifier, the resolving time $\tau$ for the system approaches $t_d$, the dead time for the G-M tube. For a less sensitive amplifier, $\tau$ lies between $t_d$ and $t_d + t_r$.

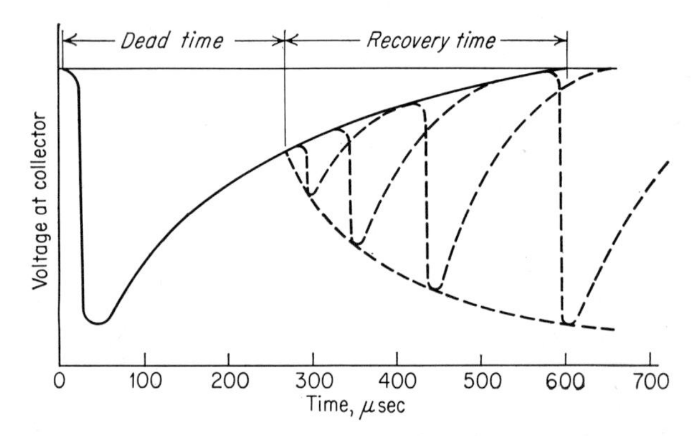


FIG. 5–7. Illustration of dead time in a typical G-M tube. [*From H. G. Stever, Phys. Rev.*, **61**:38 (1942).]

The dead time and therefore the resolving time of a G-M tube are variable, even from pulse to pulse in the same tubes. Typical values lie from $1 \times 10^{-4}$ to $2 \times 10^{-4}$ sec. This uncertainty can be avoided by fixing the inoperative period of the detection system electronically at a value somewhat greater than the dead time of the G-M tube.

The correction which must be made to the counting rate because of the finite resolving time is given by Eq. (2–3). This correction is particularly important in applications of G-M tubes because the resolving times are so large.

The resolving time for a counting system can be determined experimentally by the multiple-source method [9]. A simplified version of this, known as the two-source method, follows. It involves the comparison of the counting rate indicated by the system when two sources are counted simultaneously with the sum of the counting rates produced by each of the sources taken individually. To accomplish this, let $\dot{n}_1$, $\dot{n}_2$, $\dot{n}_{12}$, and $\dot{n}_b$ be the true rate of ionizing events in the tube due to source 1 plus background, source 2 plus background, sources 1 and 2 plus background, and background only, respectively; let $\dot{m}_1$, $\dot{m}_2$, $\dot{m}_{12}$, and $\dot{m}_b$ be the corresponding observed counting rates. Then

$$\dot{n}_1 + \dot{n}_2 = \dot{n}_{12} + \dot{n}_b \tag{5-5}$$

or, by Eq. (2–4),

$$\frac{\dot{m}_1}{1 - \dot{m}_1\tau} + \frac{\dot{m}_2}{1 - \dot{m}_2\tau} = \frac{\dot{m}_{12}}{1 - \dot{m}_{12}\tau} + \frac{\dot{m}_b}{1 - \dot{m}_b\tau} \tag{5-6}$$

Using the approximations

$$\frac{\dot{m}}{1 - \dot{m}\tau} \simeq \dot{m} + \dot{m}^2\tau \qquad \text{and} \qquad \frac{\dot{m}_b}{1 - \dot{m}_b\tau} \simeq \dot{m}_b \tag{5-7}$$

Eq. (5–6) becomes

$$\tau = \frac{\dot{m}_1 + \dot{m}_2 - \dot{m}_{12} - \dot{m}_b}{\dot{m}_{12}^2 - \dot{m}_1^2 - \dot{m}_2^2} \tag{5-8}$$

Accurate measurements of $\tau$ require highly accurate determinations of $\dot{m}_1$, $\dot{m}_2$, and $\dot{m}_{12}$, since $\dot{m}_1 + \dot{m}_2$ is nearly equal to $\dot{m}_{12}$.

**Example 5–4.** A counting rate of 15,100 counts/min is indicated by a G-M tube having a dead time of 250 $\mu$sec. What would be the counting rate if the dead-time phenomenon were not present?

*Solution.* According to Eq. (2–4), the counting rate $\dot{n}$, after the dead-time loss is accounted for, would be

$$\dot{n} = \frac{\dot{m}}{1 - \dot{m}\tau} = \frac{15{,}100}{1 - (15{,}100)(250 \times 10^{-6})/60} = 16{,}100 \text{ counts/min}$$

## G-M COUNTERS FOR BETA PARTICLES

### 5–7. *Importance of Window Thickness*

The distinguishing feature of G-M tubes for use in the counting of beta particles is the thin wall or window which is incorporated in the tube. The necessity of the thin region for admitting the particles arises from the relatively short range of the beta particles which are emitted by most radioisotopes.

A wall thickness of 30 mg/cm$^2$ is a common value for the cylindrical-type thin-wall glass tubes which are designed for beta counting. These tubes are suitable for counting high-energy beta particles. Special thin windows are required for soft betas. Commercial tubes of the type shown in Fig. 5–1*a* are available with windows as thin as 1.4 mg/cm$^2$, made from mica, mylar, or stainless steel. When these windows are not sufficiently thin, it is necessary to use windowless counters, i.e., ones in which the beta source is placed within the counter.

When the window thickness is known, an estimate can be made of the absorption due to it. This estimate is based on the exponential relationship

Eq. (1–15). Table 5–1 gives the per cent transmission as calculated by Eq. (1–15) for several different wall thicknesses and beta-ray energies.

TABLE 5–1. TRANSMISSION OF BETA PARTICLES THROUGH G-M-TUBE WALLS AND WINDOWS

| Beta source | Maximum energy of beta particle, Mev | Per cent transmission | | |
|---|---|---|---|---|
| | | 30 mg/cm² | 4 mg/cm² | 1.4 mg/cm² |
| $C^{14}$ | 0.154 | 0.03 | 1.5 | 20 |
| $Ca^{45}$ | 0.250 | 1.5 | 38 | 82 |
| $Sr^{90}$ | 0.65 | 31 | 86 | 95 |
| $P^{32}$ | 1.7 | 72 | 95.5 | 98.5 |

5–8. *Over-all Efficiency*

The over-all efficiency of a G-M tube for detecting particles will be defined as $\dot{m}/S$, where $\dot{m}$ is the counting rate and $S$ is the source strength of the sample. This efficiency depends on many factors, most of which do not remain constant from one experiment to another. Therefore it is necessary to break down the efficiency into these several factors and to make corrections for changes as they occur.

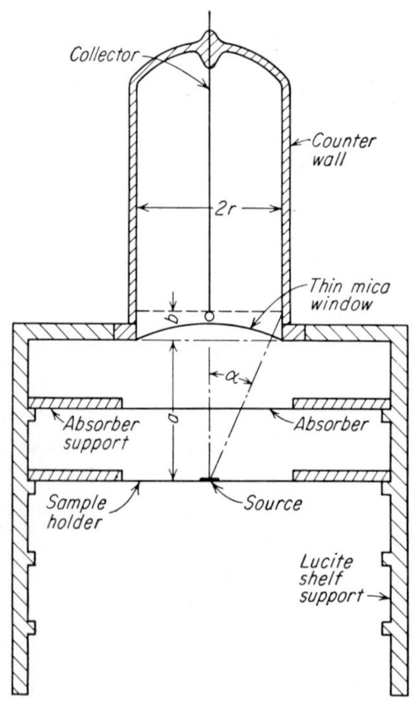


FIG. 5–8. Typical setup for an end-window tube. (*From L. R. Zumwalt, U.S. Atomic Energy Comm. Document AECU*-567, 1950.)

The details of the analysis of the over-all efficiency differ with counter types. A comprehensive study of the bell-type end-window tube has been made by Zumwalt [10]. The results of that analysis are followed here. The arrangement which is considered is shown in Fig. 5–8.

The over-all efficiency of the bell-type tube for counting beta particles may be expressed as

$$\frac{\dot{m}}{S} = G\epsilon_\beta f_m f_\tau f_w f_b f_s \qquad (5\text{–}9)$$

where $G$ = geometry factor of counting setup

$\epsilon_\beta$ = intrinsic efficiency of G-M tube for beta particles

$f_m$ = multiple-count factor
$f_\tau$ = dead-time correction
$f_w$ = correction due to absorption between source and tube
$f_b$ = source-mount backscattering factor
$f_s$ = source self-absorption factor

For precise work there are other sources of scattering which may be considered [10]; these are the air, the lining of the shield, and any other structures in the vicinity of the source or tube. Scattering by the air may give [10] up to 5 per cent increase in the number of particles reaching the counter when the source-to-tube distance is several centimeters and the particle energy is low. Scattering from the lining of the shield and from the other structures can be minimized by making these parts from low-$Z$ materials and by keeping them as far as possible from the paths of the particles. In this way, scattering from these sources can be made negligible, except for a source location quite near the shield bottom.

5–9. *Geometry*

The geometry factor $G$ accounts for the fact that only a portion of the particles start toward the tube. Initially all directions are equally probable. The quantity $G$ is the fraction of the particles from the source which start toward the sensitive volume of the counter.

The sensitive volume is considered to lie back somewhat from the window because of the tendency of charge to collect on the window and because of the finite distance that particles must travel beyond the window to initiate the discharge [10]. In Fig. 5–8 the sensitive volume is considered to be above the dotted line which is a distance $b$ from the window edge.

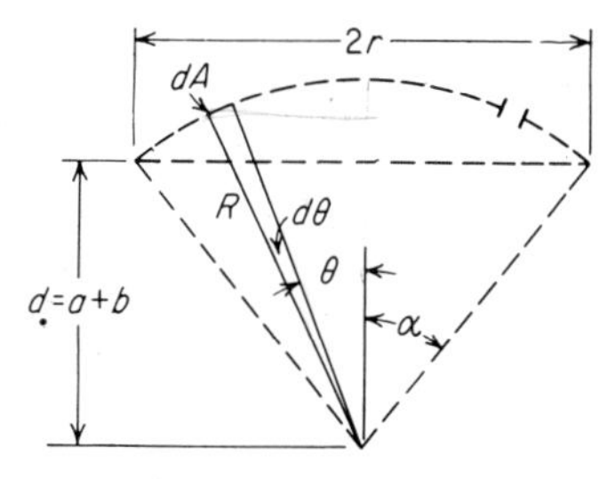

FIG. 5–9. Representation of an end-window tube for use in the calculation of the geometry factor.

For the calculation of the $G$ for the arrangement in Fig. 5–8, one can make use of the representation in Fig. 5–9, provided that the source is considered to be a point on the axis of the tube. Here the boundary of the sensitive volume is taken as the intersection of a plane with a sphere of radius $R$. The quantity $G$ is simply the ratio of the area of this segment of the sphere to the total area of the sphere. This is

$$G = \frac{1}{4\pi R^2}\int_0^\alpha 2\pi R^2 \sin\theta \, d\theta = \tfrac{1}{2}(1 - \cos\alpha)$$

$$= \frac{1}{2}\left[1 - \frac{d}{(d^2 + r^2)^{1/2}}\right] \tag{5–10}$$

Similar calculations have been carried out for extended sources [11–13].

Both the formulas for the point sources and for the extended sources have the uncertainty as to the proper value of $b$. However, Zumwalt [10] found that a value of 4 mm gave good results for a Victoreen end-window counter. This tube contained a 0.007-in. collector terminated with a glass bead. The inside diameter of the glass tube, which also served as the cathode, was 29 to 30 mm. The tube was an organic-quenched type, and it was filled with partial pressures of 9 and 1 cm Hg of argon and alcohol, respectively.

### 5–10. *Scattering and Absorption*

The factors $f_b$, $f_s$, and $f_w$ correct for the fact that the number of particles which enter the sensitive volume of the counter differs from the number which start toward it at the instant of disintegration. The product $Gf_bf_sf_w$ represents the fraction which actually reach the sensitive volume.

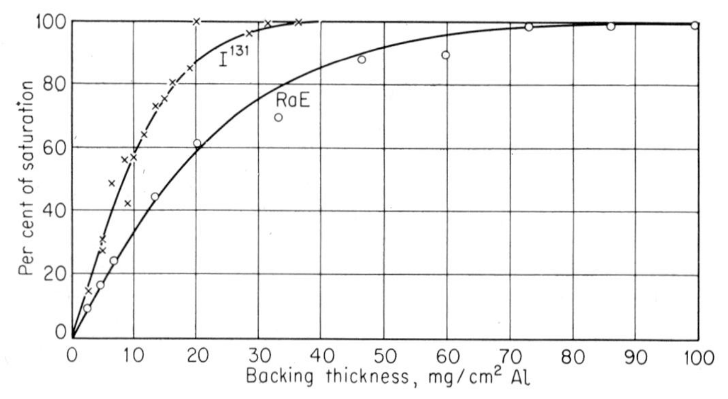


FIG. 5–10. Backscattering-growth curve for $I^{131}$ radiation (0.6 Mev maximum) and $Bi^{210}$ (1.17 Mev maximum), with aluminum backing. (*From L. R. Zumwalt, U.S. Atomic Energy Comm. Document AECU-567, 1950.*)

Backscattering is the phenomenon by which particles which originally start away from the tube are scattered back toward it. This is the result of multiple Rutherford scattering. The factor $f_b$ accounts for backscattering from the source backing material. It is defined as the ratio of the counting rate with the backscatterer in place to that with no backscattering material. Its value ranges from 1 to almost 2, depending on the thickness and atomic number of the backing material.

Figure 5–10 shows the dependence of the backscattering on the thickness of aluminum backings for two different beta emitters. It is found experimentally that the saturation thickness of backing material is about two-tenths of the maximum range of the particles in the material.

Because of the rapid dependence of backscattering on the thickness of the backing, sources are prepared either on a very thin backing, so that $f_b$ is 1, or on a sufficiently thick backing so that the saturation backscattering factors can be used. Some information on saturation backscattering appears in Fig. 5–11, where the saturation backscattering factors are plotted as a function of the atomic number of the backscatterer for several beta emitters.

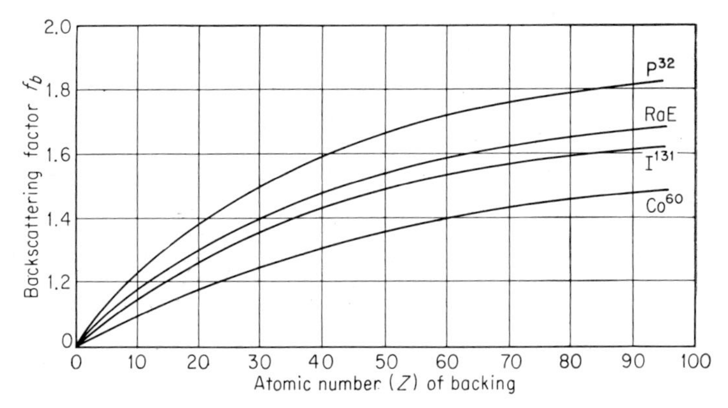


FIG. 5–11. Saturation backscattering factors of various radiations versus atomic number. (*From L. R. Zumwalt, U.S. Atomic Energy Comm. Document AECU*-567, 1950.)

The dependence of the backscattering on the energy of the primary radiation has been shown [10] to be due to the absorption by the air and the window. When this is taken into account by the methods of this section and the extrapolated counting rates are compared, the curve in Fig. 5–12 results; the backscattering factor is seen to be independent of the energy of the beta emitter.

The values of backscattering factors depend somewhat on the geometry of the counting setup. The data which were quoted above hold for a source-to-tube distance of 2.5 cm. In addition, the backing materials were in intimate contact with the sources.

The self-absorption factor $f_s$ [11–14] takes into account the effect of the finite thickness of the source on the number of particles reaching the source. Two effects compete here. One is an increase in the number of particles reaching the counter because of scattering of particles in the right direction; the other is absorption of radiation by the source.

Whenever possible, sources should be prepared so that they are sufficiently thin that this factor can be neglected. For this to be accomplished, nearly carrier-free radioisotopes need to be employed.

Equation (1–15) can be used to make a crude calculation of $f_s$, if scattering is neglected. Consider a source which emits $c_0$ beta particles per unit

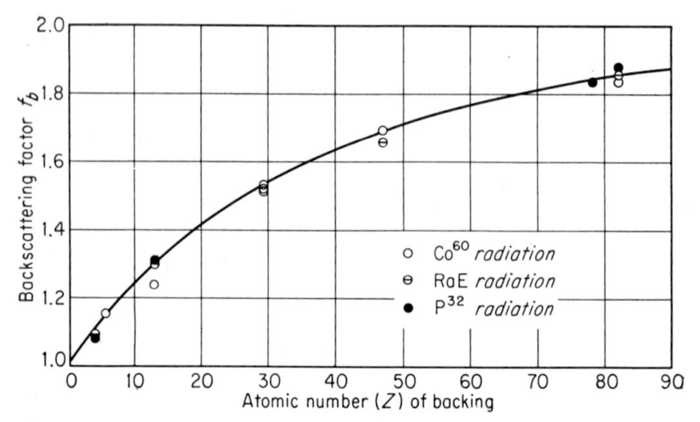


FIG. 5–12. Saturation backscattering factor (as determined by the extrapolation method) versus atomic number. (*From L. R. Zumwalt, U. S. Atomic Energy Comm. Document AECU*-567, 1950.)

time in the direction of the counter if self-absorption is neglected. If the source has a uniform thickness $s$, the contribution of a thin layer $dx$ is $dc_o = (c_o/s)\ dx$. However, the activity which escapes the source from a layer at a distance $x$ from the surface is

$$dc = \frac{c_o e^{-\mu x}\, dx}{s}$$

Therefore, the total activity leaving the source toward the counter is

$$c = \int_0^s dc = \frac{c_o}{\mu s}\,(1 - e^{-\mu s})$$

and the self-absorption factor is

$$f_s = \frac{c}{c_o} = \frac{1}{\mu s}\,(1 - e^{-\mu s}) \tag{5–11}$$

This relationship holds reasonably well for small source-to-counter distances. For large source-to-counter distances, the scattering effect may become important. It actually can cause an initial rise in the factor $f_s$ as the source thickness is increased.

When an accurate account of self-absorption must be made, it should be measured as a function of the source thickness for the particular arrangement of interest. This may be done by making a series of measurements of the counting rate in which the total activity is held constant while $s$ is changed by the addition of inactive material. The resulting data of the counting rate versus source thickness $s$, after being normalized to 1 for zero source thickness, give $f_s$ versus $s$.

The absorption factor $f_w$ is the ratio of the actual counting rate to that which would be obtained if there were no absorption between the source and the interior of the counter. The absorption is due to the tube window, the air, and any other absorbers which may be placed between the source and the tube. The quantity $f_w$ can be calculated approximately by the use of Eq. (1–15). However, it is more accurate to measure $f_w$ directly for each counting setup by the use of a series of aluminum absorbers. This is possible since aluminum, air, and mica all have the same mass absorption coefficients.

To carry out these measurements, the aluminum absorbers are placed as near the counter as possible to minimize scattering effects. The true counting rate $\dot{n}$, that is, the actual counting rate corrected for dead-time losses, is plotted on semilog paper versus the thickness of the added aluminum absorber. The resulting curve is extrapolated back to a distance $d_t$ beyond the point corresponding to zero added-absorber thickness; here $d_t$ is the entire absorber thickness between the source and the interior of tube, not counting the added aluminum absorbers. The quantity $d_t$ consists of the tube window thickness, usually specified by the tube manufacturer, the air, and any other absorbers such as a source cover. The thickness $d_a$ due to the air at 760 mm Hg and 25°C is

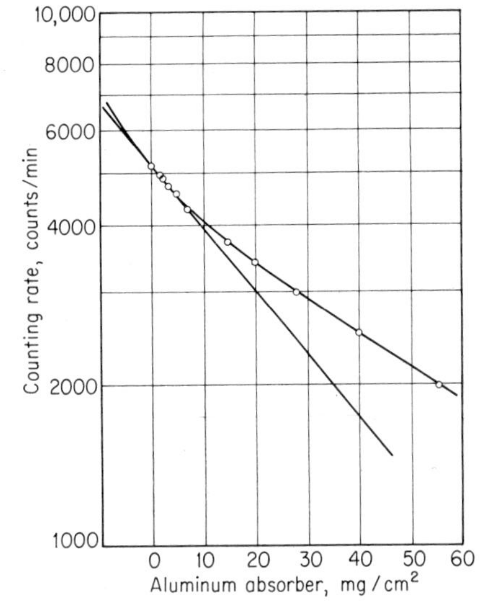


FIG. 5–13. Aluminum-absorber curve for $Bi^{210}$ radiation. (*From L. R. Zumwalt, U.S. Atomic Energy Comm. Document AECU*-567, 1950.)

$$d_a(\text{mg/cm}^2) = 1.18s(\text{cm})$$

where $s$ is the distance from the source to the tube window.

Figure 5–13 is a typical plot for use in the study of absorption. The quantity $f_w$ is the ratio of the counting rate at zero to the extrapolated counting rate at $-d_t$. Zumwalt [10] has investigated the methods of extrapolating such curves. He recommends the use of the expression

$$f_w = \frac{\dot{n}_0}{\dot{n}_{ext}} = e^{-(kd_t + k'd_t^2)} \tag{5–12}$$

where $k$ is the magnitude of the slope of the absorption curve at zero added absorber and $k'$ is given by Table 5–2.

TABLE 5–2. FACTORS FOR CORRECTING CURVATURE OF ALUMINUM-ABSORBER CURVES FOR SEVERAL ISOTOPES*

| Isotope | Maximum beta energy Mev | $k'/k$, $cm^2/mg$ |
|---|---|---|
| $Co^{60}$ | 0.31 | 0.05 |
| $I^{131}$ | 0.60 | 0.024 |
| $Bi^{210}$ | 1.17 | 0.021 |
| $P^{32}$ | 1.7 | 0.01 |

* From L. R. Zumwalt, *U.S. Atomic Energy Comm. Document* AECU-567, 1950.

**Example 5–5.** Use the data in Fig. 5–13 and Table 5–2 to calculate $f_w$ for a counting setup in which a $Bi^{210}$ source is 2.5 cm from an end-window counter having a window thickness of 2.0 $mg/cm^2$.

*Solution.* The value of $d_t$ is

$$d_t = 2.0 + (2.5)(1.18) = 4.96 \text{ mg/cm}^2$$

From Fig. 5–13 the slope at zero is 0.026 $cm^2/mg$; therefore, by Table 5–2,

$$k' = (0.026)(0.021) = 5.4 \times 10^{-4} \text{ (cm}^2\text{/mg)}^2$$

Making use of Eq. (5–12),

$$f_w = \exp[-(0.026)(4.96) - (5.4 \times 10^{-4})(4.96)^2] = \exp[-(0.129 + 0.0132)] = 0.87$$

## 5–11. *Intrinsic Efficiency and Multiple Counts*

To complete the problem of relating counting rate to source strength, one needs to know the relationship between the counting rate and the number of particles which enter the tube. This is given by the product of the factors $f_\tau$, $f_m$, and $\epsilon_\beta$.

The dead-time correction $f_\tau$ is just $\dot{m}/\dot{n}$; it can be calculated by Eq. (2–4), provided that $\tau$ is known. This factor depends on the counting rate and will need to be considered only at high rates.

The factor $f_m$ is the ratio of the number of counts, after dead-time corrections, to the number of primary discharges which occur in the sensitive volume of the tube; this ratio can be slightly greater than 1 because of multiple discharges. It increases slightly with the tube voltage, being the principal cause for the slope of the plateau of an organic-quenched tube. The multiple-discharge factor also increases as a tube ages; the increase results from the disappearance of the quenching gas as the tube is used.

The intrinsic efficiency $\epsilon_\beta$ for beta counting is defined as the fraction of the particles which, upon entering the sensitive volume of the tube, produce discharges. Its value for a G-M tube is nearly unity since a single ion pair is sufficient to trigger the discharge. The binomial-distribution law, given by Eq. (3–2), can be used to show that the probability of producing at least one ion pair in the tube is large. Assume that the path of a beta particle in the tube is divided into $N$ segments, where $N$ is sufficiently large that no one segment contains more than one ion pair. The probability $p$ of an ion pair being produced in any one segment is $b/N$, where $b$ is the total number of primary ion pairs that the beta particle will produce along the path, on an average. By Eq. (3–2), the probability $P(0)$ that no ionization will be produced in any segment is

$$P(0) = \frac{N!}{N!0!} p^0(1 - p)^N = \left(1 - \frac{b}{N}\right)^N \simeq e^{-b}$$

for large values of $N$. Thus the probability that a particle will produce a discharge while traveling a distance in which it should produce an average of $b$ primary ion pairs is given by

$$\text{Probability of discharge} = 1 - e^{-b} \tag{5–13}$$

**Example 5–6.** What is the probability that a 1-Mev beta particle will cause a discharge while traveling 1 cm through a G-M tube containing argon at a pressure of 10 cm Hg?

*Solution.* By Fig. 1–8, the primary specific ionization is 20 primary ion pairs per centimeter in air at normal temperature and pressure. Since the specific ionization is directly proportional to the atomic number of the gas and inversely proportional to the pressure, one obtains

$$b = (20)\left(\frac{18}{7.2}\right)\left(\frac{10}{76}\right) = 6.6 \text{ ion pairs}$$

Therefore the probability of a discharge is $1 - e^{-6.6} = 0.999$.

Even though the probability of producing an ion pair per unit path length is large, a few millimeters must be traveled if it is to approach unity. Thus particles which pass through a tube window near its periphery may strike the tube wall before initiating a discharge. However, if the sensitive volume is defined so as to exclude this region, as was done in Sec. 5–9, the intrinsic efficiency can be taken as 1.

In halogen-quenched tubes the sensitive volume is reduced further by negative-ion formation, as was discussed in Sec. 5–4. The fraction which the sensitive volume comprises of the total tube volume depends on the tube voltage; about eight-tenths is a typical value.

## 5–12. *Absolute and Relative Beta Counting*

In principle, the absolute activity or strength $S$ of a source can be determined from the measured counting rate $\dot{m}$ by the use of the expression for over-all efficiency. This can actually be accomplished [10] if sufficient attention is given to determining the factors for use in Eq. (5–9). However, if other methods for determining activity are available, they are usually preferable.

The most precise determinations of the absolute activities by simple counting experiments involve the comparison of the counting rate of the unknown sample with that of a standard of known activity. Beta standards are available from the National Bureau of Standards. In addition, they can be prepared in well-equipped radioisotope laboratories by the use of proportional counters, as discussed in Chap. 6, and by coincidence methods. Seliger and Schwebel [15] have discussed methods of calibrating beta standards.

In most applications of beta counting, the problem is the comparison of activities. An absolute activity measurement by comparison with a standard is only one of many possible examples. If $S_1$ and $S_2$ are the source strengths which are being compared and $\dot{m}_1$ and $\dot{m}_2$ are the corresponding counting rates, the simple relationship $S_1/S_2 = \dot{m}_1/\dot{m}_2$ holds only in exceptional cases. In general, the complete expression

$$\frac{S_1}{S_2} = \frac{\dot{m}_1}{\dot{m}_2} \frac{G_2 \epsilon_{\beta 2} f_{m2} f_{\tau 2} f_{b2} f_{w2} f_{s2}}{G_1 \epsilon_{\beta 1} f_{m1} f_{\tau 1} f_{b1} f_{w1} f_{s1}} \tag{5-14}$$

must be considered. The individual factors can be canceled out only after they have been shown to be identical.

In measurements which require the comparison of the activity of one source with that of another, the attempt should be made to prepare the sources in as nearly as possible an identical manner. The sources should have the same backing, thickness, and position. In addition, they should have the same energy spectrum, since the factors $f_w$, $f_s$, and $f_b$ all depend on energy. It is not always possible to obtain the ideal conditions with identical correction factors. In these cases corrections must be calculated, following the methods outlined in the preceding sections.

In precise work which is carried out over a period of time, it is wise to maintain periodic checks on the over-all efficiency of the counting setup. Relative values can be obtained by measurements on a reference source, the activity of which either does not change or changes by known amounts. These measurements allow the correction for changes as they occur. Probably the commonest causes of changes are the aging and the replacement of the G-M tubes.

## G-M TUBES FOR GAMMA AND X RAYS

### 5-13. *Tube Walls for Gamma- and X-ray Detectors*

The detection of X and gamma rays by G-M tubes requires the production of secondary electrons by the radiation. These secondary electrons can come from interactions with any portion of the tube, provided that these electrons can reach the sensitive volume in which they will initiate a discharge. For low-energy radiation, i.e., of the order of 20 kev, the absorption coefficient is so high that a large fraction of the photons can be absorbed directly in the filling gas. On the other hand, the absorption by the gas is negligible for high-energy photons, and the interactions in the tube wall are required in order that the detection process be sufficiently efficient for a useful device.

The intrinsic efficiency $\epsilon_\gamma$ of a G-M tube for gamma counting may be defined as the number of secondary electrons entering the sensitive volume of the tube per photon striking the tube. It will be observed that, by this definition, the attenuation of the gamma rays by the tube wall is included in the intrinsic efficiency. The efficiency depends not only on the fraction of the gammas which are absorbed by the tube but also on whether or not these secondary electrons reach the interior of the tube. Only those secondary electrons which are produced in a section of the wall which is no farther from the tube interior than their range can possibly cause a count.

An accurate calculation of $\epsilon_\gamma$ is difficult because of several complications, including the variation in the direction and in the energy of the secondary electrons and their crooked paths in the walls. However, an approximate expression can be derived; this is

$$\epsilon_\gamma \simeq \tau R_\tau + \sigma R_\sigma + 2\kappa R_\kappa \tag{5-15}$$

where $\tau$, $\sigma$, and $\kappa$ are the partial absorption coefficients of the wall material for the photoelectric, Compton, and pair-production methods of absorption, respectively, and $R_\tau$, $R_\sigma$, and $R_\kappa$ are the corresponding ranges of the secondary electrons in the wall materials.

The schematic representation in Fig. 5-14 is used to derive Eq. (5-15). The assumptions are that the gamma rays pass through the center of the tube and that one-half of the secondary electrons which originate in the shaded area, the thickness $R$ of which is the range of the secondary electrons, enter the sensitive volume. Further, the wall thickness is at least as great as the range of the most energetic electrons but not so great as to attenuate the gamma rays appreciably before they enter the shaded area. Under these conditions the contribution to the efficiency by the photoelectric absorption in one wall is $(\frac{1}{2})(1 - e^{-R_\tau \tau})$ or $(\frac{1}{2})R_\tau \tau$ since $R_\tau \tau \ll 1$. The inclusion of similar contributions by each process at both walls leads to Eq. (5-15) if it is recalled that each pair-production process results in two charged particles.

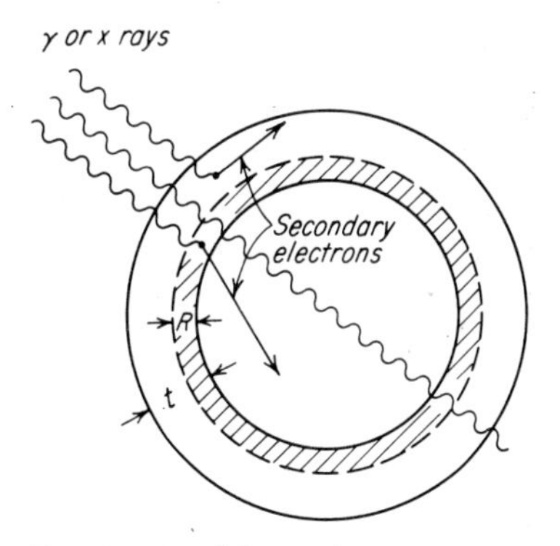


Fig. 5-14. Schematic representation of a G-M tube used for estimating the intrinsic efficiency for gamma counting.

The ranges of the secondary electrons can be obtained from Fig. 1–10, provided that their kinetic energies are known. The energies of the photoelectrons and the electrons in the pair are $h\nu$ and $(\frac{1}{2})(h\nu - 1.02)$ Mev, respectively, where $h\nu$ is the photon energy. The Compton electrons have a spectrum of energies. However, for this calculation the average energy $h\nu\sigma_a/(\sigma_a + \sigma_s)$ may be used, where $\sigma_a$ is the energy absorption portion and $\sigma_s$ is the scattering portion of the Klein and Nishina absorption coefficient (see Sec. 1–14).

In the intermediate energy region where the electrons are liberated primarily by the Compton effect, the material of the wall has little effect on the intrinsic efficiency since the range of the electrons is approximately inversely proportional to $Z$ while the Compton absorption coefficient is directly proportional to $Z$. At low energies where the photoelectric effect is the predominant one, the high-$Z$ wall materials produce the highest-efficiency counters since $\tau$ is proportional to $Z^5$. At energies sufficiently high for pair production to have the predominant effect, the high-$Z$ materials result in higher efficiencies because $\kappa$ increases as $Z^2$.

The curves in Fig. 5–15 give measured values of the dependence of efficiency on photon energy for aluminum, brass, and bismuth tube walls [16]. In addition, some values calculated for aluminum by the use of Eq. (5–15) are included. Other measurements of efficiency which check the data in Fig. 5–15 in general but not in detail have been reported [17,18]. The nearly linear increase of efficiency with energy through the region in which the Compton effect predominates is due to a similar increase in the range of secondary electrons with energy while the absorption coefficient remains fairly constant.

Data such as those in Fig. 5–15 should be taken only as approximate since the exact values of efficiency depend on the wall thickness and on the configuration of the cathode. The increase in the efficiency by the use of special cathode designs is discussed in Sec. 5–16.

### 5–14. *G-M Tubes in Radiation Survey Meters*

The dependence of the G-M tube efficiency on the gamma-ray energy is particularly important in its application in radiation survey meters. In such instruments the counting rate of the G-M tube is related to the dosage rate. In general, this relationship is an involved function of energy; therefore the scales which are supplied with these instruments give only a qualitative indication of the actual dosage rate. Sinclair [19] and Day [20] have studied the energy dependence of instruments of these types. The correction factor versus energy is shown for a typical instrument in Fig. 5–16. The correction factor is the number by which the scale reading must be multiplied to obtain the correct reading.

It is seen by Eq. (4–37) that the dosage rate in roentgens is proportional to the product of the absorption coefficient of air and the photon energy. By Eq. (5–15), the counting rate should be proportional to the product of the absorption coefficient in the tube wall material and the secondary-electron range. Therefore, in the energy range in which absorption coefficients are essentially constant, the correction factor is proportional to the ratio of the photon energy to the particle range. A decrease in this ratio

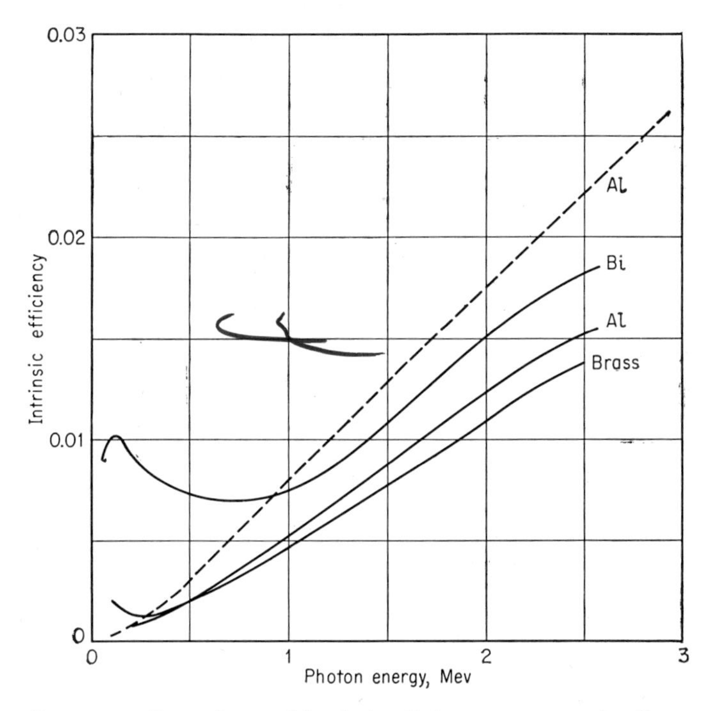


Fig. 5–15. Dependence of intrinsic efficiency on energy for three cathode materials. [*From H. Bradt et al., Helv. Phys. Acta,* **19**:77 (1946).] Dotted curve is the efficiency of an Al wall tube calculated by Eq. (5–15).

accounts for the corresponding decrease in the correction factor in Fig. 5–16 as the energy goes up from 0.3 Mev.

On the other hand, when the energy is decreased from 0.3 Mev, the photoelectric process becomes the predominant factor in the absorption process. Since the photoelectric absorption increases rapidly with the atomic number of the absorber, the absorption in the wall material predominates, and the correction factor drops rapidly as the photon energy drops.

At the very low energies, the correction factor rises again because of the excessive absorption of the photons while entering the tube. This effect is emphasized by placing the beta-ray shield over the tube. Curves for both the covered and uncovered tubes are included in Fig. 5–16.

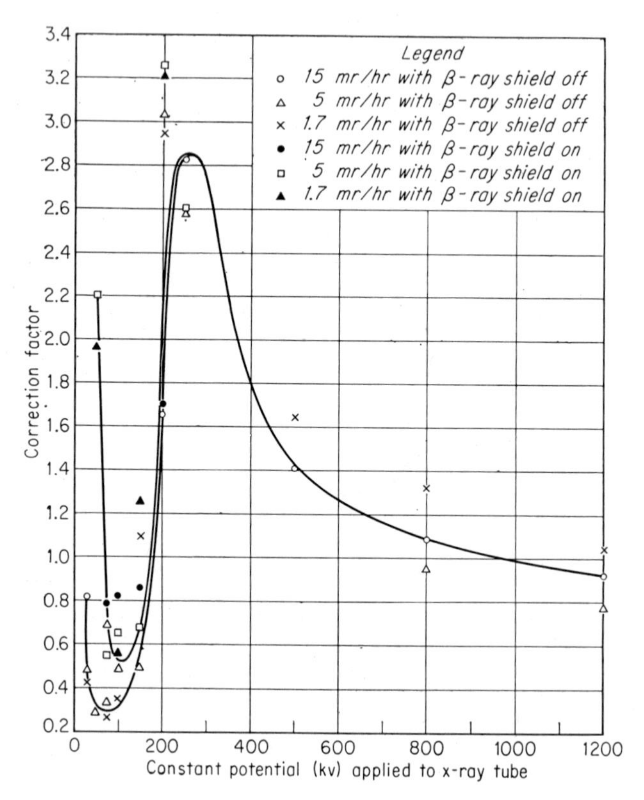


FIG. 5–16. Correction factors for the Victoreen G-M-tube survey meter 509, model 263A. [*From F. H. Day, Natl. Bur. Standards (U.S.) Circ.* 507, 1951.]

## 5–15. *Over-all Efficiency for Gamma Counting*

The counting rate of a G-M tube for detecting gammas can be related to the gamma-source strength $S$ by Eq. (5–9), provided that $\epsilon_\beta$ is replaced by $\epsilon_\gamma$, the intrinsic efficiency for detecting gammas. All other terms have the same meaning as previously.

It is important to observe that the intrinsic efficiency for gammas is about 0.01 instead of 1, as with betas. Further, its dependence on the gamma-ray energy and on the tube wall material and thickness must be taken into account. Approximate values of $\epsilon_\gamma$ can be taken from Fig. 5–15 or calculated by Eq. (5–15). However, for accurate measurements it is preferable to determine $\epsilon_\gamma$ experimentally for the particular type of tube which is being used.

The geometry factor can be treated in the same fashion as discussed in Sec. 5–9. Thus Eq. (5–10) is applicable to a source on the axis of an end-window-type tube. A common arrangement is that of a point source irradiating a cylindrical tube from the side. For the case in which a line from the source to the center of the tube is perpendicular to the tube axis, the geometry factor is given by [21]

$$G = \frac{1}{\pi}\tan^{-1}\frac{RL/2}{[(d^2 - R^2)(b^2 - R^2)]^{1/2}} + \frac{LR^2}{b^3}\left[\cos^{-1}\frac{R}{d} - \frac{R}{d}\left(1 - \frac{R^2}{d^2}\right)^{1/2}\left(1 - \frac{3R^2}{2b^2}\right) + \frac{dR}{b^2}\left(1 - \frac{R^2}{d^2}\right)^{3/2}\right] \tag{5–16}$$

where $R$ = tube radius
$L$ = length
$d$ = distance from tube center to source
$b^2 = (L/2)^2 + d^2$

In many cases the tube-to-source distance $d$ is sufficiently large that the geometry factor can be approximated by

$$G = \frac{A}{4\pi d^2} \tag{5–17}$$

where $A$ is the cross-sectional area of the tube.

The absorption in the source and between the source and the tube can often be neglected in gamma counting. In addition, because of the large penetrating power of gammas, it is relatively easy to obtain a backing material that is sufficiently thin that backscattering is negligible. However, if these factors become significant, the correction factors can be calculated or measured by the methods which were discussed in Sec. 5–10.

## SPECIAL-PURPOSE G-M TUBES

### 5–16. *High-efficiency Gamma Tubes*

It was pointed out in Sec. 5–13 that the intrinsic efficiency of G-M tubes is quite low. It is apparent from Fig. 5–15 that a small increase can be obtained by making the walls of high-$Z$ materials. In addition, gains in efficiency can be realized by using a fine-mesh-screen cathode [22] or by employing a combination of plate and fin structures fastened to the cathode [23]. A stainless-steel tube constructed in this latter manner is about five times more efficient [23] for 0.37-Mev gammas ($I^{131}$) than is a glass-wall bell-type tube of conventional construction. This gain in efficiency comes about because of the increased cathode area from which secondary electrons can reach the sensitive volume of the tube.

Graf [24] has studied multiple-section G-M tubes for gamma-ray counting. He has described a counter composed of 24 tubes in parallel. The tubes had bismuth-plated brass-screen cathodes and were all combined in the same envelope. Figure 5–17 is a schematic diagram of this device. Its efficiency was found to be several times larger than that of a conventional tube. In addition, the tube had the advantage of a dead time as low as 3 or 4 μsecs. The low dead time in this counter results from the fact that the discharges are confined to the section in which they originate. Thus, while one section may be in an insensitive condition at any given instant, as many as 23 other sections can accept an additional count.

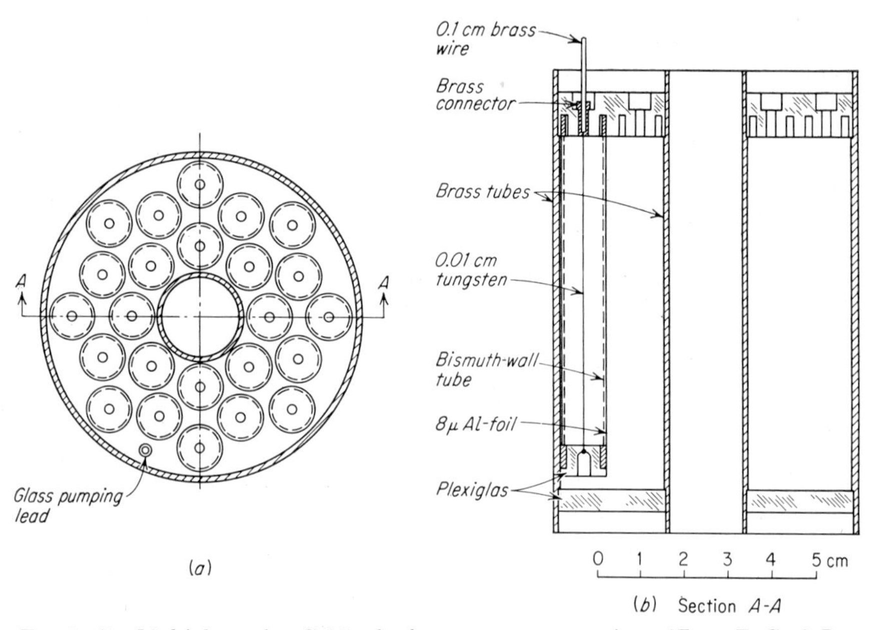


FIG. 5–17. Multiple-section G-M tube for gamma-ray counting. [*From T. Graf, Rev. Sci. Instr.*, **21**:285 (1950).]

Figure 5–18 is a schematic diagram of another counter with multiple sections. The tube has been designed for 8-kev X rays [25]. It consists of 10 cells, each approximately 1 cm square by 2.5 cm long, placed transverse to the beam. Each cell has an opening through which the beam may pass without touching the walls. The secondary electrons which are required to start the discharges are produced by absorptions in the filling gas. The tube has a very thin beryllium window in order to minimize the absorption of the soft X rays in the window. Because of its low dead time, the counter is capable of operation at rates up to 10,000 counts/sec.

## 5–17. *The Integrator Tube*

A recent extension of the G-M-tube principle is referred to as the integrator tube [26]. It has been found possible to operate specially designed tubes in high-radiation fields and to use the average current rather than a count of the individual pulses as a measure of flux.

Integrator tubes can deliver currents of the order of 50 $\mu$amp. Halogen quenching gases are employed since they are not used up during the life of the tubes. The electrodes undergo special processing in order that they can withstand the high current. The output of the tubes is quite dependent on the applied voltage so that a well-regulated high-voltage power supply is required.

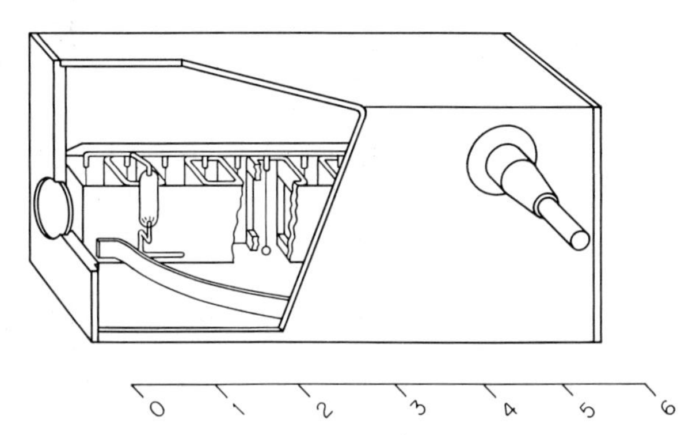

FIG. 5–18. G-M tube for 8-Mev X rays. (*Courtesy of Victoreen Instrument Company.*)

## 5–18. *Counters with Internal Sources*

Several G-M tubes have been designed in such a way that the samples can be placed within them. With such arrangements the geometry factor can be at least 0.5. In addition, since these tubes are windowless, they can be used with very weak betas such as $C^{14}$.

One type of windowless tube is known as a screen-wall counter [27]. It is so named because its cathode or wall is made of screen wire, usually about 10-mesh copper. The sample is placed on the inside surface of a cylinder which surrounds the screen cathode. After the tube is assembled with the source, it is evacuated and then filled with a mixture of argon and ethylene at 9.5 cm Hg and 0.5 cm Hg, respectively.

Other G-M tubes which were arranged so that the source could be placed within them have been described by Tait and Hagges [28] and by Brown and Miller [29]. In addition, flow-type chambers such as those described in Sec. 6–3 have been used in the G-M region.

## 5–19. *Photosensitive G-M Tubes*

Since G-M tubes are sensitive to single electrons, they will respond to photons of ultraviolet and visible light if this light is allowed to produce photoelectric emission within the tube. In the application of G-M tubes to nuclear-radiation detection, the photosensitivity is avoided by making the envelopes of the tubes opaque to light or by special treatment of the tube surfaces.

Mandeville and Scherb [30] have reviewed the development and the application of tubes in which the photosensitivity is utilized. A number of workers have succeeded in developing G-M tubes with good sensitivity in the ultraviolet region. Typical quantum efficiencies are $10^{-2}$ to $10^{-1}$ electron/quantum.

The photosensitive G-M tubes are much more sensitive to low-intensity light than are ordinary photocells, since the G-M discharge serves to produce a large current multiplication. Photomultiplier tubes (see Chap. 7) have a similar sensitivity to the photosensitive G-M tubes; however, they have the disadvantage of more complexity both in the tube proper and in the associated electronic equipment. On the other hand, the G-M tubes have a much larger dead time than the photomultiplier tubes. The photomultiplier tube is found to be preferable to the photosensitive G-M tube for most applications.

5–20. *Hollow-collector and Parallel-plate Geiger-Müller Tubes*

Until quite recently all G-M-tube designs have utilized fine wires for the collector electrodes, as has been discussed in this chapter. The small collector is required to achieve adequate quenching with most filling gases. In addition, increasing the collector diameter results in higher tube voltages, greater slopes of the plateaus, and shorter plateau lengths.

Hermsen et al. [31] have shown that the use of the low-voltage halogen-gas mixtures (see Sec. 5–4) makes possible the construction of useful G-M tubes with large-area collectors. Both cylindrical tubes with large hollow collectors and parallel-plate counters have been studied. The counting characteristics of these devices are quite good. These departures from conventional G-M-tube design result in counters with more suitable geometry for certain applications. In addition, the dead time of the large-area collector tubes can be made smaller than that in tubes with fine wires.

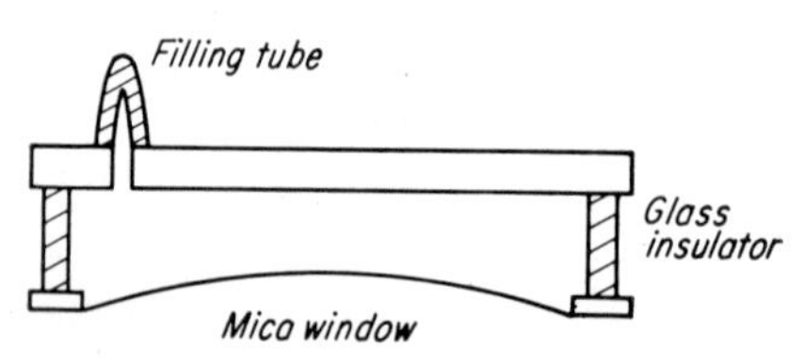


FIG. 5–19. Parallel-plate G-M tube. (*From J. Hermsen, A. M. J. Jaspers, P. Kroayeveld, and K. van Duuren, "Proceedings of the International Conference on the Peaceful Uses of Atomic Energy," vol.* 14, *p.* 275, *United Nations, New York,* 1956.)

Figure 5–19 is a schematic drawing of a parallel-plate counter. The mica window may be coated internally with a conductive coating or supported by a metal grid. The counting characteristics are given by Figs. 5–20 and 5–21. Both the counting-rate–tube-voltage curves of Fig. 5–20 and the dead-time–tube-voltage curves in Fig. 5–21 are quite depend-

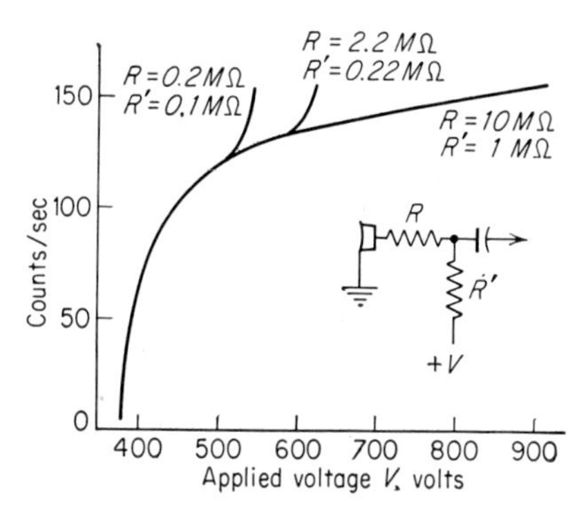


Fig. 5–20. Counting-rate–tube-voltage curves for a parallel-plate G-M tube. (*From J. Hermsen, A. M. J. Jaspers, P. Kroayeveld, and K. van Duuren, "Proceedings of the International Conference on the Peaceful Uses of Atomic Energy," vol.* 14, *p.* 275, *United Nations, New York*, 1956.)

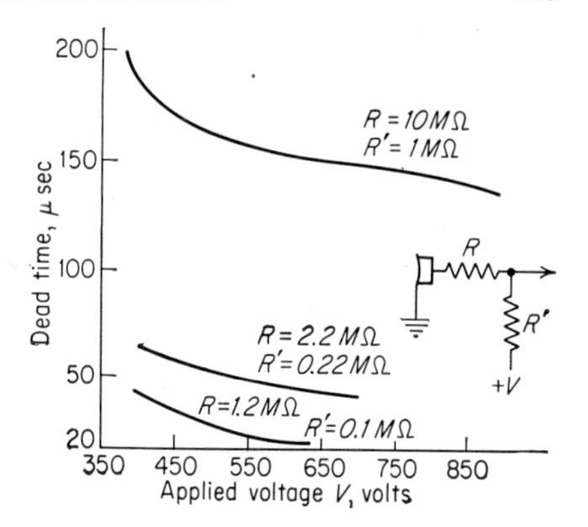


Fig. 5–21. Dead-time–tube-voltage curves for a parallel-plate G-M tube. (*From J. Hermsen, A. M. J. Jaspers, P. Kroayeveld, and K. van Duuren, "Proceedings of the International Conference on the Peaceful Uses of Atomic Energy," vol.* 14, *p.* 275, *United Nations, New York*, 1956.)

ent on the value of the series resistance $R$. High values of $R$ give good plateaus. On the other hand, the small dead times are achieved only with low values of $R$.

## 5–21. *Needle Counter*

A G-M tube development of great importance in medical diagnosis is the needle counter [32]. Figure 5–1*c* is a schematic diagram of this counter type. The envelope of the active region of these counters is a fine steel tube about 2 to 3 mm in diameter and with a wall thickness of 0.1 mm. The sensitive region may be about 1 cm in length. Because of its shape and small size, the needle counter can be used as a probe in soft tissue and similar regions.

## PROBLEMS

**5–1.** If a G-M tube which contains 90 mm Hg of argon and 10 mm Hg of alcohol has a lifetime of $10^{10}$ counts, calculate the number of molecules of alcohol dissociated per discharge, under the assumption that the end of the tube life occurs when all the alcohol molecules have been dissociated.

**5–2.** A G-M counter with a resolving time of 200 μsec is employed for 2-min counts on a source producing a counting rate of about 20,000 counts/min. Would the dead-time loss be significant in view of the other errors present?

**5–3.** If a G-M tube has a counting-rate characteristic with a plateau slope of 10 per cent per 100 volts, what regulation is required on the high-voltage power supply if no change in efficiency greater than 0.5 per cent can be tolerated?

**5–4.** Consider a beta emitter with maximum energy of 1 Mev. Estimate the percentage transmission of these particles through a G-M tube wall of a thickness of 25 mg/cm$^2$.

**5–5.** Compute the activity of a beta emitter from the following data taken with an end-window G-M tube:

| Added absorber, mg/cm$^2$ | Counting rate, counts/min | Register factor |
|---|---|---|
| 0 | 460 | 64 |
| 7.5 | 434 | 64 |
| 14.0 | 407 | 64 |
| 20.5 | 394 | 64 |
| 29.0 | 370 | 64 |
| Background | 0.5 | 64 |

Take the characteristics of the counter setup as follows: distance from source to window, 4 cm; window thickness, 2 mg/cm$^2$; source, thin (neglect self-absorption) and plated on an aluminum planchet ⅛ in. thick; resolving time, $\tau$ = 150 $\mu$sec; geometry factor, 0.05.

**5–6.** A beta source has a thickness of 30 mg/cm$^2$. Estimate the source self-absorption factor if the beta emitter emits electrons of a maximum energy of 0.25 Mev.

**5–7.** The absorption and backscattering of beta particles are used as the basis of a thickness gauge. Discuss the range of thickness for which such a gauge could be used by transmission techniques and by backscattering.

**5–8.** Discuss the errors inherent in Eq. (5–15).

**5–9.** Explain why the intrinsic efficiency of a G-M tube for gamma counting is nearly a linear function of the gamma energy from about 0.2 to 2 Mev.

**5–10.** A scheme has been proposed for locating lost golf balls by incorporating some radioactive material in the golf ball and searching for it with a G-M counter. Compute the strength in curies of a radioactive source in a golf ball that would be required to double the counting rate on the G-M counter at a distance of 10 m from the golf ball. Assume a counter with an effective cross-sectional area of 10 cm$^2$, an efficiency $\epsilon_\gamma$ of 0.01, and a background counting rate of 30 counts/min. In addition, determine the number of golf balls which would be required to produce a dosage rate of 7.5 mr/hr at 50 cm if $Co^{60}$ is used for the radioactive material.

**5–11.** Prove that Eq. (5–16) can be approximated by Eq. (5–17) as $d$ becomes large.

**5–12.** Compute the geometry factor at a perpendicular distance of 10 cm from the center of the axis of a cylindrical G-M tube with length and radius of 10 and 1 cm, respectively. Compare the approximation given by Eq. (5–17) with the more accurate value.

## REFERENCES

1. Mandeville, C. E.: *Nucleonics*, **8**:S-8 (June, 1951).
2. Wilkinson, D. H.: "Ionization Chambers and Counters," chap. 7, Cambridge University Press, London, 1950.
3. Jordan, W. H.: Personal communication.
4. Neher, H. V., and W. H. Pickering: *Phys. Rev.*, **53**:316 (1938).
5. Trost, A.: *Z. Physik*, **105**:399 (1937).
6. Spatz, W. D. B.: *Phys. Rev.*, **64**:236 (1943).
7. Liebson, S. H., and H. Friedman: *Rev. Sci. Instr.*, **19**:303 (1948).
8. Stever, H. G.: *Phys. Rev.*, **61**:38 (1942).

9. Kohman, T. D.: Article in G. T. Seaborg et al. (eds.), "The Transuranium Elements," National Nuclear Energy Series, div. IV, vol. 14B, pt. II, McGraw-Hill Book Company, Inc., New York, 1950.
10. Zumwalt, L. R.: *U.S. Atomic Energy Comm. Document* AECU-567, 1950.
11. Burt, B. P.: *Nucleonics*, **5**:28 (August, 1949).
12. Calvin, M., et al.: "Isotopic Carbon," chap. 3, John Wiley & Sons, Inc., New York, 1949.
13. Gleason, G. I., J. D. Taylor, and D. L. Tabern: *Nucleonics*, **8**:27 (May, 1951).
14. Schweitzer, G. K., and B. R. Stein: *Nucleonics*, **7**:65 (September, 1950).
15. Seliger, H. H., and A. Schwebel: *Nucleonics*, **12**:54 (July, 1954).
16. Bradt, H., et al.: *Helv. Phys. Acta*, **19**:77 (1946).
17. Jurney, E. T., and F. Maienschein: *Rev. Sci. Instr.*, **20**:932 (1949).
18. Hart, R. J., K. Russel, and R. M. Steffen: *Phys. Rev.*, **81**:460 (1951).
19. Sinclair, W. K.: *Nucleonics*, **7**:21 (December, 1950).
20. Day, F. H.: *Natl. Bur. Standards (U.S.) Circ.* 507, 1951.
21. Norling, F.: *Arkiv Mat. Astron. Fysik*, **27A**:27 (1941).
22. Evans, R. D., and R. A. Mugele: *Rev. Sci. Instr.*, **7**:441 (1936).
23. Tracerlab, Inc.: Private communication.
24. Graf, T.: *Rev. Sci. Instr.*, **21**:285 (1950).
25. Victoreen Instrument Company: Private communication.
26. Anton, N.: "Proceedings of the International Conference on the Peaceful Uses of Atomic Energy," vol. 14, p. 279, United Nations, New York, 1956.
27. Anderson, E. C., J. R. Arnold, and W. F. Libby: *Rev. Sci. Instr.*, **22**:225 (1951).
28. Tait, J. F., and G. H. Hagges: *J. Sci. Instr.*, **26**:269 (1949).
29. Brown, S. C., and W. W. Miller: *Rev. Sci. Instr.*, **19**:360 (1948).
30. Mandeville, C. E., and M. V. Scherb: *Nucleonics*, **7**:34 (November, 1950).
31. Hermsen, J., A. M. J. Jaspers, P. Kroayeveld, and K. van Duuren: "Proceedings of the International Conference on the Peaceful Uses of Atomic Energy," vol. 14, p. 275, United Nations, New York, 1956.
32. Robinson, C. V.: *Rev. Sci. Instr.*, **21**:82 (1950).

CHAPTER 6

# PROPORTIONAL COUNTERS

The operation of gas-filled chambers in the voltage region where gas multiplication is present while proportionality to the particle energy is still maintained has resulted in a very useful detector. This region, lying between those of the ionization chamber and the Geiger-Müller tube, is named the proportional region, as discussed in Sec. 2–1. Detectors in this region can be of either the pulse or the mean-level type, as was also the case with ionization chambers. The pulse-type applications are by far the most widespread, and this chapter will be devoted to them; detectors of this type are usually referred to as proportional counters.

The mean-level-type application of proportional chambers to the measurement of low radiation levels has been studied [1]. This system might result in a lower-cost instrument than is possible with ionization chambers. This potential saving arises because the proportional chamber requires a less sensitive d-c electrometer than does the ionization chamber.

The applications of both pulse-type ionization chambers and Geiger-Müller tubes for the study of single particles have been discussed in the preceding chapters. The former detectors maintain a strict proportionality between the charge which is produced and the primary ionization, but the pulse size is quite small; the latter employ quite large gas multiplication resulting in a large voltage pulse, but all dependence of the pulse size on primary ionization is lost. The proportional counters offer an important addition, since with them a quite significant gain in pulse height over that of a straight ion chamber can be achieved while at the same time proportionality is maintained.

Proportional chambers offer particular advantages in the pulse-type measurements of beta radiation, an application for which ionization chambers do not have sufficient sensitivity. For straight counting, much higher rates are possible than with G-M tubes because of the small resolving time that can be achieved. For the energy measurements of low-energy betas, the proportional chambers are capable of better resolution than scintillation detectors used for the same application.

## PRINCIPLES OF OPERATION

### 6–1. *General Considerations*

The phenomenon of gas multiplication is produced in a proportional counter in a manner similar to that described in Sec. 5–1 for a G-M tube. However, the discharges in the two detector types differ greatly in the mechanisms for their termination and in the amount of gas multiplication.

In the G-M tube the discharge is terminated when the positive-ion sheath entirely covers the collector. In the proportional counter the discharge stops when all the electrons within the gas volume are swept to the collector.

In G-M tubes the gas multiplication proceeds until a certain total number of ion pairs is produced in the tube, this quantity being independent of the primary ionization which initiates the discharge. From $10^8$ to $10^{10}$ ion pairs are produced per discharge, the exact number being dependent on the tube type and its operating conditions. In proportional counters the amount of ionization produced per discharge is a function of the primary ionization as well as of the tube characteristics and operating conditions. The practical ranges of gas multiplications are from unity up to about $10^4$, with $10^6$ being possible when the primary ionization is as low as one ion pair [2]. The region above about $10^6$ may be considered to be the transition region to G-M-tube operation.

The primary electrons in the initial ionizing event produce secondary electrons by collisions with neutral gas molecules. The emission of light photons accompanies the production of the secondary electrons. If $\epsilon$ is the probability that a secondary electron will produce a tertiary electron by photoemission, the gas-multiplication factor $M$ can be represented by

$$M = f + \epsilon f^2 + \epsilon^2 f^3 + \cdots + \epsilon^n f^{n+1} = \frac{f}{1 - \epsilon f} \tag{6–1}$$

Here $f$ represents the gas multiplication present in the initial avalanche and therefore the value which would result if there were no photoionization. The term $\epsilon f$ is considered to be less than 1.

For strict proportionality, $M$ must be independent of the primary ionization. This will be true as long as the space charge due to the positive ions is not too large or the primary electrons do not travel different distances through the region of the tube in which the multiplication occurs. When the primary ionization is a single ion pair, the multiplication factor can be $10^6$ before the space charge affects the proportionality; for larger amounts of primary ionization, the multiplication factor must be proportionately smaller. The dependence of the secondary ionization on the position of the primary ionization is avoided by the choice of geometry for the proportional-counter chambers. These chambers in all cases have a fine wire, usually of the order of 0.001-in. diameter, for the collector electrode. Consequently, the electric field is quite large in the immediate vicinity of this electrode, and essentially all the secondary ionization is produced close to the wire. Since the volume of this region is negligible compared with the

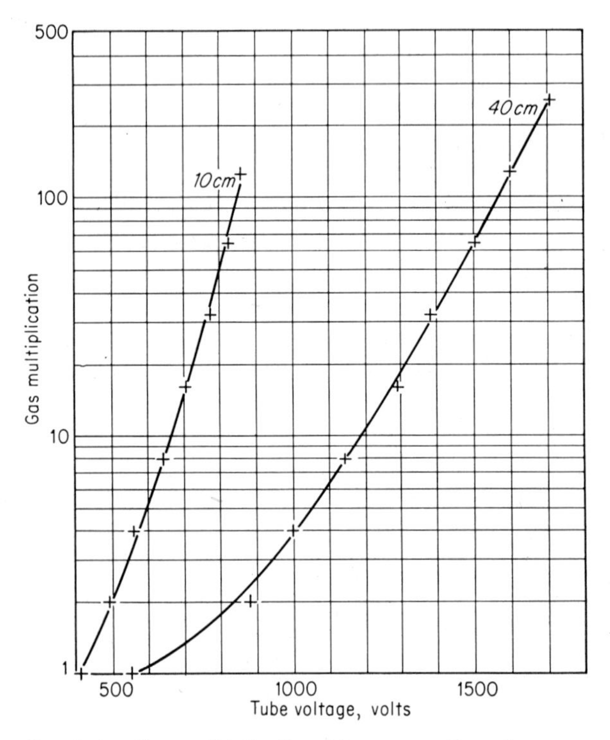


FIG. 6–1. Gas multiplication $M$ versus voltage for pressures of 10 and 40 cm Hg; argon 99.6 per cent pure; collector diameter, 0.01 in.; cathode diameter, 0.87 in. (*From B. B. Rossi and H. H. Staub, "Ionization Chambers and Counters," Chap. 4, National Nuclear Energy Series, div. V, vol. 2, McGraw-Hill Book Company, Inc., New York,* 1949.)

total volume in which the primary ionization can occur, the chances of obtaining a lower multiplication factor due to the location of the primary ionization are small.

The actual values of the multiplication factor are obtained by experiment [3]. Figure 6–1 presents the multiplication factor in argon versus the voltage which is applied between the collector and the cathode of a cylindrical tube. The argon pressure is taken as the parameter.

The addition of polyatomic gases to pure gases such as argon and helium makes $M$ less dependent on the applied voltage. For example, a mixture of 10 per cent methane and 90 per cent argon, known as "P-10 gas," makes a good filling gas for proportional counters; 4 per cent isobutane and 96 per cent helium are also quite satisfactory. The stabilizing influence of the polyatomic gases apparently comes about because their added absorption for the photons reduces the photoemission. The large values of gas multiplication can be obtained only with gases having these properties.

### 6–2. *Pulse Shapes and Resolving Times*

The analysis of pulse shapes which was carried out for G-M tubes in Sec. 5–1 applies to proportional counters as well. In fact, the analysis represents the proportional counter much better than the G-M tube, since the neglect of the space charge is quite a good assumption for the former but not for the latter.

It was pointed out in Sec. 5–1 that most of the induced charge is due to the initial motion of the positive ions. Further, it was shown that the use of circuits with time constants small compared with the collection time for the positive ions produced short pulses, the heights of which were proportional to the primary ionization and independent of its position within the chamber.

The resolving time of a proportional counter depends on its application. If the tube is used for detection only, the time by which the pulses must be separated for proper operation is much less than if energy measurements are required also.

The positive-ion sheath in a proportional-counter tube remains localized. Consequently, the tube can receive another pulse and amplify it as long as the new ion sheath is formed on the collector at another position. As the gas-multiplication factor is increased, the positive-ion sheath spreads, and the resolving time increases.

For the case in which detection only is required, the resolving time can be made as low as 0.2 to 0.5 μsec. The tube resolving time is determined by the rise time of the pulses; this is limited principally by the differences in the times required for the electrons to travel from the extreme ends of the primary-ion tracks to the collector. In the application of proportional counters, it often happens that the input amplifier and the electronic scaler rather than the detector limit the resolving power.

When the amplitude of the pulses must be measured accurately, the error in pulse size because of the presence of ionization from the preceding pulse must be avoided. Therefore, for highest-accuracy work, the interval between pulses should be at least as great as the collection time for the positive ions, or about 100 μsec. For most experiments the time between pulses can be less than this since the effect of the positive ions decreases rapidly as they move out from the immediate vicinity of the collector wire.

The size of the pulse at the input of the amplifier which follows the proportional counter can be estimated from the analysis in Sec. 5–1. A pulse of height about $0.5MN_pe/C$ is obtained, where $M$ is the gas multiplication, $N_p$ is the number of primary ions, and $C$ is the capacity of the circuit as defined in Sec. 5–1.

**Example 6–1.** Estimate the gas multiplication required to count a 10-kev electron which gives up all its energy to the chamber gas. Assume that the amplifier input capacity in parallel with the counter capacity is 20 $\mu\mu$f and that its input sensitivity is 1 mv.

*Solution.* Taking 32.5 ev as the energy required to produce an ion pair, one has

$$N_p = \frac{10^4}{32.5} = 308$$

Therefore, the gas multiplication must be given by the expression

$$M = \frac{V_{\min}C}{0.5N_pe} = \frac{(10^{-3})(20 \times 10^{-12})}{(0.5)(308)(1.6 \times 10^{-19})} = 810$$

## TYPES AND APPLICATIONS OF PROPORTIONAL COUNTERS

### 6–3. *Gas-flow Counters*

A type of detector known as a gas-flow counter is in wide-scale use. Although the principle of the gas-flow counter does not restrict it to the proportional region, most of these detectors are operated as proportional counters.

Figures 6–2 and 6–3 contain photographs of two different types of commercial flow counters. The distinguishing features of these instruments are that the counter gas flows continuously through the counter and that the sample can be placed inside the sample chamber. When employed in this fashion, the counter is said to be a windowless flow counter.

After the chamber has been opened, as in replacing a sample, the counter is purged by a rapid flow of gas. During counting, the flow rate may be reduced to about one bubble per second so that the consumption of gas is quite nominal. Both the mixture of 10 per cent methane with 90 per cent argon and that of 4 per cent isobutane with 96 per cent helium are good, all-round counter gases. However, simple gases such as argon, methane, helium, or any other gas with a small electron affinity can be used when only a small gas-multiplication factor is required, as in the case of counting alpha particles.

The flow counters have various geometries, usually not cylindrical; the counters in Figs. 6–2 and 6–3 are seen to be hemispherical. The collectors are very fine wires, usually 0.001 to 0.002 in. in diameter. The collector wire is either formed into a loop and welded to a terminal which is supported by a single insulator or is suspended as a straight wire between two insulators.

Plateaus are found in the counting-rate versus tube-voltage characteristics of a proportional counter, just as in the case of a Geiger-Müller tube. An essential difference, however, is that separate plateaus are obtained for various particle types, provided that they have sufficiently large differences in primary ionization. For example, in a counter of the type shown in Fig. 6–3, with an input amplifier having a gain of 200 followed by a scaler with its discriminator set at 0.2 volt, the counting-rate versus operating-voltage characteristic shown in Fig. 6–4 was obtained. The source employed in this measurement was an Ra-D-E-F source emitting both alpha

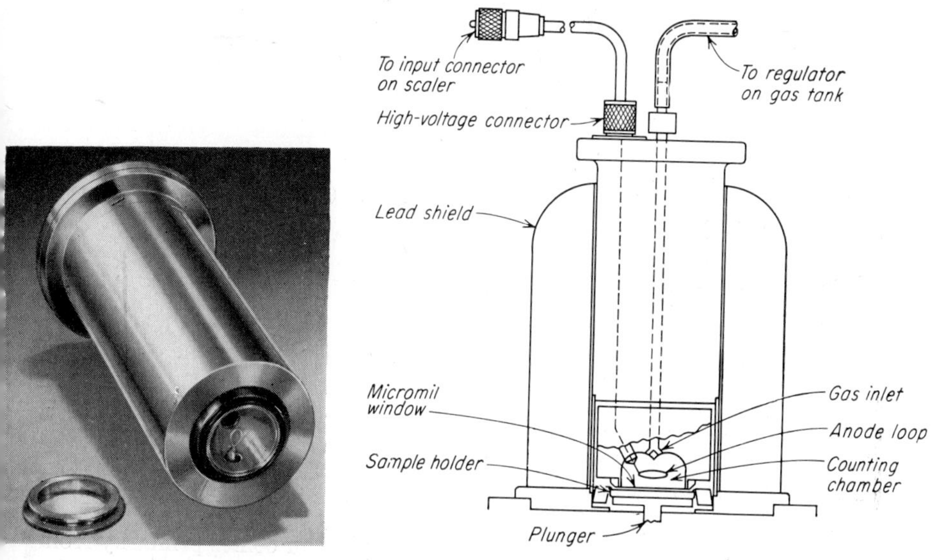


FIG. 6–2. Windowless flow counter; photograph of a chamber and a schematic diagram of a chamber mounted in the shield; the micromil window (150 $\mu$g/cm$^2$) is optional. (*Courtesy of Nuclear-Chicago Corporation.*)

and beta particles. The counting gas was 10 per cent methane in 90 per cent argon, and the collector wire was 0.001-in. platinum in the form of a loop.

The starting voltage for the alpha plateau represents the condition for which the most energetic alpha particles dissipate their entire energy in the counter and the gas-multiplication factor is just sufficient to allow the pulses to pass the discriminator. As the voltage is increased further, the region is reached where all the alphas produce pulses which pass the discriminator; this condition leads to the plateau. The proper operating voltage for counting alphas is in the middle of this plateau.

As the applied voltage is increased through the alpha plateau, the counting rate starts to rise again. This occurs when the gas multiplication be-

FIG. 6–3. Windowless flow counter; photograph of a unit both assembled and unassembled as well as a schematic diagram of the chamber. (*Courtesy of Nuclear Measurements Corporation.*)

comes sufficiently great that some beta particles are counted. After a transition region, a beta plateau is reached. Since there is a large distribution in the energy of the betas, this plateau is not as flat as the one for the alphas.

The background counting rate in the alpha plateau may be as low as 0.1 count/min. These counts come from alpha emitters present in the chamber either as contamination on the surface or as constituents of the counter wall material.

The background counting rate in the beta plateau comes primarily from the external cosmic- and gamma-radiation sources. A typical value for a chamber of the type shown in Fig. 6–3 is 50 counts/min.

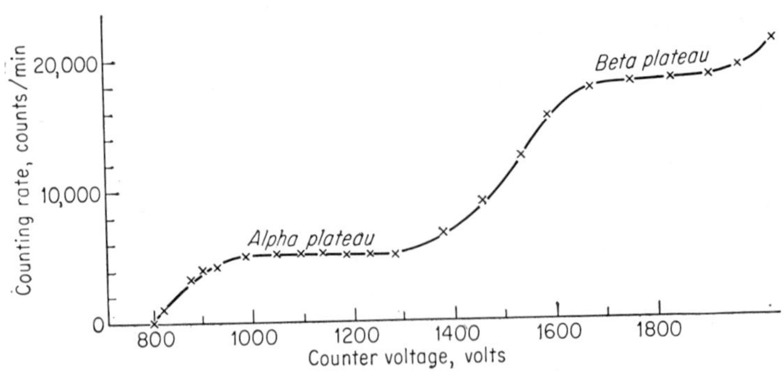


FIG. 6–4. Counting rate versus counter voltage for a flow-type proportional counter with a National Bureau of Standards Ra-D-E-F source.

## 6–4. *Alpha Counting by Proportional Counters*

Windowless flow-type counters are used widely for alpha counting. This is a particularly attractive application since the need for thin windows is avoided. Further, it is possible to carry out the alpha counting in the presence of large fluxes of betas and gammas if the detector is operated in the proportional region; the betas and secondary electrons may be discriminated against because of their low specific ionization. A limitation is reached, however, when the background of betas and gammas becomes so high that the superposition of their pulses results in signals of sufficient size and frequency to interfere with the counting of the alpha particles.

The inherently low background counting rate of flow counters makes it possible to count very small alpha activities. This fact makes them particularly useful in the field of health physics.

The over-all efficiency of a windowless flow counter depends on only a small number of factors as compared with an end-window-type G-M tube. Since these factors can be evaluated with fair accuracy, this detector type is quite useful for absolute-activity measurements of both alpha and beta emitters.

When the sample is placed within the counter, the only factors of Eq. (5–9) which need to be evaluated are geometry, backscattering, and self-absorption. The intrinsic efficiency, multiple count, and source-to-counter absorption factors can be taken as 1. In addition, because of the small resolving time, the dead-time correction factors in proportional counters can be neglected up to a counting rate of 100,000 counts/min or greater.

**Example 6–2.** Estimate the counting rate at which the dead-time loss becomes 1 per cent for both a typical proportional counter and a G-M tube.

*Solution.* By Eq. (2–3), the per cent dead-time loss is 100 $\dot{m}\tau$ per cent, where $\dot{m}$ is the actual counting rate and $\tau$ is the resolving time. Assuming dead-time values of 0.5 and 250 $\mu$secs for proportional counters and G-M tubes, respectively, leads to counting rates of

$$\dot{m} = \frac{1}{100\tau} = \frac{1}{(10^2)(0.5 \times 10^{-6})} = 2 \times 10^4 \text{ counts/sec}$$

for proportional counters and

$$\dot{m} = \frac{1}{(10^2)(250 \times 10^{-6})} = 40 \text{ counts/sec}$$

for G-M tubes.

Curtis et al. [4] have studied the use of a flow counter similar to the type in Fig. 6–3 for absolute alpha counting. The relationship between the counting rate $\dot{n}$ and the source strength $S$ is

$$\dot{n} = SGf_sf_b \tag{6–2}$$

where $f_s$ and $f_b$ are the source self-absorption and backscattering factors, respectively, and $G$ is the geometry factor.

For the arrangement shown in Fig. 6–5, the geometry factor is 0.5, to a good approximation. The counter type is known as a $2\pi$ counter since this is the solid angle from which it accepts particles. The alpha-backscattering factor, while not nearly as large as for betas, is still not negligible. Curtis et al. [4] evaluated $f_b$ by running aluminum-absorber curves. These are obtained by placing aluminum absorbers directly over the source. Figure 6–6 shows three such curves. Except for very small absorber thicknesses, the data fall on a straight line. The departure from the straight line is due to backscattered particles. Therefore, a linear extrapolation back to zero absorber allows one to correct for backscattering. The ratio of the actual counting rate at zero absorber thickness to the extrapolated rate is the backscattering factor. The backscattering factors

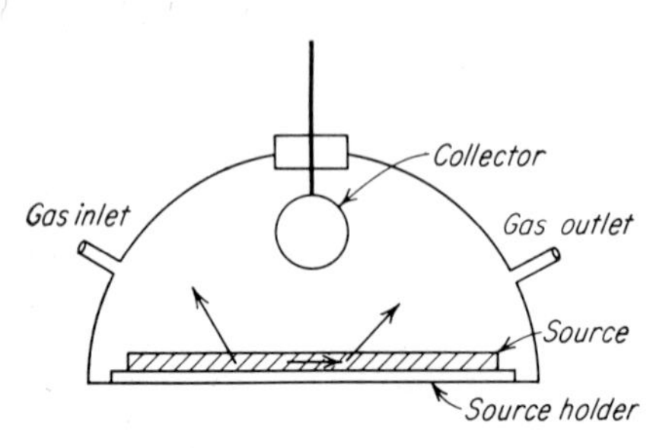


FIG. 6–5. Windowless flow counter with $2\pi$ geometry.

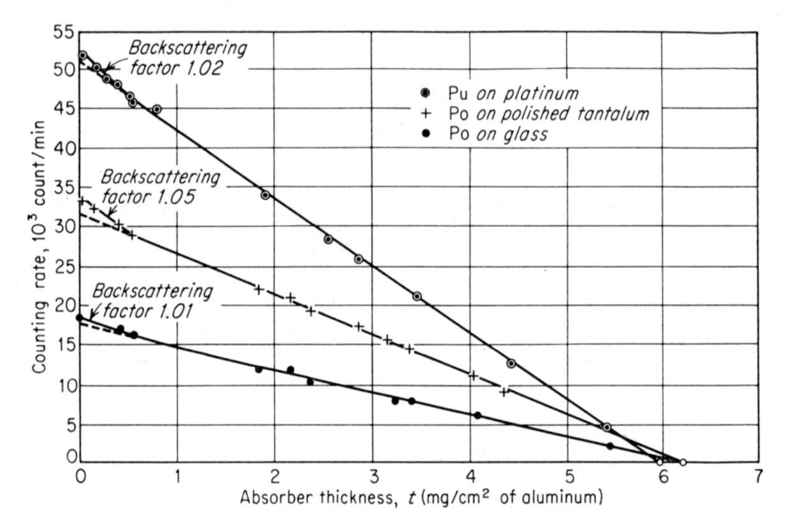


FIG. 6–6. Counting rate versus absorber thickness for a $2\pi$ windowless alpha counter. [*From M. L. Curtis, J. W. Heyd, R. G. Olt, and J. F. Eichelberger, Nucleonics,* **13**:38 (*May,* 1955).]

in Fig. 6–6 are typical. These values depend not only on the $Z$ of the backing material but also on its degree of polish.

The self-absorption factor is particularly important in $2\pi$ counters, since those particles which are emitted nearly parallel to the surface may need to travel through a large thickness of the source to reach the sensitive volume of the counter. Curtis et al. [4] have shown that the range of alpha particles from a thick source as measured by the absorber-thickness versus counting-rate curve is less than that of a thin source by $s/2$, where $s$ is the source thickness. Thus a linear extrapolation to a distance of $s/2$ back beyond zero absorber thickness gives the counting rate corrected for self-absorption.

An analytical expression for the self-absorption factor for alpha particles in a counter with $2\pi$ geometry is [5]

$$f_s = 1 - \frac{s}{2pR} \qquad \text{for } s < pR \tag{6–3a}$$

and

$$f_s = \frac{0.5R}{s} \qquad \text{for } s > pR \tag{6–3b}$$

where $s$ = source thickness
$R$ = maximum range of alpha particles in source material
$p$ = maximum fraction of $R$ which particles can spend in source and still be counted

**Example 6–3.** Compute the self-absorption factor for the $Po^{210}$ alpha particles emitted by a $PbO_2$ source of a thickness of 0.5 mg/cm² if the sensitivity of the counting system is sufficiently great that $p$ is approximately 1.

*Solution.* The range of the 5.3-Mev $Po^{210}$ alpha particles in $PbO_2$ is estimated, from Eq. (1–3), to be 14 mg/cm²; here the contribution of the oxygen to the absorption has been neglected. Therefore, by Eq. (6–3*a*), one obtains

$$f_s = 1 - \frac{s}{2pR} = 1 - \frac{0.5}{(2)(1)(14)} = 0.98$$

The uncertainty in both the backscattering and self-absorption can be avoided by the low-geometry arrangement shown in Fig. 6–7. The back-scattered radiation does not have enough energy to penetrate the thin window between the sample holder and the sensitive volume of the counter; therefore, it may be neglected. Further, an ideal source with negligible self-absorption can be achieved much more easily than with $2\pi$ geometry since, in the low-geometry case, the particles which are counted travel nearly perpendicularly through the source.

The precision of the low-geometry counter is resolved to the accurate computation of the solid angle from the source to the orifice plate. Curtis et al. [4] have used this arrangement for activity measurements from $2 \times 10^5$ to $5 \times 10^9$ disintegrations per minute and have achieved up to 0.1 per cent accuracy.

Applications such as monitoring for alpha contamination on hands and table tops require the use of detectors with thin windows, since the alpha sources are outside the detector. Proportional counters are particularly suitable for this application because of their inherently low background counting rate. For example, Simpson [6] has described a proportional counter with a large window area, having 10 collector wires in parallel. Although the chamber was enclosed by a window, argon was bubbled through the chamber to maintain the proper gas atmosphere.

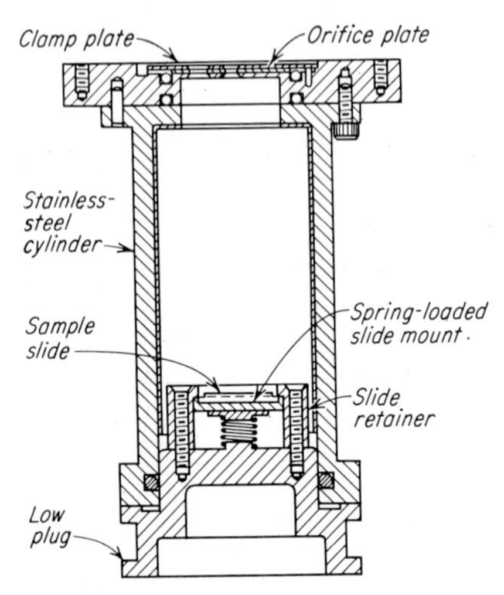


FIG. 6–7. Schematic diagram of a low-geometry flow counter for high-activity alpha counting. [*From M. L. Curtis, J. W. Heyd, R. G. Olt, and J. F. Eichelberger, Nucleonics*, **13**:38 (*May*, 1955).]

### 6–5. *Absolute Beta Activity by Flow Counters*

For the counting of betas, the flow counter can be operated in either the proportional region or the Geiger-Müller region. However, the former method of operation is usually preferred since its inherently shorter resolving time makes possible more accurate count determinations at higher counting rates.

The importance of backscattering in beta counting was discussed in detail in Sec. 5–10 in connection with end-window G-M tubes. Nader et al. [5] have studied backscattering in $2\pi$ flow counters of the type shown in Fig. 6–3. The results, along with a study of self-absorption in the same counter, are presented in Fig. 6–8.

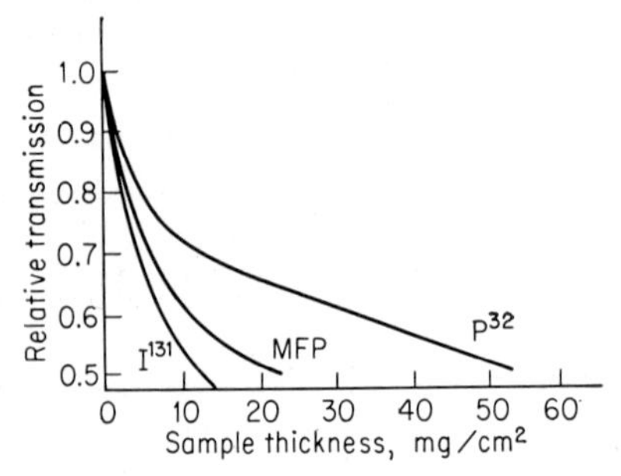


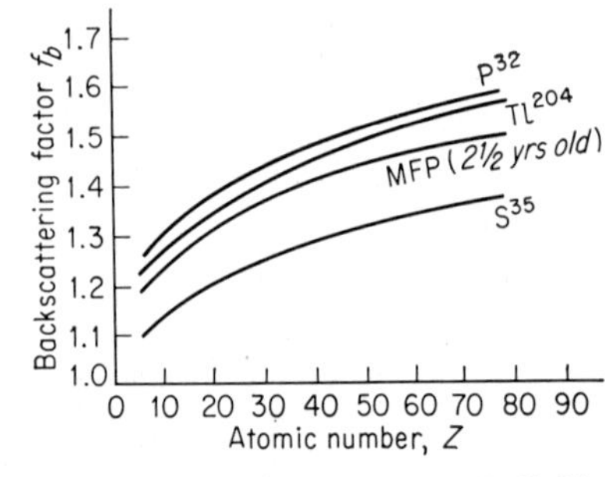


FIG. 6–8. Backscattering and self-absorption in a $2\pi$ flow counter. [*From J. S. Nader, G. R. Hagee, and L. R. Selter, Nucleonics*, **12**:29 (*June*, 1954).]

The uncertainties in the correction for backscattering have been avoided in the $4\pi$ counter described by Seliger and Cavallo [7]. The high-geometry factor is achieved by mounting the source on a thin foil in the center of a double chamber. This arrangement is shown in Fig. 6–9. The counter is divided in half by a thin aluminum diaphragm with a hole in its center. The source is mounted on a thin conductive foil suspended over this hole.

Accuracies as great as 0.5 per cent have been reported [8] for the $4\pi$ counters. Absolute-beta-activity measurements by this detector are the most precise that are available at the present time.

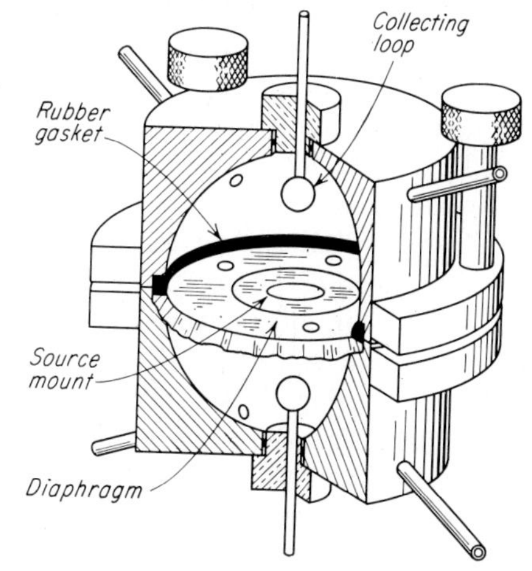


FIG. 6–9. The $4\pi$ geometry counter for absolute beta determinations. [*From H. H. Seliger and A. Schwebel, Nucleonics,* **12**:54 (*July,* 1954).]

### 6–6. *Proportional Counters for Neutron Detection*

An important class of applications for proportional counters is to neutron detection. Detectors for this purpose will be described in detail in Chap. 9.

In order to count neutrons, it is necessary to incorporate within the chamber a material from which charged particles will be released as the result of nuclear reactions which the neutrons cause. The several possible types of reactions were described in Sec. 1–16. For example, the detection of slow neutrons can be accomplished by the $B^{10}(n,\alpha)Li^7$ reaction. The energetic charged particles, both the alpha particles and the lithium ions, produce the ionization to operate the counter. The boron is incorporated in the counter either as a solid compound lining the walls or as a counter gas $B^{10}F_3$.

The ability of proportional counters to discriminate between particle types which produce different-size output pulses is particularly useful in neutron counting. Neutrons often appear along with a large background of gamma radiation. However, the gamma rays can usually be rejected since the secondary electrons which they produce cause less ionization than do the charged particles which are released by the neutron reactions.

### 6–7. *Energy-distribution Measurements and Counting of Soft Betas*

The windowless flow detectors are particularly useful for measurements on soft-beta emitters. Important examples are $C^{14}$ and $H^3$ which emit betas with maximum energies of 0.15 and 0.0185 Mev, respectively. These energies correspond to ranges of 19 and 0.7 mg/cm². Since the thinnest windows that are available for sealed detectors are from 1 to 2 mg/cm², the use of windowless counters is clearly indicated.

Jordan [9] has reviewed the application of proportional counters to measurements of the energy-distribution curves of low-energy beta emitters.

It was shown in Sec. 2–8 that these measurements can be accomplished by a pulse-height analysis of the output of a detector in which the pulse height is proportional to the particle energy. The proportional counter can be used in this fashion for low-energy electrons.

The upper limit on the electron energy that can be measured by this method is imposed by the requirement that the electron must give all its energy to the production of ionization within the chamber. The practical limit, as determined by chamber sizes and gas pressures, is around 100 to 200 kev. This has been extended to around 2 Mev by causing the electrons to spiral in axial magnetic fields.

The lower limit on the electron energy that can be measured is determined by a number of factors, including the sensitivity and noise levels of the associated amplifiers, the stability of the power supply furnishing the detector high voltage, the characteristics of the counter gas, and the statistical variations in the number of ion pairs produced by the low-energy particles. Measurements have been made successfully down to less than 1 kev. As an example, Curran et al. [10] have made an accurate determination of the beta spectrum of tritium.

## PROBLEMS

**6–1.** In a cylindrical-shape pulse ionization chamber it is primarily the motion of the electrons which causes the voltage rise, whereas in the proportional counter it is primarily the motion of the positive ions. Explain.

**6–2.** Compute the input sensitivity required for a pulse amplifier to be used with a flow-type proportional counter for fast beta particles if the system has the following characteristics: distance traveled by beta particles in chamber, 2 cm; gas multiplication, 5,000; input capacity, 10 $\mu\mu$f. Assume that the time constant of the amplifier is such that the pulse size is one-half that which would result from a very large time constant.

**6–3.** Consider a cylindrical proportional counter with a collector wire of 0.002-in. diameter and an outer electrode of ¾-in. diameter containing argon at 0.1-atm pressure. Calculate the time required to collect the positive ions when the applied voltage is 1,000 volts. Compare this time with a typical resolving time for a proportional counter, and discuss.

**6–4.** What would be the maximum thickness for a $Po^{210}$ plated source if self-absorption in the source was not to make an error of more than 0.5 per cent?

**6–5.** Explain why the minimum activity of an alpha emitter measurable by means of a proportional counter is much smaller than that of a beta emitter.

**6–6.** Consider a spherical proportional chamber for measuring beta particle energies in which the beta source is placed at the center of the chamber. If the chamber has a radius of 10 cm, calculate the pressure of argon which would be required in the chamber if the electrons which are emitted have a maximum energy of 30 kev. Repeat the calculation for krypton gas.

## REFERENCES

1. Kennedy, J. W.: *U.S. Atomic Energy Comm. Document* BNL-31, 1949.
2. Curran, S. C., A. L. Cockroft, and J. Angus: *Phil. Mag.*, **40**:929 (1949).

3. Rossi, B. B., and H. H. Staub: "Ionization Chambers and Counters," chap. 4, National Nuclear Energy Series, div. V, vol. 2, McGraw-Hill Book Company, Inc., New York, 1949.
4. Curtis, M. L., J. W. Heyd, R. G. Olt, and J. F. Eichelberger: *Nucleonics*, **13**:38 (May, 1955).
5. Nader, J. S., G. R. Hagee, and L. R. Selter: *Nucleonics*, **12**:29 (June, 1954).
6. Simpson, J. A., Jr.: *Rev. Sci. Instr.*, **19**:733 (1948).
7. Seliger, H. H., and L. Cavallo: *J. Research Natl. Bur. Standards*, **47**:41 (1951).
8. Seliger, H. H., and A. Schwebel: *Nucleonics*, **12**:54 (July, 1954).
9. Jordan, W. H.: *Ann. Rev. Nuclear Sci.*, **1**:207 (1952).
10. Curran, S. C., J. Angus, and A. L. Cockroft: *Phil. Mag.*, **40**:53 (1949).

CHAPTER 7

# SCINTILLATION DETECTORS

One of the oldest methods of nuclear-radiation detection is by the use of the scintillations produced in phosphors. It is well known that Rutherford and his collaborators used this technique for detecting alpha particles in the famous Rutherford scattering experiments. Although the basic principles remain the same, the techniques which are used have changed greatly. Probably the greatest difference in techniques is that now photomultiplier tubes instead of individuals looking through microscopes serve to register the particles. In addition, the scope of applications of the modern scintillation-type detector has broadened greatly over that of the early type.

## GENERAL CONSIDERATIONS

### 7-1. *Modern Scintillation Detectors*

The development of modern scintillation detectors was started by Coltman and Marshall [1] in 1947, at which time they reported the successful use of a photomultiplier tube for counting the light scintillations which were produced by alpha, beta, and gamma radiation. During the time which has elapsed since 1947, the scintillation detectors have become the most versatile type available for nuclear-radiation detection. These devices came into use primarily to meet a demand for counters capable of higher counting rates and shorter resolving times than were possible with the existing instruments.

An example of an important requirement for high counting rates arises in the instrumentation accompanying accelerators, such as those employing the synchrotron principle, in which the particles occur in short pulses. It is necessary to employ a fast counting rate while the pulse is on, in order that the average counting rate be reasonably high. In addition, coincidence experiments require high counting rates in the individual channels in order that the rate of true coincidences be reasonably high.

The requirement for shorter resolving time also arises in coincidence experiments. The shorter the resolving time, the less will be the ratio of chance coincidences to true coincidences.

It is interesting to compare the scintillation detector with the Geiger-Müller tube. In addition to the advantages of high counting rate and short resolving time, the scintillation counter is superior in the following respects: efficiency for gamma counting, ability to distinguish between types of radiation, number of radiation types with which it can be used, utility in measurement of particle energy, and variety of size and shape of detectors possible.

On the other hand, the Geiger-Müller tube is cheaper than the apparatus which replaces it in the scintillation detector system. Also, the requirements for the voltage regulation in the high-voltage power supply are less in the Geiger-Müller counter system since it exhibits less dependence of the counting rate on applied voltage than does the scintillation counter.

The scintillation techniques have become particularly useful in the measurement of the energy of beta and gamma rays. While pulse ionization chambers (Chap. 4) and proportional counters (Chap. 6) are quite satisfactory for the measurement of short-range particles such as alphas, they cannot be used for particles having a range larger than the dimensions of the chambers. On the other hand, the solid or liquid phosphors which are used with the scintillation detectors can absorb the beta particles or the secondary electrons produced by gammas. Consequently, measurements of the energies of these particles are possible.

### 7–2. *General System for the Scintillation Detector*

Figure 7–1 is a schematic diagram of a scintillation detector used in a counting system. The nuclear particle being detected produces a flash of light in the scintillator. By means of the light pipe and reflector, a large

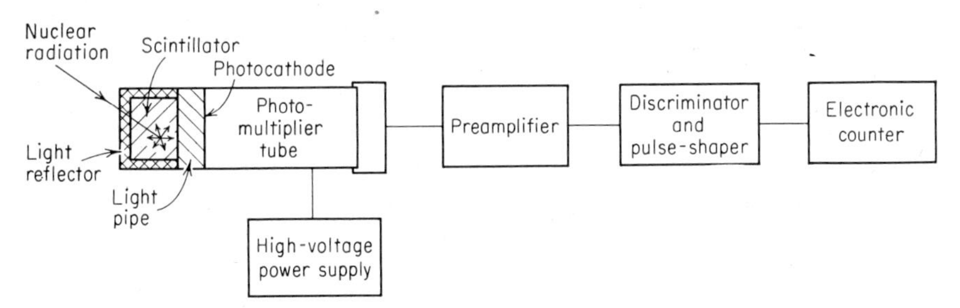


FIG. 7–1. Schematic diagram of a scintillation detector.

fraction of the light is transmitted to the photocathode of the photomultiplier tube. The photoelectrons emitted at the photocathode are multiplied many times by means of the electron-multiplier section of the photomultiplier tube. The resulting current pulse produces a voltage pulse at the input of the preamplifier. This pulse, after passing the discriminator and pulse shaper, is counted by the electronic counter. Alternatively, the electronic counter could be replaced by a differential pulse-height analyzer, as in the scintillation-type spectrometer, or by other special-purpose equipment.

For the purpose of understanding the system, one can divide the operation into six consecutive events. These are the following:

1. The absorption of the nuclear radiation in the scintillator, resulting in excitation and ionization within it
2. The conversion of the energy dissipated in the scintillator to light energy through the luminescence process
3. The transit of the light photons to the photocathode of the photomultiplier tube
4. The absorption of the light photons at the photocathode and the emission of the photoelectrons
5. The electron-multiplication process within the photomultiplier tube
6. The analysis of the current pulse furnished by the photomultiplier tube through the use of the succeeding electronic equipment

The charge $q$ appearing at the output of the photomultiplier tube can be related to the energy $E_n$ of the primary nuclear particle by considering the first five processes listed above. If $n_e$ is the number of photoelectrons released and collected in the tube and $M$ is the electron-multiplication factor, then

$$q = Men_e \tag{7-1}$$

Further, $n_e$ can be expressed as

$$n_e = E_n F_n C_{np} T_p F_p S_m f F_c \tag{7-2}$$

where $F_n \equiv$ fraction of total energy of nuclear particle absorbed in scintillator

$C_{np} \equiv$ efficiency of conversion from nuclear energy dissipated in scintillator to light energy

$T_p \equiv$ transparency of scintillator for scintillation which it produces

$F_p \equiv$ fraction of light photons which would reach photocathode if $T_p = 1$

$S_m \equiv$ sensitivity of photocathode at wavelength for maximum sensitivity in terms of photoelectrons per electron volt of light energy striking it

$f \equiv$ figure of merit expressing degree to which spectral sensitivity of photocathode matches spectral distribution of scintillation

$F_c \equiv$ fraction of photoelectrons collected by dynodes

Equation (7-2) can be seen to follow from these definitions by considering that $E_n F_n C_{np}$ is the amount of light energy in the scintillation, $T_p F_p$ is the fraction of this light which reaches the photocathode, while $S_m f F_c$ is the number of photoelectrons reaching the first dynode of the electron-multiplier section of the tube per unit of light energy striking the photocathode.

The conversion efficiency $C_{np}$, sometimes referred to as the intrinsic efficiency of the scintillator, is given by

$$C_{np} = \int_0^\infty C_{np}(\lambda)\, d\lambda$$

where $\lambda$ is the wavelength of the light and $C_{np}(\lambda)$ is the conversion efficiency per unit wavelength with which light of wavelength $\lambda$ is produced. The figure of merit $f$ is given by

$$f = \frac{\int_0^\infty C_{np}(\lambda) S(\lambda)\, d\lambda}{C_{np} S_m}$$

where $S(\lambda)$ is the sensitivity of the photocathode at the wavelength $\lambda$.

### 7–3. *Types of Scintillators*

A wide variety of scintillators is in use today. Several of the more important of these are listed in Table 7–1 along with some of their characteristics. Recently, Ramm [4] has made a comprehensive summary of the properties of scintillating materials.

The first two materials in Table 7–1 are single crystals of organic materials; nos. 3 and 4 are organic materials dissolved in organic liquids; the fifth is a solid solution of the organic compound terphenyl in polystyrene; nos. 6, 7, and 8 are single crystals of inorganic material; and no. 9 is an inorganic powder. In addition to the above materials, xenon and other inert substances in gaseous, liquid, and solid states are being employed [5,6] as scintillators.

Among the desirable properties for good scintillators are high efficiency for the conversion from the energy of nuclear particles to the energy of fluorescent radiation, transparency for their own fluorescent radiation, decay time for the fluorescent radiation of the order of a microsecond or less, and spectral distribution of the scintillation consistent with responses of available photocathodes. Requirements for other properties such as density, form, state of matter, and versatility in sizes and shapes vary with the application for which the detector is intended.

### 7–4. *The Scintillation Process*

The absorption of energy by a substance and its reemission as visible or near-visible radiation are known as luminescence. In the luminescence process the initial excitation can come from many origins. Several of these are light, mechanical strains, chemical reaction, and heating. The scintillation accompanying nuclear radiation has its origin in the excitation and ionization produced in the substance by radiation.

If the light emission occurs during the excitation or within $10^{-8}$ sec after it, the material is said to be fluorescent. The time interval of $10^{-8}$ sec is

Table 7-1. Properties of Several Scintillators*

| Scintillator | Density, g/cm³ | Wavelength of maximum, emission, A | Relative beta-ray pulse height | Alpha-beta ratio, % | Decay time, sec |
|---|---|---|---|---|---|
| 1. Anthracene crystal | 1.25 | 4,400 | 100 | 9 | $2.7 \times 10^{-8}$† |
| 2. Trans-stilbene crystal | 1.15 | 4,100 | 60 | 9 | 3 to $7 \times 10^{-9}$† |
| 3. Xylene + 5 g/liter of terphenyl + 0.01 g/liter of diphenylhexatriene | . . . | ~4,500 | 48 | 9 | |
| 4. 100 g polyvinyltoluene + 4 g terphenyl + 0.1 g diphenyl stilbene | . . . | ~3,800 | 48 | 9 | |
| 5. Terphenyl in polystyrene | 1.1 | 3,900–4,300 | 15 | . . . | $5 \times 10^{-9}$ |
| 6. NaI(Tl) | 3.67 | 4,100 | 210 | 44 | $2.5 \times 10^{-7}$† |
| 7. LiI(Sn) | . . . | 5,300 | 12 | ~93 | |
| 8. LiI(Eu) | . . . | ~4,400 | 75 | ~95 | |
| 9. ZnS(Ag) | 4.10 | 4,500† | 200 | 100 | $10^{-5}$† |

* Primarily from R. K. Swank, *Nucleonics*, **12**:14 (March, 1954).

† From J. B. Birks, "Scintillation Counters," Chap. 6, McGraw-Hill Book Company, Inc., New York, 1953.

chosen as the order of the lifetime of an atomic state for an allowed transition. If the emission occurs after excitation has ceased, the process is called phosphorescence. The duration of the phosphorescence varies with the type of luminescent material and may be from the order of microseconds to hours. Only those scintillators with the shorter durations are useful for the detection of nuclear radiation.

The number of light photons $n_p$ emitted in the time $t$ after the arrival of the ionizing particle can be represented by the exponential growth law

$$n_p = n_{p\infty}(1 - e^{-t/\tau}) \tag{7-3}$$

The time $\tau$ required for the emission of the fraction $1 - e^{-1}$ or 63 per cent of the photons is referred to as the decay time.

Most of the energy of excitation and ionization produced in the scintillator by the nuclear radiation is quickly degraded into heat, with only a small percentage of it escaping as visible or ultraviolet radiation. The quantity $C_{np}$ introduced previously is the fraction converted into light energy. Values of $C_{np}$ for scintillators in common use vary from a fraction of a per cent to around 30 per cent. Values are given for specific types of scintillators and materials in succeeding sections.

For the purpose of discussing the mechanism of the scintillation process, it is convenient to divide the materials into five classes. These are organic crystals, liquid solutions of organic materials, solid solutions of organic materials, inorganic crystals, and noble gases. These five classes will be discussed separately.

## 7-5. *Theory of Organic-crystal Scintillators*

These organic-crystal scintillators are, for the most part, aromatic hydrocarbons whose molecules contain benzene-ring structures, along with various nonaromatic substitutions. These molecules contain resonating structures.

The luminescence process in organic materials is a molecular process and can best be discussed in terms of a potential-energy diagram for the molecule [7]. A typical form for such a diagram is shown in Fig. 7-2. The two curves represent the potential energy versus the interatomic distance both for the case in which all the electrons are in the ground state and that in which the molecule contains an electron in an excited state. In each state there are allowed modes of vibration of the molecule, the energy of which is represented by the horizontal lines.

The passage of the nuclear radiation through the scintillator can result in the transfer of the molecules from the electronic ground state to an electronic excited state. The line $AA'$ represents such a transfer. According to the Franck-Condon principle [8], the transfer takes place at a fixed interatomic spacing. The point $A'$ represents a highly excited vibrational state. This extra energy is quickly dissipated as heat from the lattice vibrations, with perhaps the level $B$ being reached.

If the molecule in the electronic excited state is sufficiently stable against other processes by which its energy can be released, it will ultimately return to the ground state along the path $BB'$ by fluorescent emission. The mean life for this process, the order of $10^{-8}$ sec, is long compared with the time required for molecular vibrations. Ways in which the fluorescent emission can be prevented or quenched include (1) transfer of the energy directly from the electronic excited state to the ground state, as at the

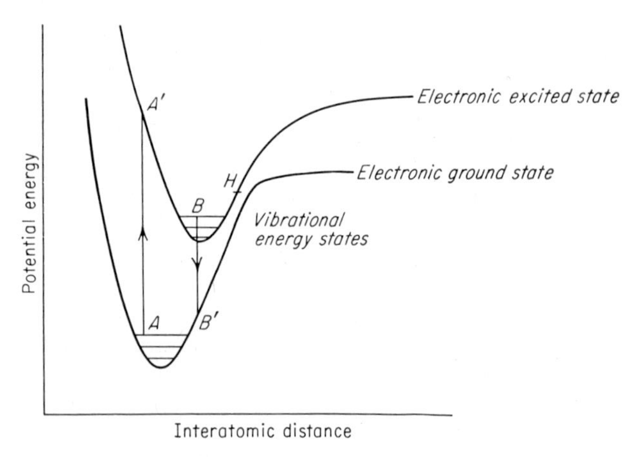


Fig. 7–2. Typical molecular-potential-energy diagram.

level $H$ where the two states come close together, and (2) the dissociation of the molecule when the level $A'$ is sufficiently high.

It can be shown by Fig. 7–2 that the organic crystals are transparent for the luminescent radiation which they produce. Here it is seen that, in general, the energy required to transfer the molecule from the ground to the excited state is larger than that released upon return. Consequently only the most energetic photons have sufficient energy to be absorbed by the production of excitation.

Numerous organic crystals have been studied [9]. To date, the most useful of these materials are anthracene and trans-stilbene.

A detailed review of the theory and properties of organic crystalline scintillators has been given by Birks [3].

## 7–6. *Theory of Organic-liquid Scintillators*

The theory and behavior of organic-liquid scintillators have been studied by Kallmann and Furst [10–12]. These materials consist of organic scintillators used as the solute in liquid organic solvents. Numerous materials have been tried as the solute. Among the most satisfactory are *p*-terphenyl, diphenyloxazole, and tetraphenylbutadiene. Several solvents appear to be satisfactory, including xylene, toluene, and phenylcyclohexane.

The scintillator efficiency increases rapidly as the concentration of the solute increases from low values. It usually passes through a rather broad maximum before the saturation concentration is reached. The solute concentration of *p*-terphenyl in toluene for maximum efficiency is about 5 g/liter.

The excitation produced in the solvent by the nuclear radiation is quickly transferred to the solute before quenching can occur. The excitation of the solute could be represented by the process $AA'$ in Fig. 7–2. This excitation energy is thus degraded and trapped by the solute and is subsequently radiated as fluorescent radiation characteristic of the solute.

The mechanism for transfer of the excitation from the solvent to the solute is not well understood. Kallmann and Furst [11] reject photon energy transfer and postulate other mechanisms, including an exchange of energy between molecules as a result of quantum-mechanical resonance. On the other hand, Birks [3] believes that the energy is transferred by photons and stresses the importance of the fluorescence of the solvent molecules in this process.

The process involving the transfer of energy from the solvent to the solute molecules explains the increase in scintillation efficiency with solute concentration. However, it is not understood why the scintillation efficiency goes through a maximum with increasing solute concentration [2].

The efficiency of a liquid scintillator can frequently be improved by the addition of so-called wavelength shifters. These substances are fluorescent materials which change the spectrum from that produced by the main solute to somewhat longer wavelengths which more nearly match the photomultiplier-tube spectral response. However, the decay time of the phosphor is usually increased somewhat.

Table 7–2 shows several important liquid scintillators. The trace of diphenylhexatriene is used as a wavelength shifter.

TABLE 7–2. IMPORTANT LIQUID SCINTILLATORS

| Solute | Concentration of solute, g/liter | Solvent |
|---|---|---|
| *p*-Terphenyl | 5 | Xylene |
| *p*-Terphenyl | 5 | Dioxane |
| *p*-Terphenyl + trace of diphenylhexatriene | 5<br>0.01 | Toluene |
| *p*-Terphenyl + trace of diphenylhexatriene | 3<br>0.01 | Phenylcyclohexane |
| 2,5-Diphenyloxazole | 4 | Xylene |
| 2-Phenyl-5-biphenyloxazole | 8 | Toluene |

It is often desirable that various compounds, including those of heavy elements, be incorporated directly into liquid solutions. This broadens the scope of applications to low-level counting, since geometrical losses are removed. These additive compounds reduce the efficiency of conversion of the scintillator by the quenching that is introduced. It has been found [13], however, that this quenching can be effectively removed by using solvents containing naphthalene, biphenyl, and other compounds in addition to the usual compounds.

### 7–7. *Theory of Scintillators in Solid Solutions*

Scintillators composed of solid solutions of organic materials such as terphenyl in polystyrene have been studied [14–17]. Swank and Buck [17] have found solid solutions which give efficiencies as high as 38 per cent of crystalline anthracene. The most promising material found by them was 1,1,4,4-tetraphenyl-1,3-butadiene in polyvinyltoluene. A concentration of about 1 g of fluor per 100 g of plastic gave the highest output.

The mechanism for the production of scintillations in solid and liquid solutions appears to be similar, with the solute and solvent playing like roles for each case. The mechanism for the transfer of energy from the solvent to the solute may differ for the two cases, however. Swank [2] has shown that it is unlikely that the energy is transferred by radiation. Sufficient experimental work for a positive identification of the transfer mechanism has not been reported at this time.

### 7–8. *Theory of Inorganic-crystal Scintillators*

The inorganic scintillators are crystals of inorganic salts, primarily the alkali halides, containing small amounts of impurities as activators for the luminescent process. The mechanism for the production of the scintillation can be described best in terms of the band picture [18,19] of solids.

A pure alkali-halide crystal is represented in the band theory by a valence band of energies which is normally completely filled with electrons and by a conduction band of energies which is normally empty. The latter lies above the former and is separated from it by a forbidden band of energies in which the electrons cannot exist. Any imperfections in the crystal, such as impurity atoms or lattice vacancies, can create energy levels in the forbidden band at isolated points throughout the crystals. Figure 7–3 is a schematic diagram of the energy levels in an alkali-halide crystal.

The passage of nuclear radiation through the crystal can raise electrons from the valence band to the conduction band. An electron in the conduction band is in an excited energy state. When it returns to the valence band, which is its ground state, this energy is given up. The electron excited to the conduction band can wander through the crystal until it comes to the vicinity of an imperfection; here it can drop to the energy level associated with the imperfection. From this new level it may drop to the valence band by the emission of radiation. This is the process of fluorescence in scintillators. Alternatively, it may lose its energy by a radiationless process, say to thermal energy or lattice vibration. This process is referred to as one of quenching, since it prevents radiation.

Still another possibility is the trapping of the electron at the energy level associated with the impurity atoms. When this occurs, the level is referred to as a metastable state. The electrons will remain in the metastable state until raised again to the conduction band. From here the electron can undergo any of the three processes just described. If, after being trapped in the metastable state, the electron drops to the valence band with the emission of radiation, the phenomenon is phosphorescence.

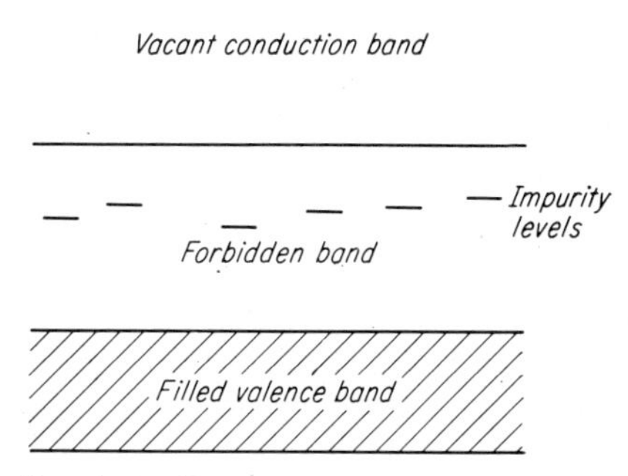


FIG. 7–3. Band picture showing the energy levels of an alkali-halide crystal with imperfections.

The inorganic crystals possess the desirable property of transparency for their own fluorescent radiation. This property exists since the photon energy is less than that energy between the valence and conduction bands; it is transitions between these bands which constitute the principal optical absorption.

The addition to the crystals of small quantities of the appropriate impurity atoms creates fluorescent centers. These impurities are known as activators. Some inorganic scintillators, along with their activators, are sodium iodide with thallium, lithium iodide with tin, and zinc sulfide with silver.

A number of other inorganic materials have been investigated as scintillators. For a survey of these, see Birks [3] and Ramm [4].

### 7–9. *Gaseous Scintillators*

The light which is emitted in gaseous scintillators is that coming from the gaseous molecules which are ionized and excited by the passage of charged particles. The noble gases are being studied [5,6] for this application. Northrop and Nobles have reported [6] that xenon scintillators look very promising.

Each excited atom or ion returns to its ground state with the emission of one or more photons of light within about $10^{-9}$ sec, giving rise to a fast light pulse. This light is primarily in the ultraviolet region, and the efficiency of conversion from light photons to photoelectrons is low. Methods of improving this efficiency include the coating of the container walls with intermediate fluorescent materials such as tetraphenylbutadiene or quaterphenyl to shift the wavelengths from the far ultraviolet to that more nearly matching the photocathode-response curve.

More recently the use of materials such as xenon in solid and liquid forms has been studied [6]. The decay constant of solid xenon is extremely short, being less than $10^{-2}$ $\mu$sec.

### 7–10. *Comparison of Scintillator Types*

There are a number of ways in which scintillator types can be compared. The particular application determines which of these aspects is the most important. In this section several properties will be discussed without reference to the applications.

The inorganic scintillators are by far the most dense. This consideration, coupled with the high atomic numbers of part of their constituents, makes them superior scintillators for gamma detection through the high absorption for this radiation. Solid xenon also shares these properties.

Except in the case of the noble gases, there appears to be no choice of scintillator types on the basis of the wavelength of maximum emission. In all other types it is possible to find scintillators which match reasonably well with the photomultiplier-tube response.

An important property for each scintillator is $C_{np}$, the efficiency of conversion from nuclear energy to light energy. Relative values of these for beta particles are tabulated in Table 7–1. To put these on an absolute basis is a little difficult, since values of $C_{np}$ for anthracene have been reported [2] from 4.2 to 10 per cent. It is seen that, in general, the inorganic scintillators have the largest conversion efficiency. Morton [21] reports that a good sodium iodide crystal will yield one useful photon for each 30 to 50 ev of beta-particle energy dissipated in the crystal. Taking the average energy per photon as 4 ev yields a value of $C_{np}$ from 8 to 13 per cent.

Comparison of scintillators on the basis of their relative response to different particle types and energies will be discussed in the next section.

From the standpoint of short resolving times, small decay times are desirable. The organics and noble-gas counters are quite superior to the inorganics on this basis. The superiority results because of the absence of phosphorescence in these materials. Stilbene crystals and solid solutions of terphenyl in polystyrene appear to have the shortest decay times, with values about $5 \times 10^{-9}$ sec.

A comparison on the basis of the availability and economy of large volumes for scintillators finds the organic liquids far in the lead. In fact, it has been reported that efficiencies up to 90 per cent of the values for pure materials have been obtained, using standard high-grade commercial materials without additional purification.

### 7–11. *Dependence of Conversion Efficiency on Type and Energy of Nuclear Radiation*

It was observed early in the use of scintillators for quantitative measurements of the energy of nuclear particles that the efficiency of conversion from particle energy to light energy is not a constant. Rather, it varies with both the type and energy of the particle. In addition, the form which these variations take depends on the scintillator type.

Extensive measurements of these effects have been made by Taylor et al. [22]. In these experiments the relative pulse heights produced by various particles bombarding anthracene, stilbene, and sodium iodide crystals were measured. The particles investigated were electrons of from 500-ev to 624-kev energies, deuterons and molecular hydrogen ions with energies of 1 to 11 Mev, protons of 1 to 5 Mev, and alpha particles of 4 to 21 Mev.

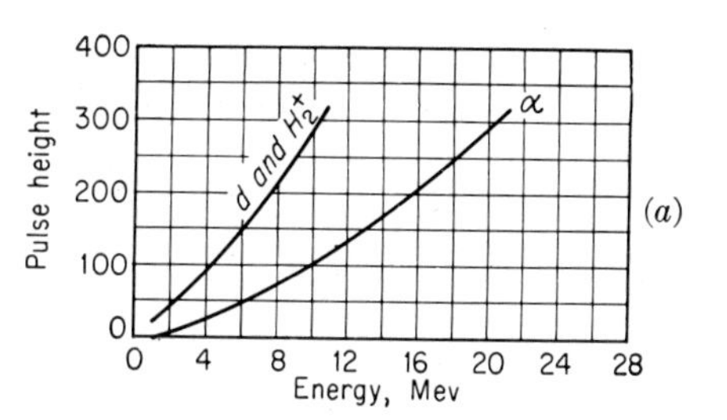


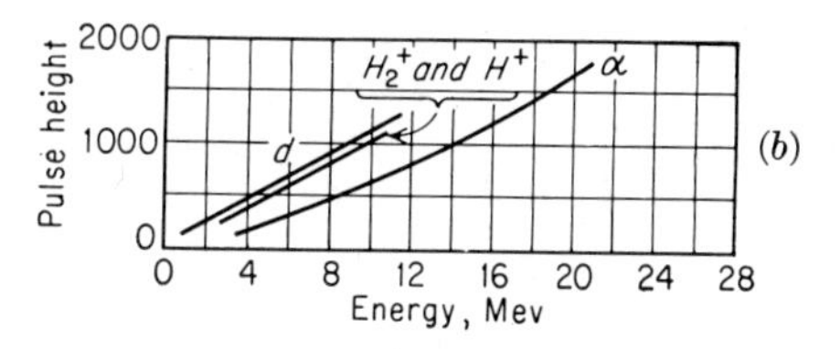


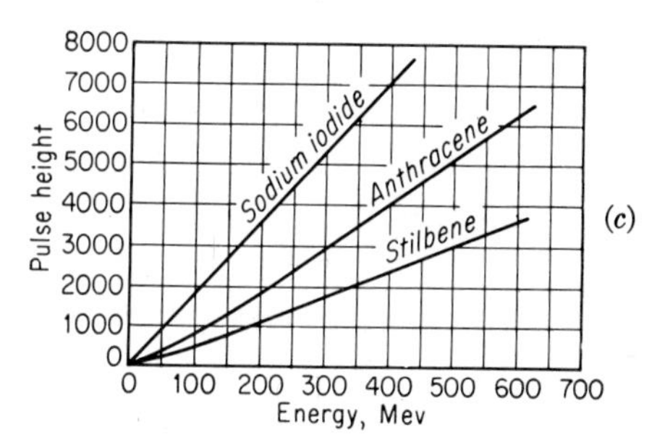


FIG. 7–4. Pulse heights in various scintillators as a function of particle energy and type. (*a*) Heavy particles in anthracene; (*b*) heavy particles in thallium-activated sodium iodide; (*c*) electrons in anthracene, stilbene, and sodium iodide. [*From C. J. Taylor, W. K. Jentschke, M. E. Remley, F. S. Eby, and P. G. Kruger, Phys. Rev.*, **84**:1034 (1951).]

With the exception of protons and deuterons in sodium iodide, which gave a linear response over the entire energy region investigated, plots of pulse height versus energy for heavy particles gave a nonlinear relation for low energies, tending toward linearity with increasing particle energy. Electrons in stilbene and anthracene show a linear response above 100 kev, while the sodium iodide curve is linear above 1 kev. Some of these results are shown in Fig. 7–4*a*, *b*, and *c*.

The effect of particle type on conversion efficiency can be represented by a plot of the ratio of scintillation amplitude to the particle energy versus particle energy. Figure 7–5 is such a plot for electrons, protons, deuterons, and alpha particles in anthracene. These curves are normalized to 100 for high-energy electrons. This behavior is characteristic of all scintillators; however, different types vary in the degree to which they exhibit this property.

A measure of the degree to which a particular scintillator is affected by the nature of the particle is obtained by comparing the conversion efficiency for 5.3-Mev alpha particles with that for high-energy electrons. The ratio of these two quantities is known as the alpha-beta ratio. This quantity is given in Table 7–1.

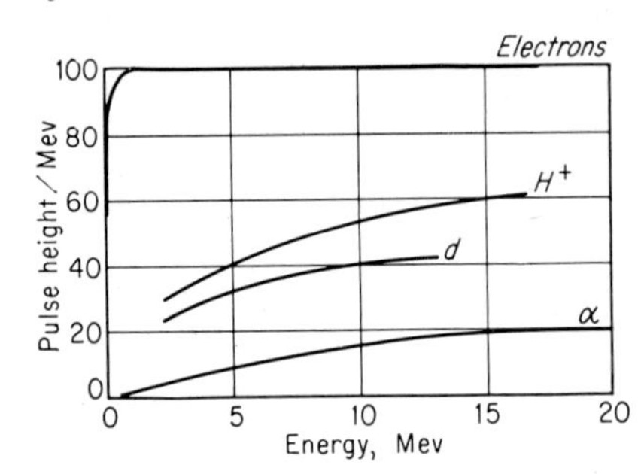


Fig. 7–5. Dependence of scintillation amplitude in anthracene on particle energy. [*From C. J. Taylor, W. K. Jentschke, M. E. Remley, F. S. Eby, and P. G. Kruger, Phys. Rev.*, **84**:1034 (1951).]

Analysis of the experimental data shows that $dL/dx$, the fluorescence per unit path length, is a unique function of the specific energy loss $dE/dx$ and is independent of the particle type. This relationship holds except for low-energy electrons; this exception has been explained by a quenching due to a surface effect [23]. Birks [24] has developed a theory to account for the decrease in conversion efficiency with specific energy loss. This theory is based on the assumption that the quenching comes from impurities which are produced through the chemical dissociation which accompanies the passage of the particles.

## SCINTILLATOR MOUNTING AND LIGHT COLLECTION

### 7–12. *Scintillator Mounting*

The physical arrangement for the scintillator and its incorporation with the photomultiplier tube are important design considerations. A primary factor is the efficient transfer of light from the point of origin in the scintillator to the photocathode.

The organic and inorganic scintillators which are prepared from single crystals are cut and shaped by specially devised techniques. Bell [25] has discussed some of these methods in his comprehensive article on the scintillation method. Plastic scintillators are machined by conventional methods, while gaseous and liquid materials are placed in the appropriate containers. Common shapes for the scintillators include solid right cylinders, flat disks, and right cylinders with recessed holes (i.e., the "well type").

The scintillator proper is encased for mechanical protection and for the control of ambient light. Further, as in the case with NaI(Tl), which is quite hygroscopic, the unit must be hermetically sealed. Figure 7–6 shows a sealed NaI(Tl) unit surrounded by a layer of MgO for light reflection and provided with a glass window for transmission of the light to the photocathode. Figure 7–7 is a sealed NaI(Tl) unit described by Bell [25] for high-resolution gamma-ray spectroscopy. Both the aluminum casing and the $\alpha$-alumina reflector are minimized in thickness to prevent the formation of secondary electrons and degraded gammas in the casing. The hypodermic needle is used for partially exhausting the air in the can. This

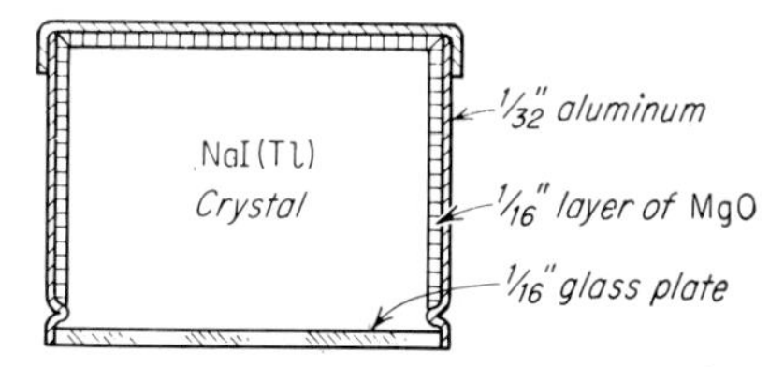


FIG. 7–6. A mounting for NaI crystals.

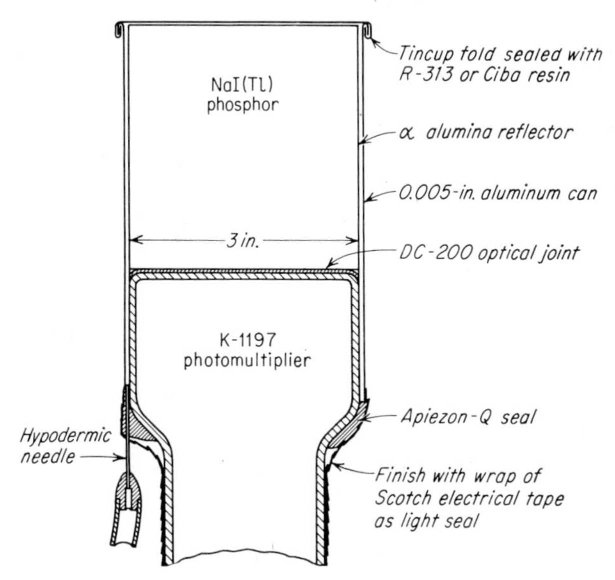


FIG. 7–7. Reduced-pressure crystal mount for use with scintillators having the same diameter as the photomultiplier tube. [*From P. R. Bell, Article in K. Siegbahn (ed.), "Beta- and Gamma-ray Spectroscopy," Interscience Publishers, Inc., New York,* 1955.]

reduced pressure forces the can down on the scintillator and holds it firmly to the phototube.

The covering over a nonhygroscopic material such as anthracene can be considerably simpler, the primary consideration being the prevention of light transmission from outside. Aluminum foil may be employed for this purpose. When used with low-energy betas, a section of the main foil cover may be removed and replaced by a much thinner aluminum window.

### 7-13. *Factors Affecting Light Collection*

The fraction of the light originating in the scintillation which ultimately reaches the photocathode can be expressed as $T_pF_p$, where $T_p$ is the transparency of the optical system and $F_p$ is the collection efficiency exclusive of the transparency. Ideally, one would like to make both of these factors unity. Practically, this can be approached in many cases.

The optical system consists of the scintillator, any reflecting or diffusing medium which may surround the scintillator, and the light path from the scintillator to the photocathode. The transparency of the system depends on the optical absorption for the optical spectrum contained in the scintillation. In addition, the distance which the light travels must be considered. The transparency can be represented by

$$T_p = e^{-\mu x} \tag{7-4}$$

where $\mu$ is the effective optical absorption coefficient and $x$ is the distance traveled by the light. In most scintillator and light-pipe materials, $\mu$ is reasonably small except at the extreme short-wavelength end of the emission spectrum. The distance $x$ depends not only on the dimensions of the system but also on the number of internal reflections which occur.

In most light-collection systems, $T_p$ approaches unity. Exceptions are those systems employing multicrystalline scintillators such as zinc sulfide and those using long light pipes.

The light-collection efficiency of a given system depends somewhat on the energy of the radiation [26]. In addition, one would expect it to be influenced by the point of origin of the scintillation in the phosphor. Consider a light flash occurring in a scintillator which has an index of refraction $n_1$. What happens to the light upon arrival at the surface of the scintillator depends upon the nature of the surface and the angle of incidence of the light with the surface. If the surface is polished and it adjoins an optically transparent medium of index of refraction $n_2$, where $n_2 < n_1$, the light will be totally reflected, provided that the angle between the light ray and the normal to the surface is greater than the critical angle

$$\theta_c = \sin^{-1} \frac{n_2}{n_1} \tag{7-5}$$

For angles less than $\theta_c$, the light is partially transmitted and partially reflected. For angles approaching zero, all but a few per cent of the light is transmitted.

If a polished reflector such as aluminized foil covers the surface, specular reflection occurs regardless of the angle of incidence of the light. Still another possibility is a roughened surface surrounded by a diffuse reflector such as magnesium oxide. Such an arrangement provides diffuse reflection.

These several arrangements are shown in Fig. 7–8. Since the usual objective is to direct as much of the light as possible from the origin of the scintillation to the photocathode, the common practice is to coat all but

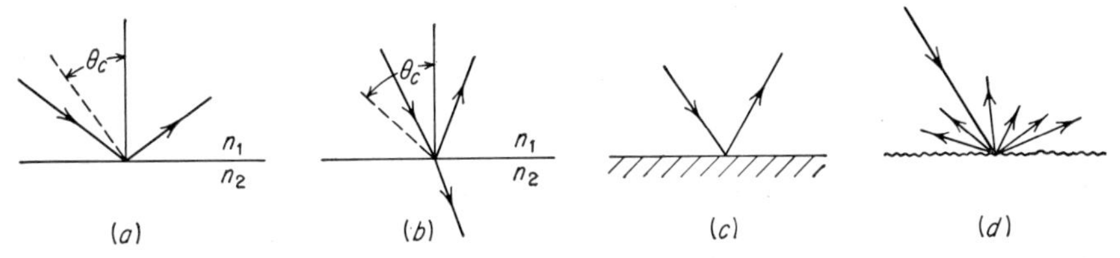


Fig. 7–8. Reflection of light at a surface. (a) Angle of incidence greater than the critical angle; (b) angle of incidence less than the critical angle; (c) polished reflecting surface; (d) diffuse reflecting.

one side of the scintillator for either specular or diffuse reflections. The photocathode is placed adjacent to the uncoated surface. This allows much of the light which starts initially in directions other than the photocathode to be reflected toward the cathode. If it arrives at the surface adjacent to the photocathode with an angle less than the critical angle $\theta_c$, it will be passed out of the scintillator toward the photocathode.

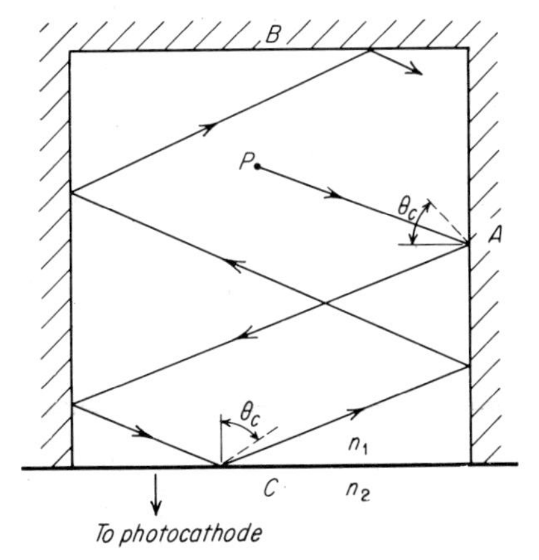


Fig. 7–9. Trapping of light in a scintillator.

If specular reflection is employed on the surface, a fraction of the light is trapped in the scintillator. This is illustrated in Fig. 7–9. Light originating at point $P$ and striking the surface $A$ at an angle of incidence less than $\theta = \sin^{-1}(n_2/n_1)$ is totally reflected when it reaches the surface adjacent to the photocathode. Thus any light from $P$ having its initial direction in a right cone of apex angle $2\theta_c$ at $P$ and a base coincident with $A$ will be totally reflected upon reaching $C$. The same situation holds for the other three surfaces parallel to $A$. Of course, if the light strikes surface $C$ or $B$ with an angle greater than $\theta_c$, it will also be totally reflected.

Ultimately the trapped light either will be absorbed in the scintillator or will escape after having its direction changed by scattering from imperfections. The fraction of the light which is trapped is largest when the surface $C$ is in contact with air or other media with an index of refraction equal to 1. As an example, for NaI(Tl), which has an index of refraction equal to 1.77, $\theta_c$ is 34.5°. If the air is replaced by lucite with an index $n_2 = 1.50$, $\theta_c$ becomes 58°, and the situation is materially improved.

The use of diffuse reflection has been found to give larger and more uniform light output than specular reflection. Borkowski and Clark [27] have had good results with NaI(Tl) scintillators by grinding the surfaces with 120-grit emery or Carborundum paper followed by packing powdered magnesium oxide around the surfaces. Alpha-aluminum oxide has been reported by Bell [25] to be more satisfactory than magnesium oxide for this purpose.

Bell has reported [25] that no advantage has been found in roughening the surface of anthracene. However, he has pointed out that the bright aluminum reflector should not be in optical contact with the crystal surface, as would be the case with a reflector evaporated directly on the surface of the crystal or with a foil joined to the crystal with Canada balsam or other material. Such a contact replaces the good reflection at the crystal surface outside the critical angle by the poorer reflection at the aluminum surface.

### 7-14. *Light Pipes*

In many applications a material known as a light pipe is placed between the scintillator and the photocathode. The polymethyl methacrylate lucite is widely used for this purpose. Plexiglas and polystyrene have been tried also [26], but the light transmission is less. Collins [28] has found that the percentage transmission of the light from a ZnS screen through a 1-ft section is 70, 60, and 50 per cent for quartz, lucite, and mineral oil, respectively.

The purpose which the light pipe serves in helping to prevent the trapping of the light in the scintillator has already been discussed. Other uses include the placing of the scintillator at a distance from the photocathode and the spreading of the light over a larger cathode area.

For several reasons, such as space limitations and ambient conditions, it may be desirable to place the scintillator at a distance from the photomultiplier tube. Several feet of light pipe has been used with success. Gradual bends in the light pipe can be made without appreciable light loss [26].

From the standpoint of constant output from the photomultiplier tube for constant light produced in the scintillator, it may be desirable to use a light pipe to spread the light more uniformly over the photocathode. This situation arises if the photocathodes have nonuniform characteristics with respect to the efficiency of emission and collection of photoelectrons. A light pipe having an area equal to that of the photocathode and a length of about ½ in. is effective in spreading the light over the entire photocathode, regardless of its point of origin in the scintillator. However, this technique is usually not required with the currently available photomultiplier tubes.

In some applications, such as in the use of a photomultiplier tube with other than a flat photocathode, the light pipe is very useful, since the shaping of the surface is much easier for the light-pipe material than for the scintillators, in case the latter are single crystals such as anthracene or NaI(Tl).

In the installation of light pipes, it is necessary to ensure good optical contact to the scintillator and the photomultiplier tube in order to minimize the amount of reflection at the interfaces. This is accomplished by inserting some transparent material between the surfaces which have first been machined so that a reasonably good fit is obtained. Bell [25] has reported that Canada balsam may be used for anthracene where the scintillation spectrum ends sharply at 4,300 A but that it is not suitable for NaI(Tl) since the spectrum of the latter extends to 3,200 A. Mineral oil or high-viscosity silicone oil, such as Dow-Corning DC-200 ($10^6$ centistokes), is suitable for use with NaI(Tl).

## PHOTOMULTIPLIER TUBES

### 7–15. *General Description of Photomultiplier Tubes*

A photomultiplier tube is a phototube in which the current of photoelectrons from the tube's cathode is multiplied many times through the process of electron multiplication. The current multiplication within the tube can be as high as a million or more. Consequently the tube is particularly suitable for detecting low light levels such as scintillations. In counting by the use of scintillation detectors, sufficient electron multiplication may be used that no additional amplification is needed between the output of the photomultiplier tube and the input of a conventional electronic scaler.

Schematic diagrams and photographs of two types of photomultiplier tubes which were designed for scintillation work are shown in Figs. 7–10 and 7–11. The essential elements in each of these tubes are the photocathode for releasing the photoelectrons, the dynodes for producing the electron multiplication, and the anode for collecting the current pulse. In order that the electrons will pass from the photocathode to each of the dynodes in succession and finally to the anode for collection, each of these elements is placed at successively higher potentials. The electron multiplication is made possible by the secondary-emission phenomenon at the dynodes. The ratio $\delta$ of the secondary to the incident current (i.e., the secondary-emission ratio) at a particular dynode determines the contribution of the dynode to the multiplication. The total multiplication $M$ given by $n$ dynodes is

$$M = \delta_1 \delta_2 \cdots \delta_n \tag{7–6}$$

As an example, to obtain a multiplication of $10^6$ with 10 dynodes requires an average $\delta$ of 4.0.

The selection of the potentials for application to the various electrodes in the tube is influenced by several considerations, including the desired

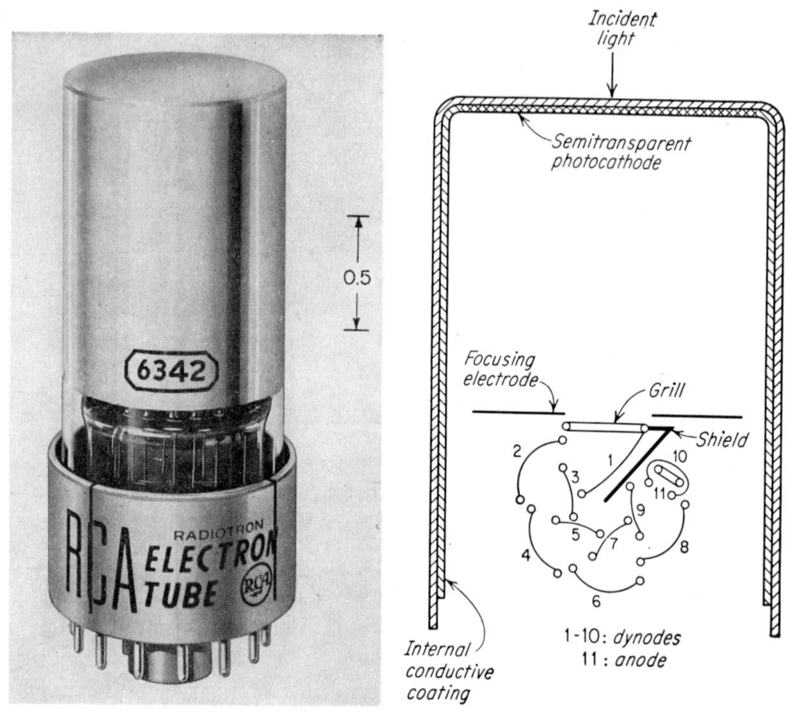


FIG. 7–10. Photomultiplier tube RCA 6342; schematic diagram and photograph. (*From G. A. Morton, "Proceedings of the International Conference on the Peaceful Uses of Atomic Energy," vol.* 14, *p.* 246, *United Nations, New York,* 1956; *photograph courtesy of RCA.*)

secondary-emission ratios, the optimizing of the collection efficiency, and the uniformity of pulse sizes (see Sec. 7–18).

### 7–16. *Photocathodes*

When the development of modern scintillation detectors was first started, the available commercial photomultiplier tubes such as the RCA 931-A were used. These tubes contain an internal metal photocathode in a semicylindrical shape. The photoemissive surface is applied to the inner surface of this plate. The efficiency for collecting light from the scintillator left much to be desired; consequently special tubes were developed. The arrangements shown in Figs. 7–10 and 7–11 are employed almost universally.* The photocathode is a semitransparent coating of the photoemissive material on the inside of the flat end of the tube envelope. The light passes from the scintillator to the photocathode (see Fig. 7–1). The photoelectrons are emitted from the opposite side into the interior of the tube.

Although a number of materials have been used successfully [29] in photoelectric tubes, only one has been used widely in scintillation counting; this is a composite cathode of antimony-cesium. These photocathodes are prepared by the evaporation of alternate layers of antimony and cesium,

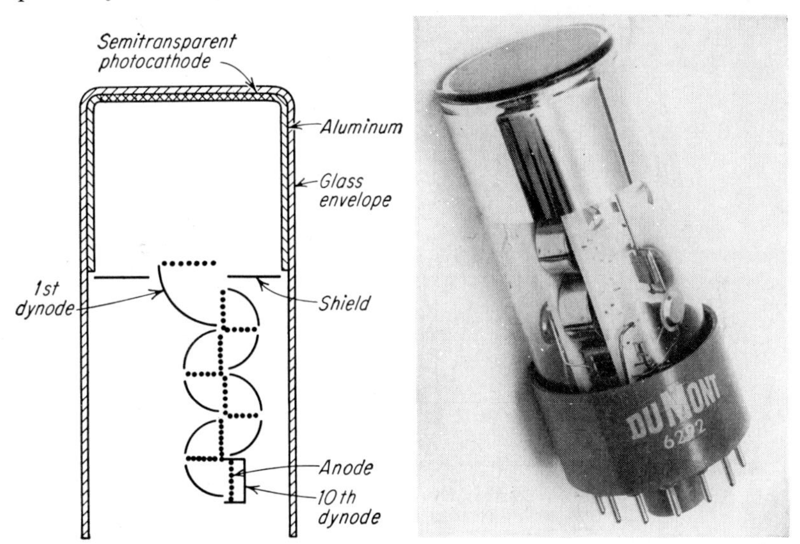


Fig. 7–11. Photomultiplier tube Du Mont 6292; schematic diagram and photograph. (*From G. A. Morton, "Proceedings of the International Conference on the Peaceful Uses of Atomic Energy," vol. 14, p. 246, United Nations, New York,* 1956; *photograph courtesy of Allen B. Du Mont Laboratories, Inc.*)

along with a controlled amount of oxidation. Apparently an intermetallic compound of $SbCs_3$ is formed with an adsorbed layer of cesium and cesium oxide.

The sensitivity of the antimony-cesium photocathode is high, and its dependence on the light wavelength is quite suitable for use with the emission spectra of the common scintillators. Figure 7–12 shows the type S-11 photocathode response curve, which is the most commonly used type, and is characteristic of such tubes as the RCA 6342 and the Du Mont 6292. The maximum sensitivity $S_m$ is 0.056 $\mu$a/$\mu$w or 0.056 photoelectron/ev of light energy. Figure 7–12 also includes $C_{np}(\lambda)$, the spectral dependence of

* The RCA 6372 utilizes a semicylindrically shaped, semitransparent photocathode with an area of 12⅜ in.$^2$ This should be a very useful tube for alpha counting if a zinc sulfide scintillator were to be coated on the outside of the envelope of the tube.

the conversion efficiency for NaI(Tl), and a commercially available* plastic scintillator. The corresponding values of the figure of merit $f$ are 0.77 and 0.92 for the NaI(Tl) and the plastic scintillators, respectively.

It is desirable that the thermionic-emission current be as small as possible in order to minimize the number of noise pulses from this source. Although commercial tubes employing Sb-Cs emit as many as 5,000 thermionic electrons/(sec)(cm$^2$) at room temperature, this is still a factor of $10^3$

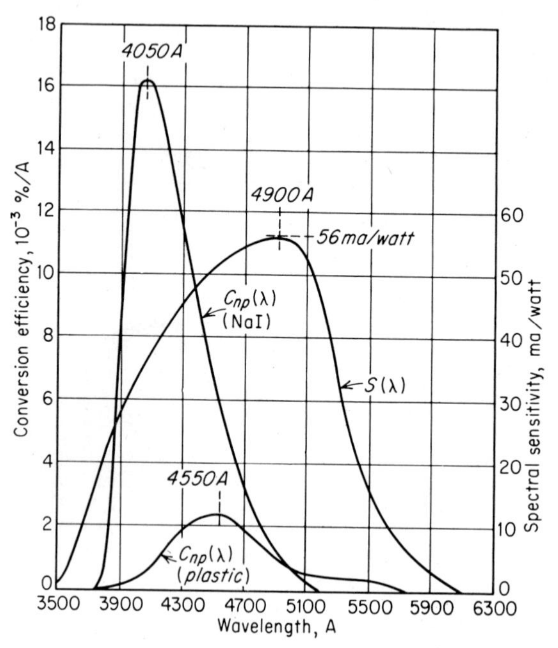


FIG. 7–12. Conversion efficiency $C_{np}(\lambda)$ of plastics and NaI(Tl) scintillators and the spectral sensitivity $S(\lambda)$ of type S–11 photocathodes. [*From L. L. Bird, Tracerlog, No.* 78, *p.* 12 (1956).]

smaller than the emission from an Ag-O-Cs surface. The difference comes about because the latter has a lower work function than the former.

New cathodes are continually under development. Morton [21] has reported that cesium-activated sodium potassium antimonide and sodium potassium antimonide are of considerable interest for photomultiplier tubes employed in scintillation counters.

## 7–17. *Electron Collection and Multiplication*

The electron-multiplier technique is the key to the whole science of scintillation detectors. The technique is also of interest in other applica-

* Distributed by Tracerlab, Inc., Boston, Mass.

tions, including electron counting; Allen [30] has discussed these applications, as well as the secondary-emission phenomenon and the choice of dynode materials.

For a number of years commercial photomultiplier tubes have employed a cesium-antimonide coating on the dynodes similar to that used for the photocathode. More recently some tubes [31,32] have incorporated silver-magnesium dynodes. This material permits higher temperature processing; therefore a higher vacuum is possible. In addition, the tubes employing

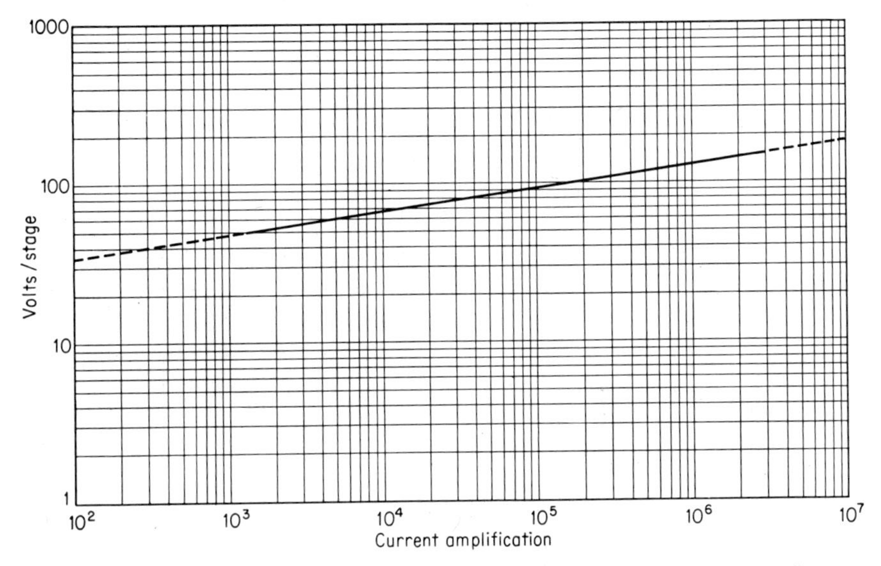


Fig. 7–13. Current amplification versus volts per stage in the Du Mont 6292. (*Courtesy of Allen B. Du Mont Laboratories, Inc.*)

silver-magnesium dynodes have been thought to be more stable at high average current density. On the other hand, Bell [25] has reported that these tubes have a change in pulse height with count rate, an effect which is not observed in tubes employing the cesium antimonide dynodes.

The secondary-emission ratio increases as the energy of the primary electrons increases until a broad maximum is reached for electrons of several hundred volts. Corresponding to this, the electron multiplication increases with increases in the voltage applied per dynode stage. This relationship is shown in Fig. 7–13. Over limited regions, $M$ can be represented by the equation

$$M = KE^n \tag{7–7}$$

where $n$ is approximately 7.

The problem of directing the photoelectrons from the cathode of the photomultiplier into the dynode structure is not negligible. However, fairly adequate schemes have been worked out. In the box structure (see Fig. 7–11) the first dynode is large in order to increase the efficiency of collection of photoelectrons. In addition, a shield is provided, the potential of which can be varied, in order to maximize the collection efficiency. It has been found [31,33] that the uniformity of response over the photocathode can be optimized by proper choice of shield voltage and that, in general, the proper voltage varies for different tubes of the same type.

The dynode system itself is an electron optical system for drawing secondary electrons away from one dynode and causing them to strike the next succeeding dynode with a minimum loss of electrons. In the box structure, each dynode, except the tenth, has a mesh screen attached to it and facing the preceding dynode. This screen is to enhance the secondary-electron collection. Since the high-voltage dynodes are relatively far from the low-voltage dynodes in the box structure, the voltage per stage can be higher than otherwise before excessive leakage currents occur. In the Du Mont 6292, as high as 190 volts per stage can be used.

The circular electrostatically focused electron multiplier is widely used. It contains shaped dynodes which have been carefully designed so as to produce electric lines of force which guide the electrons throughout the structure. The last dynode is shaped to enclose partially the anode, thus shielding it so that fluctuations of the anode potential will not disturb the interdynode focusing. A mica shield is provided between the photocathode and the anode to prevent positive-ion feedback from the anode to the cathode. Such an effect, if allowed, can result in the phenomenon known as afterpulsing [34]. The outgassing possible with silver-magnesium dynodes also helps to eliminate afterpulses.

The relative pulse size in a circular multiplier is quite sensitive to magnetic fields [35]. A field of 0.8 oersted parallel to the dynode-cage axis will reduce the pulse size to four-tenths of that with no field. This situation can be prevented with a simple magnetic shield. A cylinder of Mu metal 0.045 in. thick has been found to be effective.

The collection efficiency of the photoelectrons has been found sensitive to mechanical alignment. In the circular type, as well as the box-type dynodes, there is found to be an optimum potential for the focusing electrode to obtain the greatest uniformity of electron collection over the entire photocathode surface.

### 7–18. *Pulse-height Resolution in Photomultiplier Tubes*

The current pulses at the output of a photomultiplier tube are found always to have a distribution in size. In applications to scintillation counting, part of this distribution is due to variation in the amount of light reaching the photocathode. The remainder of the effect can be attributed to the photomultiplier tube.

Studies have been made of the size distribution of output pulses resulting from uniform-intensity light pulses [35,36]. Further, it has been shown [37] that the output pulses originating with single electrons from the photocathode also have a distribution in size. The latter distribution is due primarily to variation in the secondary-emission ratio, while the former has an additional contribution from fluctuations in the conversion efficiency from light to photoelectrons and from the collection of the electrons from the photocathode.

A measure of the uniformity of pulse sizes called the resolution is usually adopted. The resolution $R$ is defined as

$$R = \frac{(\bar{q})^2}{\overline{q^2} - (\bar{q})^2} = \frac{(\bar{q})^2}{\Delta^2} \tag{7-8}$$

where $\bar{q}$ = mean pulse amplitude
$\overline{q^2}$ = mean of the square
$\Delta^2$ = mean square deviation of $q$

For a series of identical scintillations, the reciprocal of the resolution is given by [36]

$$\frac{1}{R} = \frac{\Delta^2}{n_e^2 M^2} = \frac{\delta_e^2}{n_e^2} + \frac{\delta_1^2}{n_e m_1^2} + \frac{\delta^2}{n_e m_1 m(m-1)} \tag{7-9}$$

where $n_e$ = average no. of electrons reaching first dynode with constant light input
$\delta_e^2$ = mean square deviation in $n_e$
$m_1$ = average multiplication factor at first dynode
$\delta_1^2$ = mean square deviation in $m_1$
$m$ = average multiplication factor at each of $n - 1$ succeeding dynodes
$\delta^2$ = mean square deviation in $m$
$M$ = $m_1 m^{n-1}$, the over-all multiplication in $n$ stages

The first term in Eq. (7-9) comes from the statistical nature of the photoelectric-emission phenomenon. This follows Poisson's distribution, for which case $\delta_e^2 = n_e$.

The second and third terms are due to the first and successive dynodes, respectively. It has been found that, in general, the secondary-emission phenomenon does not follow Poisson's distribution [38]. However, for voltages of the order of 100 volts per stage, $\delta^2$ is probably about equal to $m$, as in the case of Poisson's distribution.

**Example 7-1.** Compute the pulse-height resolution in a photomultiplier tube having an average multiplication factor of 4 in each dynode for (*a*) the emission of single electrons from the photocathode and (*b*) for the collection of 10 electrons, on the average, in the first dynode.

*Solution.* By Eq. (7–9),

$$\frac{1}{R} = \frac{\delta_e^2}{n_e^2} + \frac{\delta_1^2}{n_e m_1^2} + \frac{\delta^2}{n_e m_1 m(m-1)} = 0 + \frac{(2)^2}{(1)(4)^2} + \frac{(2)^2}{(1)(4)(4)(4-1)}$$
$$= 0 + 0.25 + 0.08 = 0.33$$

where $m_1 = m = 4$ and $\delta_1^2 = \delta^2 = 4$. The quantity $n_e = 1$, and $\delta_e$ is taken as zero because each pulse is initiated by one electron only. When $n_e = 10$, then $\delta_e = \sqrt{10}$, leading to

$$\frac{1}{R} = 0.1 + 0.025 + 0.008 = 0.133$$

The corresponding values of $R$ are 3 and 7.5, respectively.

From Eq. (7–9) it is clear that the best opportunity to increase the resolution is to increase the number of electrons $n_e$ which reach the first dynode. This can be done partially by maximizing the light to the photocathode. Within the phototube the photocathode sensitivity and $F_c$, the fraction of photoelectrons collected, should be made as large as possible.

The resolution of the photomultiplier tube can also be increased by raising the multiplication per dynode. Equation (7–9) indicates that the first dynode is particularly effective in this regard. However, all photomultiplier tubes have an upper limit on the total voltage that can be applied to the tube and therefore a limit to the average multiplication factor. Nevertheless, a voltage much higher than the average can be applied to the first dynode without exceeding the maximum total voltage for the tube. Therefore, in applications where maximum resolution is desired, it is the usual practice to use a first-dynode voltage of perhaps five times the average voltage per stage for the remaining dynodes.

## 7–19. *Time Resolution in Photomultiplier Tubes*

A finite time is required for the transit of an electron through the multiplier tube. This time is inversely proportional to the square root of the voltage, being about $3 \times 10^{-8}$ and $6 \times 10^{-8}$ sec for a circular-type dynode structure and box dynode structure, respectively, with 100 volts per stage [39].

There are found to be statistical variations in this time lag, primarily due to variations in the path lengths traveled by different electrons. The root-mean-square deviation in the transit time has been found [40] to be about $0.5 \times 10^{-9}$ sec.

## 7–20. *Commercial Photomultiplier Tubes*

The development of photomultiplier tubes for scintillation counting has been an active and successful field during the past several years. Much of the effort has been toward improved resolution in pulse height. This has been approached through improved light collection, uniformity of the

TABLE 7-3. CHARACTERISTICS (APPROXIMATE) OF REPRESENTATIVE COMMERCIAL PHOTOMULTIPLIERS*

| Type | Maximum outside dimensions, in. | | Cathode | | | Dynode system | | | | Over-all voltage, volts | Light equivalent of noise, lumens |
|---|---|---|---|---|---|---|---|---|---|---|---|
| | Diam. | Length | Area $cm^2$ | Response | Av. sensitivity, $\mu a$/lumen | No. of dynodes | Type | Material | Gain | | |
| RCA: | | | | | | | | | | | |
| 5819 | $2\frac{1}{4}$ | $5\frac{13}{16}$ | 14.2 | S-11 | 50 | 10 | Circ. focused | $Cs_3Sb$ | $2.3 \times 10^6$ | 1,250 | $7 \times 10^{-11}$ |
| 6342 | $2\frac{1}{4}$ | $5\frac{13}{16}$ | 14.2 | S-11 | 60 | 10 | " | AgMg | $0.55 \times 10^6$ | 1,500 | $7 \times 10^{-12}$ |
| 6655 | $2\frac{1}{4}$ | $5\frac{13}{16}$ | 14.2 | S-11 | 50 | 10 | " | $Cs_3Sb$ | $2.3 \times 10^6$ | 1,250 | $7 \times 10^{-12}$ |
| 6199 | $1\frac{9}{16}$ | $4\frac{9}{16}$ | 7.75 | S-11 | 45 | 10 | " | $Cs_3Sb$ | $2.8 \times 10^6$ | 1,250 | $4 \times 10^{-12}$ |
| 2020 | $2\frac{1}{4}$ | $5\frac{13}{16}$ | 14.2 | S-11 | 60 | 10 | " | $Cs_3Sb$ | $2.8 \times 10^6$ | 1,250 | $7 \times 10^{-12}$ |
| 6217 | $2\frac{1}{4}$ | $5\frac{13}{16}$ | 14.2 | S-10 | 40 | 10 | " | $Cs_3Sb$ | $2.8 \times 10^6$ | 1,250 | $4 \times 10^{-11}$ |
| 6372 | $2\frac{9}{16}$ | $7\frac{3}{4}$ | 80 | S-11 | 33 | 10 | " | $Cs_3Sb$ | $2.5 \times 10^6$ | 1,200 | $1 \times 10^{-11}$ |
| 1P21 | $1\frac{5}{16}$ | $3\frac{11}{16}$ | 1.9† | S-11 | 40 | 9 | " | $Cs_3Sb$ | $8.3 \times 10^6$ | 1,250 | $5 \times 10^{-13}$ |
| 1P28 | $1\frac{5}{16}$ | $3\frac{11}{16}$ | 1.9† | S-5 | 40 | 9 | " | $Cs_3Sb$ | $5.3 \times 10^6$ | 1,250 | $7.5 \times 10^{-13}$ |
| Du Mont: | | | | | | | | | | | |
| 6291 | $1\frac{1}{2}$ | $4\frac{1}{4}$ | 6.4 | S-11 | 60 | 10 | Box | AgMg | $2 \times 10^6$ | 2,100 | |
| 6292 | $2\frac{1}{16}$ | $5\frac{5}{8}$ | 13.4 | S-11 | 60 | 10 | " | AgMg | $2 \times 10^6$ | 2,100 | |
| 6363 | . . . | $6\frac{1}{8}$ | 31.4 | S-11 | 60 | 10 | " | AgMg | $2 \times 10^6$ | 1,800 | |
| 6364 | $5\frac{1}{4}$ | $7\frac{1}{2}$ | 88.8 | S-11 | 60 | 10 | " | AgMg | $2 \times 10^6$ | 1,800 | |
| 6467 | $1\frac{1}{4}$ | $4\frac{1}{2}$ | 5.1 | S-11 | 60 | 10 | " | AgMg | $2 \times 10^6$ | 1,800 | |
| 6365 | $\frac{3}{4}$ | $2\frac{3}{4}$ | 1.26 | S-11 | 50 | 6 | " | AgMg | $3 \times 10^3$ | 1,200 | |

* From G. A. Morton, "Proceedings of the International Conference on the Peaceful Uses of Atomic Energy," vol. 14, p. 246, United Nations, New York, 1956.

† Projected area.

photocathode, conversion efficiency of the photocathode, and collection efficiency of photoelectrons.

Table 7–3 lists several of the characteristics of commercial photomultiplier tubes available in 1955. In addition, a number of new types are in development [21,31–33]. Included among these are tubes with 16-in.-diameter photocathodes.

## APPLICATIONS OF SCINTILLATION DETECTORS TO COUNTING

### 7–21. *Counting of Nuclear Particles*

It has been pointed out that some nucleonics instrumentation applications involve only the counting of nuclear particles, whereas others have additional purposes such as the measurement of energy and of time relationships. Scintillation detectors can be used for all these applications.

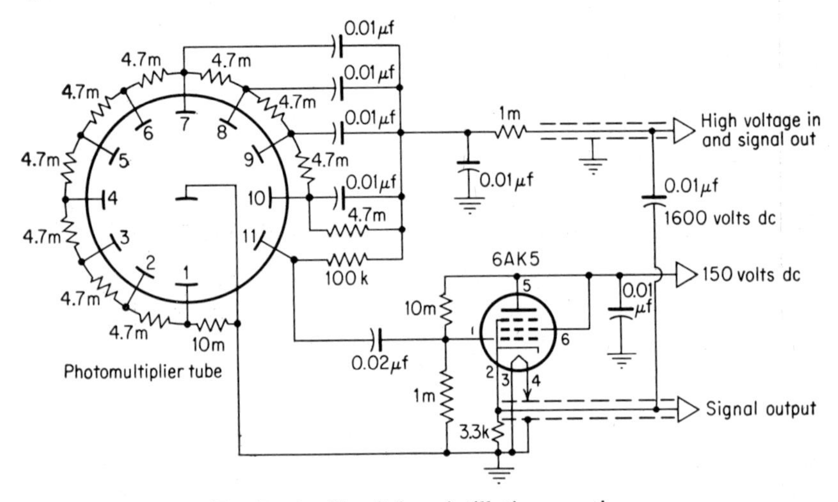


FIG. 7–14. Circuit for scintillation counting.

A simplified version of the arrangement shown in Fig. 7–1 is all that is required for counting nuclear particles. A photomultiplier tube and the appropriate scintillator and preamplifier are usually mounted as one unit. Figure 7–14 shows a preamplifier along with the voltage-divider arrangement for supplying the proper voltages to the dynodes. The output of this preamplifier can be connected directly to the input of any scaler requiring a negative pulse and having an input sensitivity of around 0.25 volt. The Geiger-Müller-tube input on most scalers serves this purpose very well. In this way, the high-voltage supply in the scaler can be used for the photomultiplier-tube high-voltage supply.

**Example 7–2.** If a scintillation counter with an anthracene scintillator is used to count 1-Mev electrons, estimate the electron multiplication that is required in the photomultiplier tube. Assume that the phototube delivers its signal to a scaler with an input capacity of 25 $\mu\mu$f and a sensitivity of 0.25 volt.

*Solution.* To deliver a pulse of at least 0.25 volt, a charge $q$ of

$$q = 0.25 \times C = 0.25(20 \times 10^{-12}) = 5 \times 10^{-12} \text{ coulomb}$$

must appear at the photomultiplier-tube anode. Assuming the values $C_{np} = 4\%$, $T_p = F_p = f = F_c = 1$ and $S_m = 0.05$, Eq. (7–2) yields a value of

$$n_e = 10^6 C_{np} T_p F_p S_m f F_c = 10^6(0.04)(0.05) = 2 \times 10^3$$

for the number of photoelectrons collected by the first dynode. The electron multiplication required is therefore

$$M = \frac{5 \times 10^{-12}}{(2 \times 10^3)e} = 1.5 \times 10^4$$

## 7–22. *Alpha-particle Counting*

Silver-activated zinc sulfide is the most satisfactory scintillator for alpha-particle counting. This material has a very high efficiency for conversion from nuclear energy to light but its transparency is low. However, by preparing the zinc sulfide scintillator in a layer of thickness comparable with the range of the alphas, the lack of transparency is avoided. Around 5 to 10 mg/cm$^2$ is the optimum thickness for detecting alphas occurring in radioactive decay.

Although other types of radiation which may be present will also produce scintillations in the zinc sulfide, these can, as a rule, be discriminated against because of their relatively small intensity.

Zinc sulfide scintillators can be coated directly on the glass envelope of the photomultiplier tube. Alternative arrangements in which the zinc sulfide is coated on a transparent material such as lucite are employed also. In this event, the transparent backing for the zinc sulfide is optically coupled to the photocathode.

## 7–23. *Gamma-ray Counting*

Inorganic crystals, especially sodium iodide activated with thallium, are used ordinarily for gamma counting. The NaI(Tl) crystals are particularly efficient for this application because of their relatively high density and atomic number.

An estimation of the efficiency of a scintillation counter for gamma rays can be made by computing the fraction of the gamma rays absorbed in passing through the scintillator. If the assumption is made that all the absorption processes, regardless of their nature, result in a count, the total absorption coefficient $\mu$, such as that given in Fig. 7–15 for NaI(Tl), is used.

For a parallel beam of gammas impinging normally on a slab of thickness $d$, the intrinsic efficiency is simply $1 - e^{-\mu d}$. For a point source on the

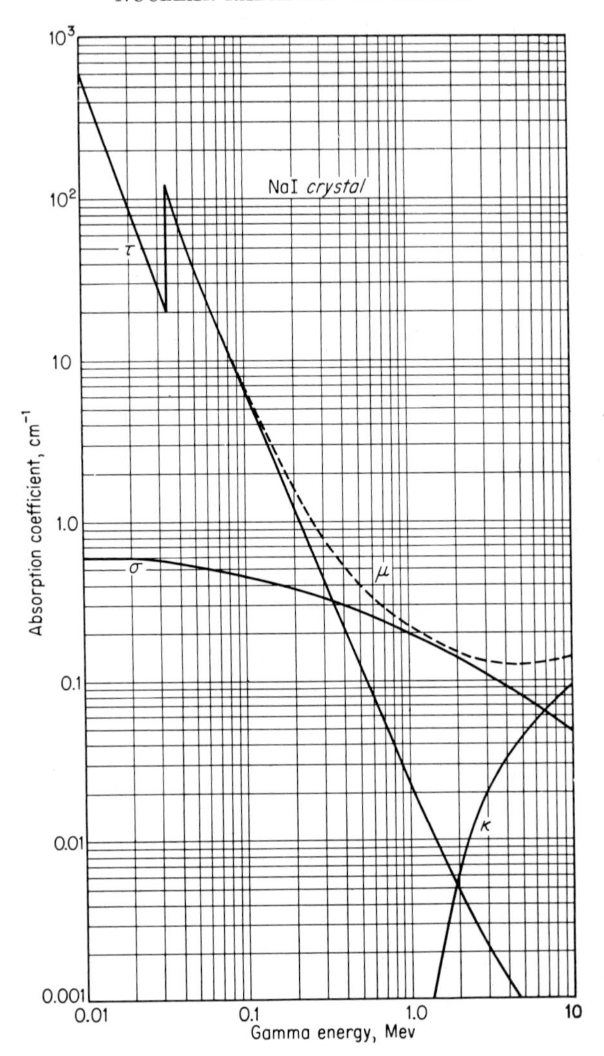


FIG. 7–15. Gamma absorption coefficients for sodium iodide versus gamma-ray energy. [*From W. H. Jordan, Ann. Rev. Nuclear Sci.*, **1**:221 (1951).]

axis of a cylindrical scintillator, as shown in Fig. 7–16, the intrinsic efficiency $\epsilon$ may be computed as

$$\epsilon = \frac{\int_{\Omega_0} (1 - e^{-\mu x})\, d\Omega}{\Omega_0} \tag{7-10}$$

where $\Omega_0$ is the solid angle subtended by the crystal measured from the source point. Values of $\epsilon$ for a 1½-in.-diameter by 1-in.-high NaI(Tl) scintillator are shown in Figs. 7–17 and 7–18, with the source-to-scintillator distance as a parameter.

**Example 7–3.** What is the maximum intrinsic efficiency of a 1-in.-thick NaI(Tl) scintillator for counting $Co^{60}$ gammas incident normally on its surface?

*Solution.* If the mean energy of $Co^{60}$ gammas is taken as 1.25 Mev, the total absorption coefficient from Fig. 7–15 is 0.19 $cm^{-1}$. This yields a maximum intrinsic efficiency $\epsilon$ of

$$\epsilon = 1 - e^{-\mu d} = 1 - \exp[-0.19 \times 2.54] = 0.38$$

Actually, the efficiency of the counter will be somewhat less than the value indicated above since the discriminator of the electronic scaler must reject some of the smaller intensity pulses. One method which has been devised [41] for

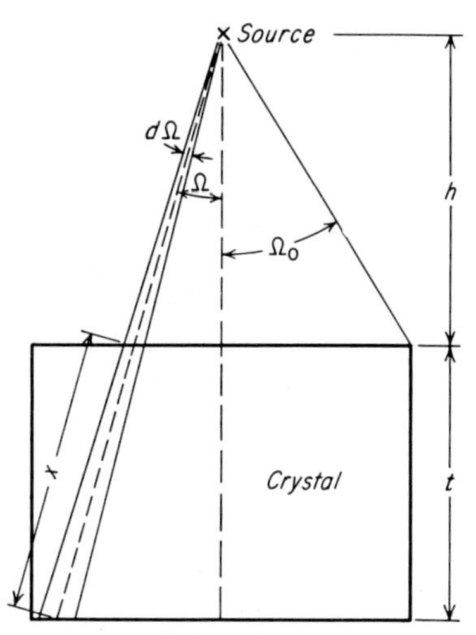


FIG. 7–16. Calculation of the intrinsic efficiency for a point source on the axis of a cylindrical scintillator.

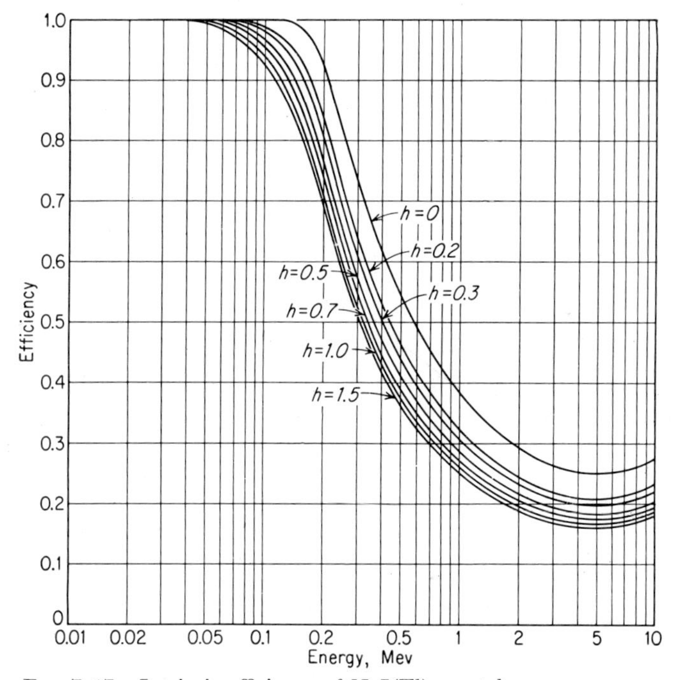


FIG. 7–17. Intrinsic efficiency of NaI(Tl) crystal versus gamma-ray energies for source-to-crystal distances of 0 to 1½ cm; crystal, 1½-in. diameter by 1 in. high. [*From P. R. Bell, Article in K. Siegbahn (ed.), "Beta- and Gamma-ray Spectroscopy," Interscience Publishers, Inc., New York,* 1955.]

removing this uncertainty is to count just the pulses whose height corresponds to the full gamma energy. Practically, this may be accomplished by taking the area under the full-energy peak of the differential pulse-height distribution curve. In Fig. 7–19 this so-called intrinsic peak efficiency is

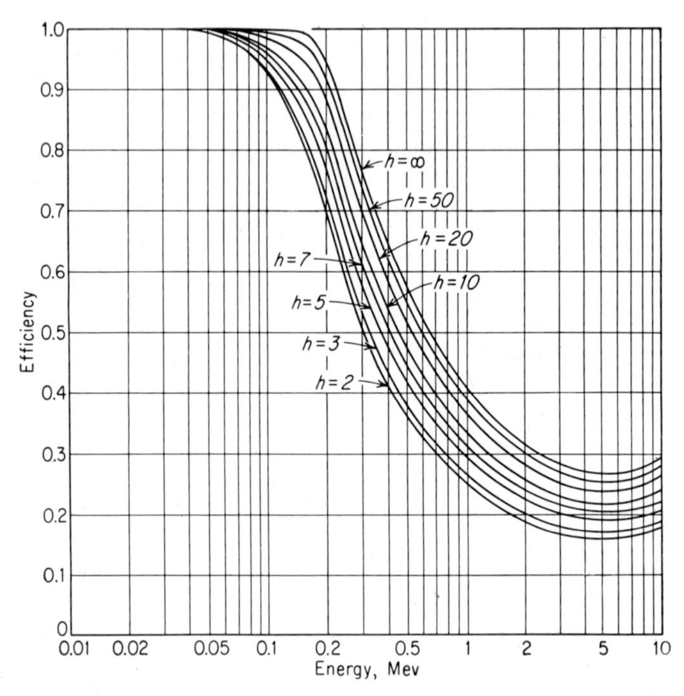


FIG. 7–18. Intrinsic efficiency of NaI(Tl) crystal versus gamma-ray energies for source-to-crystal distances of 2 cm to infinity; crystal 1½-in. diameter by 1 in. high. [*From P. R. Bell, Article in K. Siegbahn (ed.), "Beta- and Gamma-ray Spectroscopy," Interscience Publishers, Inc., New York,* 1955.]

plotted versus gamma energy for several different-size crystals as well as for different source-to-crystal distances.

The efficiency of scintillation counters for gamma rays is of the order of 100 times that for Geiger-Müller counters. This high efficiency has opened up new possibilities in measurements of low values of gamma activity. For example, scintillation detectors have been successful in locating uranium deposits from helicopters flying at 550 ft [42].

The background counting rate, as well as the total counting rate, increases when the efficiency of the counter is increased. However, if the efficiency for counting background and that for counting the source activity both increase by the same factor $C$, the accuracy which can be obtained in a fixed time is higher by a factor of $\sqrt{C}$ for the higher-efficiency detector.

Miller et al. [43] have studied the background count rate produced in NaI(Tl) scintillators due to naturally occurring radiations. Table 7–4 gives their results for 1½- by 1-in. crystals with various amounts of steel, lead, and mercury shielding. These results, of course, are dependent on the location. In addition, the residual count rate for thick shields is dependent on radioactive contaminants both in the scintillation detector proper and in its surroundings. The dependence of the background count rate on the

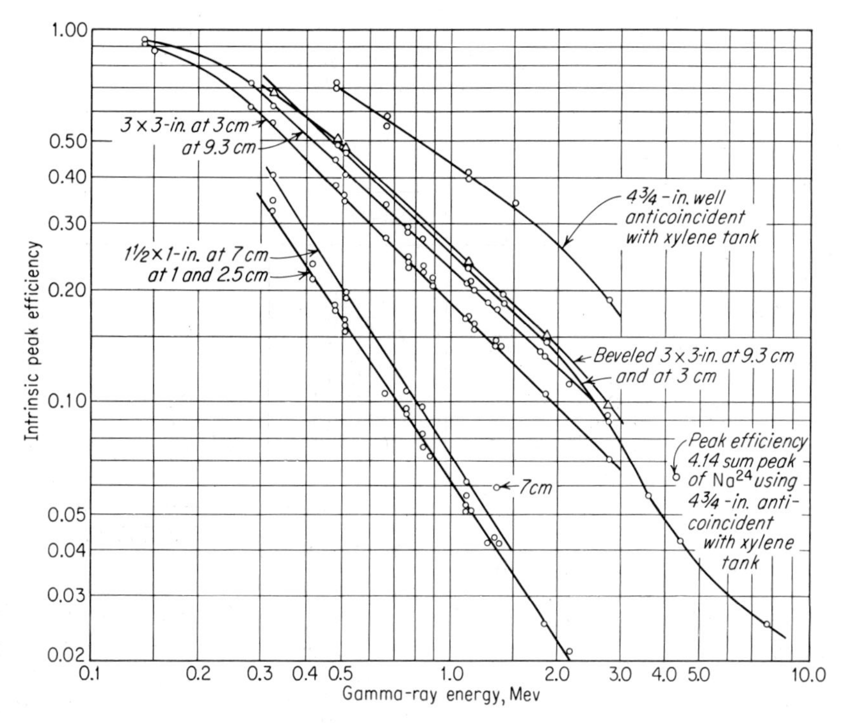


FIG. 7–19. Intrinsic peak efficiency versus gamma energy for NaI(Tl) crystals. [*From N. H. Lazar, R. C. Davis, and P. R. Bell, Nucleonics*, **14**:52 (*April*, 1956).]

range of pulse heights accepted by the counter is also indicated in Table 7–4; integral count rates for both 0.2 to 2.5 Mev and 70 kev to 2.5 Mev are included.

In the event that very short pulses are required in gamma counting, as in coincidence studies or in counting at very high rates, either the organic scintillators or the noble-gas scintillators must be used.

## 7–24. *Electron Counting*

Although all scintillator types are sensitive to electrons and beta rays to varying degrees, the organic materials are most widely used for detecting these particles. The fast response of the organic scintillators, coupled with the availability in liquid and solid solutions as well as crystalline forms, contributes greatly to their utility. Although NaI(Tl) has a higher conversion efficiency for electrons than do the organic scintillators, its slow response and the requirement for a hermetic seal limit its utility for electron detection. Further, the high atomic numbers of the constituents of NaI (Tl), while advantageous in gamma-ray detection, actually are objectionable for electrons because of the large percentage of backscattering from the scintillator.

TABLE 7-4. GAMMA-RAY BACKGROUND IN 1½- BY 1-IN. NAI(TL) CRYSTALS*

| Shielding, inches of steel | Integral background, counts/min | |
|---|---|---|
| | 0.2–2.5 Mev | 70 kev–2.5 Mev |
| None | 576.4 | |
| ¾ | 312.2 | |
| 1½ | 173.2 | |
| 3 | 84.2 | |
| 6 | 46.6 | |
| 8 | 41 | 62 |
| 8 + 2 in. Pb | 29.5 | 41 |
| 8 + 1 in. Hg | 26 | 35 |
| 8 + 2 in. Pb + 1 in. Hg | 25 | 32.5 |

* From C. E. Miller, L. D. Marinelli, R. E. Rowland, and J. E. Rose, *Nucleonics*, **14**:40 (April, 1956).

Organic-liquid scintillators are particularly useful for counting weak betas. In these applications the beta emitter may be mixed in the phosphor if the fluorescence phenomenon is not quenched by so doing. This method eliminates both detector-window absorption and self-absorption by the source.

The liquid scintillators have found wide-scale use for the counting of the soft-beta emitters $C^{14}$ and $H^3$ (tritium). These radioisotopes emit betas with peak energy of 160 and 18 kev, respectively. A primary design consideration in this application is the potential noise background due to the electrons which are emitted from the photocathodes by thermionic emission. As was pointed out in Sec. 7-16, a typical photocathode may emit around 5,000 electrons/(sec)(cm$^2$) at room temperature. A typical distribution in height of the pulses due to these electrons [37] may result in 0.1 per cent of these electrons having a pulse height corresponding to at least the average height for nine electrons starting at the photocathode. For a photocathode 1½ in. in diameter or 11 cm$^2$ in area, there would be about 55 pulses of this height per second due to thermionic emission. Unless the rate of occurrence of light pulses was at least this large, it would not be practical to count them if they released as few as nine photoelectrons. If 10 to 20 photoelectrons are taken as the practical lower limit for the number of photoelectrons, one obtains 5 to 10 kev as the minimum energy which the nuclear particle must dissipate in the scintillator under the conditions assumed in Example 7–2.

If these noise pulses are eliminated by a simple discriminator, the efficiency, particularly for tritium, is low because of the pulses that must be rejected. This situation may be improved by the careful selection of photomultiplier tubes and by refrigeration of them. For the best efficiency, the coincidence method, described below, is used.

Two photomultiplier tubes with their associated circuits receive the light from the scintillation cell, and after energy selection only those pulses which occur simultaneously (within 1 $\mu$sec or less) are passed by a fast coincidence circuit. Since the thermal noise pulses are random and uncorrelated in the two tubes, most of them are rejected in this process.

The techniques of liquid scintillators have been developed to a high state of perfection [44–47]. The manner in which the sample to be counted is incorporated with the liquid scintillator depends on its chemical nature. In the case where the scintillator solvent is toluene, a sample which is soluble in toluene may be dissolved directly in the scintillator. If the sample is not soluble in toluene but is water-soluble, then the water solution may be dissolved in the scintillator solution with the aid of absolute alcohol. Still another possibility is a sample which is finely ground and suspended in the scintillator for counting.

The addition of the sample may impair the efficiency of the scintillator. Such quenching may be corrected for by the use of an internal standard. Accurate standards are available for both tritium and $C^{14}$.

Efficiencies of 70 per cent have been achieved for counting cholesterol ($C^{14}$) in a xylene-terphenyl-diphenylhexatriene scintillator, while better than 30 per cent has been reported for stearic acid ($H^3$) in the same scintillator [48].

### 7–25. *Neutron Counting*

Applications of scintillation counting to neutron measurements will be discussed in Chap. 9. In general, the advantages which arise are similar to those for detection of other particles. These advantages include small sensitive volume of the detector, high counting rates, high efficiency, and geometric flexibility.

A number of materials for neutron scintillators are available. In these the detection of the neutrons is made possible through the charged particles which are released by various neutron-induced reactions.

### 7-26. *Dependence of Counting Rate on Photomultiplier-tube Voltage*

The existence of plateaus in the counting-rate versus detector-voltage curves has been discussed in connection with both Geiger-Müller and proportional counters. The term plateau refers to a range of voltages on the curve where the slope is markedly less than in other ranges. A plateau with zero or, at the most, a small slope only is desirable since this ensures that the efficiency of the detector will be insensitive to small changes in the power-

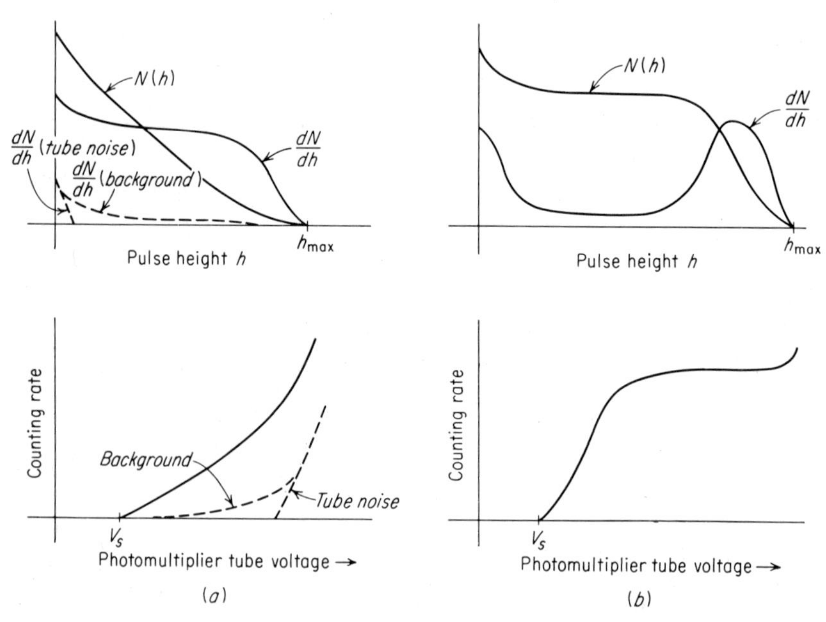


FIG. 7-20. Relationship between the pulse-height-distribution and the counting-rate–phototube-voltage curves.

supply voltage. In scintillation counting a plateau does not exist, in general, although under certain conditions one may be found.

The counting-rate multiplier-tube-voltage curve can be predicted if the distribution in height of the pulses from the photomultiplier tube is known. A number of factors contribute to this pulse-height distribution curve, as discussed in Sec. 7-28.

Figure 7-20 illustrates the relationship between a pulse-height distribution curve and the corresponding counting-rate versus voltage curve. The curves marked $dN/dh$ are known as the differential pulse-height curves; they show the number of pulses per unit pulse height versus the pulse height $h$. The quantity $(dN/dh)\,dh$ represents the number of pulses with height between $h$ and $h + dh$. The curves marked $N(h)$ are the integral pulse-height curves; that is, $N(h)$ has the meaning

$$N(h) = \int_h^\infty \frac{dN}{dh}\,dh$$

For the curves of $N(h)$ and $dN/dh$, the photomultiplier-tube voltage is considered to be constant.

The counting-rate curve is obtained from that of $N(h)$ by the following considerations. The pulses being counted at a certain photomultiplier voltage are all of those for which the electron multiplication is sufficient to produce a voltage pulse at least as large as the setting of the discriminator. If $V_s$ and $M_s$ designate the photomultiplier voltage and multiplication, respectively, when counting starts, the pulse-height distribution for this condition is such that $h_{\max}$ is just equal to the discriminator voltage setting $v_d$. Increasing the phototube voltage to $V$ corresponds to expanding the pulse-height scale by the factor $(V/V_s)^7$. The resulting counting rate can be determined by the value of $N(h)$ which occurs at a pulse height of $v_d$ on the expanded scale.

In the absence of a plateau, as in Fig. 7–20*a*, it is particularly important to use a power supply with good voltage regulation. This is evident from Eq. (7–7). If $h_d(V)$ represents the pulse height $h$ which equals $v_d$ for a given value of $V$, then

$$\frac{dh_d}{h_d} = -7\,\frac{dV}{V}$$

That is, a 1 per cent change in the photomultiplier-tube voltages makes a 7 per cent change in the value of the abscissa on the integral pulse-height curve. The corresponding change in counting rate would be $(dN/dh)_{h_d} dh_d$.

The dotted curves in Fig. 7–20 represent the background due to ambient nuclear radiation and that due to tube noise, respectively. The latter is the counting rate one would measure if the scintillator were removed. An operating voltage just at the point where tube noise sets in would give the highest possible efficiency at the lowest background.

While the distributions in Fig. 7–20 are meant only to be illustrative rather than to apply to a particular radiation type, examples leading to each distribution can be given. Scintillations from a continuous beta spectrum would result in a distribution similar to Fig. 7–20*a*. On the other hand, monoenergetic particles, e.g., alphas, produce a distribution similar to Fig. 7–20*b*. Furthermore, monoenergetic gammas with a high-$Z$ scintillator such as NaI(Tl) have a voltage characteristic with a plateau if the crystal is large enough.

### 7-27. *Resolving and Dead Time in Scintillation Counters*

The resolving time $\tau_r$ for counting measurements was introduced in Sec. 2-7 as the minimum time which must exist between successive events if they are to be counted as two events. At a counting rate $\dot{m}$, a fraction $\tau_r \dot{m}$ of the events is lost because of this dead time.

The resolving time in a Geiger-Müller counter is 100 $\mu$sec or more, while in a scintillation counter it can be a small fraction of a microsecond. Therefore the scintillation counter can be used at a much higher counting rate than the Geiger-Müller tube.

In the usual case, the resolving time in a system employing a scintillation counter is determined by the recovery time of the electronic scaler. In conventional scalers this is from 1 to 5 $\mu$sec. Special circuits [49,50] with a fixed dead time of 0.2 $\mu$sec have been developed.

To have the resolving time determined by the electronic circuit requires that the decay time $\tau$ of the scintillator be much less than $\tau_r$. The time dependence of the charge arriving at the anode of the photomultiplier is

$$q = q_0 e^{-t/\tau}$$

under the conditions that any dispersion due to the electron multiplication is neglected. To obtain the fastest response, the voltage pulse accompanying the collection of charge is differentiated, and the resulting voltage pulse drives the scaler. The voltage is proportional to $e^{-t/\tau}$. If the quantity $e^{-\tau_r/\tau}$ is sufficiently small, the pulse will have dropped below the discriminator setting by the time the electronic circuit has recovered.

The organic scintillators, particularly stilbene with a decay time of about 0.005 $\mu$sec, can be used with a circuit resolving time of 0.1 $\mu$sec or less. Consequently, counting rates up to $10^5$ per second can be accommodated with less than 1 per cent dead-time loss.

When the counting rate is large enough that it is necessary to make a dead-time correction, an experimental determination should be made of the dead time. The two-source method (Sec. 5-6) will suffice for this determination.

Still another important consideration is the limitation on the accuracy to which the time occurrence of events can be determined. This limitation, designated as the time resolution, arises because of fluctuations in the time interval between the passage of the nuclear particle through the scintillator and the triggering of the timing circuit. The triggering corresponds to the reaching of a certain level of charge collection at the photomultiplier-tube output.

The time resolution is determined by the time spread in the passage of electrons through the photomultiplier (see Sec. 7-19), the fluorescent decay time $\tau$ of the scintillator, the total number $n_e$ of electrons emitted at the photocathode, and the number of cathode electrons $n_t$ required for triggering the timing circuit. Estimates of the root-mean-square deviations, $t_{rms}$, in time-interval measurement for three different scintillators are given [21] in Table 7–5.

TABLE 7–5. ESTIMATES OF TIME RESOLUTION IN THREE SCINTILLATORS*

| Type | $n_e$ | $\tau$(sec) | $n_t$ | $t_{rms}$(sec) |
|---|---|---|---|---|
| Liquid | 100 | $3 \times 10^{-9}$ | 17 | $2.2 \times 10^{-10}$ |
| Trans-stilbene | 300 | $6 \times 10^{-9}$ | 25 | $1.7 \times 10^{-10}$ |
| Anthracene | 500 | $36 \times 10^{-9}$ | 7 | $3.3 \times 10^{-10}$ |

* From G. A. Morton, "Proceedings of the International Conference on the Peaceful Uses of Atomic Energy," vol. 14, p. 246, United Nations, New York, 1956.

## SCINTILLATION DETECTOR AS A SPECTROMETER

### 7–28. *General Considerations*

As was pointed out earlier, one of the important properties of a scintillation detector is its ability to give an indication of the energy of the incident nuclear radiation. Because of this property, the differential pulse-height distribution curves from a scintillation detector can be used to determine the energy spectrum of the incident particles. Systems of this type have been used extensively both as beta- and gamma-ray spectrometers. Bell [25] has recently written an excellent review of these applications.

Factors determining the relationship between the charge released at the photomultiplier-tube anode and the nuclear-particle energy have been discussed in the previous section. For spectrometer applications it is important that these factors remain nearly constant for all particles of the same energy; i.e., a group of monoenergetic particles should result in a group of pulses of the same height. In practice, a spread of distribution of pulse sizes is experienced. This spread can be expressed in terms of the resolution $R$ in Eq. (7–8) or by $W_{1/2}$, the percentage full width of the pulse-height distribution curve at one-half of the maximum. The quantity $W_{1/2}$ is calculated as

$$W_{1/2} = \frac{\Delta h_{1/2}}{h_{\max}} \times 100\%$$

where $h_{\max}$ is the pulse height corresponding to the maximum in the curve while $\Delta h_{1/2}$ is the pulse-height interval between the points at which one-half of the maximum value occurs. If it is assumed that the pulse-height distribution follows the "normal" error curve, the relationship between $W_{1/2}$ and $R$ is $W_{1/2} = 236/R^{1/2}$, where $W_{1/2}$ is expressed as a percentage. Making use of Eq. (7–9), $W_{1/2}$ can be written as

$$W_{1/2} = \frac{236}{(n_e)^{1/2}}\left[1 + \frac{\delta_1^2}{m_1^2} + \frac{\delta^2}{m_1 m(m-1)}\right]^{1/2} \tag{7-11}$$

where $n_e$ now has the meaning of the average number of electrons reaching the first dynode per monoenergetic particle striking the scintillator, and the other symbols have the meanings assigned previously in Sec. 7–18.

Since the value 1 is the controlling term in the bracket of Eq. (7–11) (see Example 7–1), it is clear that the major effect on the resolution can come through $n_e$. Consequently, maximizing the efficiency of the conversion from nuclear energy to light, the collection of the light, the photoemission, and the collection of the electrons leads to the best resolution for a given energy of radiation.

The effect of the fluctuations in the secondary emission of the dynodes on the resolution was discussed in Sec. 7–18. The optimization of the dynode voltage to improve this situation was also covered.

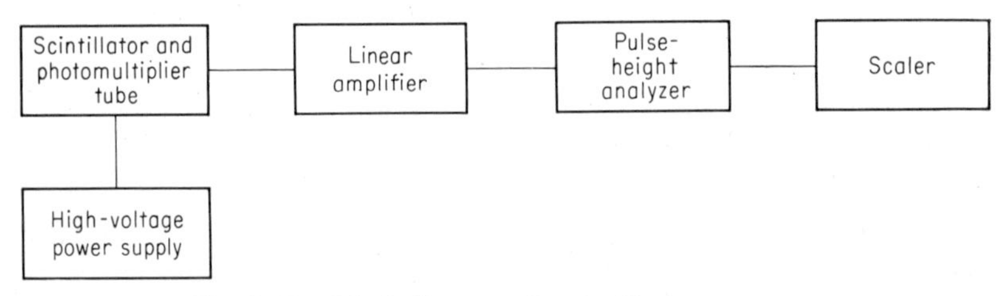


FIG. 7–21. Block diagram of a scintillation spectrometer.

There are a number of nonbasic factors which can decrease the resolution capability of the scintillation detector. Among these are optical imperfections in the crystal, nonuniformity of the photocathode, instability in the photomultiplier, fluctuations in the high voltage applied to the photomultiplier, and excessive noise in the photomultiplier.

The resolution of scintillation detectors for gamma-ray spectrometers has been discussed by several investigators [51–55]. Recent studies [56] which compare the resolution obtainable when the light is from a scintillator with that resulting with light from an artificial light flash indicate that there is a large contribution to the width that is intrinsic to the scintillator. This effect needs further study.

With reasonable care, 10 per cent full-width resolution can be obtained for the 0.661-Mev gamma ray of $Cs^{137}$ with an NaI(Tl) crystal. Under good conditions this may be lowered to about 6 per cent [25].

Figure 7–21 is a block diagram of a scintillation spectrometer. The fundamentals of pulse-height analysis were introduced in Sec. 2–8, and a single-channel analyzer was discussed. As the sample activity is reduced, the time required for obtaining a certain accuracy is increased. The time element makes the use of a single-channel pulse-height analyzer impractical for low-activity samples, as well as for specimens with short half-lives. Multichannel analyzers have been developed which help to avoid this limitation. In these instruments determinations of the counting rates can be made in as many as 20 or more channels simultaneously. A discussion of pulse-height analyzers can be found in Chap. 10 and in the comprehensive articles of Van Rennes [57].

7–29. *Gamma-ray Scintillation Spectrometers.*

The wide-scale use of scintillation detectors as gamma-ray spectrometers has been made possible by the availability of large single crystals of NaI(Tl) and the development of end-window photomultiplier tubes with high resolution. Gamma rays interact with the NaI(Tl) crystals by three mechanisms: photoelectric effect, Compton effect, and pair production. The partial absorption coefficients due to these effects are shown in Fig. 7–15. In each of the processes, a portion of the primary photon energy goes into the kinetic energy of electrons—negative electrons in the photoelectric and Compton processes and both negative electrons and positrons in pair production. The remainder of the energy goes into secondary photons. Except when the interaction occurs near the surface and the electron escapes the scintillator before coming to rest, the kinetic energy of the electron goes into the production of light. The secondary photons may or may not release further electrons and thus lose light-producing energy to the scintillator. If light is produced, it adds to that caused by the electrons released in the primary process, and the total light output is proportional to the primary photon energy $E\gamma$. These separate stages of the interactions occur so nearly simultaneously compared with the decay time of the phosphor that their light outputs will not be resolved in time but will show up as a single pulse of light.

In the photoelectric process the secondary photon is an X ray, and because of its low energy it is absorbed in the scintillator essentially every time. Consequently the photoelectric process results in a light pulse of energy proportional to the primary gamma energy except for the surface effect mentioned above.

In the Compton process a relatively large fraction of the primary energy may go into the scattered gamma. This depends on the scattering angle and the energy of the primary gamma. The energy of the scattered gamma is given by Eq. (1–26).

In pair production an energy equal to twice the rest-mass energy of an electron, or 1.02 Mev, is required for producing the pair. Consequently the total kinetic energy of the pair is only $E - 1.02$ Mev. However, when annihilation of the positron occurs, two 0.51-Mev photons are produced.

Both the scattered gamma in the Compton effect and the annihilation radiation accompanying pair production escape the scintillator a large part of the time except in very large NaI(Tl) or other high-density crystals. Thus, with the intermediate-size crystals, the pulse distribution from monoenergetic gamma rays contains both pulses representing the entire gamma energy and those representing but a fraction of the energy. As the crystal

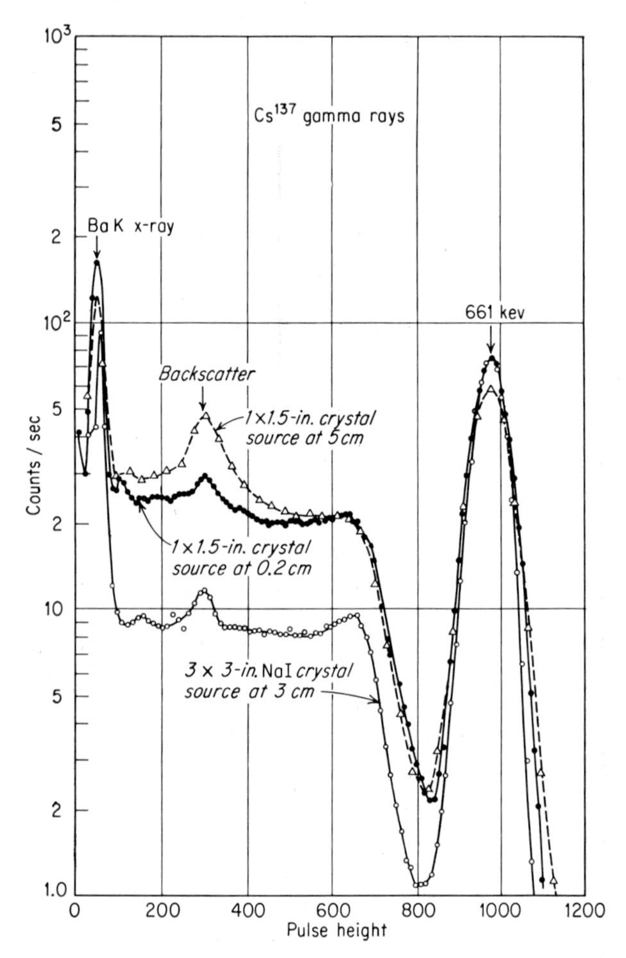


FIG. 7–22. Pulse-height distribution curves of $Cs^{137}$ gammas taken by 1- by 1.5-in.-diameter and 3- by 3-in.-diameter NaI(Tl) scintillators. [*From P. R. Bell, Article in K. Siegbahn (ed.), "Beta- and Gamma-ray Spectroscopy," Interscience Publishers, Inc., New York*, 1955.]

size is increased, the latter become a small fraction of the total. The differential pulse-height distribution curves of $Cs^{137}$ gamma rays, shown in Fig. 7–22, illustrate this effect. The full-energy peak, designated as 661 kev, is seen to increase, while the lower-energy distribution decreases when the scintillator size is changed from 1 in. high by 1½-in. diameter to 3 in.

high by 3-in. diameter. This effect is illustrated further in Fig. 7–23, in which the ratio of the area under the full-energy peak to the full area under the pulse-height distribution curve is plotted versus the photon energy. The ratio of the partial absorption coefficient of NaI(Tl) due to the photoelectric effect to the total absorption coefficient is also shown for comparison purposes; the latter is the ratio which would occur in the pulse-height curves if no absorption of the secondary gammas took place.

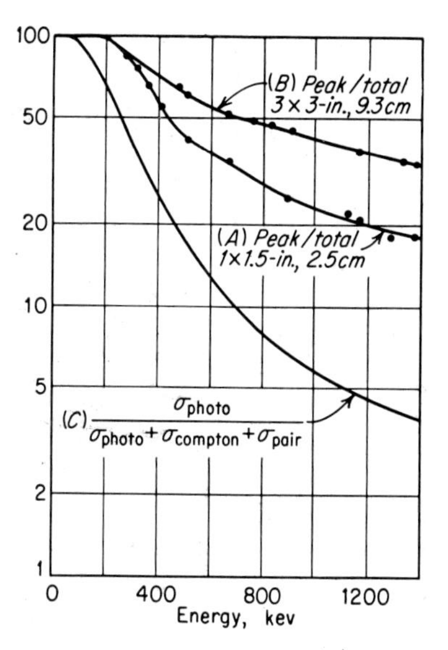


FIG. 7–23. Peak-total ratios for two different-size NaI(Tl) crystals; also, the ratio of photoelectric absorption to total. [*From P. R. Bell, Article in K. Siegbahn (ed.), "Beta- and Gamma-ray Spectroscopy," Interscience Publishers, Inc., New York,* 1955.]

Spectrometers which employ crystals sufficiently large that most of the pulses appear under the full-energy peak are known as total-absorption spectrometers. Bell [58] has described such a spectrometer; it employs a scintillator equivalent to a 5¼-in. sphere with a ¼-in.-diameter hole drilled to its center for positioning the source.

When it is required that the spectrum obtained with a scintillation spectrometer be such that several groups of monoenergetic gammas can be identified, it is desirable that each energy gamma result in but one pulse size. This is especially true when the lower-energy gammas have small intensities relative to the higher-energy gammas. In this case the total-absorption peak of the lower-energy gamma can be lost easily in the Compton recoil-electron continuum of the higher-energy gamma, if such a continuum exists. The total-absorption spectrometer approaches the resolution which is required for the separation of several gamma-ray energies.

A one-to-one correspondence between gamma-ray energy and pulse height can also be obtained with smaller crystals (dimensions around 1 in.) by the use of more than one scintillator and photomultiplier tube. Two such devices are the two-crystal spectrometer and the pair spectrometer. A two-crystal spectrometer [59] employs a coincidence arrangement (see Chap. 10) so that only the Compton recoil electrons which are accompanied by a scattered gamma of a fixed angle (around 135°) are allowed into the pulse-height analyzer. Thus all other pulses are eliminated. The two-crystal spectrometer achieves resolutions comparable with the single-crystal type. However, it has the disadvantage of requiring a source which is a factor of a thousand or more times larger because of the small fraction of particles actually accepted by the analyzer.

The pair spectrometer [60] employs three crystals in a row, each being viewed by a different photomultiplier tube. The output of the center crystal goes to the pulse-height analyzer. A triple-coincidence arrangement is employed so that the analyzer accepts only the pulses from the center crystal which are accompanied by scintillations in the two adjoining crystals. The gamma rays to be analyzed are allowed to strike the center crystal. A triple coincidence can occur in the pair-production process when the two annihilation quanta which accompany the destruction of the positron interact one each with the two adjoining crystals. Thus the pulses which are analyzed are those giving the total kinetic energy of the pair. This energy is $E_\gamma - 1.02$ Mev. The source strength required by the pair spectrometer is not as large as with the two-crystal spectrometer. One microcurie of a 2.7-Mev gamma ray has been found satisfactory [60] for the former.

### 7–30. *Medical Scintillation Spectrometry*

The techniques of the single-channel scintillation spectrometer have been applied [61] to radioiosotope measurements in medical diagnosis and therapy. By counting only those pulses appearing under the full-energy peak, scattered radiation will not be detected. This fact, coupled with the use of specially designed collimators, leads to accurate position measurements. Further, background counting rates are much lower because only those background pulses that occur in the selected channel are registered.

### 7–31. *Beta-ray Scintillation Spectrometers*

Anthracene crystals are used most widely as the scintillators in beta-ray spectrometers. NaI(Tl) can be used also. The considerations outlined in Sec. 7–24 indicate the preference for the former. However, anthracene does have the disadvantage of a nonlinear light-energy response below 100 kev [22], making a correction required in the correlation of pulse height and energy.

The scintillators are usually prepared with an area similar to that of the cathode of an end-on-type photomultiplier tube and a thickness at least as great as the range of the maximum-energy beta particles. A typical crystal might have a thickness of ¼ in. and a diameter of 1 in. A thin aluminum foil as a cover can serve the dual purpose of a light reflector to aid in the light collection and a protection against the ambient light.

A distortion of the beta spectrum occurs if any of the beta particles are backscattered out of the scintillator and therefore dissipate but part of their energy in it. The arrangement shown in Fig. 7–24 helps to avoid this, to a large extent. The electrons hit the bottom of the hole, and if they are backscattered they have but small chance of escaping the scintillator, because of the shape of the opening.

A number of secondary effects exist which must be accounted for in accurate beta-ray spectroscopy [25]. These include coincident gamma-ray transitions which, if absorbed, add light to the beta-induced scintillations and absorption by window, reflector, air, or any other absorber between the source and the scintillator.

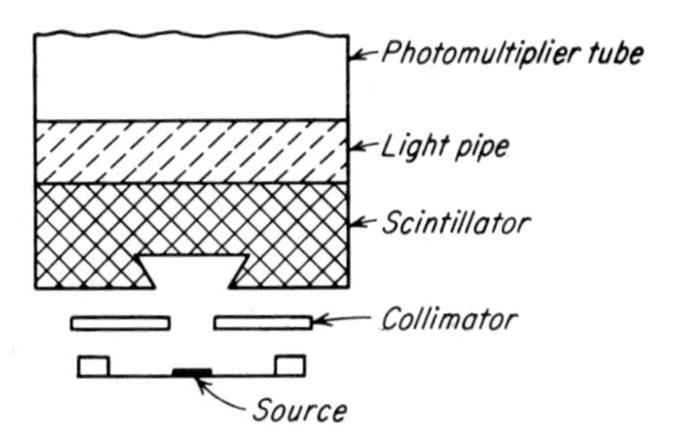


FIG. 7–24. Arrangement for the prevention of loss of backscattered electrons in a beta-ray spectrometer.

Scintillation-type beta spectrometers can be used with much weaker sources than can the magnetic type. This is possible because the fraction of the beta particles entering the scintillator can be made to approach 50 per cent, whereas in a magnetic type only a per cent or less can be employed. In addition, errors due to self-absorption in the source can be avoided to a greater extent in the scintillation spectrum because sources of larger area and smaller activity can be used than in the magnetic type.

## FURTHER APPLICATIONS OF SCINTILLATION DETECTORS

### 7–32. *Wide Utility of Scintillation Detectors*

No attempt will be made in this book even to list all the types of experiments in which scintillation detectors have been employed. To do so would involve enumerating nearly every type of nucleonics instrumentation problem which has been met in recent years.

A discussion of many applications of scintillation counters is found in Birks [3] and in Curran [62]. In the present discussion emphasis is on special applications which are made possible through the particular characteristics possessed by scintillator detectors.

### 7–33. *Measurements for Very-high-energy Particles*

A review article by Wouter [63] describes the application of scintillation detectors to measurements with high-energy particles. These measurements include particle-scattering experiments and meson experiments.

A typical proton-scattering experiment employs a collimated incident beam from the 184-in. frequency-modulation cyclotron impinging on a target. The beam may consist of $10^7$ protons of 340 Mev, emerging during 25 $\mu$sec and repeated about 60 times per second. The flux as measured by a detector of narrow aperture may result in a dozen true proton counts per second. The scattered protons are accompanied by a background flux perhaps a hundred times larger consisting of deuterons, protons, high-energy electrons, mesons, and gammas coming from inelastic scattering in the surrounding matter. The spectrum of this background ranges up to 340 Mev, but most of it is around a few Mev.

Measurements of this sort by the use of a gas-type instrument such as a proportional counter are seriously limited by the extent of the discrimination which is possible and by the resolving power of the instrument. The scintillation detector avoids, in a large part, both of these factors.

In a proportional counter the pulse sizes from the low-energy background particles are often as large as or larger than those due to the high-energy particles. This occurs since the specific ionization of the high-energy particles is much smaller than that of the lower-energy particles and since the distance traveled by each group of particles is essentially the same as the chamber dimensions. On the other hand, in the scintillation detector, because of its higher density, the range of the background particles in the scintillator is much less than the scintillator dimensions; therefore the ratio of the pulse heights due to the two groups of particles is considerably better, and much more effective discrimination results.

### 7–34. *Investigation of Short-lived Nuclear Isomers*

Many nuclei possess metastable excited states known as isomeric states. The common mode of decay to the ground state is by gamma emission. Each isomer has a characteristic half-life. Half-lives ranging from less than $10^{-9}$ sec to several years are known.

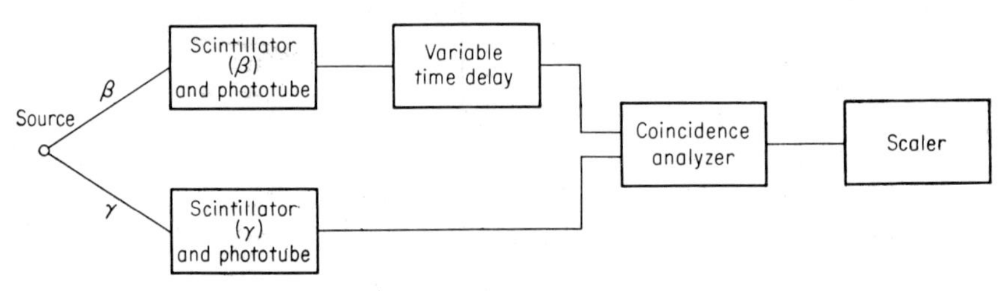


FIG. 7–25. Delayed-coincidence method for half-life measurements.

For the longer half-life measurements, Geiger-Müller counters have been used. However, these detectors cannot be used for half-lives less than $10^{-6}$ sec because their resolving times are of this order. The short resolving time of the scintillation counter has allowed the extension of the half-life measurements down to $10^{-9}$ sec.

The block diagram for the half-life measurements is Fig. 7–25. The measurement makes use of the fact that the formation of the isomeric state is accompanied by the emission of a beta particle. Coincidence counts between the gamma ray accompanying decay of the isomer and the beta particle accompanying the formation of the isomer can be made if the pulse accompanying the latter is delayed. The variation of the coincidence rate with the delay time gives the half-life of the isomer directly. Decay periods of numerous isomers with values from $10^{-6}$ to $10^{-9}$ sec have been measured by McGowan [64] and others. McGowan [64] has also extended the method to the measurement of the amplitude distribution of the radiation from the isomer as well as from the parent nuclei.

### 7–35. *Large-volume Liquid Scintillators*

Much of the wide utility of scintillation detectors rests in the versatility which is possible in the size and shape of the scintillators. Large-volume liquid scintillators are particularly interesting for applications where other-type detectors give zero or a very small counting rate because of the small flux subtended and/or the small efficiency for interaction with the particles. Cosmic-rays measurement is one area in which the large liquid scintillator is being employed to increase the rate at which data are collected.

Harrison, Cowan, and Reines [65] used a large liquid scintillator successfully for studying the neutrino. They measured the cross section for the reaction

$$\nu + {}_1H^1 \rightarrow {}_1e^0 + {}_0n^1$$

In this experiment a large tank was used, since the cross section for the reaction is quite small. The tank contained 300 liters of toluene-terphenyl-$\alpha$ naphthyl phenyloxazole as a liquid scintillator with cadmium propionate added. The tank was cylindrical in shape and was equipped with 90 photomultiplier tubes in spiral rows on the walls. The tubes were divided into two groups and connected in parallel to the two inputs of a coincidence analyzer. The positrons cause a pulse to enter one channel. The neutrons which are created with an energy of a few kev are first slowed down to thermal neutrons. Once they reach thermal energies, they are captured by the cadmium, and the capture gamma produces a scintillation which passes to the other channel of the coincidence analyzer. By delaying the pulse originating with the positron, the neutrino-induced reaction described above can result in a count.

### 7–36. *Dosimetry Applications of Scintillation Detectors*

The light emission in a scintillator is a good measure of the absorbed radiation energy, under the appropriate conditions. These applications have been reviewed by Ramm [4]. The most widespread use is for the dosimetry of gamma radiations, but the dosimetry of neutrons and charged particles has been investigated also.

In dosimetry applications the scintillation detector is usually employed as a mean-level device. The average current is proportional to the scintillator light output within a certain range. The useful current range of the photomultipliers and consequently the range of dose rates detectable with a given system are limited at low and high currents by dark currents and photomultiplier fatigue, respectively. For a given multiplication factor $M$, the dark current at room temperature is about $8 \times 10^{-14}M$ amp; it is therefore of the order of $10^{-7}$ to $10^{-8}$ amp for the most frequently used multiplication factor of about $5 \times 10^{5}$. At anode currents of $10^{-5}$ amp and above, appreciable fatigue of the multiplier has been observed. This current range corresponds to a practical range of dose rates from $10^{-4}$ to 1 r/hr with an anthracene crystal of 20 g.

Except for the photon-energy dependence of the relationship between absorbed particle energy and light output, as described in Sec. 7–11, the latter can be taken as proportional to the gamma-energy absorption in the scintillator. Accordingly, subject to the limitations imposed by the attenuation of the gamma radiation in the scintillator, the establishment of secondary-electron equilibrium, and the dependence of the absorption on atomic numbers of the scintillator constituents, the photomultiplier-tube output can be calibrated in dose rate.

The dependence of the response of a scintillation-type dosimeter on photon energy has been studied by comparison with an air-wall ionization chamber [4]. The theoretical prediction of this relative response has been made for anthracene crystals of four different thicknesses. This particular calculation neglects the energy dependence of the conversion efficiency.

## PROBLEMS

**7–1.** What pulse size would a 50-kev electron produce at the input of a pulse amplifier having an input capacity of 20 $\mu\mu$f in a system using an anthracene crystal and a Du Mont 6292 photomultiplier tube with 130 volts per stage? Make reasonable assumptions on any other parameters of the system as necessary.

**7–2.** Compute the conversion efficiency of an NaI scintillator from Fig. 7–12.

**7–3.** Use Fig. 7–12 to compute the figure of merit of an NaI scintillator employed with a type S-11 photocathode.

**7–4.** Consider a counting system employing scintillation detectors in which the resolving time for the system is limited by the decay of the luminescence and is approximately equal to the decay time of the scintillator. Calculate the counting rate at which the counting losses are 1 per cent for both anthracene and NaI scintillators.

**7–5.** Discuss the significance of Figs. 7–4 and 7–5 to the utilization of the various scintillator types for energy spectrometers.

**7–6.** Prove that the units for spectral sensitivity of microamperes per microwatt and photoelectrons per electron volt are equal.

**7–7.** Compute the pulse-height resolution in a 10-dynode photomultiplier tube for which the average multiplication factor for the first dynode is 4 and that for each succeeding dynode is 3. Assume that 10 electrons are emitted from the photocathode.

**7–8.** Calculate the efficiency of a scintillation counter using a 1-in.-thick NaI(Tl) crystal for counting $Co^{60}$. Assume that the gamma rays strike the scintillator in perpendicular incidence and that the discriminator is set to receive all the scintillations from the crystal, regardless of their size.

**7-9.** Compare the results obtained in Prob. 7-8 with the values obtained from Figs. 7-17 to 7-19. Explain.

**7-10.** Compute the theoretical ratio of the area under the photoelectric peak to the total area for a differential pulse-height distribution curve obtained with a large NaI(Tl) crystal irradiated with a $Cs^{137}$ source.

## REFERENCES


1. Coltman, J. W., and F. H. Marshall: *Phys. Rev.*, **72**:528 (1947).
2. Swank, R. K.: *Nucleonics*, **12**:14 (March, 1954).
3. Birks, J. B.: "Scintillation Counters," chap. 6, McGraw-Hill Book Company, Inc., New York, 1953.
4. Ramm, Wolfgang J.: Article in G. J. Hine and G. L. Brownwell (eds.), "Radiation Dosimetry," Academic Press, Inc., New York, 1956.
5. Eggler, C., and C. M. Huddleston: *Phys. Rev.*, **95**:600 (1954); *Nucleonics*, **14**:34 (April, 1956).
6. Northrop, J. A., and R. Nobles: *Nucleonics*, **14**:36 (April, 1956).
7. Slater, J. C.: "Quantum Theory of Matter," chap. 8, McGraw-Hill Book Company, Inc., New York, 1951.
8. Kittel, C.: "Introduction to Solid State Physics," p. 317, John Wiley & Sons, Inc., New York, 1953.
9. Sangster, R. C.: *MIT Laboratory for Nuclear Science and Engineering Tech. Rept.* 55, Jan. 1, 1952.
10. Kallmann, H., and M. Furst: *Phys. Rev.*, **78**:621 (1950).
11. Kallmann, H., and M. Furst: *Phys. Rev.*, **79**:857 (1950).
12. Kallmann, H., and M. Furst: *Phys. Rev.*, **81**:853 (1951).
13. Kallmann, H., M. Furst, and F. H. Brown: *Nucleonics*, **14**:48 (April, 1956).
14. Schorr, M. G., and F. L. Forney: *Phys. Rev.*, **80**:474 (1950).
15. Kuski, W. S.: *Phys. Rev.*, **82**:230 (1951).
16. Pichut, L., and Y. Koechlin: *J. Chem. Phys.*, **48**:225 (1951).
17. Buck, W. L., and R. K. Swank: *Nucleonics*, **11**:48 (November, 1953).
18. Mott, N. F., and R. W. Gurney: "Electronic Processes in Ionic Crystals," Clarendon Press, Oxford, 1940.
19. Seitz, F.: "The Modern Theory of Solids," chap. 13, McGraw-Hill Book Company, Inc., New York, 1940.
20. Muehlhause, C. O.: *U.S. Atomic Energy Comm. Document* BNL-242 (T-38), 1953.
21. Morton, G. A.: "Proceedings of the International Conference on the Peaceful Uses of Atomic Energy," vol. 14, p. 246, United Nations, New York, 1956.
22. Taylor, C. J., W. K. Jentschke, M. E. Remley, F. S. Eby, and P. G. Kruger: *Phys. Rev.*, **84**:1034 (1951).
23. Birks, J. B.: *Phys. Rev.*, **86**:569 (1952).
24. Birks, J. B.: *Phys. Rev.*, **84**:364 (1951).
25. Bell, P. R.: Article in K. Siegbahn (ed.), "Beta- and Gamma-ray Spectroscopy," Interscience Publishers, Inc., New York, 1955.
26. Timmerhaus, K. D., E. B. Giller, R. B. Duffield, and H. G. Drickamer: *Nucleonics*, **6**:37 (June, 1950).
27. Borkowski, C. J., and R. L. Clark: Personal communication.
28. Jordan, W. H., and P. R. Bell: *Nucleonics*, **5**:30 (October, 1949).
29. Sommer, A.: "Photoelectric Tubes," chap. 3, Methuen & Co., Ltd., London, 1951.

30. Allen, J. S.: *Proc. IRE*, **38**:346 (1950).
31. Linden, B. R.: *Nucleonics*, **11**:30 (September, 1953).
32. Engstrom, R. W.: *Nucleonics*, **12**:26 (March, 1954).
33. Linden, B. R.: *Nucleonics*, **12**:20 (March, 1954).
34. Davidson, P. W.: *Nucleonics*, **10**:33 (March, 1952).
35. Engstrom, R. W., R. G. Stoudenheimer, and A. N. Glover: *Nucleonics*, **10**:58 (April, 1952).
36. Swank, R. K., and W. L. Buck: *Nucleonics*, **10**:51 (May, 1952).
37. Morton, G. A., and J. A. Mitchell: *Nucleonics*, **4**:16 (January, 1949).
38. Allen, J. S.: *Proc. IRE*, **38**:346 (1950).
39. Smith, R. V.: *Nucleonics*, **14**:55 (April, 1956).
40. Morton, G. A.: *Nucleonics*, **10**:39 (March, 1952).
41. Lazar, N. H., R. C. Davis, and P. R. Bell: *Nucleonics*, **14**:52 (April, 1956).
42. Cowper, G.: *Nucleonics*, **12**:29 (March, 1954).
43. Miller, C. E., L. D. Marinelli, R. E. Rowland, and J. E. Rose: *Nucleonics*, **14**:40 (April, 1956).
44. Hayes, F. N., D. G. Ott, and B. S. Rogers: *Nucleonics*, **13**:38 (December, 1955).
45. Hayes, F. N., D. G. Ott, and V. N. Kerr: *Nucleonics*, **14**:42 (January, 1956).
46. Williams, D. L., F. N. Hayes, R. J. Kandell, and W. H. Rogers: *Nucleonics*, **14**:62 (January, 1956).
47. Hayes, F. N., E. C. Anderson, and J. R. Arnold: "Proceedings of the International Conference on the Peaceful Uses of Atomic Energy," vol. 14, p. 188, United Nations, New York, 1956.
48. Keuffel, J. W.: *Nucleonics*, **10**:41 (March, 1952).
49. Cooke-Yarborough, E. H.: *J. Sci. Instr.*, **26**:96 (1949).
50. Wells, F. H.: *J. Sci. Instr.*, **29**:111 (1952).
51. Morton, G. A., and J. A. Mitchell: *RCA Rev.*, **9**:632 (1948).
52. Seitz, F., and D. W. Mueller: *Phys. Rev.*, **78**:605 (1949).
53. Wright, G. T.: *J. Sci. Instr.*, **31**:377 (1954).
54. Robinson, K. W.: *Nucleonics*, **10**:34 (March, 1952).
55. Connolly, R. E., and M. B. Leboent: *Anal. Chem.*, **25**:1095 (1953).
56. Kelley, G. C., P. R. Bell, R. C. Davis, and N. H. Lazar: *Nucleonics*, **14**:53 (April, 1956).
57. Van Rennes, A. B.: *Nucleonics*, **10**:20 (July, 1952); **10**:23 (August, 1952); **10**:32 (September, 1952); **10**:51 (October, 1952).
58. Bell, P. R.: *Nucleonics*, **12**:53 (March, 1954).
59. Hofstadter, R., and J. A. McIntyre: *Phys. Rev.*, **78**:619 (1950)L.
60. Maienschein, F. C., and J. K. Barr: *Phys. Rev.*, **82**:917 (1951)L.
61. Francis, J. E., P. R. Bell, and C. C. Harris: *Nucleonics*, **13**:82 (November, 1955).
62. Curran, S. C.: "Luminescence and the Scintillation Counter," chap. 10, Academic Press, Inc., New York, 1953.
63. Wouter, L. F.: *Nucleonics*, **10**:48 (August, 1952).
64. McGowan, F. K.: *Phys. Rev.*, **76**:1730 (1949); **81**:1066 (1951); **79**:404 (1950).
65. Harrison, F. B., C. L. Cowan, Jr., and F. Reines: *Nucleonics*, **12**:44 (March, 1954).

CHAPTER 8

# PHOTOGRAPHIC EMULSIONS AND OTHER DETECTION METHODS

Four important types of nuclear-radiation detectors have been considered in detail in the preceding chapters. In addition to these methods, there are a number of other detection systems which might be discussed. A brief treatment of several of these methods is included in this chapter.

In the organization of this book it has been necessary to make a rather arbitrary decision as to which detectors would be treated in detail in separate chapters and which would be covered in this chapter. The main criterion which has been applied is the extent to which the particular detector type has found general utility.

Some of these detection methods perhaps deserve a more detailed treatment than is afforded them here. However, the attempt has been made to include sufficient information that the reader can understand the basic features of the methods and evaluate their utility. In addition, reference to comprehensive discussions of the techniques are included for those readers needing more information.

## NUCLEAR-EMULSION TECHNIQUES

### 8–1. *Description of Techniques*

When charged particles pass through photographic emulsions, they can produce latent images along their paths. Upon development of the film, the grains of silver appear along the tracks of the particles. A variety of information can be obtained from a study of the tracks. Counting of the individual paths gives a measure of the number of nuclear particles entering the plate. A study of the detailed structure of the tracks leads to the determination of the mass, charge, and energy of the particles. Further, a detailed analysis can be made of an extremely complicated event involving several particles. In other words, these tracks give one essentially a direct observation of phenomena which otherwise would remain purely conceptual. Without such observations, many hypotheses would have only statistical substantiation through observations of great numbers of events instead of finding their direct verification through observations of single events.

Several comprehensive review articles have been written on nuclear-emulsion techniques. One of the most recent of these, by Goldschmidt-Clermont [1], has emphasized measurements on the tracks and processing techniques. Rotblat [2] has presented a very useful introduction to the basic techniques, along with much information on procedures and applications. Powell and Occhialini [3] as well as Yagoda [4] have written books containing many microphotographs of nuclear tracks. Many applications to the field of meson physics have been reviewed by Powell [5]. Other reviews include those of Rossi [6], Fowler and Perkins [7], Beiser [8], Vigneron [9], and Shapiro [10].

Both nuclear emulsions and cloud chambers have the property of being able to record the paths of nuclear particles. Therefore these two detector types share the ability to determine in detail the nature of nuclear events. Each of these detectors possesses certain advantages over the other. The nuclear emulsions are superior to cloud chambers in the following respects:

1. Stopping power. The stopping power in a nuclear emulsion is around a thousand times that in a cloud-chamber gas because of a similar difference in densities. This means that not only can larger portions of the paths of high-energy particles be recorded but also there exists a much higher probability for initiation of nuclear events in the emulsion. These advantages can be exploited by the use of thick emulsions or by stacks of thinner emulsions.

2. Duration of sensitivity. The data recorded in a nuclear emulsion can be collected over a period of time approaching several weeks. During this period the detector is continually operative. The limitation of the exposure time comes from the fading of the latent image. On the other hand, a cloud chamber, whether it be the expansion or the diffusion type, can be operative only during the time the conditions in the chamber are proper for track formations and the camera is set for recording the picture of the track. In an expansion chamber this might be $\frac{1}{10}$ sec for each expansion of the chamber, with the expansion occurring perhaps two times each minute. Although the sensitive time is greatly improved in the diffusion chamber, the operative time does not begin to approach that of the nuclear emulsions.

3. Mechanical features. The nuclear emulsions are particularly advantageous because of their light weight, small size, and ruggedness.

On the other hand, the cloud chambers have certain advantages. These are as follows:

1. Accuracy. The nuclear emulsion tends to shrink during development. Unless special precautions are taken to prevent it, the thickness may shrink to a value between 50 and 75 per cent of the predevelopment thickness. In addition, the composition of the emulsions varies from batch to batch,

leading to an uncertainty in the range-energy relationships. Since the cloud chambers are not subject to this type of difficulties, the accuracy of the measurements taken with these instruments is much higher.

2. Use in a magnetic field. Cloud chambers are often operated in magnetic fields so that a particle's momentum can be determined from measurements of the radius of curvature of the track which it produces. This cannot be accomplished readily in nuclear emulsions because of the frequency of scattering of particles by constituents of the emulsion; some successful work of this type has been carried out, however [11–13].

### 8–2. *Emulsion Types for Nuclear-track Applications*

Special nuclear emulsions have been developed for nuclear-track work since ordinary optical emulsions are not suitable. Tracks in the latter appear as widely separated, large grains, making it impossible to make accurate measurements of track lengths. In addition, the low sensitivity of these emulsions, coupled with a large background fog of individual grains, makes it impossible to observe tracks of low specific ionization. Nuclear emulsions have as much as four times the silver bromide content of optical emulsions. The grains are small, 0.1 to 0.6 $\mu$ in size, and are well separated, in contrast to the larger interlocking grains in optical plates.

A number of nuclear emulsions are available for nuclear-track work. Some of these films along with several of their characteristics are listed in Table 8–1.

It appears that several ionizing events are necessary to make a grain developable. Consequently, for a particular type of particle in any given emulsion there may be a maximum particle energy above which the specific ionization is not large enough to cause tracks. These maximum energies are listed in Table 8–1 where they are applicable. In the event that the value of the critical specific ionization for the emulsion is less than that at the minimum in the specific-ionization curve of the particle, particles with all energies are detectable.

The film sensitivities are controlled primarily through the use of sensitizers. In addition, the sensitivity of a given type of film can be varied within wide limits by the developing techniques [14,15].

Nuclear emulsions can be obtained from the manufacturers in a wide variety of sizes and shapes. These emulsions are produced regularly in thicknesses ranging from a few microns to 1,200 $\mu$. They may be obtained on a glass backing plate or without the backing. The latter, sometimes called "pellicules" or "stripped emulsions," are very useful for stacking into a large sensitive volume.

The composition of the emulsion is important, not only as it affects the sensitivity of the film but also as it determines the range-energy relationships of charged particles in the emulsions. In addition, it determines the

TABLE 8–1. CHARACTERISTICS OF COMMERCIAL EMULSIONS

| Manufacturer | Ilford* | | | | Eastman Kodak† | | | | |
|---|---|---|---|---|---|---|---|---|---|
| Type | D1 | E1 | C2 | G5 | NTC | NTA | NTB | NTB2 | NTB3 |
| Mean grain diameter, $\mu$ | 0.12 | 0.14 | 0.16 | 0.30 | 0.1–0.3 | 0.2–0.3 | 0.2–0.3 | 0.2–0.3 | 0.2–0.3 |
| Highest ratio of $v/c$ for singly charged particles | ... | 0.2 | 0.31 | 1.0 | ... | ... | 0.33 | 0.69 | 0.99 |
| Highest detectable energy of electrons, Mev | ... | ... | 0.03 | All | ... | ... | 0.03 | 0.2 | 0.4 |
| Highest detectable energy of protons, Mev | ... | 20 | 50 | All | ... | 20 | 50 | 375 | 750 |
| Highest detectable energy of alpha particles, Mev | Low energy | 500 | 1,500 | All | Low energy | 200 | 800 | All | All |
| Highest detectable energy of fission products | All | All | All | All | All | All | All | All | All |

* From Ilford Research Laboratories, Ilford, London, England.

† From Eastman Kodak Company, Rochester, N.Y.

type of interactions which nuclear radiation undergoes in the film. Table 8–2 gives the composition of Ilford G5 emulsion as well as its density and other properties.

The addition of special materials to the emulsions makes possible the selection of particular nuclear reactions. As an example, the addition of $B^{10}$ makes the emulsion a very efficient neutron detector, as is discussed in Chap. 9.

TABLE 8–2. DATA ON ILFORD G5 EMULSIONS*

| Composition | | Properties | |
|---|---|---|---|
| Element | Concentration, g/cm³ | | |
| Silver | 1.82 | Density | 3.838 g/cm³ |
| Bromine | 1.34 | Atoms/cm³ | $8.0 \times 10^{22}$ |
| Iodine | 0.012 | Mean $A$ | 29 |
| Carbon | 0.277 | Mean $Z$ | 13 |
| Hydrogen | 0.053 | Mean $Z^2$ | 456 |
| Oxygen | 0.25 | | |
| Sulfur | 0.007 | | |
| Nitrogen | 0.074 | | |

* From Ilford Research Laboratories, Ilford, London, England.

The choice of the emulsion type depends on the application to which the emulsion is made (see Sec. 8–6). The sensitivity of the film must be large enough to allow sufficient grain density for detection. On the other hand, if it is too sensitive, the grain density will be so high that the individual grains cannot be distinguished and grains cannot be counted.

Further information on the commercial types of emulsions can be obtained from the manufacturers and from the literature referred to above.

## 8–3. *Processing and Examination of Nuclear-track Plates*

Special developing techniques have been worked out for use with nuclear emulsions. The necessity of the special methods arises because of the great thickness, the high silver content, and the sensitivity of the gelatin to distortion. The review by Goldschmidt-Clermont [1] includes an excellent description of current techniques.

Perhaps the simplest method to achieve even development of emulsions with moderate thickness is to choose a slow developer with a long induction time. It penetrates through the emulsion in a time appreciably less than the developing time itself. Standard X-ray film developer, such as D19, is suitable for thicknesses up to 100 $\mu$. This method can be extended to thicknesses of up to 400 μ by further slowing down the developing action through reduction of the temperature to 4°C [16].

The most widely used method today is the temperature-development technique [17]. This method is based on the difference in the temperature coefficients of the diffusion and developing processes. It has been used successfully for development of emulsions having thicknesses up to 2,000 μ. A developer is chosen whose chemical effects are more reduced at low temperatures than is its diffusion speed. Therefore the developer is allowed to diffuse evenly throughout the emulsion at about 5°C. Then the plate is taken out of the bath and allowed to heat up, for example, to 28°C, at which temperature the development takes place. Table 8–3 is a typical development schedule for a 600-μ plate.

The selection of a developer in this technique is very important. Amidol (2,4-diaminophenol hydrochloride) is one of the most satisfactory types [1].

TABLE 8–3. EXAMPLE OF TEMPERATURE-DEVELOPMENT SCHEDULE*

| Operation | Bath | Temperature, °C | Time |
|---|---|---|---|
| Development: | | | |
| Preliminary soaking | Distilled water | Cooling to 5 | 120 min |
| Cold stage | Boric acid-amidol† | 5 | 120 min |
| Warm stage: | | | |
| Slow heating | Dry‡ | 5–28 | 5 min |
| Development | Dry | 28 | 60 min |
| Slow cooling | Dry | 28–5 | 5 min |
| Stop bath | Acetic acid, 0.2% | 5–14 | 120 min |
| Silver-deposit cleaning§ | | | |
| After development: | | | |
| Washing | Running water | 14 | 120 min |
| Fixing | Hypo, 40%¶ | Cooling to 5 | Until clear |
| Slow dilution | Water¶ | 5 | 100 hr |
| Glycerine bath | Glycerine, 2% | 5 to ambient | 120 min |
| Drying | . . . . . . . . . . . . . . | 20 | 7 days |

* From Y. Goldschmidt-Clermont, *Ann. Rev. Nuclear Sci.*, **3**:141 (1953).

† Composition given in Y. Goldschmidt-Clermont, Table II, *Ann. Rev. Nuclear Sci.*, **3**:141 (1953).

‡ Wipe the plate surface with a soft tissue.

§ Remove the silver deposited on the surface with a soft tissue.

¶ Add sodium sulfate in increasing concentration up to 10 per cent if swelling is excessive.

The shrinkage of the emulsion which accompanies the development places a serious limitation on the accuracy of measurements made by nuclear-emulsion techniques. Substantial control of this shrinking has been attained [18] by soaking in glycerine, thus filling the voids which are left by the removal of the unsensitized silver halides.

In order that accurate results may be obtained and that the observer may be relieved from optical strain, it is important that proper optical equipment be available. This has been emphasized by Powell [19]. The requirements for the optical equipment, along with descriptions of several systems which have been used, are covered by Rotblat [2] and Goldschmidt-Clermont [1]. The chief instrument is an ordinary microscope with an individual as an observer. A binocular microscope with inclined eyepieces is recommended for the comfort of the observer. Requirements for the microscope include small depth of focus, large working distance, precise vertical movement with an accurate scale for depth measurements, precise motion of the mechanical stage with an accurate position indicator, a protractor for angle measurement, and eyepiece scales.

In regard to the mechanical construction of the microscopes, it appears that the domain of the nuclear-emulsion technique starts just about where the technique in medicine and biology stops. However, special models for the nuclear-emulsion technique have been made by Cooke, Troughton, and Simms in England; Koristka in Italy; Leitz in Germany; and Bausch and Lomb in the United States. Microscope objectives which meet the optical requirements for a nuclear-emulsion microscope include the following: Cooke (magnification 45, numerical aperture 0.95, working distance 1.5 mm); Leitz (×53, n.a. 0.95, w.d. 1 mm); Koristka (×55, w.a. 0.95, w.d. 1.35 mm); and others. These objectives are useful for the detailed study of selected events.

For scanning of plates while looking for large events or for counting tracks produced by particles with high specific ionizations, lower magnification can be used. Nevertheless, oil-immersion lenses are desirable since they help to minimize difficulty arising because the surfaces of the emulsions are not perfectly smooth. Oil-immersion lenses such as the Leitz (×22, n.a. 0.65, w.d. 2.3 mm) meet this need.

When photomicrographs of the tracks are required at high magnifications, it is necessary to take a series of photographs at consecutive sections along the track and fit these together in a mosaic. Morrison and Pickup [20] have described a useful method of taking these photomicrographs.

### 8–4. *Range-Energy Relationships in Emulsions*

Commonly the energy of a particle is measured by the determination of its range in the emulsion. For this determination it is necessary that the entire path of the particle be within the emulsion and that the identity of the particle be known.

A considerable amount of work, both theoretical and experimental, has been devoted to the establishment of precise range-energy relationships for various types of nuclear emulsions [21–24]. As an example, Fig. 8–1 is a set of range-energy curves for various particles in the Ilford C2 emulsion.

Other similar curves are available from the suppliers of the emulsions.

Changes in the emulsion composition, for example, in the water content, affect range measurement. For accurate measurements it is common practice to calibrate the emulsion under the conditions of exposure and develop-

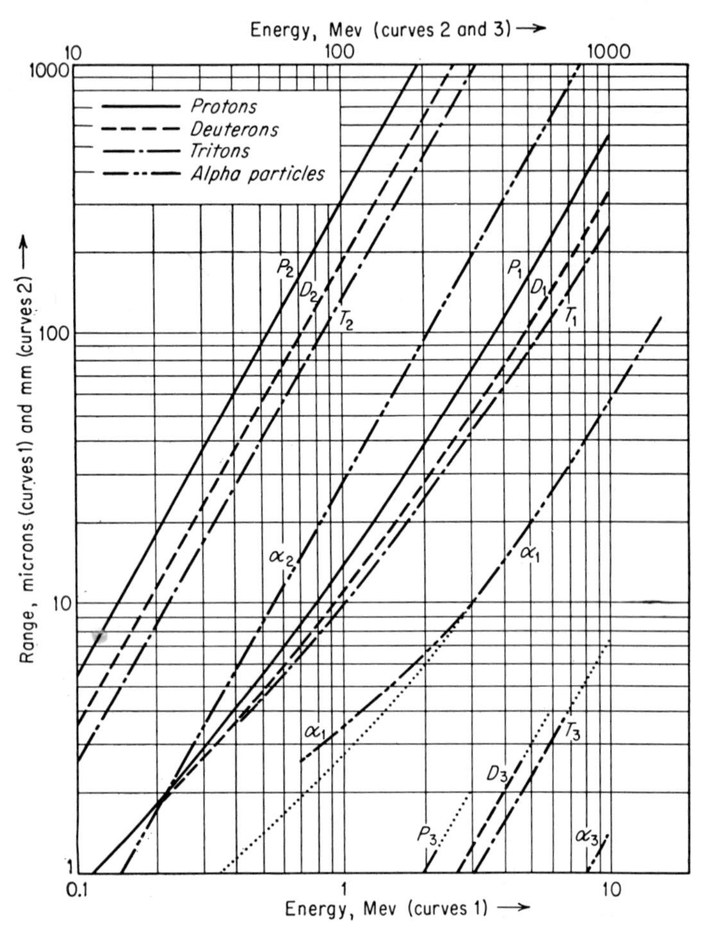


FIG. 8–1. Range-energy relationships for various particles in the Ilford C2 emulsion. [*Data from L. Vigneron, J. phys. radium,* **14**:145 (1953); *reprinted from Y. Goldschmidt-Clermont, Ann. Rev. Nuclear Sci.,* **3**:141(1953).]

ment to be employed in the experiment. This can be done by using particles of known range.

In the absence of the range-energy curves for a variety of particles, the relationships of the type given by Eqs. (1–5) and (1–6) can be used to complete the curves, provided that a curve for another particle type is available. The factor $C$ in Eq. (1–6) is approximately 1.5 $\mu$ for emulsions.

8–5. *Energy Loss and Grain Counting*

Only a small fraction of the energy lost by a charged particle while passing through an emulsion is used in the production of latent images that can be brought out during development. Nevertheless, within limits, depending on the type of emulsion and the nature and degree of the development, the number of developed grains per unit path length $dN/dx$ is a function of the rate of energy loss $dE/dx$. Thus one can write

$$\frac{dN}{dx} = f\left(\frac{dE}{dx}\right) \tag{8–1}$$

However, at the two extremes of the specific ionization, limiting cases are reached. For sufficiently low specific ionization, the grains will not develop, and no tracks appear. On the other hand, for sufficiently high specific ionization, all grains along the path of the particle are developable, and the grain density reaches a saturation value, independent of the particle energy. A typical maximum density is 2 grains/$\mu$ for commercial emulsions. Figure 8–2 shows the grain density versus rate of energy loss for underdeveloped Eastman Kodak NTA [25, 26] and for Ilford G5 [27] emulsions.

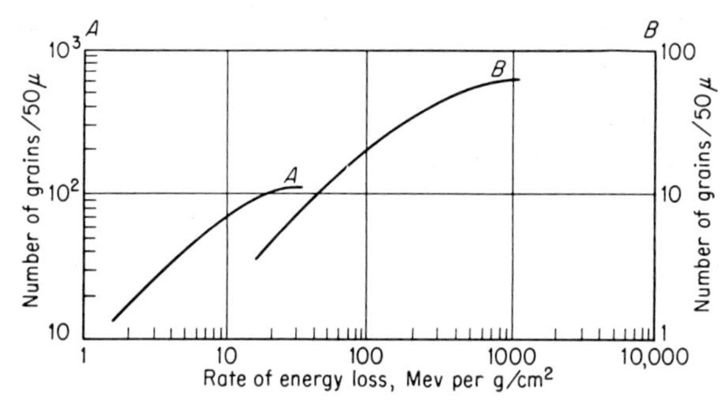


FIG. 8–2. Grain density versus rate of energy loss in underdeveloped Eastman Kodak NTA (curve $B$) [*from H. L. Bradt and B. Peters, Phys. Rev.*, **80**:943 (1950)] and Ilford G5 (curve $A$) [*from P. H. Fowler, Phil. Mag.*, **41**:169 (1950)] emulsions.

The masses of particles can be compared through the use of grain-density measurements along with total grain count or range measurements. These relationships are particularly useful when the charges of the particles are the same, e.g., in the case of singly charged particles. By means of Eqs. (1–1) and (8–1), one can write

$$\frac{dN}{dx} = f_1(v) \tag{8–2}$$

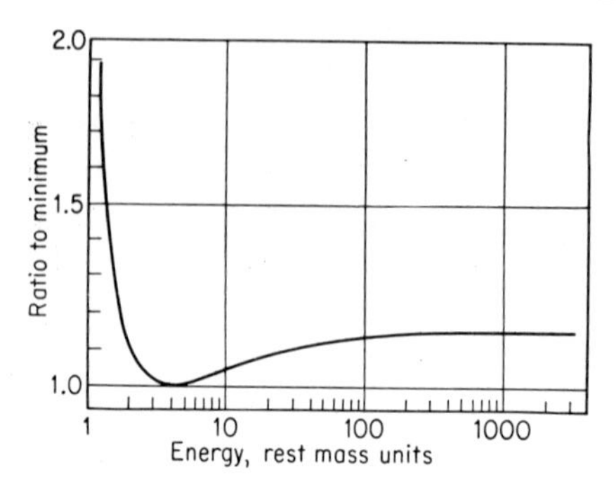


FIG. 8–3. Predicted relative grain density in silver bromide as a function of particle energy. [*From M. M. Shapiro and B. Steller, Phys. Rev.*, **87**:682 (1952).]

where $v$ is the particle velocity; i.e., the grain density is dependent only on the particle's velocity. This is illustrated in Fig. 8–3 where the relative grain density in an emulsion is plotted as a function of energy in rest-mass units, the latter quantity being a function of velocity only.

From Eqs. (1–5) and (8–2), one can write

$$\frac{dN}{dx} = f_1(v) = f_2\left(\frac{R}{M}\right) \tag{8-3}$$

where $R$ is the residual range of the particle and $M$ is its mass. Thus, if on two tracks made by particles $A$ and $B$ one finds points where the track densities are equal, that is, $(dN/dx)_A = (dN/dx)_B$, then

$$\frac{R_A}{M_A} = \frac{R_B}{M_B} \tag{8-4}$$

where $R_A$ and $R_B$ are the residual ranges of $A$ and $B$, respectively, from the points of equal grain density. Consequently, if the mass of one particle is known and the residual range of both are measured, the mass of the unknown particle can be calculated.

**Example 8–1.** Figure 8–4 is a plot of grain density versus residual range for protons and $\mu$ mesons on Ilford C2 plates. Use these data to determine the ratio of the proton to $\mu$-meson masses.

*Solution.* By Eq. (8–4), the ratio of the residual ranges at equal grain densities is $R_p/R_\mu = M_p/M_\mu$. From Fig. 8–4 this ratio is seen to be 1:55/0.18 = 8.6 and 3.5/0.38 = 9.2 at grain densities of 18 and 16, respectively. The average of these two values is 8.9, comparing favorably with the accepted value of 8.8.

The total grain count $N$ can be related to the mass $M$ in the following manner. Rewriting Eq. (8–3),

$$\frac{dN}{dx} = -\frac{dN}{dR} = -\frac{d(N/M)}{d(R/M)} = f_2\left(\frac{R}{M}\right)$$

Integrating, one obtains

$$\frac{N}{M} = f_3\left(\frac{R}{M}\right)$$

where $N$ is the total number of grains in that portion of the track having a residual range of $R$. Consequently, at a given velocity or grain density, $N/M$ is a constant, and

$$\frac{N_A}{M_A} = \frac{N_B}{M_B} \tag{8-5}$$

In the study of the tracks of heavy, multicharged particles, ordinarily grain counting is not feasible because of the high density of the tracks. Two other methods have been developed for this purpose. The first method is the counting of $\delta$ rays, i.e., the secondary electrons ejected from the atoms as the heavy charged particles pass them. This method has been discussed by Bradt and Peters [25, 26]. They have pointed out that the number of $\delta$ rays, with energies lying between certain limits, produced per unit path

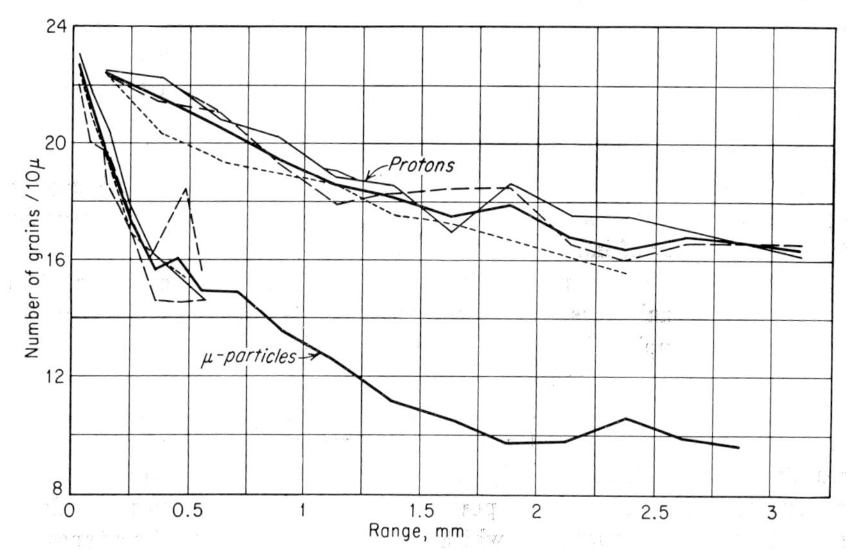


FIG. 8–4. Grain density versus residual range for protons and 36 mesons, in Ilford C2 plates. [*From R. Brown et al., Nature,* **163**:82 (1949).]

length is given by $N_\delta = Kz^2/\beta^2$, where $z$ is the particle charge, $\beta$ is $v/c$, and $K$ is a constant. When this relationship is used, curves can be drawn of $N_\delta$ versus residual range $R$ for various values of $z$. From these curves, values of $z$ can be determined from the $\delta$-ray counts.

The second method for studying heavy particles is based on the observation of the thinning down of the track near the end of its range. The ionization along tracks of multiple charged particles shows a characteristic taper corresponding to a gradual loss of charge by electron capture [28].

As a charged particle passes through an emulsion, it suffers numerous small-angle deflections as a result of Coulomb interaction at collisions with nuclei. The theory of small-angle scattering has been given by Williams [29]. Numerous comparisons of theory and experiment have been made. These have been reviewed by Berger [30] and by Gottstein et al. [31].

## 8–6. *Applications of Nuclear Emulsions*

It is to be expected that nuclear emulsions, with their property for obtaining permanent records of the details of nuclear events, coupled with their extreme simplicity, would have found many important applications. That this is indeed the case is borne out by an examination of the literature for the past 10 years. The reviews referred to in Sec. 8–1 are convenient for this purpose. A few of the applications are mentioned below.

Nuclear emulsions are widely used in autoradiography. In this technique the elements under study are tagged with radioisotopes. The positions of these radioisotopes in the systems under investigation are indicated by tracks in nuclear emulsions placed in contact with the system. This technique has found applications in botany, biology, crystallography, and metallurgy. Radioisotopes emitting both alpha and beta particles can be employed.

Often scattering experiments are carried out by using emulsions. Further, nuclear-scattering cameras in which the number, nature, and angular orientation of particles are recorded in nuclear emulsions are important tools in the study of induced nuclear reactions.

Emulsions have been used for measuring the activity of alpha emitters with very long half-lives. The long period of sensitivity is the important factor for this application. Through this technique, nuclides thought previously to be stable have been identified as alpha emitters.

Many applications have been found in cosmic-ray research. The small size and the long period of sensitivity of nuclear emulsions make them readily adaptable to balloon flights. In addition, the detail registered concerning the particles, making possible their identification, is particularly advantageous in a situation in which as large a number of particle types are involved as in cosmic radiations.

The nuclear stars (or nuclear evaporations) produced by both cosmic rays and radiation from high-energy particle accelerators are studied largely by nuclear emulsions. These events occur when a nucleus in the emulsion receives such intense excitation that a number of its elementary particles gain sufficient energy to penetrate the potential barrier. The energy for the evaporations comes from the mass conversion of the captured particles.

One particularly active use of emulsions is in the study of mesons. Most of the determinations of the mass and of the decay schemes of mesons have been made in this manner.

Numerous applications of nuclear emulsions to neutron measurements have been made. Some of these are discussed in Chap. 9.

### 8–7. *Photographic Films as Dosimeters*

Photographic film is in wide use for monitoring personnel for the radiation dose due to X, $\gamma$, and $\beta$ radiation [32]. This is accomplished through calibration procedures which relate the density of the photographic deposit in the film to the dose of radiation received by it.

Photographic films lend themselves to dosage determinations over a large range of dosage rates. The response to X and gamma radiation is independent of rate for intensity ratios of at least 1 to 10,000 [33]. By selection of films of different sensitivities, film dosimeters covering a wide range of doses can be devised. For example, Du Pont 502 film can be used from about 100 mr to 10 r, while the Eastman spectroscopic film 548–0 double-coat is suitable from 500 to 10,000 r [33].

The response of photographic film varies with the X- and gamma-ray energy; in particular, it rises as the photon energy decreases below about 150 kev. By a suitable selection of absorbers, so chosen that their absorption versus energy response matches the film density-energy characteristic, the film dosimeter can be made essentially energy-independent. For example, a filter composed of 1.49 mm of tin and 0.25 mm of lead matches the Eastman 548–0 double-coat film [33].

The application of photographic film to the dosimetry of beta rays has been studied by Dudley [34]. He concludes that, if proper reliance is placed on calibration, accurate results can be achieved.

The measurement of thermal-neutron dosage by photographic film has been studied by Kalil [35]. This may be accomplished through the comparison of the film densities under cadmium and brass filters. These filters are chosen so that both attenuate the gamma radiation by the same amount. However, because of the $(n,\gamma)$ reactions induced in the cadmium by the thermal neutrons, the film exposure produced behind the cadmium is higher than that behind the brass when thermal neutrons are present. Differential density measurements are calibrated in terms of thermal-neutron exposure.

The photographic film can be worn as a badge or in the form of a finger ring. The badge form is shown in Fig. 8–5. Ordinarily it contains two or more pieces of film of different sensitivities so that different ranges of gamma dosage can be measured simultaneously. The films are usually about 1½ by 2 in. They are wrapped in a thin, light-tight paper and placed in a frame, along with the necessary filters (usually about 1 mm of cadmium) to improve the energy response, to discriminate between betas and hard gammas and between thermal and fast neutrons, as required. The filters cover only portions of the film so that "windows," or openings, exist through which the various types of radiations can pass.

The opacity of the different portions of the film after development allows the dose due to the various types of radiation to be estimated. For practical purposes, each type of film requires its own calibration curve.

As an alternative method for the measurement of neutron dosage, track counts may be made in a nuclear emulsion such as Eastman Kodak NTA. The fast neutrons produce tracks through the scattered protons with which they share their energy, while the slow neutrons interact with the emulsion by the reaction $N^{14}(n,p)C^{14}$. The tracks are counted under a microscope after the development of the film, and the number of tracks per unit area is

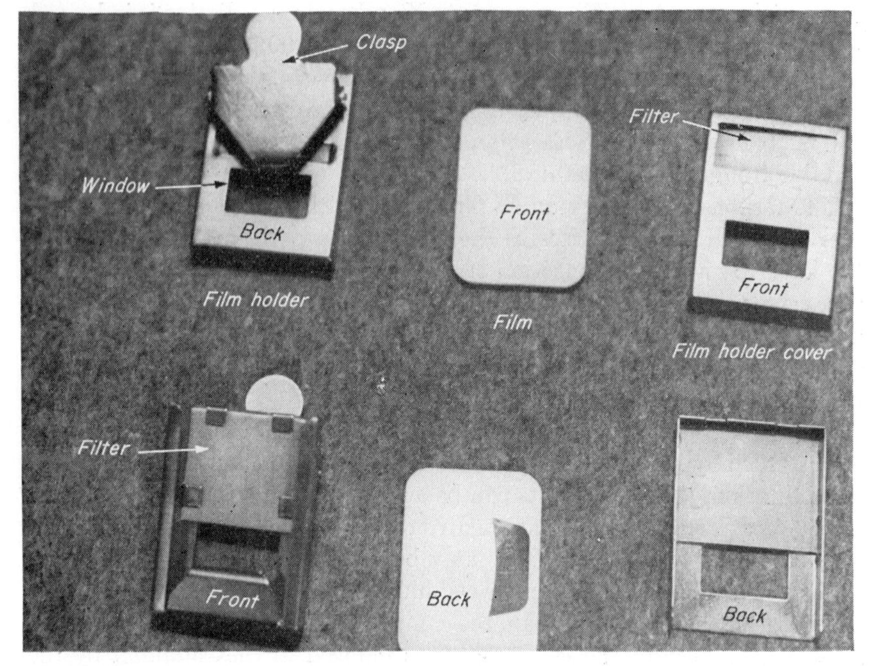


FIG. 8–5. Film-badge dosimeter.

interpreted in terms of neutron flux. Since the cadmium filter passes only fast neutrons, a differential count allows one to distinguish between fast and slow neutrons.

## CLOUD CHAMBERS

### 8–8. *Principles of Operation*

The operation of cloud chambers depends on the existence of a supersaturated region in a gas containing a condensable vapor. In the absence of nuclei or centers for condensation, the supersaturation condition can exist with essentially no accompanying condensation. Lord Kelvin has shown that the saturation vapor pressure in the vicinity of a drop increases with the curvature of the liquid surface. Consequently, the vapor pressure which represents supersaturation for a flat surface is below saturation if the drop is sufficiently small. For a given supersaturation in a region, there exists a given critical drop size below which the drop will evaporate and above which it will grow.

Dust and other particles can serve as centers for condensation because of their size. Also, ions of either sign serve as nuclei for condensation because their presence reduces the saturation vapor pressure in their immediate vicinity. It is the latter phenomenon which causes the track of charged particles to appear as vapor trails in cloud chambers.

There are two forms of cloud chambers, namely, the expansion type and the diffusion type. They are distinguished by the methods employed for obtaining a supersaturated region. These systems are illustrated schematically in Figs. 8–6 and 8–7.

The expansion cloud chamber and its applications are described in a book by J. G. Wilson [36] and the article by Das Gupta and Ghosh [37]. In this

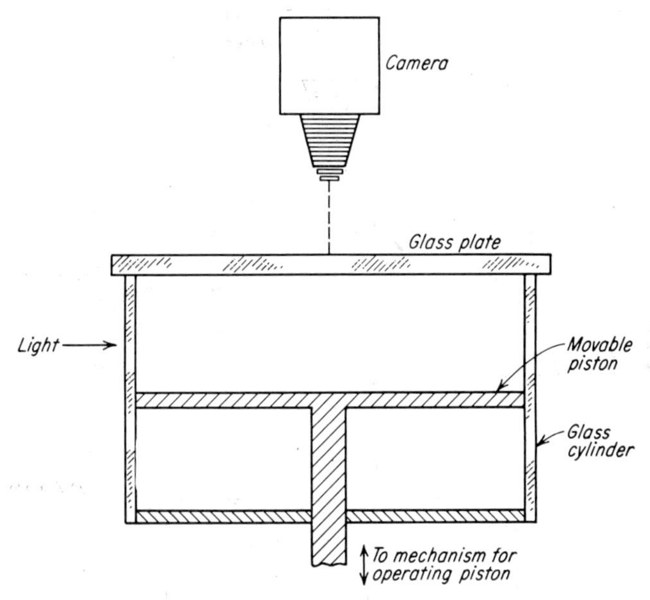


FIG. 8–6. Expansion cloud chamber.

type of chamber, a gas containing a condensable vapor is allowed to come to equilibrium, with sufficient liquid present to produce saturation. After the equilibrium is reached, an adiabatic expansion which causes supersaturation is produced. Following the expansion, heat flows slowly into the chamber, raising the temperature and decreasing the degree of supersaturation. The sensitive time, i.e., the time during which conditions are right for track formation, varies from a few milliseconds to 2 or 3 sec, depending on the particular design.

The theory of the diffusion cloud chamber has been summarized by Snowden [38] in his general review article. This type of chamber operates by the diffusion of a condensable vapor from a warm region where it is not saturated to a cold region where it becomes supersaturated. Most chambers in current use are arranged for downward diffusion. The vapor is introduced at the top, this being the warm end. The location and extent of the supersaturated region depend on the geometrical design and temperature differences in the chamber.

A number of combinations of gas and vapors have been found to function satisfactorily. In a diffusion-type chamber, methyl and ethyl alcohol vapors appear to be the most successful. Air is satisfactory for the gas from 20 cm to 4 atm, and hydrogen from 10 to 20 atm [39]. In expansion cloud chambers, air with water and argon with alcohol are in common use.

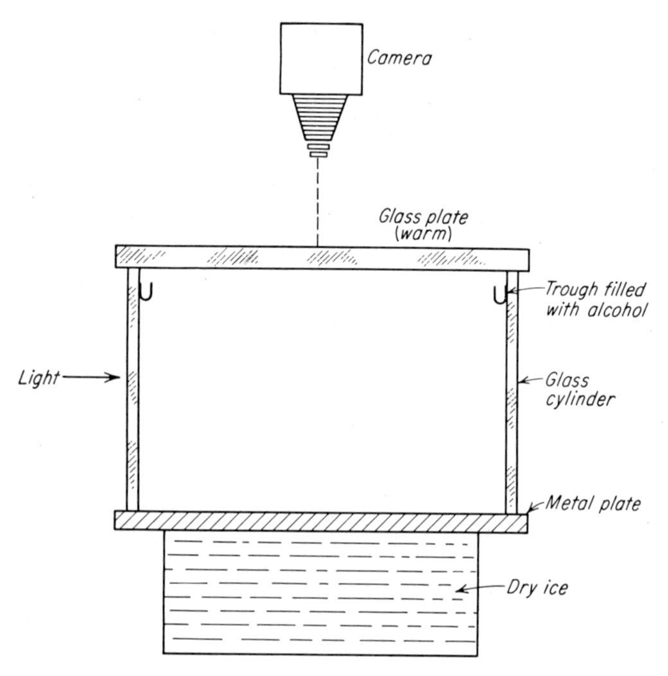


Fig. 8–7. Diffusion cloud chamber.

In each chamber type it is necessary to apply electric fields to remove unwanted ions. Fields of the order of 20 to 50 volts/cm are adequate. Any ambient ionizing radiation such as cosmic rays continually produces ions in the chamber. If those ions produced above the sensitive region in the diffusion chamber are not removed before they reach the sensitive region, the ion density may become high enough to remove the supersaturated condition and thus prevent the appearance of the tracks. In an expansion chamber these unwanted ions produce a general background of fog. The usual practice is to remove the field immediately before the expansion in an expansion chamber and immediately before the opening of the shutter of the camera in a diffusion chamber.

Cloud chambers are usually operated at atmospheric pressure. However, in certain applications it is advantageous to use a considerably higher or lower pressure. For low-energy particles whose range would be too short at atmospheric pressure, reduced pressures can be used. Joliot [40] has described a chamber which he operated at various pressures down to 10 mm Hg. High-pressure chambers can be employed to study a larger portion of the range of high-energy particles than would be possible with atmospheric pressure. Johnson et al. [41] have described a chamber designed to operate up to 200 atm. When filled with argon, this instrument has a stopping power equivalent to 1 cm of lead.

### 8–9. *Comparison of Expansion- and Diffusion-type Cloud Chambers*

In a recent article, Fretter [42] has reviewed the developments that have been made in cloud-chamber and bubble-chamber (see Sec. 8–10) techniques since 1951. This period has seen the development of both the diffusion cloud chamber and the bubble chamber into important methods of nuclear-particle detection.

It is clear from Figs. 8–6 and 8–7 that the diffusion chamber is simpler than the expansion chamber from the standpoint of mechanical features because of the absence of moving parts. Also, it follows as a result of the different principles of operation that the fraction of the total time useful for observing tracks is much larger for the diffusion- than for the expansion-type chamber.

Since the diffusion cloud chamber is continually sensitive, it cannot be operated in a background much above the normal cosmic-ray level. The presence of a high background reduces the amount of vapor present for recording the event of interest. However, if the background is pulsed along with the phenomena of interest, it produces no limitations on the method. Expansion cloud chambers are not affected adversely by either continuous or pulsed background.

The sensitive region in a diffusion chamber does not extend immediately adjacent to surfaces placed in it, since the surfaces disturb the diffusion currents passing them. A similar situation does not exist in the expansion cloud chamber. Consequently, those experiments requiring the placement of objects in the sensitive region can be carried out more satisfactorily in the latter-type chamber. Experiments of this type include the use of absorbers to control the energy of the radiation and the use of radiators such as lead to induce nuclear interactions. In the way of a further limitation, the sensitive layer in a diffusion chamber is no more than 3 in. thick and cannot be made vertical to detect cosmic rays.

The diffusion cloud chamber (also the bubble chamber) can be operated with fillings of hydrogen at relatively high density, whereas it is inconvenient to use an expansion chamber at a high pressure of hydrogen. The high-pressure-hydrogen chambers have made possible experiments such as those performed by the Brookhaven group concerning meson production in (n,p) collisions [43].

At the present time the largest portion of serious cloud-chamber work employs the expansion type. This would appear to be because of the larger experience in the design of this chamber type rather than an overwhelming superiority over the diffusion chamber.

### 8–10. *Bubble Chambers*

The bubble chamber is an additional nuclear-particle detector which produces visible particle tracks. It shares with nuclear emulsions the advantages of a high density. It has the further advantage that its sensitive volume can be filled with a hydrogen-rich medium in contrast to the complex nuclear structure of the silver and bromine in nuclear emulsions.

The bubble chamber has been developed as a result of a systematic set of experiments carried out by Glaser [44–46]. This work has been reviewed by Fretter [42].

The bubble chamber utilizes the instability of superheated liquids against bubble formation. Glaser was able to demonstrate that the ions formed by the passage of ionizing particles through a superheated liquid could create condensation nuclei for the formation of bubbles.

Liquid hydrogen and diethyl ether are the liquids which are used in two successful types of bubble chambers. The former is maintained as a liquid at a temperature just above the boiling temperature for atmospheric pressure by pressurization to a few atmospheres, while the diethyl ether is kept from boiling by operation at 350 lb/in$^2$ and 157°C. In each case the superheated condition is achieved by a sudden release of the pressure.

The tracks of the particles are photographed by means of a high-speed flash light which occurs just a few milliseconds after the creation of the superheated condition. In fact, for the diethyl ether the chamber remains sensitive for only about 10 msec after the expansion; this makes possible much better time resolution than can be achieved with any other type of device for recording particle tracks.

The bubble chamber promises to be very useful with high-energy particle accelerators where large stopping powers are desirable, particularly for experiments in which the presence of hydrogen nuclei is desirable.

**Example 8–2.** Estimate the dimensions of a high-pressure (10-atm) hydrogen-filled cloud chamber with the same total stopping power as a 6-in. bubble chamber.

*Solution.* Taking the dimensions as inversely proportional to the density of the media, one has for $D$, the dimension of the cloud chamber, the expression

$$D = \frac{6\rho_{\text{B.C.}}}{\rho_{\text{C.C.}}} = \frac{6 \times 0.07}{4.7 \times 10^{-4}} = 894 \text{ in.}$$

where 0.07 g/cm$^3$ and $4.7 \times 10^{-4}$ g/cm$^3$ are the densities of liquid hydrogen and gaseous hydrogen at 10 atm, respectively.

## CRYSTAL COUNTERS

### 8–11. *Mechanism of the Crystal Counter*

In 1945 Van Heerden published a thesis [47] describing the use of single crystals of silver chloride for the detection of nuclear particles. Other crystals which have been used with varying degrees of success by subsequent investigators include diamond, cadmium sulfide, silver bromide, thallium bromide, thallium iodide, sulfur, sodium chloride, and zinc sulfide. A detailed review of crystal counters has been written by Hofstadter [48].

A crystal counter consists of a small crystal in the form of a rectangular parallelepiped. Two opposite parallel faces are coated with electrodes. The detector is used in a circuit similar to that for a pulse ionization chamber, with the applied voltage being several hundred volts.

In the absence of ionizing radiation, no current flows in the external circuit, since the crystals are insulators. However, when charged particles pass through the crystals, electrons are raised to the conduction band, leaving behind "positive holes" in the valence band. The presence of the electric field causes the electrons and holes to drift toward the positive and negative electrodes, respectively. As a result, charge is induced in the external circuit, and the particle detection is made possible.

The fate of the freed electrons and holes can be (1) to reach the electrodes, (2) to recombine with other holes and electrons after wandering for some distance, or (3) to reach trapping states situated throughout the crystal lattice. The trapping of the charges is undesirable, since it results in a space charge which reduces the electric field. Continued bombardment can result in the reduction of the field to a very low value.

The crystal counter can be considered analogous to the gas ionization chamber with the gas dielectric being replaced by a solid. However, the space charge which occurs in the crystal has no analogy in the gas ionization chamber.

### 8–12. *Status of the Crystal Counter*

The status of crystal counters has been summarized by Chynoweth [49]. Potentially, these detectors have a number of useful properties. These include (1) high stopping power, making possible detection of high-energy particles by small-volume detectors; (2) proportionality between absorbed particle energy and pulse height; (3) fast rise time of pulses, making possible high counting rates; and (4) absence of "window" such as that necessary in a gas chamber. On the other hand, these detectors have disadvantages. The most serious of these is the formation of the space charge in the crystal. Other disadvantages include the requirement for cooling below room temperature and variations in the counting efficiency from crystal to crystal.

Fortunately all the advantages held by the crystal counter are shared by the scintillation counter. Consequently the latter has become a very important detector (see Chap. 7), while the former has found but little use. The development of crystals having several orders of magnitude lower trap density is required to alter this situation significantly.

The successful application of single crystals of germanium to fast-neutron dosimetry has been described by Cassen [50]. His dosimeter consisted of a wafer of intrinsic germanium 4 mm long, 2 mm wide, and 0.75 mm thick. Short lengths of copper wire were soldered to the crystal ends, and the unit was encapsulated in plastic. This type of dosimeter has proved particularly useful for the measurement of neutron dose in animals.

The change in the electrical conductivity of the germanium is a function of the integrated neutron dose. This change is explained in the following manner. The fast neutrons produce germanium-atom recoils which dislodge neighboring germanium atoms from their normal lattice sites, causing lattice defects which act as electron traps. The holes in the normally filled Fermi band act as positive carriers, giving the crystal additional conductivity. At ordinary temperature this increase in conductivity is masked by the normal conductivity produced by electrons. Thus for maximum sensitivity the germanium resistance must be measured before and after the irradiation at a reduced temperature, usually that of solid carbon dioxide.

The change in conductivity was found to be a linear function of dose from about 150 rep up to tens of thousands of rep. Linearity could be obtained at lower doses by sufficient preexposure of the crystals.

## PARTICLE COUNTING BY ČERENKOV RADIATION

### 8–13. *Production of Cerenkov Radiation*

During the early days of the studies of the effects of nuclear radiation, there were several reports of weak glowing in the vicinity of strong radioactive sources. The first detailed study of this phenomenon was made by Cerenkov [51] in 1934; it has subsequently come to be known as the Cerenkov effect or, alternatively, as Cerenkov radiation.

A theoretical explanation for Cerenkov radiation, based on classical electromagnetic theory and optics, has been presented by Frank and Tamm [52]. Their theory includes equations for the intensity of the light, the angular correlation with the direction of the exciting radiation, the polarization, and the spectral characteristics. A presentation of a portion of this theory due to Jelley [53] follows.

A charged particle of high energy passes through a dielectric and produces local polarization along its path. This is illustrated in Fig. 8–8. Immediately after the passage of the charged particle, the polarized molecules return to their quiescent states with the emission of light. When the velocity of the particle is slower than that of light in the medium, the light pulses from the individual molecules interfere destructively and are damped out. On the other hand, if the velocity of the charged particle is greater than that of light in the dielectric, the wavelets from the individual molecules reinforce each other by constructive interference. The resulting pulse of light produced by the passage of the charged particle through the dielectric is known as Cerenkov radiation. Thus, for the production of Cerenkov radiation in a medium of index of refraction $n$, the velocity $v$ of the charged particle must be greater than that of light in the medium; that is,

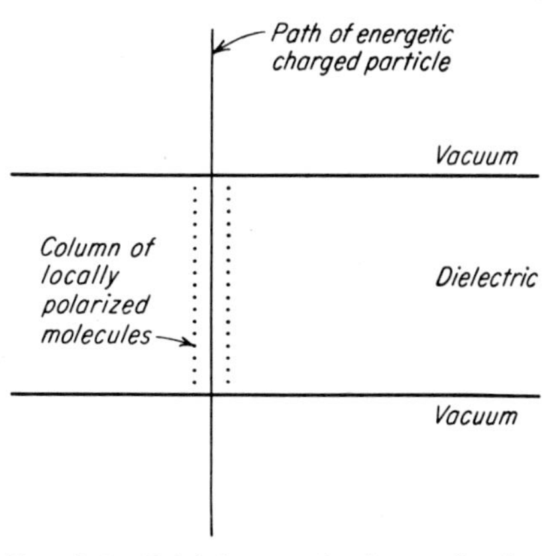


FIG. 8–8. Initial stages in the production of Cerenkov radiation.

$$v > \frac{c}{n} \quad \text{or} \quad \beta > \frac{1}{n} \tag{8–6}$$

where $c$ is the velocity of light in a vacuum, or $2.99793 \times 10^{10}$ cm/sec, and $\beta$ is $v/c$.

The production of constructive interference is illustrated in Fig. 8–9. The wavelets of light which are sent out while the particle moves from $A$ to $B$ are seen to produce a wavefront $BC$. The condition for constructive interference is that the time for the light to travel the distance $AC$ be equal to the time required for the particle to travel from $A$ to $B$. That is,

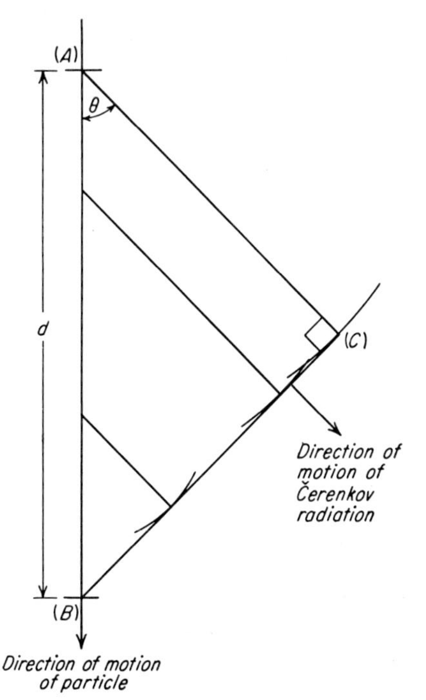


FIG. 8–9. Constructive interference in the production of Cerenkov radiation.

$$\frac{d \cos \theta}{c/n} = \frac{d}{v} \quad \text{or} \quad \cos \theta = \frac{1}{\beta n} \tag{8–7}$$

Here it is assumed that the particle velocity remains constant while moving from $A$ to $B$.

Figure 8–9 shows the wavefront in one half of one plane only. In the

spatial situation it is seen that the light is emitted in a conical shell of half angle $\theta$ extending all around the axis of the particle path.

A derived practical formula, obtained from the work of Frank and Tamm, gives for $I$, the number of photons radiated per centimeter of path in the frequency interval $\Delta\nu$, the value

$$I = \frac{4\pi^2 e^2}{hc^2} \Delta\nu \left(1 - \frac{1}{\beta^2 n^2}\right) = \frac{2\pi\Delta\nu}{137c} \sin^2\theta \tag{8-8}$$

The visible spectrum covers a frequency interval of about $3 \times 10^{14}$ cycles/sec. Using this value for $\Delta\nu$ yields a value of 450 $\sin^2\theta$ photons per centimeter of path for $I$.

The Cerenkov effect is analogous to two mechanical phenomena: (1) the bow wave from a ship which is moving faster than the velocity of surface waves and (2) the shock wave produced in air when a projectile passes through it at a supersonic velocity.

TABLE 8–4. THRESHOLD ENERGY, DIRECTION OF PROPAGATION, AND INTENSITY OF PHOTONS DUE TO CERENKOV RADIATION IN LUCITE

| Particle | Threshold energy, Mev | 100-Mev particles | | 500-Mev particles | |
|---|---|---|---|---|---|
| | | $\theta$, deg | $I$ visible range, photons/cm | $\theta$, deg | $I$ visible range, photons/cm |
| Electrons. . . . . . . . . . | 0.173 | 48 | 250 | 48 | 250 |
| $\pi$ mesons. . . . . . . . . . | 49 | 31 | 120 | 46 | 232 |
| Protons. . . . . . . . . . . | 320 | Below threshold | . . . | 29 | 106 |

The preceding equations have been used to compute the quantities tabulated in Table 8–4. The threshold energy refers to the energy below which Cerenkov radiation does not appear. The angle $\theta$ is the half angle of the cone of radiation, and $I$ is the number of photons in the visible band per centimeter of path.

### 8–14. *Considerations Involved in the Applications of Cerenkov Detectors*

If nuclear radiation of sufficient intensity is available, a photographic method may be employed to record the Cerenkov radiation. Such a system has been used by Mather [54] for the precise measurement of the photon energy produced by the 184-in. Berkeley cyclotron. In this measurement a photographic film was used in conjunction with the appropriate optical system to measure the angle $\theta$. The particle energy was computed from Eq. (8–7).

Most applications of Cerenkov radiation to the study of nuclear radiation involve the detection of single particles. In these equipments photomultiplier tubes are used to detect the light which is produced in the radiator. The term radiator refers to the medium in which the Cerenkov radiation is produced. In this respect, the arrangement is the same as in scintillation detectors. In principle, the two detector systems differ only in the replacement of the scintillator by the radiator. The radiators have the advantage that the light pulses are shorter, of the order of $10^{-10}$ sec, and that there is no phosphorescent glow, as occurs sometimes in scintillators. The radiators have the serious disadvantage, compared with the scintillators, of a low light output. For example, an electron traveling near the speed of light in lucite produces 250 photons of visible light per centimeter of path. If all these photons are collected at the photocathode and conversion efficiency to photoelectrons is of the order of 0.1 (see Chap. 7), then only about 25 electrons are produced, on an average. As discussed in Sec. 7–24, it would be difficult to discriminate between these pulses and the photomultiplier-tube noise. The discrimination is made easier by the use of a longer particle path, say of several centimeters, in the radiator. Another way in which the discrimination can be effected is to require fast coincidence between two phototubes viewing the same radiator or between two phototubes viewing two radiators through which a common particle passes.

In the choice of a radiator material, the index of refraction is an important consideration. From the standpoint of maximum light intensity, $n$ should be as high as possible. On the other hand, the requirement to discriminate between particle types through adjusting the threshold energy by means of $n$ may call for a low value of $n$. High angular discrimination, as required in precision velocity measurements, requires a radiator with a small dependence of $n$ on optical wavelength. Further, the material should have a low density and low atomic number in order that the rate of energy loss and the scattering be as small as possible when angle determinations are to be made. In addition, the radiator should have good transparency in the band to which the phototubes respond.

Lucite has proved to be the most generally useful radiator material. Its index of refraction is relatively high, being 1.5; its optical dispersion is somewhat less than most glasses; its transparency is good; and its density and effective atomic number are low. Water has also proved to be a useful radiator material.

One of the most important factors in the application of Cerenkov radiation to nuclear-particle detection is the dependence of the angle of travel of the radiation on the particle velocity, as given by Eq. (8–7). Not only does this make possible the determination of the velocity but also the discrimination between particles of differing velocities. It should be stressed, however, that, for any given particle type, velocity discrimination by means of angular determination is possible over only a limited range of energies. The lower limit occurs at the threshold energy for the Cerenkov effect, while the upper limit occurs when the relativistic mass increase causes the particle velocity to be insensitive to energy.

Another important feature of the Cerenkov detector is the ease of construction of the radiator. Further, the material is economical because the requirements on purity are quite moderate.

## 8–15. *Applications of Cerenkov Detectors*

Cerenkov counting can be used with high efficiency only for quite energetic particles. In the first place, the particle must be moving faster than light in the dielectric in order to radiate. Further, it must be capable of moving a considerable distance to irradiate sufficient photons for efficient detection. Consequently, the application of Cerenkov counters is limited to experiments with either cosmic rays or high-energy particle accelerators.

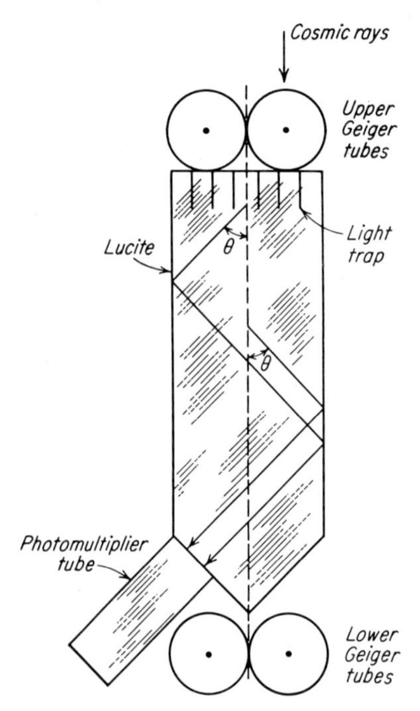


FIG. 8–10. Detector to study upward and downward components of cosmic rays. [*From J. R. Winckler, Phys. Rev.*, **85**:1054 (1952).]

In the field of cosmic radiation, the applications are limited, since most of the particles have very high energy and therefore values of $\beta$ approximately equal to 1. Consequently, these particles all produce the same radiation in the radiator. Nevertheless, interesting applications have been developed.

Winckler [55] has made use of the directional properties of the Cerenkov radiation to measure the ratio of the upward to downward components of cosmic radiation traveling in and out of the atmosphere. Figure 8–10 is a schematic diagram of this apparatus. The system has three separate detector channels: the photomultiplier tube operating by Cerenkov radiation and the upper and lower pairs of Geiger tubes, respectively. Particles passing downward are detected by all three channels and produce triple coincidences. Particles traveling upward produce no signal in the photomultiplier tube since the light is trapped at the top of the lucite; therefore upward particles produce double coincidences only.

Applications of Cerenkov detectors to experiments with a 450-Mev cyclotron have been described by Marshall [56]. The counters used can be classified either as focusing or nonfocusing types. Figure 8–11 is an example of a focusing type. The radiator consists of a lucite cylinder

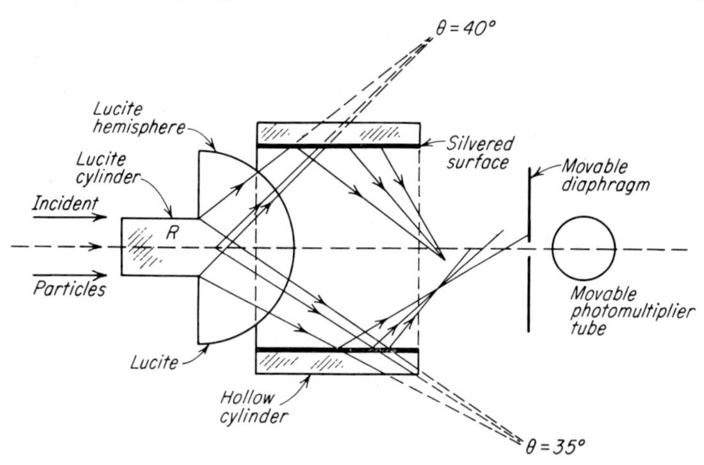


FIG. 8–11. Cerenkov detector having focusing property. [*From J. Marshall, Phys. Rev.*, **86**: 685 (1952).]

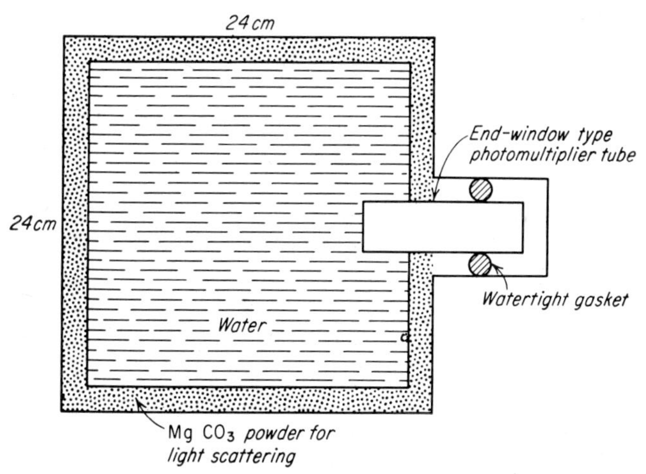


FIG. 8–12. Nonfocusing-type Cerenkov detector. [*From J. Marshall, Phys. Rev.*, **86**: 685 (1952).]

coupled to a lucite hemisphere. The system is such that radiation produced at a given angle $\theta$ is focused to a point, regardless of its point of origin in the radiator. This situation is illustrated for $\theta = 40°$ and $\theta = 35°$. By moving the diaphragm and the photomultiplier along the axis of the system, it is possible to select various values of $\theta$.

Figure 8–12 shows a nonfocusing-type Cerenkov counter. It is composed of an end-window-type photomultiplier tube in direct optical contact with the water. The walls are coated with a waterproof $MgCO_3$ powder to produce diffuse reflection.

Marshall has used these detectors satisfactorily in several fields; these include counting of electrons, protons, and $\pi$ mesons and the counting of high-energy electrons to the exclusion of protons and neutrons. In addition, by use of the focusing-type detector, the velocity of $\pi$ mesons has been determined. The velocity measurements are possible since the value of $\theta$ is in a convenient range for velocity discrimination.

Hildebrand [57] has reported the use of a type 5819 photomultiplier tube with a water radiator to count 145-Mev $\pi$ mesons. He has found that this process is 100 per cent efficient.

## ELECTRON MULTIPLIERS

### 8–16. *Use of Electron Multiplier for Nuclear-particle Counting*

The electron-multiplier principle plays a central role in two detector systems which have been discussed already, i.e., the scintillation counter and the Cerenkov counter. However, in each of these detectors the nuclear particles produce light as an intermediate step in the process. The light causes the emission of the photoelectrons, and the electron-multiplier section of the photomultiplier tube multiplies the number of electrons to a pulse which is sufficiently large for measurement.

The electron multiplier can be used for particle detection without the inclusion of the intermediate steps. In such a system the multiplication process is used for increasing the charge of the primary nuclear particle to an amount sufficiently large for counting.

Allen [58] has applied the electron-multiplier particle counter to a mass spectrograph for counting positive ions and electrons. He also reports [59] applying an electron multiplier to an electron spectrometer and as an alpha-particle detector. Stone [60] has studied the use of an electron-multiplier tube equipped with a thin window for beta-particle counting. The electron-multiplier tube is arranged so that the particles to be counted strike a target at the beginning of the electron-multiplier section of the tube. The dynode arrangement shown in Fig. 7–11 was used by both Allen and Stone. A background counting rate occurs primarily because of the thermionic emission from the target and the first dynodes. This background rate can be kept to a low value by the use of relatively high-work-function materials. Silver-magnesium alloys have proved satisfactory, having good secondary-emission properties as well as a relatively high work function.

The efficiency of the tube depends largely on the secondary-emission ratio of the target for the particles which strike it. If the secondary emission is 1 or greater, the efficiency can be 100 per cent, provided that the collection of secondary electrons from the target into the dynode section is good and the discriminator is set properly. Allen [59] has reported 100 per cent efficiency for counting alpha particles. On the other hand, Stone [60] has found that only about 6 per cent of $Sr^{90}$ betas striking the silver-magnesium target result in counts. This is due to the fact that the secondary-emission ratio drops off rapidly with increase in the energy of the electrons. The principal advantage of the electron-multiplier particle counter is that it can be inserted directly into a vacuum chamber without an intervening window.

## CHEMICAL DOSIMETERS

### 8–17. *Chemical Effects Induced by Nuclear Radiation*

It has long been known that the passage of nuclear radiation through matter may produce chemical changes in it. However, it is only quite recently that any of these effects have found important uses for the measurement of radiation. The present development is closely associated with the wide-scale use of kilocurie-strength radiation sources, for it is in these high-radiation fluxes that the chemical systems find their applications. The principal use is in the measurement of absorbed energy or the dose due to the radiation.

The chemical effects are a result of the excitation and ionization produced by the passage of the radiation. The mechanisms for the production of these chemical changes are not understood in detail. Many times it is qualitatively and sometimes quantitatively true that all types of nuclear radiations produce the same chemical effect when equal energies are dissipated in the material. For discussion of the quantitative differences it is convenient to divide nuclear radiation into two groups. These groups are (1) light (fast) particles such as beta rays and (2) heavy (slow) particles including alpha particles, accelerated charged particles such as protons and deuterons, and fission products at the instant of fission. X and gamma rays are in the group with electrons since they produce their effects through secondary electrons. Neutrons may be in either group, depending on the nature of their interaction with matter.

The basis for the division into the two groups lies in the difference in the specific ionization of the light and heavy particles. The specific ionization is from two to three orders of magnitude higher for group 2 than for group 1. Not only does this mean that the primary ion pairs along the paths of the particles are correspondingly closer, but in addition the secondary delta tracks or spurs along the tracks are also closer together. These spurs are secondary tracks of ionization which are produced by the electrons ejected in the primary-ionization process.

8–18. *Irradiation of Water*

Because of its importance in the systems for chemical dosimetry, the chemical effects induced by nuclear radiation in water will be discussed. The radiation-induced decomposition of water has been more thoroughly studied than any other system. However, considerable work remains to be done before all the quantitative aspects of the phenomenon have been worked out [61].

The primary phenomenon in the irradiation of water is the formation of the free radicals H and OH. These may react to form the products $H_2$ and $H_2O_2$ as well as to recombine to form water. Possible reactions are

$$H + H \rightarrow H_2 \tag{8–9}$$

$$OH + OH \rightarrow H_2O_2 \tag{8–10}$$

and

$$H + OH \rightarrow H_2O \tag{8–11}$$

Additional reactions leading to the removal of the $H_2$ and $H_2O_2$ from the systems and the recombination into water are

$$H + H_2O_2 \rightarrow H_2O + OH \tag{8–12}$$

and

$$OH + H_2 \rightarrow H_2O + H \tag{8–13}$$

For the higher specific ionization, as with the slow heavy particles, the yield of $H_2$ and $H_2O_2$ increases, indicating the increased importance of the reactions given by Eqs. (8–9) and (8–10). This dependence of the yield of $H_2$ and $H_2O_2$ on specific ionization is explained in the following manner: When the specific ionization is low and the accompanying delta tracks are far apart, the free radicals diffuse from their point of origin into the main body of the system, reacting with $H_2$ and $H_2O_2$ according to Eqs. (8–12) and (8–13) in preference to the free-radical reactions, Eqs. (8–9) to (8–11). On the other hand, where the specific ionization is high and the local density of free radicals correspondingly high, the reactions between free radicals proceed more rapidly.

Equations (8–12) and (8–13) taken together are chain reactions which reestablish the free radicals. Other reactions can work to break the chain. Possible ones are

$$OH + H_2O_2 \rightarrow HO_2 + H_2O \tag{8–14}$$

and

$$HO_2 + H \rightarrow H_2O_2 \tag{8–15}$$

This indicates that, when water solutions are exposed to radiation, oxidizable solutes will be oxidized by the OH radicals, and reducible solutes will be reduced by H radicals.

8–19. *Requirements of Chemical Systems for Dosimetry*

The desirability of making absorbed-dose measurements in terms of absorbed energy was pointed out in Chap. 4. This has been emphasized by the establishment of the rad as a unit by the International Commission on Radiological Units. The rad is an absorbed dose of 100 ergs/g.

A common approach to the measurement of the absorbed energy has been through the determination of the ionization in an air ionization chamber (see Chap. 4). The material in question is replaced by the chamber. The quantity $J$, the ionization per unit mass in the gas, is related to $dE/dm$, the energy absorbed per unit mass of the material, by the equation

$$\frac{dE}{dm} = S_m w J \tag{8–16}$$

where $w$ is the energy required per ion pair formed in the gas and $S_m$ is the ratio of the mass stopping power of the material to that of the gas. This method is capable of accurate results when applied carefully. In fact, it has been used recently by Cormack et al. [62] for the calibration of the aqueous ferrous sulfate chemical dosimeter. In the theory, the ratio of the energy absorbed in the material to the ionization in a small air cavity in the material is calculated, assuming that the system consists only of the material and the cavity within it. This requirement can be met by making the walls of the ionization chamber from material equivalent (from the standpoint of energy absorption) to the material in which the energy absorption is being made. A very important but tedious part of the calculation is the computing of the average value of $S_m$. In general, $S_m$ is a function of electron energy, and an average value of it must be calculated for each energy in the spectrum of radiation to which Eq. (8–16) is to be applied.

To avoid the complications described above with their possible inherent inaccuracies, it is desirable for the dosimeter and the sample to have the same, or nearly the same, mass stopping power. In addition, the dosimeter and sample should be geometrically alike, to eliminate any geometry effect. Finally, to avoid erroneous results due to changes in magnitude and distribution of the radiation flux when the sample is replaced by the dosimeter, the absorption of radiation which is produced by each system should be similar.

These requirements for dosimeters to use with liquid and solid samples are difficult to meet with ionization chambers. On the other hand, chemical dosimeters, being composed of solids or liquids, the volumes and shapes of which can be readily varied, are ideally suited. Further, the chemical changes which are produced can be related simply to energy absorbed or to the dose.

It is convenient to class chemical dosimeters into two groups: (1) those employing water as a solvent and (2) all other systems. The aqueous systems include the oxidation of ferrous ions in ferrous sulfate solution and the reduction of ceric ions in ceric sulfate solutions. Under the second group are included a number of the systems which will be summarized in a later section.

Miller [63] has listed the desirable characteristics for aqueous dosimeters. In brief, the amount of chemical change brought about by a unit dose should be independent of (1) the concentration of the reactant and the product, (2) the dose rate, (3) any other conditions likely to change during exposure, such as pH, content of dissolved gas, etc., and (4) the type and spectrum of the radiation. In addition, (5) the analytical procedure should be as simple as possible, (6) the ordinary analytical grade reagents should be usable without further purification, and (7) the solutions should be usable in their normal condition of equilibrium with the atmosphere. In practice, condition 4 is found to be the most difficult to satisfy. All systems have been found to give different results when irradiated with particles of group 1 (see Sec. 8–17) from those obtained with particles of group 2.

### 8–20. *Description of Ferrous Sulfate Dosimeter*

The chemical reaction which is in the most wide-scale use for dosimetry is the oxidation of ferrous ions to ferric in 0.8 normal solutions of sulfuric acid. This system has been found to be satisfactory over a wide range of conditions. In addition, careful calibrations relating the quantity of the reaction products to the absorbed energy have been run for this dosimeter.

Several methods have been used satisfactorily for preparing the solution. Weiss, Allen, and Schwarz [64] recommend the following procedure: Dissolve 2 g $FeSO_4 \cdot 7H_2O$ or $Fe(NH_4)_2(SO_4)_2 \cdot 6H_2O$, 0.3 g NaCl, and 110 $cm^3$ concentrated (95–98%) $H_2SO_4$ (analytical reagent grade) in sufficient distilled water to make 5 liters of solution. (The chloride ions inhibit the oxidation of ferrous ions by certain organic impurities in the system. This eliminates the need for triply distilled water and recrystallized ferrous sulfate in making up the solution.)

The sample containers are filled with this solution and placed in the position where the radiation intensity is to be measured. The containers should be clean glass or polystyrene with at least 8-mm inner diameter. The duration of the irradiation period should be noted accurately.

The common method for determining the amount of ferric ion which has been produced by the radiation is spectrophotometric analysis. The ferric ion has an absorption maximum at approximately 304 m$\mu$. To determine the amount of iron, the transmission of the irradiated sample is compared with that of a nonirradiated sample. A Beckman model DU spectrophotometer equipped with a thermostated hydrogen lamp and quartz cells is quite satisfactory.

The dose rate is given [64] by the formula

$$R(\text{r/hr}) = \frac{10^9}{\epsilon b Y t} (A_{\text{sample}} - A_{\text{blank}}) \tag{8-17}$$

where $A_{\text{sample}}$ and $A_{\text{blank}}$ = absorbancy (optical density) of irradiated and unirradiated solutions, respectively

$\epsilon$ = molar extinction coefficient

$Y$ = ferrous sulfate yield, micromoles ($\mu M$) of ferric ions per liter per 1,000 r

$b$ = sample thickness, cm.

$t$ = irradiation time, hr

The value of $\epsilon$ should be determined on the spectrophotometer to be used. A representative value [64] is 2,174 liters/(mole)(cm) at 23.7°C; it has a rather large temperature coefficient of + 0.7 per cent per degree Centigrade [65].

**Example 8–3.** If the spectrophotometric measurement of the ferrous sulfate solution in a chemical dosimeter indicates a transmittance through a 2-cm cell of 0.9 and 0.4 before and after irradiation, calculate the dose received by the dosimeter.

*Solution.* The absorbancy $A$ is calculated from the transmittance $T$ as

$$A = \log \frac{1}{T}$$

resulting in values of 0.041 and 0.38 before and after irradiation. By Eq. (8–17), the total dose $D$ is

$$D(\text{r}) = \frac{10^9}{\epsilon b Y} (A_{\text{sample}} - A_{\text{blank}}) = \frac{10^9(0.38 - 0.041)}{2{,}174 \times 2 \times 15.3} = 5.1 \times 10^3 \text{ r}$$

where the yield $Y$ has been taken as 15.3 $\mu M$ of ferric ions per liter per 1,000 r (see Sec. 8–21).

## 8–21. *Yield of Ferrous Sulfate Dosimeter*

It has become customary to express the yield of chemical dosimeters in $G$ units. The value of the yield in $G$ units is the number of molecules produced or converted for each 100 ev of energy absorbed. The value of $Y$ in micromoles of ferric ions per liter of 0.8 $N$ solution per 1,000 r is 0.99 $G$ if 1 r is taken to be equivalent to 93 ergs/g in water.

For several years there have been discrepancies up to 25 per cent in the various measured values of $G$. Recent measurements indicate that the lower values are the more nearly correct. Table 8–5 includes these values, along with the references to the papers in which they are reported. The value of 15.45 ± 0.11, determined by Schuler and Allen [68], is probably the most accurate one.

TABLE 8–5. YIELDS OF FERROUS SULFATE DOSIMETER

| *Ionization Method* | | |
|---|---|---|
| Authority | Radiation | $G$(molecules/100 ev) |
| Hochanadel and Ghormley* | $Co^{60}$ $\gamma$ rays | 16.7 |
| Cormack, Hummel, Johns, and Spinks† | 24.5-Mev X rays | 15.5 or 16.4 |
| | $Co^{60}$ $\gamma$ rays | 15.8 or 16.0 |
| *Calorimetric Method* | | |
| Authority | Radiation | $G$(molecules/100 ev) |
| Hochanadel and Ghormley* | $Co^{60}$ $\gamma$ rays | $15.6 \pm 0.3$ |
| Lazo, Dewhurst, and Burton‡ | $Co^{60}$ $\gamma$ rays | $15.8 \pm 0.3$ |
| *Power-input Method* | | |
| Authority | | $G$(molecules/100 ev) |
| Hochanadel and Ghormley* | | 16.5 |
| Schuler and Allen§ | | $15.45 \pm 0.11$ |

* From G. J. Hochanadel and J. A. Ghormley, *J. Chem. Phys.*, **21**:880 (1953).

† From D. V. Cormack, R. W. Hummel, H. E. Johns, and J. W. T. Spinks, *J. Chem. Phys.*, **22**:6 (1954).

‡ From R. M. Lazo, H. A. Dewhurst, and B. Burton, *J. Chem. Phys.*, **22**:1370 (1954).

§ From R. H. Schuler and A. O. Allen, Paper at meeting of Radiation Research Society, New York, May 17, 1955.

In the ionization method of calibration, the current in an ionization chamber is converted to energy in the fashion discussed in Sec. 8–19. Cormack et al. [62] have given the details of this calibration.

The calorimetric method of calibration requires the use of microcalorimetric techniques because the rate of heat input is so small. These techniques are discussed in Sec. 8–29.

In the power-input method of calibration, the energy absorbed in the dosimeter is determined from measurement of the voltage, beam current, and duration of a cathode-ray beam which enters the dosimeter.

Although the range of conditions over which the yield remains constant at the value discussed above is large, certain factors must be kept in mind in the application of these dosimeters. One important limitation arises because the yield is dependent on the presence of oxygen in the solution; therefore the yield differs in aerated and deaerated solutions. As the reaction proceeds in aerated solutions, oxygen is consumed (see Sec. 8–22). The yield stated above is obtained when oxygen is present. When all the oxygen which was initially present in the solution is consumed, the yield drops off. This is indicated on the curve of the ferric-ion concentration versus dose in Fig. 8–13 by the break in the curve. The yield has been found [69] to be independent of the ferrous-ion concentration from $10^{-2}$ to

$4 \times 10^{-5} M$ and of dose rates from $\frac{1}{50}$ to 200 r/sec. The exact limits of these ranges need further study.

One important limitation of the ferrous sulfate dosimeters is the dependence of the yield on the type of radiation. Particles producing a higher specific ionization produce a lower yield. For example, alpha particles have been reported [63] to give a yield of about one-half that of electrons. For light fast particles the yield is independent of the energy over a large range, at least from 100 kev to 24.5 Mev. There is some indication [63] that low-energy betas such as those from tritium produce a lower yield than high-energy betas.

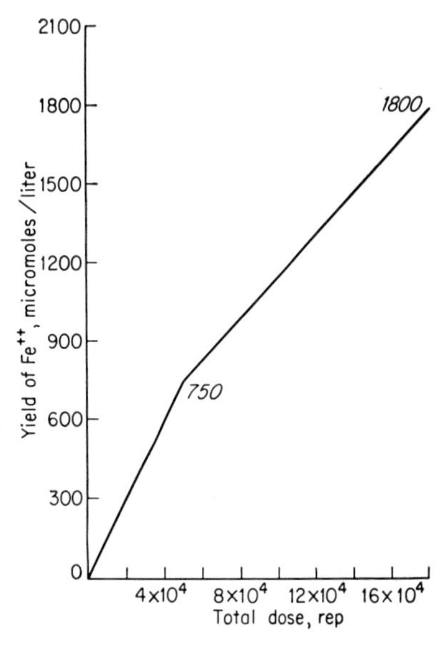


FIG. 8–13. Micromoles of $Fe^{++}$ oxidized as a function of the total dose absorbed. (*From J. Weiss, A. O. Allen, and H. A. Schwarz, "Proceedings of the International Conference on the Peaceful Uses of Atomic Energy," vol. 14, p. 179, United Nations, New York,* 1956.)

### 8–22. *Radiation Chemistry in Ferrous Sulfate System*

The following mechanisms have been proposed to describe the oxidation of the ferrous ions in an aerated solution. The process starts with the formation of the free radicals H and OH by the dissociation of water, as described in Sec. 8–18. These free radicals in turn bring about the oxidation reaction. The equations of several possible reactions are

$$H_2O \rightleftarrows H + OH \tag{8–18}$$

$$Fe^{++} + OH \rightarrow Fe^{3+} + OH^- \tag{8–19}$$

$$H + O_2 \rightarrow HO_2 \tag{8–20}$$

$$Fe^{++} + HO_2 \rightarrow Fe^{3+} + HO_2^- \tag{8–21}$$

$$HO_2^- + H^+ \rightleftarrows H_2O_2 \tag{8–22}$$

$$Fe^{++} + H_2O_2 \rightarrow Fe^{3+} + OH^- + OH \tag{8–23}$$

$$H^+ + OH^- \rightleftarrows H_2O \tag{8–24}$$

The importance of the oxygen in the process is clear from these equations. The maximum theoretical ratio between the oxidation yield in the aerated and evacuated solutions is 4; in practice, a value of about 2.7

is obtained. It is also clear from this why the yield drops off with the depletion of the oxygen after large doses.

The fact that the yield drops at low concentrations of the ferrous ion is attributed to the relative slowness of the reaction given by Eq. (8–23). If sufficient time is allowed between irradiation and analysis, the yield will be normal, as this reaction will have time to go to completion.

The drop in yield with types of nuclear radiation which produce high specific ionization is due to the loss of free radicals through the reaction given by Eqs. (8–9) to (8–11). As explained in Sec. 8–18, these reactions are aided by the large ion density.

### 8–23. *Ceric Sulfate Dosimetry*

Solutions of ceric sulfate for dosimetry are prepared by adding reagent-grade ceric sulfate to 0.8 *N* sulfuric acid. When this solution is subjected to nuclear radiation, ceric ions are reduced to cerous ions.

The cerous-ion concentration is determined by measurement of the difference between the final and initial ceric-ion concentrations. The ceric-ion concentration is determined spectrophotometrically by measurement of the absorption at 320 m$\mu$, the wavelength for maximum absorption. Since the difference method is used in analysis, it is advantageous to start with an initial ceric-ion density of the order of the change which is expected during the irradiation; of course, the initial concentration must always be somewhat greater than the expected change.

The yield for the ceric sulfate dosimeter is ordinarily determined relative to the yield for the ferrous sulfate dosimeter. The ratio $G_{Fe}/G_{Ce}$ has been reported [69] as $5.96 \pm 0.03$ for a wide range of conditions. It has been found to be independent of the initial ceric-ion concentration in the range from $3.2 \times 10^{-2}$ to $10^{-5}$ *M* and of energy from 100-kev X rays to 2-Mev gamma rays. It drops to 4.3 for 11-kev X rays and to 2.8 for tritium betas [70]. The dose rate appears to have no effect on the yield from ½ to approximately 500 r/sec. There is no dependence of the yield on oxygen concentration. Therefore no break in the curve of cerous-ion concentration versus dose is found, as in the corresponding case for the ferrous sulfate dosimeter.

### 8–24. *Comparison of the Ferrous Sulfate and Ceric Sulfate Dosimeters*

In general, it is found advantageous to use the ceric sulfate dosimeter for the very intense sources and the ferrous sulfate dosimeter for the somewhat weaker sources. The ferrous sulfate dosimeter is preferable at the lower doses because of its higher yield. It can be used down to 4,000 r with the spectrophotometric analysis. Rødstam and Svedberg [71] report that by using $Fe^{59}$ as a tracer a ferrous sulfate dosimeter can be used in the range from 0 to 100 r with 2-r accuracy. Their method depends on the separation of ferrous and ferric ions by solvent extraction.

The break in the curve at about 50,000 r (see Fig. 8–13) limits the usefulness of the ferrous sulfate dosimeter for large doses. It can be used at higher doses if the proper calibrations are available. However, another practical limitation arises at doses around 1 million rep because of the high initial concentration of the ferrous ion that is required. This type of solution auto-oxidizes and complicates the blank determination.

On the other hand, because of its low yield, the ceric sulfate is of no use for doses of a few roentgens. However, it can be used satisfactorily at doses of millions of roentgens. Another advantage of this dosimeter is the sensitivity of the concentration determination. There is a greater change in optical density per unit change in concentration.

One disadvantage of the ceric sulfate dosimeter arises because of the rigid requirement for the surfaces in contact with the solution. It has been found [67], for example, that the irradiation of the solution in plastic vessels gives very erratic results. Further, Nicksic and Wright [72] have pointed out errors that arise from exposure to light. However, by exercising special care in avoiding all unnecessary exposure to light, accurate results can be obtained.

### 8–25. *Gamma-ray and Neutron Dosimetry by Gas Evolution from Aqueous Solutions*

Hart and Gordon [73] have successfully applied the gas evolution from aqueous solutions for gamma-ray and neutron dosimetry. The dosimeter used for gammas was a 1.0-m$M$ (millimolar) potassium iodide solution while that for neutrons was a 1.0-m$M$ potassium iodide solution plus a 50-m$M$ boric acid solution.

It is found that the rate of gas evolution is proportional to the rate of energy absorption. This can be expressed as

$$\frac{dN}{dt} = G\frac{dE}{dt} \tag{8–25}$$

where $N$ is the total number of molecules of gas evolved and $E$ is the energy absorbed in units of 100 ev. Thus a volume of gas proportional to the total dose is released. The gas volume is measured at constant pressure in a gas-manometer system.

It was pointed out in Sec. 8–18 that, when pure water is irradiated, back reactions given by Eqs. (8–12) and (8–13) occur. In this event, rather than an amount of hydrogen proportional to the total dose, one obtains an equilibrium quantity proportional to the rate of energy absorption. However, the presence of the iodine radical in the potassium iodide solution inhibits this back reaction through the reduction of the number of OH free radicals by the process

$$I^- + OH \rightarrow I + OH^-$$

Further, oxygen is produced from the decomposition of the $H_2O_2$ by radiation.

The boric acid in the neutron dosimeter brings about the absorption of neutrons accompanied by the emission of an alpha particle through the $(n,\alpha)$ reaction in $B^{10}$. The alpha particles produce the decomposition of the water.

The yield by the gammas from $Co^{60}$ is 0.575 total molecule of gas per 100 ev absorbed, including 0.383 of hydrogen and 0.192 of oxygen. For the neutrons in the thermal column of a reactor, the total yield of the boric acid solution is 2.03, with 1.35 due to hydrogen and 0.68 due to oxygen.

The main advantage of this type of dosimeter over the other chemical dosimeters is its ability continuously to monitor the energy flux through the rate of gas evolution. Hart and Gordon [73] have evaluated this system as an excellent means of monitoring the gamma-ray and neutron fluxes in reactors with neutron fluxes in the range from $10^{11}$ to $10^{15}$ neutrons/(cm²)(sec).

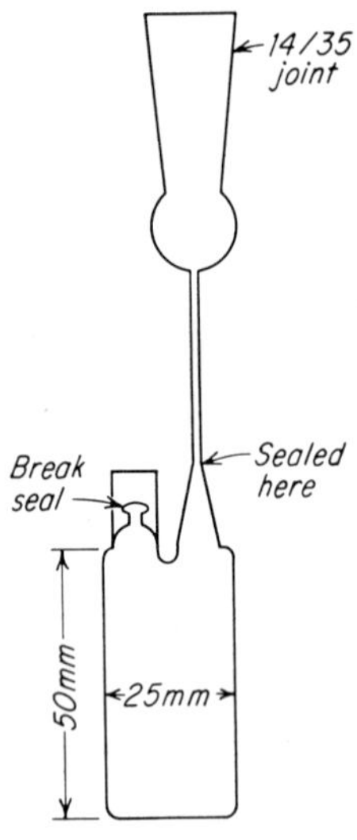


Fig. 8–14. Quartz reaction vessel for the nitrous oxide dosimeter. (*From S. Dondes, "Proceedings of the International Conference on the Peaceful Uses of Atomic Energy," vol. 14, p. 176, United Nations, New York, 1956.*)

### 8–26. *Other Chemical Dosimeters*

A number of other chemical systems have been proposed for use as dosimeters [63]. Two of these appear to be particularly useful. They are the nitrous oxide dosimeter described by Dondes [74] and the acid production in chlorinated hydrocarbons as discussed recently by Taplin [75].

The reaction vessel for the nitrous oxide dosimeter is shown in Fig. 8–14. In use, it is filled with purified nitrous oxide to a pressure of 650 mm. After the vessel has been irradiated for a measured time interval, its seal is broken in a vacuum, and measurement is made of the amount of nitrogen and oxygen formed by the irradiation. Before this determination is made, the remaining nitrous oxide, as well as the radiation-produced nitrogen dioxide, is condensed out in a liquid nitrogen bath.

Figure 8–15 shows the calibration curve of a nitrous oxide dosimeter. Above $3 \times 10^7$ r, nitrogen oxide is readily perceptible by the color change. Thus the dose above this value can be measured colorimetrically with the vessel unopened. Doses from $10^6$ to $3 \times 10^7$ r may be measured colorimetrically by increasing the length of the vessel from 2 to 50 in. Above $10^{10}$ r, the decomposition of nitrous oxide reaches an equilibrium, so that the dosimeter is no longer accurate.

The acid production from the irradiation of chlorinated hydrocarbons, such as chloroform, trichloroethylene, or tetrachloroethylene, is a linear function of the radiation dose over a broad range [75]. The acid products may be determined directly by color changes in pH-indicator dyes or indirectly either by simple acidometric titrations or other available means.

A comprehensive discussion of the characteristics of those systems and of their applications to dosimetry has been made by Taplin [76]. The resorcinol-stabilized chlorinated hydrocarbon-aqueous pH-indicator dye systems are judged to rank with the ferrous sulfate and ceric sulfate

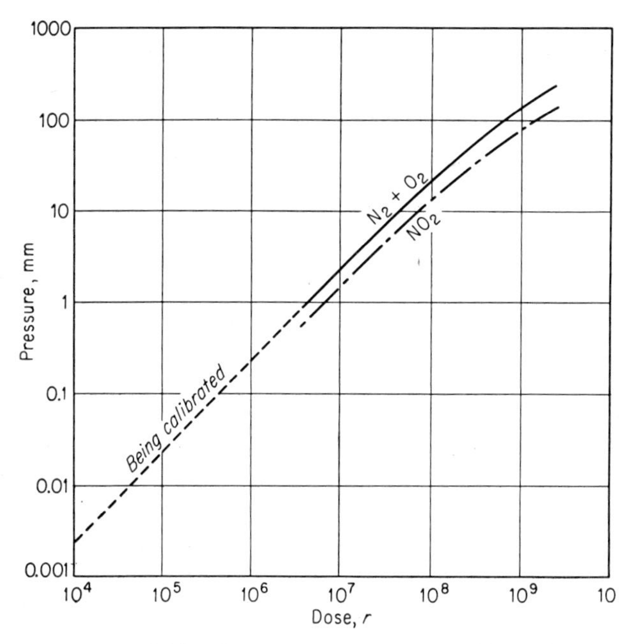


FIG. 8–15. Calibration curve for a nitrous oxide dosimeter. (*From S. Dondes, "Proceedings of the International Conference on the Peaceful Uses of Atomic Energy," vol.* 14, *p.* 176, *United Nations, New York*, 1956.)

dosimeters in their importance and general utility. The former system extends the useful range down to 10 r.

## 8–27. *Dosimetry by Silver-activated Phosphate Glass*

Radiation-induced changes in the absorption, luminescence, and other properties of solids have been used to measure radiation doses [69]. Silver-activated phosphate glass is a particularly useful material in this regard. Although the effects produced in glass are not primarily chemical in nature, a discussion of this dosimeter type is included at this point because of the features which it has in common with the chemical systems.

Schulman [77, 78] has developed two ranges of dosimeters utilizing silver-activated phosphate glass. A personnel dosimeter [77], covering the range from 10 to 600 r, utilizes the phenomenon of radiophotoluminescence, while a high-level dosimeter [78], useful from $10^3$ to $10^6$ r, makes use of changes in optical absorption.

Radiophotoluminescence is the phenomenon by which new stable photoluminescent centers are created in certain materials by the action of ionizing radiation. After irradiation, the material will fluoresce under light of the proper wavelength (usually in the near-ultraviolet), while unirradiated glass will not fluoresce under the same conditions.

The ionizing radiation liberates electrons within the glass. These are trapped by the $Ag^+$ ions of the glass, thus reducing the ions to atomic silver centers. These atomic silver centers produce the new absorption band used in the detection of larger doses. They also serve as the origin of the photoluminescence. One form of the radiophotoluminescent dosimeter [77] consists of a ¾- by ¾- by $\frac{3}{16}$-in. glass block. The glass is rough-ground and painted black on all but one ¾- by ¾-in. face (the "ultraviolet entrance face") and one ¾- by $\frac{3}{16}$-in. face (the "fluorescence exit face"). After exposure of the glass, the dose which it has received is measured by a fluorimeter. In this measurement a 931 A photomultiplier tube equipped with an orange filter is used to measure the light passing through the fluorescence exit face while the ultraviolet entrance face is being irradiated with light in the region of 3,650 A. The sensitivity of the system allows the measurement of doses as little as 2 r.

For the high-dose measurements by absorption, polished glass plates 0.5 mm thick and 1 cm square have been used [78]. In this application, optical transmission measurements are made. These data are converted to absorption coefficients, with corrections being applied for absorption and reflection losses in the unirradiated glass. In Fig. 8–16 the absorption coefficient is plotted as a function of dose; the light wavelength at which the absorption measurements are made is used as the parameter. For low doses, adequate optical-density changes are obtained when the measurements are made at 3,500 A. For higher doses the optical density at 3,500 A is much too high for convenient measurement, and the dose is determined from measurements at longer wavelengths.

## CALORIMETRIC METHODS

### 8–28. *Utility of Calorimeters for Nuclear Measurements*

A calorimeter, a device for the measurement of quantities of heat, has found applications in most fields of physics, including that of nuclear measurements. The calorimeter is very useful for the determination of the radiation-energy absorption in material, since ultimately the absorbed energy is degraded into heat. Ideally, at least, one builds a calorimeter containing a sample of the material in which the measurement of the absorbed dose is required, exposes this sample to the radiation field, and measures the total heat produced in it. Practically, of course, all parts of the calorimeter may absorb energy from the radiation, so that provisions must be made for distinguishing between the heat generated in the sample material and that being produced in the rest of the apparatus.

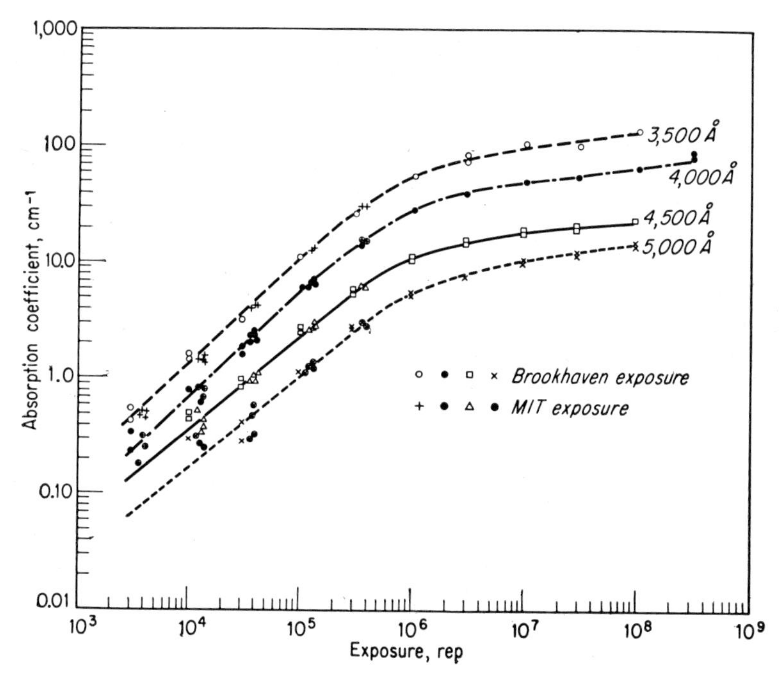


FIG. 8-16. Dose dependence of absorption of silver-activated glass for various wavelengths of light. [*From J. H. Schulman, C. C. Klick, and H. Rabin, Nucleonics,* **13**:30 (*February,* 1955).]

The other broad class of applications of calorimeters is the measurement of the absolute activity of radioactive samples. In this process either all or a known fraction of the energy of the nuclear particles which are emitted by the source is dissipated as heat in the calorimeter. This can usually be achieved by placing the source inside the calorimeter. However, if the source must be outside, the calorimeter can be equipped with a window for admitting the radiation. In either case the interior of the calorimeter is so arranged as to absorb either all or a known part of the radiation. The basic relationship between the rate of heat input $H$, the sample activity $A$, and the average energy dissipated in the calorimeter per particle $\bar{E}$ is

$$H(\text{watts}) = (1.603 \times 10^{-13})A\bar{E} \qquad (8\text{-}26)$$

where $A$ is expressed in particles per second and $\bar{E}$ in Mev. If $A$ is expressed in curies, the relationship becomes

$$H(\text{watts}) = (5.94 \times 10^{-3})A(\text{curies})\bar{E}(\text{Mev}) \qquad (8\text{–}27)$$

It is clear that the measurement of the rate of heat input allows the determination of either the activity or the average energy dissipated but not both simultaneously.

**Example 8–4.** Calculate the minimum activity of $Po^{210}$ which may be measured by means of a calorimeter that is capable of operating with heat input rates as low as $10^{-3}$ watt.

*Solution.* Except in $10^{-3}$ per cent of the cases, $Po^{210}$ emits only alpha particles. Further, these alpha particles are monoenergetic (5.30 Mev). All the alpha energy can be dissipated in the calorimeter. Therefore if all but the principal radiation is neglected, the minimum activity is given by Eq. (8–27) as

$$A = \frac{H}{(5.94 \times 10^{-3})\bar{E}} = \frac{10^{-3}}{(5.94 \times 10^{-3})(5.30)} = 31.8 \text{ millicuries}$$

In activity measurements of beta and alpha emitters, where gamma rays accompany these particles, it is necessary either to absorb all the gamma rays, to make provisions for the gamma rays to escape from the calorimeter, or to correct for the energy dissipated by them in the calorimeter. Often the system can be designed with sufficiently thin walls to allow the escape of most of the gamma radiation so that the remaining correction is small.

The main advantage of the calorimetric method for activity measurements arises from its inherent accuracy. Sources of errors such as backscattering, self-absorption, instrument resolving time, and the like which are present in counting methods are avoided. The main limitation of the calorimetric method is its lack of sensitivity. For high accuracies the sample must be present at least in millicurie amounts and preferably in curie amounts. Another limitation arises from the time required to reach thermal equilibrium. This is ordinarily of the order of hours and consequently prevents the use of the system with radioisotopes of half-lives the order of a day or less.

### 8–29. *Types of Calorimeters*

The principal problem in the design of calorimeters for radiation measurements arises from the small rate of heat input that is usually encountered. Therefore calorimeters for this purpose are often referred to as microcalorimeters.

A survey of the types of calorimeters in use has been given by Myers [79]. This is a review article including a comprehensive bibliography on both calorimeter design and application to radiation measurements. The types of calorimeters which have found general usefulness are the twin differential, the isothermal, and the adiabatic calorimeters.

the sample from that produced in the rest of the apparatus. Figure 8–18 is a schematic diagram of a reactor-radiation calorimeter designed by Richardson, Allen, and Boyle [86].

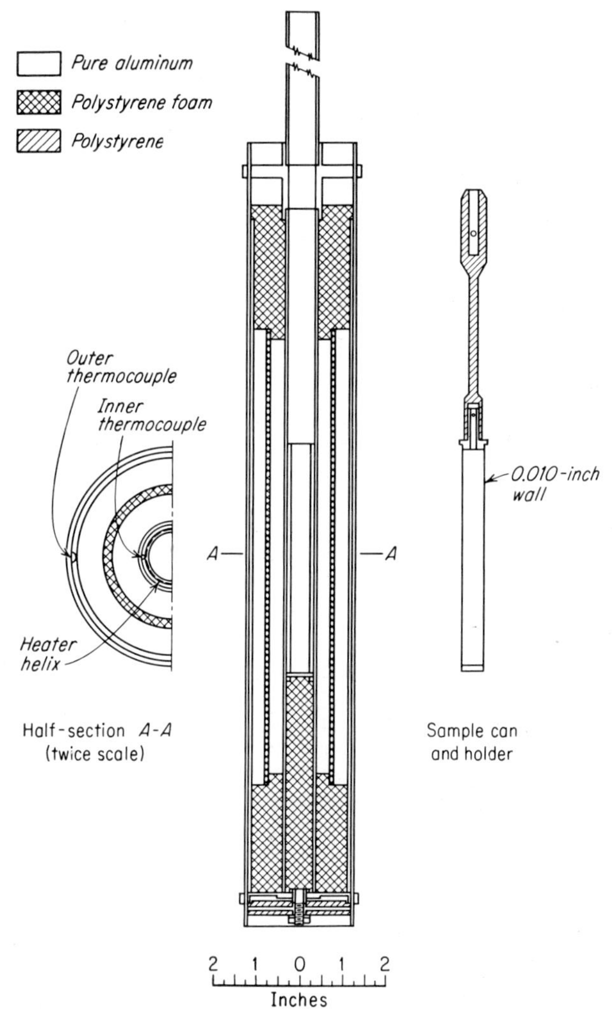


FIG. 8–18. Dosimeter for nuclear reactor radiation. (*From D. M. Richardson, A. O. Allen, and J. W. Boyle, "Proceedings of the International Conference on the Peaceful Uses of Atomic Energy," vol. 14, p. 209, United Nations, New York, 1956.*)

The calorimeter consists essentially of two coaxial aluminum tubes with a thermocouple embedded in each. The sample can is supported inside the center tube by means of a polystyrene insulator. The heat generated within the inner assembly is conducted mainly across the air gap between the two tubes, good thermal insulation being provided at the ends of the inner tube. Convection currents between the two cylinders are minimized by a thin sleeve of polystyrene foam in the middle of the air space. A helical heater composed of copper wire is embedded in the inner cylinder for calibration purposes. By means of this, the relationship between the heater power input and the temperature difference between the two cylinders is determined. This is a linear curve with a slope of 0.012 cal/sec for a 1°C temperature difference.

In the use of the calorimeter, the energy absorption rate in the sample is obtained by subtracting the rate determined for the calorimeter without the sample from that with the sample in place.

## PROBLEMS

**8-1.** Compute the number of atoms in a grain of Ilford G5 emulsion having the mean grain diameter of this emulsion type.

**8-2.** Make use of the data in Figs. 8-1 and 8-4 to estimate the total number of grains produced by a 1-Mev proton while giving up all its energy in an Ilford C2 emulsion. From this, estimate the average energy required per grain formed.

**8-3.** Designate a suitable emulsion type for use with each of the following particles, indicating the reasons for the choice in each case: 10-Mev alphas, 100-Mev protons, 1-Mev alphas, 1-Mev betas, and 1,000-Mev deuterons.

**8-4.** Consider a cloud chamber of 20-cm diameter, containing air. Calculate the pressure that is required in the chamber if the tracks of 1-Mev protons are to span a distance equal to the chamber radius. Repeat for 100-Mev protons.

**8-5.** Calculate the threshold energy for the production of Cerenkov radiation in water by each of the following particle types: alphas, protons, electrons, and $\pi$ mesons. The index of refraction of water is 1.33.

**8-6.** An electron passing through water produces Cerenkov radiation which is emitted at an angle of 45° to the direction of the electron travel. Calculate the particle energy and the number of photons produced per centimeter of path traveled by the particle.

**8-7.** What is the total dose in rads received by a ferrous sulfate dosimeter in which $10^{-5}$ mole of ferric ions is produced per gram of the solution?

**8-8.** Calculate the change in optical density which occurs in a ferrous sulfate dosimeter upon receiving a total dose of $10^4$ rads. Assume that the molar extinction coefficient for the particular spectrophotometer is 2,174 liters/(mole) (cm).

**8-9.** Calculate the rate of hydrogen-gas evolution when pure water is subjected to a dose rate of $10^7$ rads/hr.

**8-10.** What would be the sensitivity required in a calorimeter for use in measuring the activity of a $C^{14}$ source as small as 1 curie?

**8-11.** A calorimeter of the type shown in Fig. 8-18 is used to measure the rate of energy deposition in plastic irradiated by 1-Mev gamma radiation. Calculate the energy-deposition rate when a 10-g sample is placed in a gamma field of $5 \times 10^{13}$ gammas/(cm²)(sec).

## REFERENCES

1. Goldschmidt-Clermont, Y.: *Ann. Rev. Nuclear Sci.*, **3**:141 (1953).
2. Rotblat, J.: Article in O. R. Frisch (ed.), "Progress in Nuclear Physics," vol. 1, Academic Press, Inc., New York, 1950.

3. Powell, C. F., and G. P. S. Occhialini: "Nuclear Physics in Photographs," Clarendon Press, Oxford, 1947.
4. Yagoda, H.: "Radioactive Measurements with Nuclear Emulsions," John Wiley & Sons, Inc., New York, 1949.
5. Powell, C. F.: *Repts. Progr. in Phys.*, **13**:350 (1950).
6. Rossi, B.: "High Energy Particles," chap. 3, Prentice-Hall, Inc., Englewood Cliffs, N.J., 1952.
7. Fowler, P. H., and D. H. Perkins: Article in "Fundamental Mechanism of Photographic Sensitivity," Butterworth & Co. (Publishers) Ltd., London, 1951.
8. Beiser, A.: *Revs. Mod. Phys.*, **24**:273 (1952).
9. Vigneron, L.: *J. phys. radium*, **14**:121 (1953).
10. Shapiro, M. M.: *Revs. Mod. Phys.*, **13**:58 (1941).
11. Dilworth, C. C., S. J. Goldsack, Y. Goldschmidt-Clermont, and F. Levy: *Phil. Mag.*, **41**:1032 (1950).
12. Goldsack, S. J., and N. Page: *Phil. Mag.*, **42**:570 (1951).
13. Demeur, M., C. C. Dilworth, and M. Schönberg: *Nuovo cimento*, **9**:92 (1952).
14. Faraggo, H., A. Bonnet, and M. J. Cohen: *J. phys. radium*, **13**:105A (1952).
15. Gaillond, M., and C. Haerny: *Science et inds. phot.*, **23**:221 (1952); *Mém. soc. vaudoise des sci. nat.*, **10**:271 (1952).
16. Summerfield, M. B.: *Phys. Rev.*, **89**:340 (1953).
17. Dilworth, C. C., G. P. S. Occhialini, and R. M. Payne: *Nature*, **162**:102 (1948).
18. Rosen, L.: "Proceedings of the International Conference on the Peaceful Uses of Atomic Energy," vol. 4, p. 97, United Nations, New York, 1956.
19. Powell, C. F.: *Nature*, **145**:155 (1940).
20. Morrison, A., and E. Pickup: *Phys. Rev.*, **74**:706 (1948).
21. Vigneron, L.: *J. phys. radium*, **14**:145 (1953).
22. Richards, H. T., et al.: *Phys. Rev.*, **83**:994 (1951).
23. Gailar, O., et al.: *Rev. Sci. Instr.*, **24**:126 (1953).
24. Lees, C. F., G. C. Morrison, and W. G. V. Roser: *Proc. Phys. Soc. (London), A*, **66**:13 (1953).
25. Bradt, H. L., and B. Peters: *Phys. Rev.*, **80**:943 (1950).
26. Bradt, H. L., and B. Peters: *Phys. Rev.*, **74**:1828 (1948).
27. Fowler, P. H.: *Phil. Mag.*, **41**:169 (1950).
28. Freier, P., et al.: *Phys. Rev.*, **74**:1818 (1948).
29. Williams, E. J.: *Proc. Roy. Soc. (London): A*, **169**:531 (1938).
30. Berger, M. J.: *Phys. Rev.*, **88**:58 (1952).
31. Gottstein, K., et al.: *Phil. Mag.*, **42**:708 (1951).
32. Ehrlich, M.: *Natl. Bur. Standards (U.S.)* NBS-1073, 1952.
33. Ehrlich, M., and S. H. Fitch: *Nucleonics*, **9**:5 (September, 1951).
34. Dudley, R. A.: *Nucleonics*, **12**:24 (May, 1954).
35. Kalil, F.: *Nucleonics*, **13**:91 (1955).
36. Wilson, J. G.: "The Principles of Cloud-chamber Technique," Cambridge University Press, London, 1951.
37. Das Gupta, N. N., and S. K. Ghosh: *Revs. Mod. Phys.*, **18**:227 (1946).
38. Snowden, M.: Article in O. R. Frisch (ed.), "Progress in Nuclear Physics," vol. 3, Academic Press, Inc., New York, 1953.
39. Alston, M. H., A. V. Crewe, and W. H. Evans: *Rev. Sci. Instr.*, **25**:547 (1954).
40. Joliot, F.: *J. phys. radium*, **5**:216 (1934).
41. Johnson, T. H., S. Benedetti, and R. P. Shutt: *Rev. Sci. Instr.*, **14**:265 (1943).
42. Fretter, W. B.: *Ann. Rev. Nuclear Sci.*, **5**:145 (1955).
43. Fowler, W. B., R. P. Shutt, A. M. Thorndike, and W. L. Whittemore: *Phys. Rev.*, **95**:1026 (1954).

44. Glaser, D. A.: *Phys. Rev.*, **87**:665 (1952); **91**:496 (1953); **91**:762 (1953); **97**:474 (1955).
45. Glaser, D. A.: *Nuovo cimento*, **11 (Suppl. 2)**:361 (1954).
46. Glaser, D. A.: *Sci. American*, **192**:46 (February, 1955).
47. Van Heerden, P. J.: "The Crystal Counter, a New Instrument in Nuclear Physics," N. V. Noord Hollandsche Uitgevers Maatschappij, Amsterdam, 1945.
48. Hofstadter, R.: *Nucleonics*, **4**:2 (April, 1949); **4**:29 (May, 1949).
49. Chynoweth, A. G.: *Am. J. Phys.*, **20**:218 (1952).
50. Cassen, B.: "Proceedings of the International Conference on the Peaceful Uses of Atomic Energy," vol. 14, p. 218, United Nations, New York, 1956.
51. Cerenkov, P. A.: *Compt. rend. acad. sci. U.R.S.S.*, **2**:451 (1934).
52. Frank, I., and I. Tamm: *Compt. rend. acad. sci. U.R.S.S.*, **3**:109 (1937).
53. Jelley, J. V.: *Atomics*, **4**:81 (1953).
54. Mather, R. L.: *Phys. Rev.*, **84**:181 (1951).
55. Winckler, J. R.: *Phys. Rev.*, **85**:1054 (1952).
56. Marshall, J.: *Phys. Rev.*, **86**:685 (1952).
57. Hildebrand, R. H.: *Rev. Sci. Instr.*, **24**:463 (1953).
58. Allen, J. S.: *Phys. Rev.*, **55**:966 (1939).
59. Allen, J. S.: *Rev. Sci. Instr.*, **18**:739 (1947).
60. Stone, R. P.: *Rev. Sci. Instr.*, **20**:935 (1949).
61. Allen, A. O., C. J. Hochanadel, J. A. Ghormley, and T. W. Davis: *J. Phys. Chem.*, **56**:575 (1952).
62. Cormack, D. V., R. W. Hummel, H. E. Johns, and J. W. T. Spinks: *J. Chem. Phys.*, **22**:6 (1954).
63. Miller, N., and J. Wilkinson: *Discussions Faraday Soc.*, **12**:50 (1952).
64. Weiss, J., A. O. Allen, and H. A. Schwarz: "Proceedings of the International Conference on the Peaceful Uses of Atomic Energy," vol. 14, p. 179, United Nations, New York, 1956.
65. Bastian, R., R. Weberling, and F. Palilla: *Anal. Chem.*, **25**:284 (1953).
66. Hochanadel, C. J., and J. A. Ghormley: *J. Chem. Phys.*, **21**:880 (1953).
67. Lazo, R. M., H. A. Dewhurst, and B. Burton: *J. Chem. Phys.*, **22**:1370 (1954).
68. Schuler, R. H., and A. O. Allen: Paper at meeting of Radiation Research Society, New York, May 17, 1955.
69. Weiss, J.: *Nucleonics*, **10**:28 (July, 1952).
70. Hardwick, T. J.: *Discussions Faraday Soc.*, No. **12**:203 (1952).
71. Rødstam, G., and T. Svedberg: *Nature*, **171**:648 (1953).
72. Nicksic, S. W., and J. R. Wright: *Nucleonics*, **13**:104 (November, 1955).
73. Hart, E. J., and S. Gordon: *U.S. Atomic Energy Comm. Document* ANL-4844, 1952.
74. Dondes, S.: "Proceedings of the International Conference on the Peaceful Uses of Atomic Energy," vol. 14, p. 176, United Nations, New York, 1956.
75. Taplin, G. V.: "Proceedings of the International Conference on the Peaceful Uses of Atomic Energy," vol. 14, p. 227, United Nations, New York, 1956.
76. Taplin, G. V.: Article in G. J. Hine and G. L. Brownell (eds.) "Radiation Dosimetry," Academic Press, Inc., New York, 1956.
77. Schulman, J. H., W. Shurcliff, R. J. Ginther, and F. H. Attix: *Nucleonics*, **11**:52 (October, 1953).
78. Schulman, J. H., C. C. Klick, and H. Rabin: *Nucleonics*, **13**:30 (February, 1955).
79. Myers, O. E.: *Nucleonics*, **5**:37 (November, 1949).
80. Cannon, G. V., and G. H. Jenks: *Rev. Sci. Instr.*, **21**:236 (1950).
81. Bayly, J. G.: *Can. J. Research*, **28A**:529 (1950).
82. Laughlin, J. S., and J. W. Beattie: *Rev. Sci. Instr.*, **22**:572 (1951).

83. Horning, R. M., M. F. Katzer, R. L. McKisson, and C. C. Old: *U.S. Atomic Energy Comm. Document* LRL-70.
84. Maton, W. R. E.: *Atomic Energy Research Establishment*, AERE-C/R-1133.
85. Laughlin, J. S., S. Genna, M. Danzker, and S. J. Vacirca: "Proceedings of the International Conference on the Peaceful Uses of Atomic Energy," vol. 14, p. 163, United Nations, New York, 1956.
86. Richardson, D. M., A. O. Allen, and J. W. Boyle: "Proceedings of the International Conference on the Peaceful Uses of Atomic Energy," vol. 14, p. 209, United Nations, New York, 1956.

CHAPTER 9

# NEUTRON-DETECTION METHODS

In the preceding chapters specific types of nuclear-radiation detectors have been discussed. In general, each of these instruments is applicable for several radiation types. Many of these systems can be adapted to neutron measurements. These applications are discussed in the present chapter. Because of several considerations peculiar to neutrons and because of the special importance of neutron measurements, it is considered highly desirable to devote a separate chapter to this subject.

## GENERAL CONSIDERATIONS

### 9-1. *Types of Neutron Measurements*

In Chap. 1 the interaction of neutrons with matter was discussed. The variety of possible processes and the importance of the neutron energy to the probability for the various processes were emphasized. Since the detection of neutrons requires the interaction of neutrons with matter, it is clear that consideration of the neutron energy is important. Therefore one of the major concerns of this chapter is the energy dependence of the measuring processes. This study also leads to information concerning the distribution in energy of the neutrons.

The energy dependence is often complicated by the degradation of the neutron energy through slowing-down processes concurrent with the measuring process. Consequently it is necessary to discuss the slowing-down processes as they affect the measurements.

Neutron radiation often occurs along with other radiation types, particularly with gamma rays. The extent to which the particular neutron-detection system discriminates against gamma rays needs to be investigated.

The measurement of the energy which is absorbed from the neutrons by matter that is placed in radiation fields is another important application to be covered. These measurements are known as neutron dosimetry. They are important in the field of health physics and in that of radiation damage to construction materials for reactors.

### 9-2. *Nuclear Processes Used in Neutron Detection*

It has been pointed out that the detection of nuclear particles requires some type of interaction of the radiation with the detector. For radiation consisting of charged particles, the interaction is through the excitation and ionization which are produced by the primary particles, while for gamma-ray detection it must come through the secondary electrons which the photons release. In the case of neutrons there are several mechanisms by which the interaction with matter takes place; these were listed in Chap. 1. Each of these processes is the basis of a potential method of detection. The most useful ones are as follows:

1. Neutron-induced transmutations in which the product particles make possible the detection; examples are (n,$\alpha$), (n,p), (n,$\gamma$), and (n,fission) reactions. The alpha particle, the proton, the gamma ray, or the fission products give instantaneous information concerning the neutron.
2. Neutron-induced transmutations which result in radioactive product nuclei. The subsequent decay of the radioactive nuclei gives information on the neutron flux which induced the radioactivity.
3. Elastic scattering by neutrons in which the recoil particle is charged and is capable of being detected. The most important example of this process is the elastic scattering of a neutron by a proton; to the latter particle can be imparted up to 100 per cent of the neutron energy.

Neutron-detection systems consist of the material required to bring about one of the nuclear processes listed above, along with means for measuring or indicating the results of the nuclear process. This latter part of the detection system may be one of the several conventional systems for detection of charged particles or photons, as required. In the following sections several of these detector systems are discussed.

## NEUTRON-DETECTOR CHAMBERS USING $B^{10}$

### 9-3. *The* $B^{10}$(n,$\alpha$) *Reaction*

The $B^{10}$(n,$\alpha$) reaction is widely used for thermal-neutron detection. A number of factors make it highly satisfactory for this purpose. The cross section of the reaction has a large value and a simple energy dependence over a wide range of energy values. The reaction is easy to detect even in the presence of comparatively large gamma fluxes because of the high specific ionization and the large energy of the charged particles which are released. The material $B^{10}$ is available in its isotopic form, and its chemical properties are such that it can be incorporated successfully in the detector.

The reaction is exothermic, with an energy release of 2.78 Mev. The ground state of the $Li^7$ product nucleus may be formed directly, with the entire energy being shared by the $Li^7$ and the alpha particle; alternatively, an intermediate excited state of $Li^7$ may be formed, followed by the emission of a 0.48-Mev gamma. The probability of reaching the ground state directly is only 0.07 for reactions induced by thermal neutrons; it rises to a maximum of about 0.7 for 1.8-Mev neutrons, followed by a drop to less than 0.5 for 2.5 Mev [1].

For the capture of a neutron of energy $E$, the kinetic energy $E_{ke}$ of either $E + 2.30$ Mev or $E + 2.78$ Mev will be shared by the alpha particle and the lithium recoil nucleus. If the captured neutron is thermalized, $E$ is approximately zero, and the energies of the lithium nucleus and the alpha particle in the predominant case are

$$E_{\text{Li}} = \frac{E_{ke} M_\alpha}{M_\alpha + M_{\text{Li}}} = \frac{(2.30)(4.00)}{4.00 + 7.02} = 0.88 \text{ Mev}$$

and

$$E_\alpha = \frac{E_{ke} M_{\text{Li}}}{M_\alpha + M_{\text{Li}}} = 1.47 \text{ Mev}$$

respectively.

The energy dependence of the cross section $\sigma$ for the $B^{10}(n,\alpha)$ reaction is shown in Fig. 1–21. This cross section is found to have the $1/v$ dependence up to about 100 ev and therefore can be represented by the expression

$$\sigma = \frac{\sigma_o v_o}{v} \tag{9–1}$$

when $v_o = 2.2 \times 10^5$ cm/sec and $\sigma_o = 4{,}010$ barns.

9–4. *Reaction Rate in a Detector Containing* $B^{10}$

The reaction rate in a detector containing $B^{10}$ can be obtained by a generalization of Eq. (1–37). The contribution $dR$ to the reaction rate by neutrons between the energy $E$ and $E + dE$ in the volume element $dV$ is

$$dR = N(x,y,z)\sigma(E)\phi(E,x,y,z)\, dE\, dV \tag{9–2}$$

where $N(x,y,z)$ = no. of $B^{10}$ atoms per unit volume at point $x,y,z$
$\sigma(E)$ = $B^{10}(n,\alpha)$ cross section at energy $E$
$\phi(E,x,y,z)$ = flux per unit energy interval at point $x,y,z$

The total reaction rate would be represented by the integral throughout the entire detector volume and over the complete neutron-energy spectrum. That is,

$$\text{Reactions per sec} = \int_{\text{vol}} \int_0^\infty N(x,y,z)\sigma(E)\phi(E,x,y,z)\, dV\, dE \tag{9–3}$$

If the flux is considered to be independent of the position in the detector and the total number of $B^{10}$ nuclei is represented by $N_T$, then Eq. (9–3) becomes

$$\text{Reactions per sec} = N_T \int_0^\infty \sigma(E)\phi(E)\, dE \tag{9–4}$$

If the neutron spectrum contains only neutrons in the energy range for which Eq. (9–1) holds, Eq. (9–4) becomes

$$\text{Reactions per sec} = N_T\sigma_o v_o \int_0^{100\text{ ev}} n(E)\,dE = N_T\sigma_o v_o n \qquad (9\text{–}5)$$

where $n$ is the number of neutrons per unit volume, irrespective of energy up to 100 ev.

The above results which allow the calculation of the neutron density are independent of the distribution in energy of the neutrons as long as their energies lie below 100 ev. If, in addition, the average velocity $\bar{v}$ of the neutrons is known, the total flux can be calculated from the expression

$$n\bar{v} = \frac{(\text{reactions per sec})\bar{v}}{N_T\sigma_o v_o} \qquad (9\text{–}6)$$

For the case of Maxwell-Boltzmann distribution in energy (see Sec. 1–19), $\bar{v}$ is $1.128v_o$ at 20°C.

The $B^{10}(n,\alpha)$ reaction has been employed in many detection systems. These include ionization chambers, proportional counters, scintillation detectors, and nuclear emulsions. In addition, the neutron-sensitive thermopile (see Sec. 9–31) is based on this reaction.

### 9–5. *Boron-trifluoride-filled Gaseous Detectors*

To achieve a useful gaseous detector, the $B^{10}$ atoms must be introduced in the chamber in such a way that the charged particles which are released by the reaction can enter its interior and produce ionization. Because of the rather short range of these particles, one is limited to thin layers of solid boron or to gaseous compounds of boron.

The $BF_3$-filled counters have been constructed in various forms [2]. Ordinarily a cylindrical construction is employed. Various diameters, center wires, and gas filling pressures are used. A typical $BF_3$ counter has a cathode and center-wire diameters of 0.87 and 0.002 in., respectively, an active length of 6 in., and a filling pressure of 12 cm Hg with 96 per cent enriched $BF_3$. When it is used for pulse operation with a pulse-amplifier sensitivity of 4 mv, the operating voltage is 1,400 volts. If $p(E)$ represents the probability that a $B^{10}(n,\alpha)$ reaction caused by a neutron of energy $E$ will register a count, then from Eq. (9–5) one obtains the expression for the counting rate as

$$\text{Count/sec} = NV\sigma_o v_o \int_0^{\infty} p(E)n(E)\,dE \qquad (9\text{–}7)$$

where $N_T$ has been replaced by $NV$, the products of the density of $B^{10}F_3$ atoms and the chamber volume. The counter is ordinarily used with a counting system which requires that the pulse size exceed a certain minimum size to be counted. This in turn requires that the total energy which the alpha particle and the lithium nucleus dissipate in the chamber exceed a certain threshold value $E_T$. For reactions occurring at a sufficient distance from the chamber wall that the entire energy is dissipated in the chamber, this condition is easy to achieve, since even with thermal neutrons this energy is at least 2.30 Mev. The fact that for some reactions the charged particles hit the chamber walls reduces $p(E)$ somewhat below 1. However, since in practice the chamber dimensions are usually larger than the particle ranges and the threshold energy $E_T$ is much less than the total energy available, the function $p(E)$ can be taken as 1, to a good approximation. This can be seen from the fact that the plateau in the counting rate versus counter voltage is quite flat. Figure 9–1 is such a curve for the $BF_3$ proportional counter described above. The flat portion of the curve indicates that essentially all the reactions within the tube are being counted.

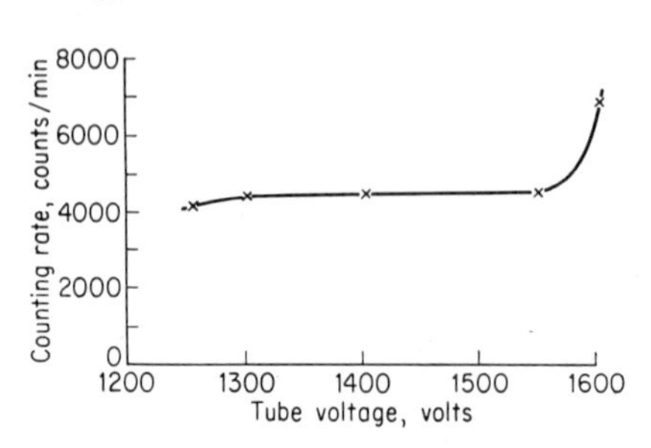


FIG. 9–1. Counting-rate–tube-voltage curve for a $BF_3$-filled proportional counter.

The sensitivity of the counter may be defined as counts per second per unit neutron flux. From Eq. (9–7), one obtains

$$\text{Sensitivity} = NV\sigma_0 \frac{v_0}{\bar{v}} \tag{9–8}$$

For a Maxwell-Boltzmann distribution, this becomes

$$\text{Sensitivity} = \frac{4{,}010 \times 10^{-24} NV}{1.128}$$

where $N$ is the number of $B^{10}$ atoms per cubic centimeter and $V$ is the sensitive volume of the counter.

**Example 9–1.** Compute the thermal-neutron sensitivity of the $BF_3$ counter described above, i.e., a sensitive volume of 58 cm³ and filling gas 96 per cent enriched $BF_3$ at 12 cm Hg.

*Solution.* The density of $B^{10}$ atomsi s obtained by the product of the molar density and Avogadro's number; that is,

$$N = \frac{(6.02 \times 10^{23})(12)(0.96)}{(76)(22.4 \times 10^3)} = 4.1 \times 10^{18} \text{ atoms/cm}^3$$

From Eq. (9–8), one obtains

$$\text{Sensitivity} = \frac{4{,}010 \times 10^{-24} NV}{1.128} = \frac{(4{,}010 \times 10^{-24})(4.1 \times 10^{18})(58)}{1.128}$$

$$= 0.83 \text{ count/sec per unit neutron flux}$$

The validity of Eq. (9–8) requires that the flux remain constant throughout the counter volume. This condition requires that only a vanishingly small fraction of the neutrons which pass through the chamber are absorbed. In addition to simplifying the expressions for counting rate, this condition ensures that the detector does not disturb the neutron flux. In a medium in which neutrons are diffusing, the absorption of neutrons upon passage through the counter lowers the flux at the counter, since these neutrons are not available for scattering back through it. The perturbation of the neutron flux by the detector will be discussed further in connection with neutron-flux measurements by foils.

The extent to which the absorption in the counter may be neglected can be estimated by considering the probability that a neutron will pass through the counter without being absorbed. This probability is given by Eq. (1–34) as $e^{-\Sigma_a d}$, where $\Sigma_a$ is the macroscopic absorption cross section and $d$ is the distance through the $B^{10}$. The value of $\Sigma_a$ for $B^{10}F_3$ gas at atmospheric pressure is $0.1(0.025/E)^{1/2}$ cm$^{-1}$, when $E$ is the neutron energy in electron volts. As long as $\Sigma_a d \ll 1$, the absorption is negligible. Thus, in a counter operated at atmospheric pressure, the absorption could be neglected for 0.025-ev neutrons in counters with dimensions up to approximately 1 cm.

The efficiency of a neutron counter is defined as the fraction of the neutrons which, upon entering the counter, result in a count. The probability of the absorption of a neutron passing a distance $d$ through the $B^{10}$ is $1 - e^{-\Sigma_a d}$. Therefore, in general, the efficiency depends on the size and shape of the counter and on the direction of incidence of the neutrons as well as on the other properties of the counter. For the special case of a collimated neutron beam traveling parallel to the tube axis, the efficiency is

$$\text{Efficiency} = 1 - e^{-\Sigma_a d} \tag{9–9}$$

where $d$ is the length of the sensitive volume measured along the tube axis.

**Example 9–2.** Compute the efficiency of the counter described in Example 9–1 for counting thermal neutrons traveling parallel to the tube axis, provided that the length of the sensitive volume is 6 in.

*Solution.* By Eq. (9–9), the efficiency is

$$\begin{aligned}\text{Efficiency} &= 1 - e^{-\Sigma_a d} = 1 - e^{-N\sigma_a d}\\ &= 1 - \exp\left[(4.1 \times 10^{18})(4{,}010 \times 10^{-24})\left(\frac{0.025}{E}\right)^{1/2}(15.2)\right]\end{aligned}$$

where $E$ is the neutron energy in electron volts. For $E = 0.025$ ev, the efficiency is 22 per cent.

### 9–6. *Boron-lined Counters*

Boron can be introduced into a chamber as a solid coating on its walls or on plates provided for that purpose. The use of the solid rather than the $BF_3$ gas has the advantage that more satisfactory counter filling gases can be employed. The boron must be applied in thin layers. This is desirable from the standpoint of reasonable transparency to neutrons from outside the counter. In addition, the only reactions which are effective in causing counts are those which occur sufficiently close to that surface of the boron that at least one of the charged particles can escape the boron into the counter gas. By Eq. (1–3), the range of the 1.47-Mev alphas which are produced by the thermal neutrons is 0.85 mg/cm² in boron. Therefore a thickness of greater than 0.85 mg/cm² would be useless from the counting standpoint. Actually, it would be detrimental, since it would absorb some neutrons before they reach the sensitive layer adjacent to the counter gas. From Eq. (1–44), one obtains for the mean free path for absorption of neutrons

$$\lambda(\text{g/cm}^2) = \frac{W}{0.602\sigma} \tag{9–10}$$

where $W$ is the atomic weight of the element and $\sigma$ is the cross section in barns. For $B^{10}$ at 0.025 ev, $\lambda$ is 4.2 mg/cm².

The plateaus in the counting-rate versus tube-voltage curves are found to be less flat for boron-lined counters than those for $BF_3$ counters. This situation arises since the charged particles produce varying ionization in the chamber gas, depending on the energy which they lose in escaping the

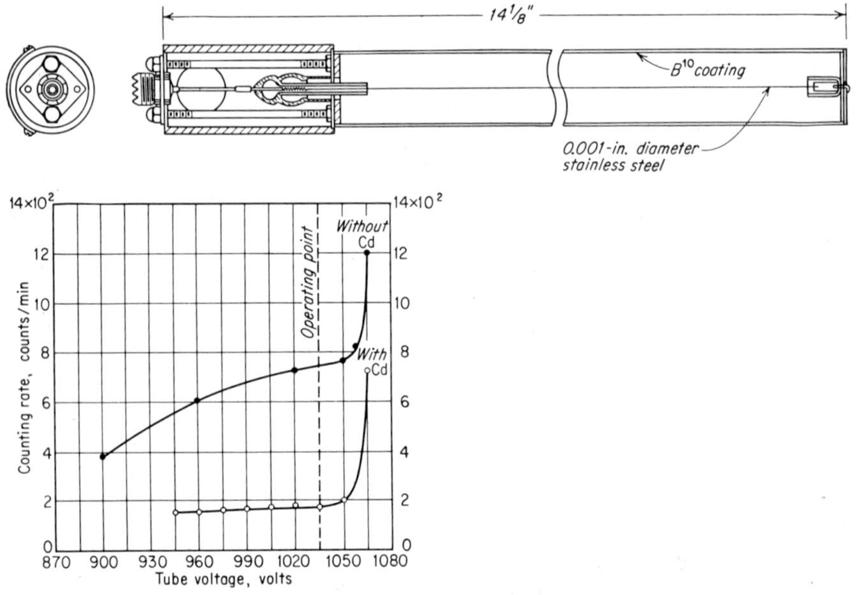


FIG. 9–2. Diagram of a $B^{10}$-lined counter and the counting-rate versus tube-voltage curve obtained with a pulse-amplifier sensitivity of 2 mv; filling gas of helium plus 5 per cent ether at 10 cm Hg pressure. (*From "The Reactor Handbook," vol. 2, p. 951, U.S. Atomic Energy Commission Document, McGraw-Hill Book Company, Inc., New York,* 1955.)

boron film. Figure 9–2 is the characteristic curve as well as the schematic diagram for such a counter. With the operating point as indicated, the counter sensitivity is 5 to 10 counts/sec per unit neutron flux.

Lowde [3] has described a $B^{10}$ chamber capable of high-efficiency detection of thermal neutrons. The whole instrument was contained in a cylinder of $2\frac{5}{16}$-in. length and $1\frac{3}{16}$-in. diameter. The counter was a multiple-plate type; 12 parallel plates of 1-mm spacing and carrying 0.5-mg/cm² $B^{10}$ layers were employed. The counter gas was 5 atm of argon. The counting-rate versus tube-voltage curve was found to have a good plateau; the operating voltage was 75 volts when operated in the ionization-chamber region with a high-gain pulse amplifier. Its efficiency is reported [3] to be 24 per cent for thermal neutrons.

## 9–7. *Current Ionization Chambers Using* $B^{10}$

For sufficiently high neutron fluxes, the neutron detectors can be operated as current-type ionization chambers. If one assumes that the entire 2.3 Mev of energy from the $B(n,\alpha)$ reaction produces ionization by dissipating 32 ev per ion pair, one reaction per second produces $1.13 \times 10^{-14}$ amp. For a chamber with sensitivity $S$, the current is

$$I = 1.13 \times 10^{-14}\Phi S \tag{9–11}$$

where $\Phi$ is the flux. Thus a chamber of a sensitivity of one reaction per second per unit neutron flux would produce currents from $10^{-4}$ to $10^{-10}$ amp for fluxes from $10^{10}$ to $10^{4}$ neutrons/(cm²)(sec), respectively. This flux range is approximately that over which the current ionization chamber would operate most successfully.

If a current chamber with coated electrodes is to have a high sensitivity with a minimum volume, its electrode area should be made as large as possible. The parallel-plate arrangement described in the previous section has been applied for this purpose [4]. A schematic diagram of this instrument, called the PCP (parallel-circular-plate) chamber is shown in Fig. 9–3. This instrument, containing 16 parallel surfaces, each coated with $B^{10}$ to a thick-

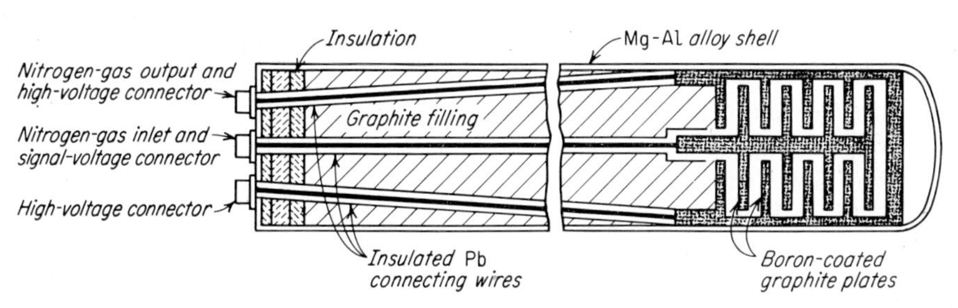


FIG. 9–3. Parallel-circular-plate (PCP) ionization chamber. (*From R. K. Abele and J. Gundlach, U.S. Atomic Energy Comm. Document AECD*-3494, 1951.)

ness of 0.3 mg/cm$^2$, has a diameter of $2\frac{15}{16}$ in. and a total length of 33 in. Its sensitivity to a streaming flux of thermal neutrons, traveling parallel to its axis, is $5 \times 10^{-15}$ amp per unit neutron flux. The material from which the chamber is constructed, including the graphite and the Mg-Al alloy shell, is chosen so as to avoid the production of high induced radioactivity under neutron bombardment.

In the pulse-type proportional counter, the gamma-ray background which often accompanies neutrons is discriminated against through the use of a pulse-height selector, provided that it is not so high that excessive pile-up of pulses for secondary electrons occurs. This type of discrimination is not possible in current-ionization-chamber instruments.

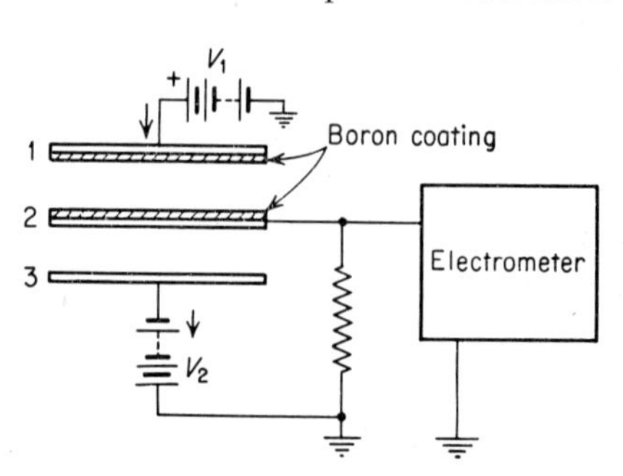

FIG. 9–4. Compensated ion chamber.

The current due to gamma radiation can be minimized by the use of the smallest practical ratio of chamber volume to coated electrode area. However, for effective discrimination, the differential or compensated chambers must be used. This system requires two chambers. One contains $BF_3$ or a boron lining and is sensitive to both neutrons and gamma rays; the other contains no boron and is sensitive to gamma rays only. If, when the chambers are exposed only to gamma rays, the two currents are balanced, then the differential current which results when neutrons and gamma rays are both present is a measure of the neutron flux. The balancing of the currents can be accomplished by adjusting the gas pressure, the chamber sizes, or the collecting voltages.

Figure 9–4 is a schematic diagram of a gamma-compensated ion chamber incorporated in a measuring circuit. The space between plates 1 and 2 forms one chamber while that between 2 and 3 forms the other. If the volumes and pressures are properly adjusted, the net current will be zero when the chambers are exposed to a uniform gamma flux in the absence of neutron radiation. Therefore the net current which is measured by the electrometer is due to neutrons only.

Figure 9–5 is a drawing of a gamma-compensated ion chamber which is used in the Materials Test Reactor at Arco, Idaho. Although the sensitive portion of the chamber is only about 6 in. long, the total length of the chamber is 36 in. Thus the cables from the chamber are far removed from the region of high neutron flux. The electrodes consist of three graphite cups. The position of the inner cup is adjustable so that the compensating volume is variable. This adjustment is needed particularly when there is a gradient in the gamma flux. The chamber which is sensitive to neutrons has a $B^{10}$

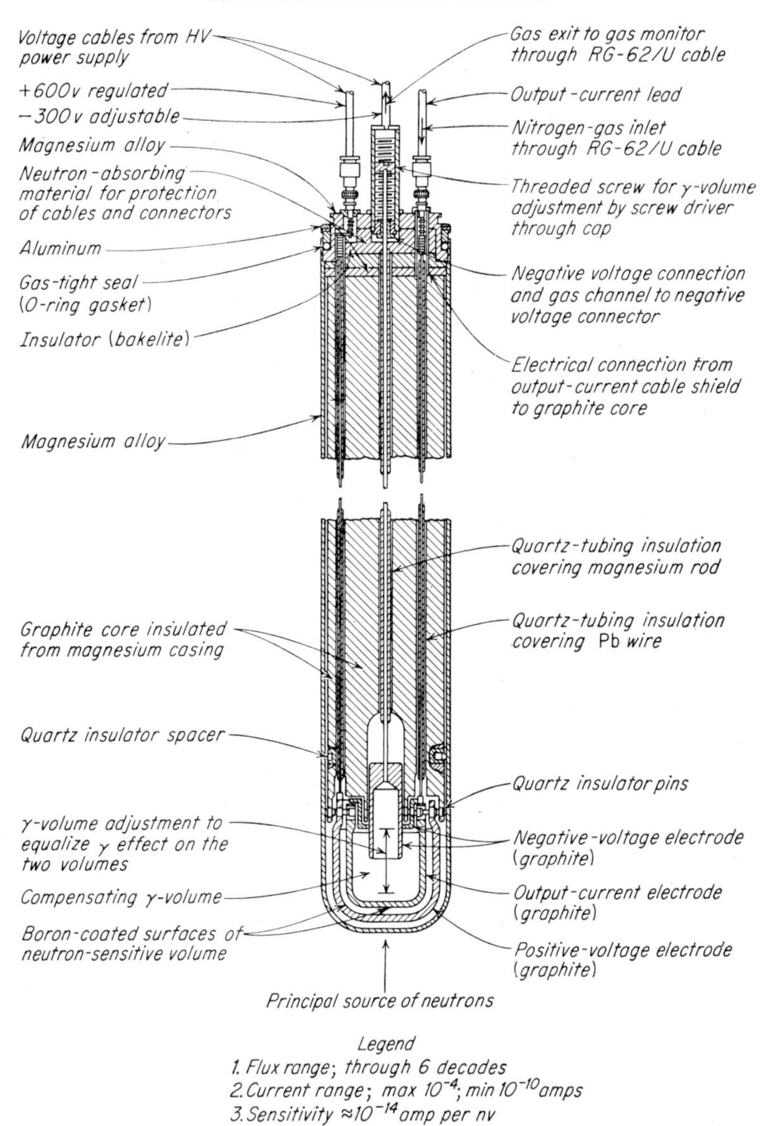


FIG. 9-5. Gamma-compensated ion chamber used in the Materials Test Reactor. (*From "The Reactor Handbook," vol. 2, p. 960, U.S. Atomic Energy Commission Document, McGraw-Hill Book Company, Inc., New York,* 1955.)

lining. The instrument can be used at least over a $10^6$-fold range of neutron flux, and the corresponding current range is from $10^{-4}$ to $10^{-10}$ amp.

As an alternative, the gamma compensation can be accomplished electrically; the construction details of this type of chamber are shown in Fig. 9-6. This chamber is circular in cross section. The center electrode, which is part of the gamma-compensating volume, is shaped to produce a weak electric-field region so that the slope of the current-voltage characteristic is greater in the gamma-compensating volume than in the neutron-sensitive volume. Provided that the compensating volume is slightly larger than the neutron-sensitive volume, a combination of applied voltages can be found

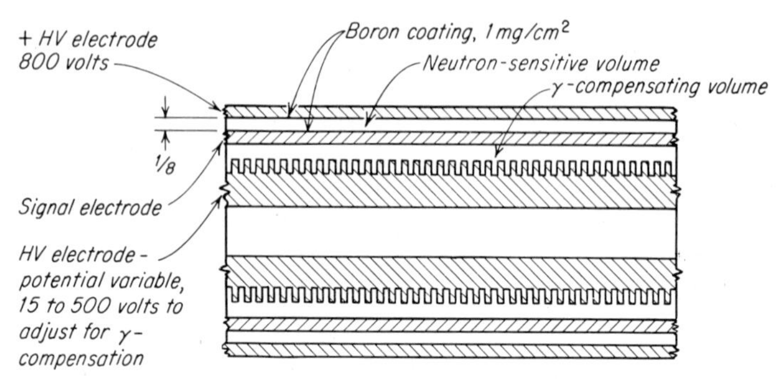


FIG. 9–6. Cross section of an electrically compensated ion chamber. [*From H. S. McCreary, Jr., and R. T. Bayard, Rev. Sci. Instr.*, **25**:161 (1954).]

at which gamma compensation results. A chamber of this type, filled with nitrogen at 1 atm, was found [5] to have a sensitivity of $4 \times 10^{-14}$ amp per unit thermal flux.

## 9–8. *Fast-neutron Detection by* $B^{10}$ *Counters*

Because of the drop in the cross section for the $B^{10}(n,\alpha)$ reaction with an increase in the neutron energy, the sensitivity of the base $B^{10}$ counter is quite small for fast neutrons. Considerable improvement can be realized by enclosing the counter in a neutron moderator in such a way that the neutrons are slowed down before entering the counter tube. However, the efficiency of such an arrangement is usually dependent on the source energy and the detector-source geometry. These factors make the interpretation of measurement quite difficult, particularly when the source has a heterogeneous energy distribution.

Hanson and McKibben [6] have devised moderator-tube arrangements in which the efficiency is essentially independent of energy from about 10 kev to about 3 Mev. This detector system is known as the "long counter," because of its long range of flat response. One of the "long-counter" designs is shown in Fig. 9–7.

In the use of the "long counter" the neutrons enter from the open end of the counter. The counts which occur come largely from thermal neutrons in the case of both fast and slow incident neutrons; that is, the counts which the fast neutrons produce come largely after the neutrons are slowed down by the moderator. The slow neutrons do not penetrate far into the paraffin, on an average. Some of them are scattered back out of the paraffin. Their reactions with the counter occur largely near the entrance end of the detector tube. The holes in the front face of the paraffin serve to increase the efficiency for slow neutrons by reducing the number of neutrons which are backscattered by the face of the paraffin.

On the other hand, the fast neutrons penetrate the paraffin much farther before they are slowed down and cause a count by entering the detector tube. Also, some of the fast neutrons will escape through the sides of the paraffin. The several factors mentioned here combine in such a way as

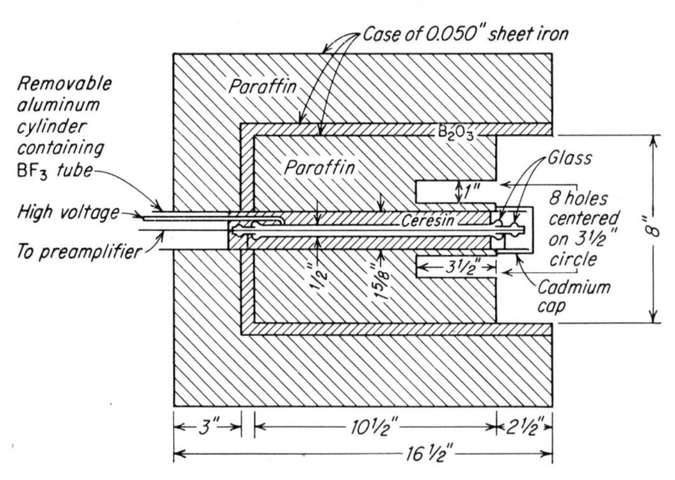


FIG. 9–7. "Long counter" designed by Hanson and McKibben. [*From A. O. Hanson and J. L. McKibben, Phys. Rev.*, **72**:673 (1947).]

to make the efficiency independent of neutron energy. The layer of boron trioxide is added to reduce the background due to the neutrons which enter in directions other than through the front face of the counter. The absolute sensitivity of the counter is such that it gives about one count for $10^5$ neutrons emitted isotropically from a source 1 m from the face.

Nobles et al. [7] have reexamined the energy dependence of the "long counter." They have reconfirmed the general flat response but have discovered local fluctuations at 2.08 and 2.99 Mev. These are believed to be due to resonances in carbon scattering.

## FISSION CHAMBERS

### 9–9. *Fission Reaction for Neutron Detection*

The fission reaction, so basic in many aspects of nuclear science and engineering, is important also in nuclear-radiation detection. In these applications use is made either of the kinetic energy of the fission products or of their resulting radioactivity. The ionization produced as the fission products are brought to rest is utilized extensively in ionization and proportional chambers, here designated as fission chambers; the fission-product radioactivity is employed as discussed in Sec. 9–15 under the category of foil detectors.

A number of factors contribute to the utility of fission chambers. The wide choice of fissionable materials allows the selection of the energy dependence and of the efficiency. The large energy released per reaction makes it possible to discriminate against much larger fluxes of gamma rays than with detectors employing the (n,$\alpha$) or similar reactions. This latter property makes the fission chambers particularly useful for the measurement of the small values of neutron flux which are present in the start-up

TABLE 9–1. APPROXIMATE VALUES OF FAST-FISSION THRESHOLDS

| Material | Threshold, Mev | Material | Threshold, Mev |
|---|---|---|---|
| $U^{238}$ | 1.45 | $Th^{232}$ | 1.75 |
| $Np^{237}$ | 0.75 | $Pa^{232}$ | 0.5 |
| | | $Bi^{209}$ | 50 |

and shutdown of a reactor. These neutron fluxes are accompanied by large gamma-ray fluxes so that the discrimination is very important. For this type of application $B^{10}$ chambers are unsuitable.

Fission chambers containing the thermal-fissionable nuclei $U^{233}$, $U^{235}$, or $Pu^{239}$ are efficient thermal-neutron detectors. Their cross sections follow more or less a $1/v$ dependence so that the considerations in Sec. 9–4 concerning the relationship between reaction rate and thermal flux apply here as a crude approximation.

Materials which are fissionable by only fast neutrons are useful for fast-neutron counting, particularly when it is desirable to discriminate against slow and intermediate-energy neutrons. All energies below the threshold are excluded from the counting. Table 9–1 lists several fissionable materials of interest for fast-fission chambers, along with their threshold energies.

Ordinarily the fissionable materials are incorporated into the chambers in the form of thin foils rather than as gases. The gaseous fission compounds have been found to be poor counter gases because of excessive negative-ion formation and corrosion.

### 9–10. *Examples of Fission Chambers*

Various authors have discussed the construction and characteristics of fission counters [8–12]. Three of these detectors will be described here.

Where high efficiency is desired, a large amount of fissionable material is incorporated into the chamber through the use of a multiple-plate construction. Baer and Bayard [9] have described a detector of this type. The chamber is shown in Fig. 9–8. It is housed in an aluminum case 2 in. in diameter and 10 in. long. The chamber contains four concentric aluminum electrodes. The electrodes are coated with $U_3O_8$, enriched to 90 per cent $U^{235}$, with coating thicknesses of 2.0 mg/cm²; the total coated area in the counter is 1,020 cm². The sensitivity for thermal neutrons is 0.7 count/sec per unit neutron flux. The background counting rate is 5 counts/sec. The instrument has a useful range from 10 to $2 \times 10^5$ neutrons/(cm²)(sec). It

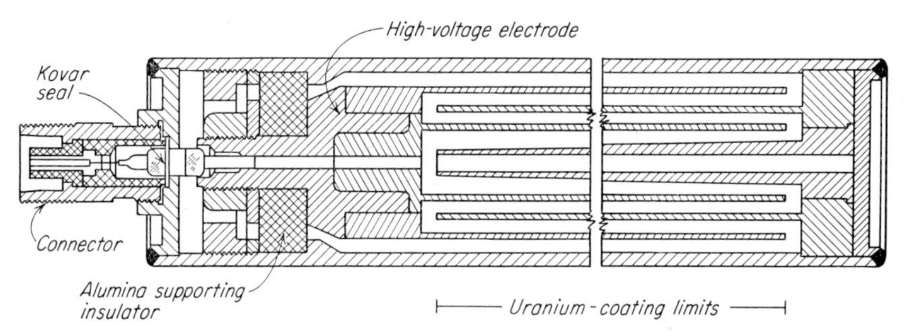


FIG. 9–8. High-efficiency fission chamber. [*From W. Baer and R. T. Bayard, Rev. Sci. Instr.*, **24**:138 (1953).]

will operate over this range in a gamma flux up to $10^{10}$ gamma rays/(cm²)(sec). When operated with a linear amplifier of gain $10^5$, its operating voltage is 300 volts, and the counting-rate–chamber-voltage characteristic has a good plateau.

One is ultimately limited in the maximum amount of fissionable material which can be placed in a counter if the material is an alpha emitter. If the rate of alpha particles is too high, there is a tendency for the alpha particles to pile up so that pulses produced by them may be counted and produce a high background.

Wiegand [12] has described the use of bismuth in a fission chamber for the detection of neutrons with kinetic energy greater than 50 Mev, the threshold energy for the fission process in bismuth. The chamber was the multiple-plate type having a total of 28 plates. These plates had a total area of 500 cm² and were coated with a bismuth layer of 1 mg/cm². The chamber was used with 84-Mev neutrons. The probability of the neutron producing a fission in traveling through the chamber was found to be $10^{-6}$. The cross section for the fission process was estimated as 0.05 barn.

Nobles and Smith [10] have described a miniature fission chamber for the determination of neutron distributions within critical and subcritical assemblies. Figure 9–9 is a line drawing of this chamber. The envelope of the counter is milled from cold-rolled steel in two sections. When properly hand-soldered together, this steel provides the necessary strength for containing the filling pressure of 4 atm of argon. The electrode, a 0.021-in.-thick stainless-steel plate supported by a hermetical seal, is coated with a thickness of 100 $\mu g/cm^2$ of the fissionable material. The chamber dimensions and gas pressure are such that the heavily ionizing fission fragments expend a large amount of their energy in the gas. Most of the longer-range alpha particles from the natural activity of the fissionable material expend

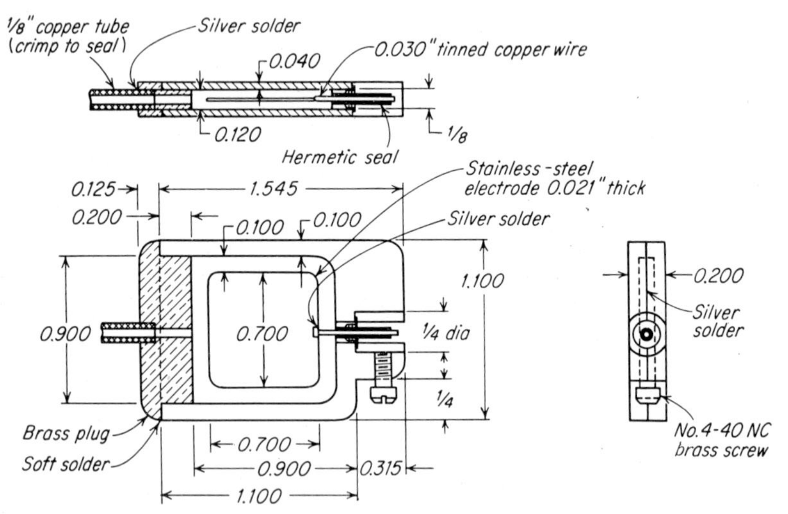


FIG. 9–9. Construction of a miniature fission chamber. [*From R. G. Nobles and A. B. Smith, Nucleonics,* **14**:60 (*January,* 1956).]

the larger part of their energy in the chamber walls, and pulse pile-up of high-alpha activity is minimized. The sensitivity of the counter, of course, depends on the fissionable material which is used and the energy distribution of the flux. A typical value of efficiency is $2 \times 10^{-5}$ count/sec per unit neutron flux for a virgin neutron spectrum with an electrode coating of $U^{235}$.

## PROTON RECOIL

### 9–11. *Introductory Considerations*

The most widely used methods for the detection of fast neutrons involve the (n,p) scattering process. By this process the neutrons give at least part of their energy to protons, and the ionization and excitation which the latter produce make possible the detection.

The use of the (n,p) scattering has the advantage that the cross section is relatively large (see Fig. 1–18), and its variation with energy is well known. A serious disadvantage is the fact that the proton energy ranges from 0 to $E_n$ for a neutron energy of $E_n$. However, this range of energies can be taken into account in the interpretation of measurements, and accurate results can be obtained.

If $\Theta$ is the angle between the incoming neutron and the recoil proton, measured in the laboratory coordinate system, then the proton-recoil energy $E$ can be shown to be [13]

$$E = E_n \cos^2 \Theta \tag{9-12}$$

where $E_n$ is the neutron energy before the collision. For neutron energies below 10 Mev, the scattering is isotropic in the center-of-mass coordinate system. From this condition it can be shown that all neutron energies from $E_n$ to 0 are equally probable after a single scattering. That is, if monoenergetic neutrons of energy $E_n$ are scattered, the probability $p(E)\,dE$ that their energy will lie between $E$ and $E + dE$ after scattering is

$$p(E)\,dE = \frac{dE}{E_n} \tag{9-13}$$

If a region contains $N_T$ protons in a uniform flux of monoenergetic neutrons with energy $E_n$, the number of recoil protons per unit time is

$$\text{Recoil protons per sec} = N_T \phi_{E_n} \sigma(E_n) \tag{9-14}$$

where $\sigma(E_n)$ is the cross section for the scattering of neutrons of energy $E_n$ by a proton. The number of protons produced per unit energy range, designated as $N_p(E)$, is obtained from the product of Eqs. (9–13) and (9–14) as

$$N_p(E)\,dE = N_T \phi_{E_n} \frac{\sigma(E_n)}{E_n}\,dE \tag{9-15}$$

To obtain the relationship between the neutron flux and the detector output, one must consider the contribution of the spectrum of the protons as given by Eq. (9–15) to the detector response. This will be discussed for both the pulse chamber and the current chambers in the following sections. Similar considerations apply for scintillation detectors, nuclear emulsions, and other systems employing the proton-recoil phenomenon.

### 9–12. *Pulse Chambers Employing Proton Recoil*

The hydrogen which is required for the proton-recoil counters can be introduced either in a solid or gaseous form. Suitable solid materials include paraffin, polyethylene, and glycerol tristearate. These materials, referred to as radiators, serve as the source of the protons which enter the sensitive region of the detector. For gaseous chambers, hydrogen gas can be used. It has the disadvantage of a small stopping power for the recoil proton. This situation is improved by the use of a mixture of hydrogen with a heavy noble gas such as argon, krypton, or xenon. Heavy hydrogenous compounds such as ethane and methane are used also. The latter are not satisfactory for chambers operated under pulse conditions requiring positive-ion collection; the ion mobility is too small.

If one assumes that the pulse height produced in the detector by each recoil proton is proportional to the proton energy, one can write an expression for the counting rate. When used with an electronic counter which accepts all pulses produced by protons with energy greater than a threshold value $E_T$, the counting rate $C(E_n,E_T)$ for neutrons of energy $E_n$ is

$$C(E_n,E_T) = \int_{E_T}^{E_n} N_p(E)\,dE = N_T\phi_{E_n}\frac{\sigma(E_n)}{E_n}(E_n - E_T) \qquad (9\text{–}16)$$

Here Eq. (9–15) has been used for the distribution in energy $N_p(E)$ of the recoil protons. The sensitivity of the detector is

$$\text{Sensitivity} = \frac{C(E_n,E_T)}{\phi_{E_n}} = \frac{N_T\sigma(E_n)}{E_n}(E_n - E_T) \qquad (9\text{–}17)$$

The threshold energy is usually about 0.1 Mev since pulse heights lower than this cannot be readily distinguished from those produced by background gammas.

To investigate the dependence of the sensitivity on neutron energy, one can approximate the energy dependence of $\sigma(E_n)$ by the $1/v$ law; that is,

$$\sigma(E_n) \simeq \sigma(E_T)\left(\frac{E_T}{E_n}\right)^{1/2} \qquad (9\text{–}18)$$

This is a fair approximation for neutron energies from 0.1 to 10 Mev. Using this, the sensitivity in Eq. (9–17) becomes

$$\text{Sensitivity} = N_T\sigma(E_T)\left(\frac{E_T}{E_n}\right)^{3/2}\left(\frac{E_n}{E_T} - 1\right) \qquad (9\text{–}19)$$

Figure 9–10 is a plot of this sensitivity normalized at the maximum value. It is seen that it is relatively independent of energy over a wide range. For example, if $E_T$ is 0.1 Mev, the sensitivity would not be expected to vary by more than 25 per cent over the range of neutron energies from about 0.15 to 1 Mev.

**Example 9–3.** Estimate the sensitivity of a proton-recoil counter with a sensitive volume of 100 cm³ containing hydrogen gas at 2-atm pressure.

*Solution.* The sensitive volume contains $N_T$ protons, where

$$N_T = (2.68 \times 10^{19})(2)(2)(100) = 1.07 \times 10^{22} \text{ protons}$$

since there are $2.68 \times 10^{19}$ molecules/cm³ at normal temperature and pressure. If $E_T$ is taken as 0.1 Mev, $\sigma(E_T)$ is 13 barns, from Fig. 1–18. By Eq. (9–19), the sensitivity is

$$\text{Sensitivity} = N_T\sigma(E_T)\left(\frac{E_T}{E_n}\right)^{3/2}\left(\frac{E_n}{E_T} - 1\right) = (1.07 \times 10^{22})(13 \times 10^{-24})(3)^{-3/2}(3 - 1)$$

$$= 0.05 \text{ at the maximum value } \frac{E_n}{E_T} = 3$$

The above calculation is indicative of the order of magnitude of the sensitivity of this counter type. It is seen to be quite low compared with that of $B^{10}$ counters for thermal neutrons.

The condition that the pulse height be proportional to the proton-recoil energy is quite hard to meet in practice. The major difficulty is the wall

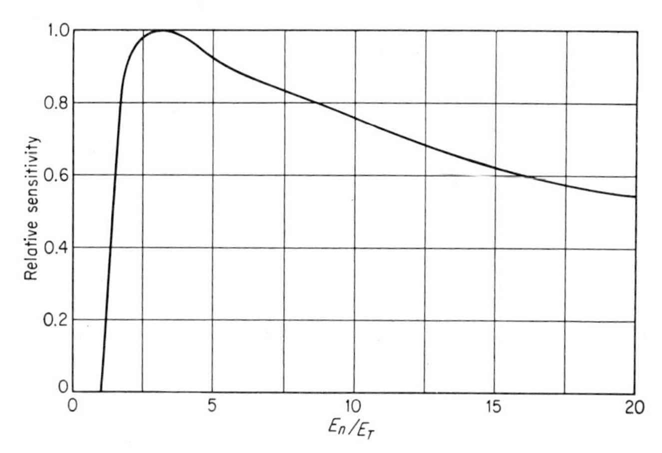


FIG. 9–10. Relative sensitivity of a pulse-type proton-recoil counter under the assumption that the pulse height is proportional to the proton energy; $E_n$ is the neutron energy and $E_T$ is the amplifier threshold energy.

effect. Recoil protons which are produced nearer to the wall than their maximum range in the chamber gas may hit the wall and dissipate part of their energy in it. In this event the pulse height is reduced.

The range of recoil protons in standard air and in paraffin is given in Table 9–2 for several energies. It is clear that, particularly for high-energy

TABLE 9–2. SOME TYPICAL PROTON-RECOIL RANGES

| $E_p$, Mev | Range, cm of standard air | Range, mg/cm² of paraffin |
|---|---|---|
| 1 | 2.3 | 3.2 |
| 2 | 7.1 | 9.7 |
| 5 | 34 | 47 |
| 10 | 115 | 160 |
| 15 | 238 | 330 |

protons, many protons will strike the chamber wall in a reasonable-size chamber. The wall effect can be minimized by the use of high pressure and heavy gases. For example, in a mixture of 5 atm of krypton and 4 atm of hydrogen, the range of 2-Mev protons is only about 1 cm. If this gas were used in a chamber with dimensions of several centimeters, the wall effect would be negligible for neutrons of energy up to at least 2 Mev.

If the pulse heights are to be proportional to the proton-recoil energies, not only must the protons dissipate their entire energy in the chamber gas, but also the collection of the ionization must be accomplished properly. The relationship between the pulse height and the ionization was discussed in detail in Chap. 4. The proportionality is maintained if both the positive and negative ions are completely collected. This type of operation, known as ion-pulse, is limited severely in the maximum counting rate. When the electrons only are collected, the resolving time is much less. However, only particular types of electron-pulse chambers maintain the required proportionality between pulse height and ionization; these are proportional counters (see Chap. 6) and gridded ionization chambers (see Chap. 4).

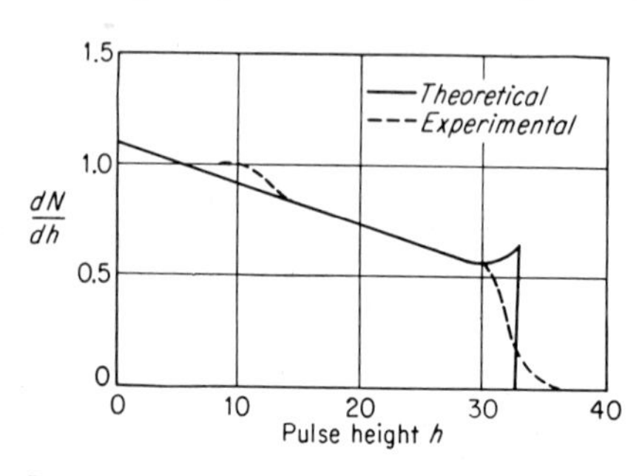


FIG. 9–11. Comparison of the experimental differential pulse distribution with the computed distribution for the Skyrme et al. proportional counter. [*From T. H. R. Skyrme, P. H. Tunnicliffe, and A. G. Ward, Rev. Sci. Instr.*, **23**:204 (1952).]

Skyrme, Tunnicliffe, and Ward (14) have described a proportional counter for the measurement of neutron flux in the energy range 0.1 to 1 Mev. In this development, end and wall corrections are calculated. The counter has a sensitive region 2 in. in diameter and 6 in. long and is operated at 1-atm pressure of hydrogen or methane. It is especially designed to simplify the end and wall corrections. With this detector, monoenergetic neutron fluxes can be determined to an accuracy of better than 5 per cent. Figure 9–11 shows a comparison of the experimental and the calculated pulse distribution for this detector with a neutron energy of 910 kev. The solid line is the computed curve. The agreement is found to be quite good over most of the range. It is interesting to compare the pulse distribution in Fig. 9–11 with the constant distribution which would be predicted by Eq. (9–15) for no wall effect.

### 9–13. *Characteristics of Proton-recoil Pulse Chambers*

It is clear from the preceding discussion that the characteristics of proton-recoil counters depend on many factors. As a consequence, it is not possible to make general statements concerning such characteristics as the efficiency, energy response, and directional properties. Instead, detailed discussions on specific proton-recoil counters must be consulted. Rossi and Staub [13] have discussed several different counter designs.

The proportional counter designed by Hurst, Ritchie, and Wilson [15] will be discussed as an example. This counter is shown in Fig. 9–12. Its response to a collimated beam of neutrons is such that the number of counts produced is approximately proportional to the dose received by the tissue in the neutron-energy range from 0.2 to 10 Mev.

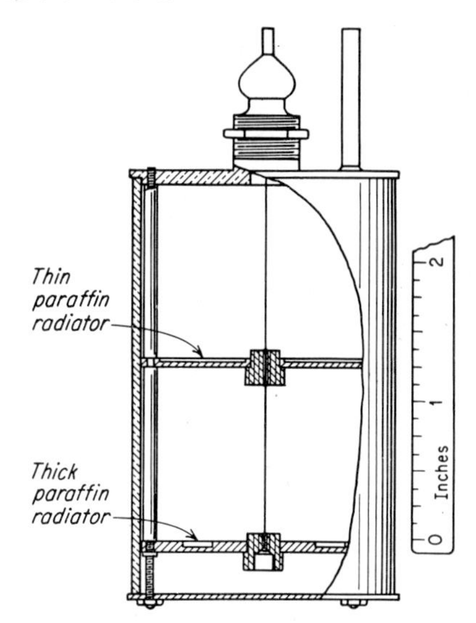


FIG. 9–12. Fast-neutron counter tube. [*From G. S. Hurst, R. H. Ritchie, and H. N. Wilson, Rev. Sci. Instr.*, **22**:981 (1951).]

The hydrogenous materials are present in the counter in three forms: (1) methane gas to 13.2 cm Hg, (2) a thin polyethylene radiator (13 mg/cm$^2$) for low-energy neutrons, and (3) a thick polyethylene radiator (100 mg/cm$^2$) for high-energy neutrons. Argon gas at 30 cm Hg is added to decrease the range of the recoil protons. The energy responses of the three sources of protons combine in such a way as to give the desired over-all response.

Figure 9–13 gives the contribution of each of the three proton sources to the response for a range of neutron energies. These curves assume that all protons having greater than 0.2-Mev energy upon leaving the radiator are counted. The thin-radiator response drops at the low energy because of the proton-energy absorption in the radiator and at the high energy because of the decrease in the cross section for the scattering. The response for the gas follows Eq. (9–17), with $E_T = 0.2$ Mev. The contribution of carbon recoils is neglected. The response of the thick absorber is negligible at low energies because of the high absorption of the protons. It makes a contribution only as protons from within the radiator can add their contribution to that from the surface layers. It will be observed that the surface area of the high-energy radiator is much less than that of the low-energy radiator.

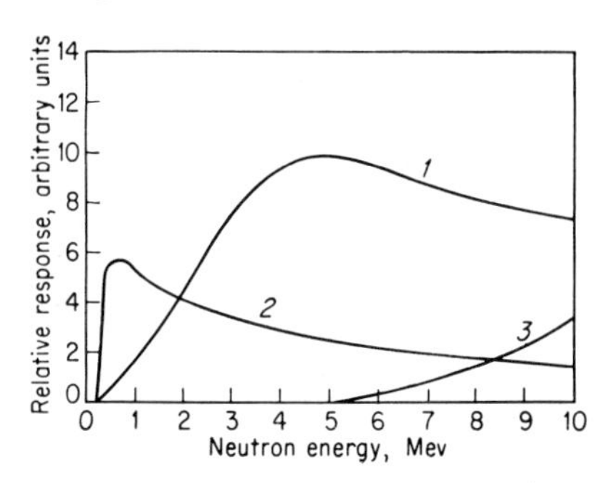


FIG. 9–13. Relative integrated count rate versus neutron energy for thin hydrogenous radiator (curve 1), hydrogenous gas (curve 2), and thick hydrogenous radiator (curve 3). [*From G. S. Hurst, R. H. Ritchie, and H. N. Wilson, Rev. Sci. Instr.*, **22**:981 (1951).]

Figure 9–14 shows the measured-sensitivity curve versus energy along with the curve for tissue dose per unit neutron flux. It is seen that the response of the counter matches quite well the tissue-dose curve. Therefore the count rate can be taken as proportional to the tissue-dose rate.

From Fig. 9–14 the sensitivity is seen to be about $1.5 \times 10^{-2}$ count/sec per unit neutron flux from 12 down to 6 Mev and to drop to $0.8 \times 10^{-2}$ around 1 Mev. This counter has the ability to discriminate against gammas. For the condition under which the sensitivity curve in Fig. 9–14 was taken, a 25-millicurie radium source placed at 5 cm from the end of the counter produced a counting rate of only 4 counts/sec. This corresponds to a gamma-dose rate of about 3 r/hr.

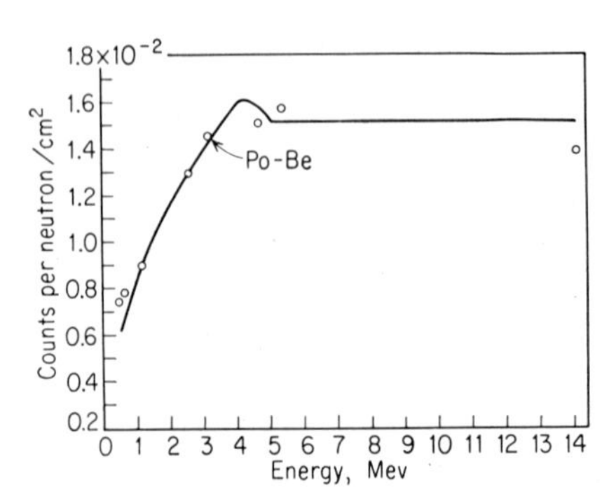


FIG. 9–14. Measured response (plotted points) and normalized tissue-dose curves (solid curve) versus neutron energy for the Hurst counter. [*From G. S. Hurst, R. H. Ritchie, and H. N. Wilson, Rev. Sci. Instr.*, **22**:981 (1951).]

It should be stressed that the results given here are for neutrons traveling along the axis of the counter. The response at a direction perpendicular to the counter drops to one-half.

The predictions of the sensitivity of a proton-recoil counter to a polyenergetic-neutron source would require knowledge of both the variation of the counter response with energy and the energy spectrum of the neutron source. Unless this information is available, specific calibrations are required. As an example, Reddie and Whipple [16] have described a simple fast-neutron counter useful for health-physics measurements. The counter is a 5.25-cm-diameter chamber 30 cm long with a 0.001-in.-diameter tungsten wire as a cathode. When operated with 1 atm of methane, with a radium-beryllium neutron source, the counter has a sensitivity of 0.04 count/sec per unit neutron flux. The unit is insensitive to gamma radiation up to dosage rays of at least 20 r/hr.

## 9–14. *Mean-level Ionization Chambers with Proton Recoil*

For sufficiently large neutron fluxes, the current in an ionization chamber containing hydrogen can be measured. If, again, the ionization produced in the chamber by each recoil proton is proportional to the proton energy and if the contributions from recoils other than protons are neglected, an idealized expression for the saturation current can be written; from Eq. (9–15) one obtains

$$I = \frac{e}{w}\int_0^{E_n} EN_p(E)\,dE = \frac{e}{2w}N_T\phi_{E_n}\sigma(E_n)\,E_n \tag{9–20}$$

In this expression, $e$ is the electronic charge, and $w$ is the energy required per ion pair produced. Using Eq. (9–18) to approximate $\sigma(E_n)$ and substituting numerical values,

$$I(\text{amp}) \simeq 3.2 \times 10^{-38} N_T \phi_{E_n} \left(\frac{0.1}{E_n}\right)^{1/2} E_n \qquad (9\text{–}21)$$

where $E_n$ is the neutron energy in Mev.

**Example 9–4.** Compute the current sensitivity of a mean-level ionization chamber for 1-Mev neutrons if the chamber has a volume of 1,000 cm$^3$ and contains hydrogen under conditions of normal temperature and pressure.

*Solution.* The number of hydrogen atoms $N_T$ in the chamber is

$$N_T = (2.68 \times 10^{19})(10^3)(2) = 5.36 \times 10^{22}$$

By Eq. (9–21) the current sensitivity is

$$\frac{I(\text{amp})}{\phi_{E_n}} = 3.2 \times 10^{-38} N_T (0.1 E_n)^{1/2} \simeq (3.2 \times 10^{-38})(5.36 \times 10^{22})(0.1)^{1/2}$$
$$= 5.5 \times 10^{-16} \text{ amp per unit flux}$$

In general, the above results must be modified for wall effects. However, these may be essentially eliminated by the use of the Bragg-Gray principle if the chamber walls and gas have the same chemical composition. For example, Rossi and Failla [17] have discussed tissue-equivalent materials for use as gas and wall materials.

Another Bragg-Gray chamber designed by the British has been described by Rossi and Staub [13]. Figure 9–15 shows this instrument. The chamber is filled with ethylene ($C_2H_4$), and the walls are coated with polyethylene or paraffin to a thickness greater than the range of the most energetic protons in the chamber. The coating is made conductive by a thin layer of silver.

Both the hydrogen and the carbon atoms undergo recoil in these chambers. The contribution of the hydrogen to the current is given by Eq. (9–21). The contribution of the carbon is given by a similar expression, that is,

$$I_c = \frac{e}{w} N_{cT} \phi_{E_n} \sigma_c(E_n) \bar{E}_c \qquad (9\text{–}22)$$

where $\bar{E}_c$ is the average energy of the recoil carbon atoms.

Usually gamma rays accompany neutron radiation. As with the $B^{10}$ chambers, compensated ion chambers (see Sec. 9–7) are used to separate the effect of the neutron flux from that of the gamma flux. A novel method of eliminating the gamma flux has been used with the chamber in Fig. 9–15. Two identical chambers are made, one as described above and one with the hydrogen replaced by deuterium in both the gas and the wall coating. With identical gamma and neutron fluxes, the contributions of the gamma rays and the recoil carbon atoms to the current are identical to both chambers. The difference current is given by

$$\Delta I = \phi_{E_n} \frac{e}{w} N_T \frac{E_n}{2} \left[ \sigma_{\mathrm{H}}(E_n) - \frac{8}{9} \sigma_{\mathrm{D}}(E_n) \right] \tag{9-23}$$

where $\sigma_{\mathrm{H}}(E_n)$ and $\sigma_{\mathrm{D}}(E_n)$ are the scattering cross sections of hydrogen and deuterium, respectively. The quantity $\frac{1}{2} \times \frac{8}{9} E_n$ is the average energy of the recoil deuterium nuclei.

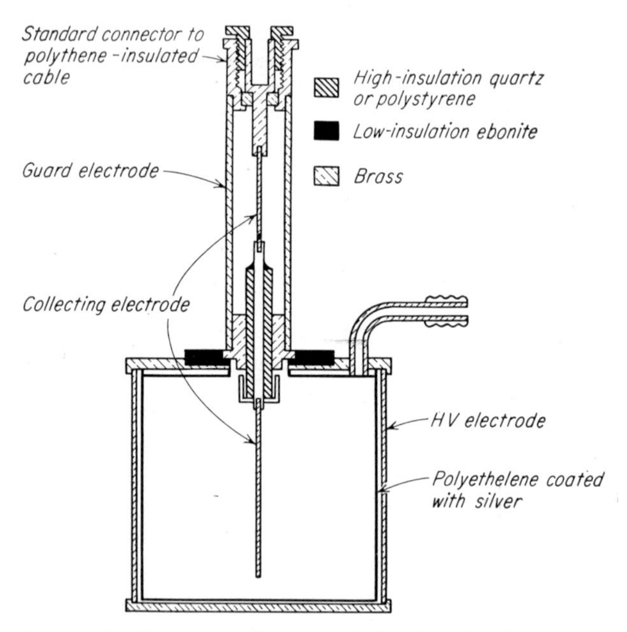


FIG. 9–15. Proton-recoil current ionization chamber for absolute flux measurement. (*From B. B. Rossi and H. H. Staub, "Ionization Chambers and Counters," chap.* 9, *National Nuclear Energy Series, div.* V, *vol.* 2, *McGraw-Hill Book Company, Inc., New York,* 1949.)

A compensated recoil-proton chamber for the measurement of fast-neutron intensity has been described by Gamertsfelder [18] and by Ray [19]. This instrument, consisting of twin ionization chambers mounted with a yoke between them, is called "Chang and Eng" in the National Laboratories; Fig. 9–16 is a schematic diagram of this instrument. The chamber containing methane is sensitive to both gammas and neutrons, while that containing argon responds to gammas only. The chambers, constructed of $\frac{1}{8}$-in. brass, are each 6 in. long and $3\frac{1}{2}$ in. in diameter. The detector is a Lindemann electrometer (see Chap. 4) operated by the rate-of-drift method. Adjustment for the gamma compensation is obtained by placing the instrument in a neutron-free gamma flux and varying the pressure until no deflection of the galvanometer occurs. The pressures are approximately 27 lb/in.$^2$ of argon and 50 lb/in.$^2$ of methane. The maximum permissible dosage rate of fast neutrons produces a charging rate of the electrometer of about 0.02 volt/sec.

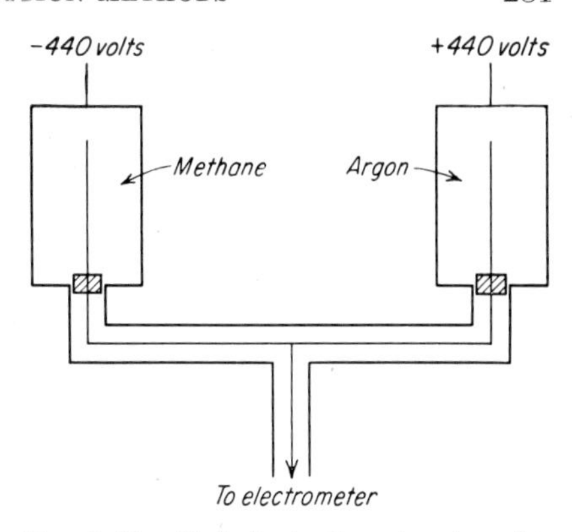


FIG. 9-16. Twin ionization chambers for the measurement of fast-neutron flux. (*From W. H. Ray, U.S. Atomic Energy Comm. Document AECD-2357,* 1944.)

## NEUTRON DETECTION BY INDUCED ACTIVITY

### 9-15. *Introductory Considerations*

It occurs quite frequently that transmutations induced by neutrons have radioactive species as product nuclides. The activity of the product radioisotope can often be used for the measurement of the amount and energy distribution of the neutron flux which induced the radioactivity. A detector employing this principle is referred to as a neutron-activation detector.

In neutron measurements by induced activity, the stable material is exposed to the neutron flux for a measured period of time. Following the irradiation, the material is removed from the neutron field, and a determination is made of the activity which has been induced in it.

Neutron-activation detectors have a number of advantages:

1. Controlled sensitivity over a wide range. Through the choice of materials with different cross sections, it is possible to make measurements down to low fluxes [less than 1 neutron/(cm$^2$)(sec)] and up to the largest values obtainable with a controlled reactor.

2. Small size. The detectors may be thin foils or small pellets. Consequently it is possible to introduce them in the medium in which the measurements are to be made without the introduction of voids. Further, the effect of neutron absorption can be made negligible either by the selection of the foil or by the application of a small correction.

3. Activity measurements can be separated from irradiations. Since the irradiations are made first and the activity measurements follow at a later time, it is sometimes possible to obtain measurements at locations where it would be otherwise very difficult or impossible to instrument them.

4. Selection of desired energy response. The cross section for the production of the radioactivity varies with the neutron energy; different nuclides have different response curves. Therefore it is possible to select, within limits, materials appropriate for various neutron-energy ranges. Detectors using materials requiring neutrons above a certain energy to cause activation are referred to as threshold detectors. Detectors which are particularly

sensitive to a narrow range of energies because of a resonance peak are known as resonance detectors.

The fact that the measurements by means of induced activity have two steps, i.e., the irradiation followed by the activity measurements, makes the method unsuitable for certain types of neutron measurements. It could not be used, for example, to measure the time dependence of a flux which is continually changing; this application requires a detector such as an ionization chamber which gives an instantaneous indication of the neutron flux.

The neutron-activation detectors may be used in any form suitable from the standpoint of handling during the irradiation and the measurement of activity. A common form, particularly for metallic materials, is in a thin foil. Such detectors are often referred to as foil detectors. Other forms include pellets pressed from powdered material, powder held by plastic films, platings on backing material, and liquids.

The activity measurements are carried out by one of the detection methods described in the previous chapters. The sample preparation for activity measurements depends on the form of the material and the type of detector. For example, the activity of a foil is commonly measured by wrapping it around a thin-wall Geiger-Müller tube or by placing it in front of a thin-window Geiger-Müller tube. In the case of liquid samples, the activity measurements may be made by a dipping counter if the activity is sufficiently large or by the evaporation of samples on a planchet for smaller specific activities.

9–16. *Relationship between Measured Activity and Neutron Flux*

Consider an activation detector in which the radioactive species of interest is being produced at a rate $R$. The rate of change of the number of radioactive atoms is the difference between the rate of production $R$ and the rate of decay or the activity of the detector. Since the activity is the product of the number of radioactive atoms $A$ and the decay constant $\lambda$, this relationship can be written as

$$\frac{dA}{dt} = \lambda R - \lambda A \tag{9–24}$$

The rate of production $R$ can be expressed by Eq. (9–3), where $N$ is the number of nuclides per unit volume of the type being activated and $\sigma$ is the cross section for the neutron process which causes the activation. In general, $R$ may be a function of time. However, a very useful case is a constant $R$. This assumes that the neutron flux remains constant. It also neglects the small decrease in the number of stable atoms $N$ which remain to be activated as they are destroyed by activation. Under these conditions, the solution of Eq. (9–24) is

$$A = R(1 - e^{-\lambda t}) = A_s(1 - e^{-\lambda t}) \tag{9–25}$$

where $t$ is measured from the start of the irradiation and the activity is assumed to be zero at $t = 0$. The symbol $A_s$ is the saturation activity, i.e., the activity approached for an irradiation long compared with the mean life $1/\lambda$.

If the activity at the end of the irradiation is $A_o$ and a count is made on the detector between $t_1$ and $t_2$ measured from the end of the exposure, the number of counts $C$ totalized will be

$$C = F\epsilon \int_{t_1}^{t_2} A_o e^{-\lambda t'} dt' + B = F\epsilon \frac{A_o}{\lambda} (e^{-\lambda t_1} - e^{-\lambda t_2}) + B \qquad (9\text{–}26)$$

The quantity $F$ is a fraction of the total activation detector used for activity determination, $\epsilon$ is the over-all efficiency of the counting system, and $B$ is the total background counts occurring in the interval $t_1$ and $t_2$.

Combining Eqs. (9–25) and (9–26), one obtains for $A_s$, the saturation activity,

$$A_s = \frac{\lambda(C - B)}{F\epsilon(1 - e^{-\lambda t_o})(e^{-\lambda t_1} - e^{-\lambda t_2})} \qquad (9\text{–}27)$$

where $t_o$ is the irradiation time.

For the case in which the neutron flux is constant throughout the detector, the saturation activity is given by Eq. (9–3) as

$$A_s = N_T \int_0^\infty \sigma_a(E)\phi(E)\, dE \qquad (9\text{–}28)$$

where $N_T$ is the total number of target atoms in the detector and $\sigma_a(E)$ is the cross section for activation at the energy $E$. This equation, taken in connection with Eq. (9–27), relates the measurement of the foil activity to the neutron flux.

### 9–17. *Requirements for Activation-detector Materials*

There are several general considerations concerning the suitability of a material for use in an activation detector; these can be grouped into properties of the detector material and properties of the activation products.

1. Detector material. The magnitudes of the cross section of the activation process and its dependence on energy are important. If the fluxes are low, a high cross section is required in order to obtain sufficient activation for accurate measurements. On the other hand, in a high neutron flux a small cross section is required in order to avoid detector activities so high as to be inconvenient for measurement. In addition, it is important to consider the energy dependence of the cross section in light of the energy range in which the detector is to be used. The material should be available without impurities with high-activation cross sections. It is desirable if its form is such that it can be handled conveniently as a detector. A thin foil is a very useful form.

TABLE 9-3. PROPERTIES OF ACTIVATION DETECTORS (THERMAL AND RESONANCE DETECTORS)

| Element | Detector material | | | Activation product | | |
|---|---|---|---|---|---|---|
| | Thermal* activation cross section, barns | Resonance† energy, ev | Resonance§ activation integral, barns | Nuclide | Half-life¶ | Principal activity¶ |
| In | 145 | 1.45 | 2,640 | $In^{116}$ | 54.1 min | $\beta^-$ (1 Mev), $\gamma$ (several energies) |
| Au | 96 | 4.9 | 1,558 | $Au^{198}$ | 2.7 days | $\beta^-$ (0.963 Mev), $\gamma$ (0.41 Mev) |
| I | 5.5 | 20–200 | 140 | $I^{128}$ | 24.99 min | $\beta^-$ (2.0 Mev) |
| Dy | 2,600 | 54 | | $Dy^{165}$ | 139.2 min | $\beta^-$ (1.25, 0.88, 0.42 Mev), $\gamma$ (0.09, 0.36, 0.76 Mev) |
| Co | 36.0 | 135 | 49.3 | $Co^{60}$‡ | 5.28 years | $\beta^-$ (0.31 Mev), $\gamma$ (1.33 Mev, 1.17 Mev) |
| Mn | 13.4 | 330 | 11.8 | $Mn^{56}$ | 2.58 hr | $\beta^-$ (2.81 Mev), $\gamma$ (0.822 Mev) |
| Na | 0.56 | 3,000 | 0.24 | $Na^{24}$ | 15.0 hr | $\beta^-$ (1.39 Mev) $\gamma$ (1.37, 2.75 Mev) |
| V | 4.5 | 4,200; 13,000 | 2.2 | $V^{52}$ | 3.76 min | $\beta^-$ (2.1 Mev) $\gamma$ (1.5 Mev) |
| Cl | 0.56 | 26,000 | | $Cl^{38}$ | 37.5 min | $\beta^-$ (5.0, 2.8, 1.1 Mev) $\gamma$ (2.2, 1.6 Mev) |

* Taken at 0.025 ev; from J. Hughes and J. A. Harvey, "Neutron Cross Sections," U.S. Atomic Energy Commission Document, McGraw-Hill Book Company, Inc., New York, 1955. † Location of principal peak; from J. Hughes and J. A. Harvey, "Neutron Cross Sections," U.S. Atomic Energy Commission Document, McGraw-Hill Book Company, Inc., New York, 1955. ‡ The 10.7-min $Co^{60}$ decays into the 5.28-year $Co^{60}$. § From R. L. Macklin and H. S. Pomerance, "Proceedings of the International Conference on the Peaceful Uses of Atomic Energy," vol. 5, p. 96, United Nations, New York, 1956. ¶ From J. M. Hollander, I. Perlman, and G. T. Seaborg, *Revs. Mod. Phys.*, **23**:613 (1953).

2. Properties of the activation product. It is necessary that the radioactive product be such that activity measurements can be made conveniently and interpreted correctly. It is desirable that there be a single radioactive species in the product. If it is a combination of two or more radioactive products, the half-lives should be sufficiently different that the activity of the main product of interest can be measured. The half-life of the main product should be neither too short nor too long. If it is too short, the activity decays too rapidly in transferring it from the irradiation to the counting equipment. If the half-life is too long, both the irradiation times and the counting times will be excessively long. Half-lives from a few seconds to several years have been used successfully. The radiation emitted by the product should be relatively high-energy betas and gammas so that self-absorption in the detector will not be excessive and activity measurements can be made conveniently.

Tables 9–3 and 9–4 list several useful activation detectors along with

TABLE 9–4. CONVENIENT THRESHOLD DETECTORS

| Reaction | Effective* threshold, Mev | $\sigma_c$,* barns | Half-life of reaction product |
|---|---|---|---|
| 1. $P^{31}(n,p)Si^{31}$ | 2.5 | 0.075 | 2.6 hr |
| 2. $S^{32}(n,p)P^{32}$ | 2.9 | 0.30 | 14.3 days |
| 3. $Mg^{24}(n,p)Na^{24}$ | 6.3 | 0.048 | 15.0 hr |
| 4. $Al^{27}(n,p)Mg^{27}$ | 5.3 | 0.08 | 9.8 min |
| 5. $Al^{27}(n,\alpha)Na^{24}$ | 8.6 | 0.11 | 15.0 hr |
| 6. $Ni^{58}(n,p)Co^{58}$ | 5.0 | 1.23 | 72 days |
| 7. $Si^{28}(n,p)Al^{28}$ | 6.1 | 0.19 | 2.3 min |
| 8. $C^{12}(n,2n)C^{11}$ | 20† | ... | 20.4 min |
| 9. $Ag^{107}(n,2n)Ag^{106}$ | 9.6† | | |
| 10. $I^{127}(n,2n)I^{126}$ | 10† | ... | 13 days |

* Effective thresholds and average cross sections for 1 through 7 calculated by P. M. Uthe; see P. M. Uthe, Attainment of Neutron Flux-Spectra from Foil Activations, Thesis, Air Force Institute of Technology, Wright-Patterson Air Force Base, Ohio, 1957; neutron flux assumed to be the fission spectrum.

† From B. L. Cohen, *Nucleonics*, **8**:29 (February, 1951); *Phys. Rev.*, **81**:184 (1951).

some of their more pertinent properties. These are seen to cover a wide range of thermal-neutron cross sections, resonance energies, half-lives, and threshold energies.

### 9–18. *Thermal-neutron Detection by Thin Foils*

Neutron-activation detectors are often used in the form of layers sufficiently thin that the absorption of neutrons in the layers is quite small.

These layers may be metallic foils, lacquer films impregnated with the detector material, plating on backings of low neutron absorption, or other similar arrangements. Detectors of this type may be referred to as thin foils.

The saturation activity in thin foils can be expressed by Eq. (9–28). It is often convenient to replace the total number of target atoms $N_T$ by

$$N_T = \frac{d_m A N_o}{W} \tag{9–29}$$

where $d_m$ = thickness of detector material, g/cm$^2$
$W$ = atomic weight
$A$ = foil area
$N_o$ = Avogadro's number

In detectors used for thermal and resonance neutrons, it is convenient to divide the activity into two parts according to whether it is produced by thermal neutrons or by epithermal neutrons with energy in the resonance peaks. In the thermal region the activation cross section follows the $1/v$ dependence, given by Eq. (9–1). For the epithermal range, $\sigma(v)$ is the superposition of the $1/v$ dependence and a resonance contribution. Accordingly, Eq. (9–28) can be written

$$A_s = N_T\left[\int_{\text{thermal}} \frac{\sigma_{oa}v_o}{v} n(v)\, v\, dv + \int_{\text{epithermal}} \sigma_a(v)\, n(v)\, v\, dv\right] \tag{9–30}$$

where the first integral is taken over the velocity range of the thermal neutrons and the second is over the epithermal range.

This equation can be rewritten as

$$A_s = A_{st} + A_{se} = N_T n_{th} v_o \sigma_{oa} + A_{se} \tag{9–31}$$

where $A_{st}$ and $A_{se}$ are the saturation activities due to thermal and epithermal neutrons, respectively, and $n_{th}$ is the volume density of thermal neutrons.

The activities due to the two groups of neutrons can be separated experimentally by means of the cadmium difference method. The foil is sandwiched between cadmium sheets. The absorption cross section of cadmium varies with energy in such a way that the cadmium absorbs most of the neutrons with energy less than about 0.4 ev (thermal neutrons) but passes most of the epithermal neutrons (see Fig. 1–20). Thus the total saturation activity induced in the foil protected by cadmium, designated as $A_s$(Cd), will be due to epithermal neutrons. However, it will be less than $A_{se}$, the activity due to epithermal neutrons captured by the unprotected foil, because there is absorption of some of these neutrons by the cadmium. The correction factor $F_{\text{Cd}}$ is

$$F_{\text{Cd}} = \frac{A_{se}}{A_s(\text{Cd})} \tag{9–32}$$

This correction factor depends on the type and weight of the foil as well as the cadmium thickness. This correction is largest for those detectors which have the lowest values for the resonance peak. In the case of indium, the correction is several per cent in practice (see next section).

Combining Eqs. (9–31) and (9–32), one obtains for the activity $A_{st}$ due to thermal neutrons

$$A_{st} = A_s - F_{\text{Cd}} A_s(\text{Cd}) \tag{9–33}$$

where $A_s$ and $A_s(\text{Cd})$ are the saturation activity of the foil without and with the cadmium shield, respectively.

If the foil is truly thin in the sense described above, it produces no effect on the neutron flux when introduced into the radiation field, and the preceding equations based on no neutron absorption are applicable. However, in practice, this assumption is often not realized. In the measurements of small fluxes, a foil sufficiently thin to produce no perturbation may not be activated sufficiently for accurate counting. Also a thin foil may be too fragile to handle.

The effect on the neutron flux of a foil in which there is a small but not neglibible absorption can be treated as a perturbation to the theory discussed above for the simple case. The perturbation arises from two causes: a reduction of the neutron flux inside the detector due to the absorption by the outside layers and a depression of the neutron flux directly outside the detector due to the absorption in the foil. The latter effect is present only in a medium in which neutron diffusion is taking place. The flux depression occurs since the neutrons absorbed in passing through a detector are not available to diffuse back to the detector site and bolster the neutron flux. The perturbation can be introduced as a correction factor $F_{th}$ defined as

$$F_{th} = \frac{A'_{st}}{A_{st}} \tag{9–34}$$

where $A'_{st}$ is the activation which the thermal neutrons would produce if it were not for the flux depression and $A_{st}$ is the measured activation as given by Eq. (9–33).

Combining Eqs. (9–31), (9–33), and (9–34), one writes the expression for the density of thermal neutrons. This is

$$n_{th} = F_{th} \frac{A_s - F_{\text{Cd}} A_s(\text{Cd})}{N_T v_0 \sigma_{0a}} \tag{9–35}$$

Again as discussed in Sec. 9–4, the thermal-neutron flux can be obtained from $n_{th}$ by multiplying by $\bar{v}$, the average velocity of the neutrons.

Bothe [23] has worked out the correction factor $F_{th}$ through the use of the diffusion theory. His results for the reduction of the activity in a sphere of radius $R$ were

$$F_{th} = 1 + \frac{\alpha}{2}\left[\frac{3RL}{2\,\lambda_{tr}(R+L)} - 1\right] \qquad \text{for } R \gg \lambda_{tr}$$

and

$$F_{th} = 1 + \frac{0.34\alpha R}{\lambda_{tr}} \qquad \text{for } R \ll \lambda_{tr} \tag{9-36}$$

In the above expressions, $L$ and $\lambda_{tr}$ are the diffusion length (see Table 9–5) and the transport mean free path, respectively, in the medium outside the detector, and $\alpha$ is the probability that a neutron will be absorbed in a single traversal of a detector. For an isotropic flux,

$$\alpha = 1 - e^{-\Sigma_a d}(1 - \Sigma_a d) + \Sigma_a^2 d^2 E_1(-\Sigma_a d) \tag{9-37}$$

where $\Sigma_a$ is the macroscopic absorption cross section for the absorber and $d$ is its average thickness ($d = R$ for a sphere). $E_1(-\Sigma_a d)$ is the exponential integral of the argument $\Sigma_a d$. Figure 9–17 is a plot of $\alpha$ versus $\Sigma_a d$. The quantity $\Sigma_a$ should be evaluated at the effective energy for absorption. In $1/v$ absorbers and a Maxwell-Boltzmann distribution, the effective energy is $(4/\pi)kT$; its value at 20° is 0.032 ev.

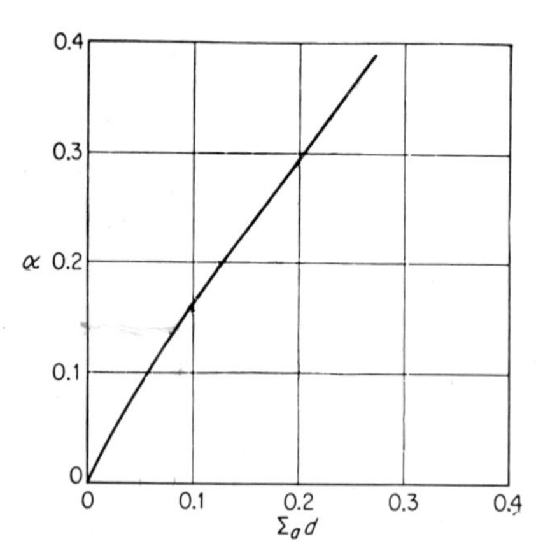


FIG. 9–17. Average probability of absorption for neutrons in an isotropic flux while passing through an absorber of thickness $d$ and macroscopic absorption cross section $\Sigma_a$.

Tittle [24] and Klema and Ritchie [25] have shown experimentally that the above expression can be used without modification for an absorber in the form of a disk of radius $R$ and thickness $d$.

When a detector is placed in a neutron beam, the situation is modified considerably. The foil produces no flux depression because diffusion is absent. The reduction of flux inside the detector can be accounted for by Eq. (1–34). The probability that a neutron will be absorbed in passing through a detector of thickness $d$ and absorption cross section $\Sigma_a$ is $1 - e^{-\Sigma_a d}$. Therefore, if $I(E)$ is the intensity of neutrons per unit energy interval, the reaction rate in a foil of area $A$ is

$$R = A\int_0^{\infty} I(E)(1 - e^{-\Sigma_a d})\,dE \tag{9-38}$$

For $\Sigma_a d \gg 1$ the detector is said to be black and $R$ becomes

$$R(\text{black}) = A\int_0^{\infty} I(E)\,dE \tag{9-39}$$

or simply the product of the foil area and the total beam current.

TABLE 9–5. THERMAL-DIFFUSION PROPERTIES OF MODERATORS*

| Moderator | Density, g/cm$^3$ | $L$, cm | $\lambda_{tr}$, cm |
|---|---|---|---|
| $H_2O$ | 1.0 | 2.76 | 0.425 |
| Paraffin | 0.9 | 2.42 | 0.395 |
| $D_2O$ | 1.1 | 171 | 2.4 |
| Beryllium | 1.8 | 31 | 2.6 |
| Graphite | 1.62 | 50 | 2.7 |

* From C. W. Tittle, *Nucleonics*, **9**:60 (July, 1951).

## 9–19. *Indium Foils for Thermal-neutron Detection*

Indium foils are widely used for neutron detection. The nuclear reaction is

$$_{49}\text{In}^{115} + {}_0n^1 \rightarrow {}_{49}\text{In}^{116}$$

followed by the radioactive-decay process

$$_{49}\text{In}^{116} \rightarrow {}_{50}\text{Sn}^{116} + {}_{-1}e^0$$

The radioisotope $\text{In}^{116}$ has a metastable and a ground state with half-lives of 54.1 min and 13 sec, respectively.

There are other activities which can be induced in $\text{In}^{115}$, including those resulting from (n,2n), (n,p), and (n,$\alpha$) reactions by fast neutrons. In addition, the less abundant stable isotopes $\text{In}^{113}$ (4.5 per cent relative abundance) can have induced activities by both thermal and fast neutrons.

In spite of the extremely complicated set of periods induced in indium, the 54.1-min period can be counted almost exclusively. The 13-sec period can be eliminated by waiting a short time between the end of the activation and the beginning of the counting. For example, in 3 min the isomeric state with the 13-sec period will have only 0.01 per cent of its initial activity remaining, while the state with the 54.1-min period will still have 95 per cent of the activity it had when the activation was terminated. The radioisotopes induced by fast neutrons do not appear under normal conditions. However, it is well to be aware of the possibility of their existence and to account for their presence if necessary.

Tittle [24] has made measurements of the cadmium correction factor $F_{\text{Cd}}$ for various thicknesses of cadmium as a function of indium-foil thickness. These results are given by Fig. 9–18. The flux-depression correction term $F_{th}$ can be calculated for indium through the use of Eq. (9–36) along with Fig. 9–17.

**Example 9–5.** Compute the flux-depression correction term for a 3-cm-diameter indium foil of 100-mg/cm$^2$ thickness when used in ordinary water.

*Solution.* The quantity $\Sigma_a d$ is

$$\Sigma_a d = \frac{tN_o\sigma_a}{W} = \frac{(0.1)(6.02 \times 10^{23})(175 \times 10^{-24})}{115} = 0.092$$

where $t$, $N_o$, $\sigma_a$, and $W$ are the foil thickness in grams per square centimeter, Avogadro's number, the indium absorption cross section at 0.032 ev, and the atomic weight of indium, respectively. Therefore $\alpha$ is 0.155, from Fig. 9–17. Using the form of Eq. (9–36) for $R \gg \lambda_{tr}$, one obtains

$$F_{th} = 1 + \frac{\alpha}{2}\left[\frac{3RL}{2\lambda_{tr}(R+L)} - 1\right] = 1 + \frac{0.155}{2}\left[\frac{(3)(1.5)(2.76)}{(2)(0.425)(1.5+2.76)} - 1\right] = 1.19$$

Example 9–5 indicates that the thermal-depression factor may be quite a significant correction for indium. An indium foil which is sufficiently thin for the flux depression to be negligible is quite fragile to handle. In material such as cobalt, which has a much smaller cross section, it is possible to employ foils sufficiently thin that the flux depression can be neglected. In addition, the use of the detector material in the form of a plating allows one to use quite thin foils.

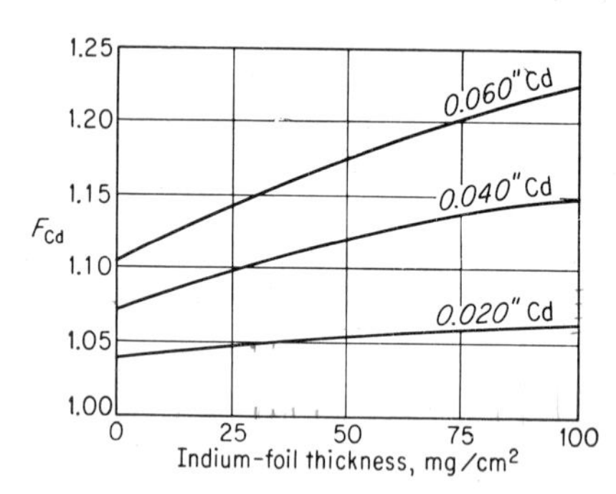


FIG. 9–18. Cadmium correction factor $F_{Cd}$ as a function of indium-foil thickness for various Cd thicknesses. [*From C. W. Tittle, Nucleonics,* **9**:60 (*July,* 1951).]

One may define the sensitivity of the foil method of neutron detection as the saturation activity induced in the foil per unit neutron flux. For thermal neutrons this is given by Eq. (9–35) as

$$\text{Sensitivity} = \frac{N_T\sigma_{oa}}{1.128F_{th}} \quad (9\text{–}40)$$

when the activation that is produced by epithermal neutrons is neglected. The average velocity has been taken as $1.128v_o$, the case for the Maxwell-Boltzmann distribution.

**Example 9–6.** Compute the thermal-neutron sensitivity of the indium foil described in Example 9–5.

*Solution.* By Eq. (9–40), the sensitivity is

$$\text{Sensitivity} = \frac{N_T\sigma_{oa}}{1.128F_{th}} = \frac{(0.10)(7.0 \times 0.602)}{115}\,\frac{145}{(1.128)(1.19)}$$

$$= 0.4 \text{ disintegration/sec per unit neutron flux}$$

The lower limit of the flux at which indium foils are useful depends on the efficiency of the counting equipment, the background counting rate, and the accuracy which is required. The practical lower limit is a few neutrons per square centimeter per second.

Most of the applications of indium foils have been to relative measurements. However, Koontz and Jarrett [26] have made an extensive study of the use of this technique for absolute thermal-flux measurement. They estimate that the accuracy of these measurements is 5 per cent.

### 9–20. *Resonance Neutron Measurements by Thin Foils*

If one defines the ratio of the saturation activities of the bare foil to that of the cadmium-covered foil as the cadmium ratio $R_{\text{Cd}}$, one may write

$$\frac{A_{st}}{A_{se}} = R_{\text{Cd}} - 1 \tag{9–41}$$

Here the cadmium-covered foil is considered to be corrected by means of Eq. (9–32). Using Eqs. (9–30) and (9–31), one can write

$$\frac{n_{th}v_0\sigma_{oa}}{\int_{0.4\ ev}^{\infty} \sigma_a(E)\phi(E)dE} = R_{\text{Cd}} - 1 \tag{9–42}$$

A useful case is that of neutrons slowing down with a $1/E$ spectrum; that is, $\phi(E)$ is given by $K/E$, where $K$ is a constant. The constant $K$ can be found from Eq. (9–42) by replacing $\phi(E)$ by $K/E$. Thus,

$$K = \frac{n_{th}v_0\sigma_{oa}}{(R_{\text{Cd}} - 1)\int_{0.4\ ev}^{\infty} \frac{\sigma_a(E)}{E}\,dE} \tag{9–43}$$

The integral in Eq. (9–43) is known as the resonance activation integral. Values of this integral have been measured for a number of substances. Typical values, taken from the extensive tabulation of Macklin and Pomerance [21], are given in Table 9–3. Further discussion of the measurement of these integrals and of their use has been given by Hughes [27].

Equation (9–43) can be used for the experimental determination of $K$ and therefore of the neutron flux per unit energy interval in the energy region where the $1/E$ spectrum exists. The measurement of $K$ involves the determination of $R_{\text{Cd}}$ and the thermal-neutron density, as in Sec. 9–18, and the knowledge of the resonance activation integral and the thermal-activation cross section.

The activation above the cadmium cutoff can be divided into two portions, that due to $1/v$ absorption and that due to resonance absorption; the sum of these two contributions gives the resonance activation integral as tabulated in Table 9–3. The theoretical value of the $1/v$ contribution, obtained by evaluating the integral

$$\int_{0.4\ ev}^{\infty} \sigma_{oa}\left(\frac{0.025}{E}\right)^{\frac{1}{2}} \frac{dE}{E}$$

is $0.5\sigma_{oa}$.

It can be seen from Table 9–3 that materials having large resonance peaks at low energy have their resonance activation integral determined primarily by the resonance phenomenon. For example, in indium where the resonance activation integral is 2,640 barns, the $1/v$ contribution is only $0.44 \times 145$, or 64, barns. Consequently, measurements made with a foil of this type are characteristic of the energy at which the peak occurs. This property has been utilized [27], for example, in the measurement of the slowing-down density at specific energies.

On the other hand, in materials such as sodium in which the resonance peaks are located at high energies, the resonance absorption integral is seen to be essentially due to the $1/v$ absorption. These materials give one information characteristic of the entire energy spectrum down to 0.4 ev and may be referred to as $1/v$ absorbers.

### 9–21. *Threshold Detector Using Induced Activity*

A number of neutron-induced reactions exist which have a threshold energy which must be exceeded before the reaction proceeds. Several of these reactions which are useful for fast-neutron detection are listed in Table 9–4; included also are the half-life of the radioactive product and the approximate threshold energy for the reactions. Lists of some other threshold detectors along with a discussion of their uses has been given by Cohen [28].

For the (n,2n) reactions the thresholds for the reactions can be calculated accurately from energy considerations. On the other hand, for the (n,p) reactions the thresholds calculated on the energy basis are considerably lower than the effective threshold. This difference arises because of the necessity of the penetration of the Coulomb barrier by the proton. In the usual case, the cross section rises slowly from the energy threshold, and the effective threshold can be defined only in terms of a particular application.

The saturation activity of a threshold detector is given by Eq. (9–28). In the case of the $P^{31}$(n,p) and the $S^{32}$(n,p) reactions, there is a fortunate occurrence of resonances which cause the cross sections to rise quite rapidly and to remain rather constant thereafter. The cross sections for many other activation processes are not as simple. In any event, the actual cross section can be replaced by an idealized cross section having a step rise at the energy $E_T$ from zero to a constant value $\sigma_c$, if an assumption for $\phi(E)$, the differential energy flux, is made. This is accomplished by the relationship

$$A_s = N_T\sigma_c \int_{E_T}^{\infty} \phi(E)\,dE = N_T \int_0^{\infty} \sigma_a(E)\phi(E)\,dE \tag{9–44}$$

where $\sigma_a(E)$ is the actual energy-dependent cross section for the process. The value $\sigma_c$ is set as the mean value above the threshold, and $E_T$ is then computed. The values of $E_T$ listed in Table 9–4 have been calculated under the assumption that $\phi(E)$ is a fission spectrum.

By the use of two types of foils with thresholds $E_{T1}$ and $E_{T2}$, the total flux in the energy interval $E_{T1}$ to $E_{T2}$ can be ascertained from Eq. (9–44). Hurst et al. [29] have utilized threshold detectors in this fashion for determining neutron spectra. In addition to induced activation as discussed above, they have made extensive use of fission threshold reactions as listed in Table 9–1. For the latter measurements, the resulting fission-product activity was used to determine the flux. By the use of the following reactions, histograms representing a complete spectra can be constructed: Au and Au plus Cd for the thermal flux; $Pu^{239}$ shielded with $B^{10}$ for the total fast flux*; $Np^{237}$ for the total flux above 0.74 Mev; $U^{238}$ for the total flux above 1.5 Mev; and $S^{32}$ for the total flux above 2.5 Mev.

Uthe [30] has discussed the errors that are incurred by applying the energy thresholds which are determined under the assumption of the fission spectrum to other than the fission spectrum. He has concluded that these errors can be quite significant and has developed another method for analyzing the data obtained by the threshold detectors. This method, known as the polynomial method, utilizes the foil-activation data to determine the coefficients of a polynomial in energy. This polynomial is the energy-dependent ratio of the actual differential flux spectrum to the fission spectrum.

TABLE 9–6. THRESHOLD DETECTORS EMPLOYED WITH SCINTILLATORS*

| Nuclear reaction | Threshold, Mev | Detector material | Minimum detectable flux, neutrons/(cm²) (sec) |
|---|---|---|---|
| $U^{238}$(n,f) | 1.1 | Uranium nitrate | 6.6 |
| $P^{31}$(n,p)$Si^{31}$ | 2.0 | $NH_4H_2PO_4$ in "phoswich"† | 200 |
| $S^{32}$(n,p)$P^{32}$ | 2.0 | Fused sulfur | 230 |
| $Ag^{107}$(n,2n)$Ag^{106}$ | 9.6 | Silver orthophosphate in "phoswich" | 350 |
| $I^{127}$(n,2n)$I^{126}$ | 10 | NaI(Tl) crystal | 20 |
| $C^{12}$(n,2n)$C^{11}$ | 20 | Anthracene | 2.3 |
| $Bi^{209}$(n,f) | 50 | Bismuth nitrate | |

* From F. P. Cowan and J. F. O'Brien, "Proceedings of the International Conference on the Peaceful Uses of Atomic Energy," vol. 14, p. 213, United Nations, New York, 1956.

† The term "phoswich" refers to a slotted scintillator with the detector material embedded in the slots.

In general, the threshold detectors are too insensitive for use in low flux levels such as those encountered in health-physics monitoring. Cowan and O'Brien [31] have obtained great improvement in the sensitivity by the use of scintillation detectors in which the activated materials are an integral part of the scintillator. Table 9–6 gives the nuclear reaction, the

* The use [29] of a 1-cm shield of $B^{10}$ produces an approximate threshold of 0.5 kev for the fission reaction in $Pu^{239}$.

threshold energy, the detector materials, and the minimum detectable flux.

### 9–22. *The Szilard-Chalmers Reaction*

In neutron detection by induced activity, one can increase the total activity in the detector for a given neutron flux by increasing the detector size until complete absorption of the neutrons takes place within the detector. This increased activity does not necessarily result in a proportionally larger counting rate in the measuring instrument, because of self-absorption of the induced radiation. However, in the event that the radioactive product can be separated from the detector material, a large gain in the system sensitivity can be realized.

Chemical separation methods may be possible when the product is a different element, as with (n,p) and (n,$\alpha$) reactions. However, for several reactions, for example, (n,$\gamma$) and (n,2n), a change to a different element does not occur. Szilard and Chalmers have devised a technique for separating radioactive nuclei, induced by the (n,$\gamma$) reaction, from their isotopic environment. This technique utilizes the fact that the emission of gamma rays in the (n,$\gamma$) process causes a recoil of the product nucleus. In some cases the recoil energy is sufficiently large to break the chemical bond and thereby change the chemical state of the product nucleus as compared with the normal nucleus. In favorable circumstances, 100 per cent separation of the radioactive nucleus can be obtained.

Specific Szilard-Chalmers reactions and applications of this technique have been discussed in the summary by McKay [32]. As an example, the Szilard-Chalmers reaction is used widely in connection with the (n,$\gamma$) reaction from manganese. If the manganese is present in a water solution of potassium permanganate, the recoil of the $Mn^{56}$ forms $MnO_2$ which is insoluble and can be filtered out. Detectors of this type have been used for comparison of the activities of artificial neutron sources. The source is placed inside a large container of the potassium permanganate solution. The water serves as a moderator for the fast neutrons. Such a system can be used with neutron-source strengths as low as 1 neutron/sec.

## SCINTILLATION DETECTORS FOR NEUTRONS

### 9–23. *Introduction*

Table 9–7 lists existing types of neutron scintillation detectors and compares several of their characteristics. The detectors are grouped according to the type of scintillator employed. The reaction by which the neutrons produce the energetic charged particles that are required to bring about the detection process is listed under the column designated nuclear reaction. The composition of the detector is broken down as follows:

Table 9-7. Neutron Scintillation Counters*

| Type | Composition: Nuclear host | Composition: Atomic host | Composition: Scintillator | Composition: Shifter | Nuclear reaction | Sensitivity: Neutron energy, kev | Sensitivity: Gamma ray | Pulse height relative to NaI(Tl) | Time response, μsec | Reference |
|---|---|---|---|---|---|---|---|---|---|---|
| Noble gas | $[He^3]$ | $He^3$ + Xe | Xe | Quaterphenyl | $He^3$(n,p) | <500 | Low | ½ | 0.002 | 33 |
| | $B^{10}$ | Xe | Xe | Quaterphenyl | $B^{10}(n,\alpha)$ | <10 | Low | ½ | 0.002 | |
| | $U^{235}$ | Xe | Xe | Quaterphenyl | $U^{235}$(n,f) | <10 | Low | ½ | 0.002 | |
| Diatomic gas | $[H_2]$ | $H_2$ + ? | ? | Sodium salicylate | H(n,n) | >20 | Low | ~½ | 0.002 | |
| Organic liquid | Toluene | Toluene | PPO† | POPOP‡ | H(n,n) | >500 | High | ~1/100 | 0.002 | |
| | Triethyl benzene + methyl borate or | Triethyl benzene | PPO† | POPOP‡ | $B^{10}(n,\alpha)$ | <50 | High | 1/100 | 0.5 | 34 |
| | cadmium octoate | Triethyl benzene | PPO† | POPOP‡ | H(n,n)H + $Cd^{113}(n,\gamma)$ | >1,000 | Low | 1/100 | 0.002 | 35 |
| Organic solid | Anthracene | Anthracene | Anthracene | None | H(n,n) | >100 | High-low | ~1/20 | 0.03 | 36 |
| | Polystyrene or polyvinyltoluene | Plastic | *p*-Terphenyl | Tetraphenylbutadiene | H(n,n) | >300 | High | ~1/50 | 0.003 | 37 |
| Inorganic solid | $Li^6I$ | LiI | Eu | None | $Li^6(n,\alpha)$ | <50 | High | ⅓ | 2 | 38 |
| | $[Li^6H]$ | LiH | ? | None | H(n,n) + $Li^6(n,\alpha)$ | >100 | Low | ~½ | 1 | 39 |
| | $B_2^{10}O_3$ | ZnS | Ag | None | $B^{10}(n,\alpha)$ | <10 | Low | $\gtrsim 1$ | 0.2 | 40 |
| | Lucite + ZnS | ZnS | Ag | None | H(n,n) or *S*(n,p) | >100 | Low | $\gtrsim 1$ | 0.2 | |
| | $B^{10}$ | NaI | Tl | None | $Li^{7*}(\gamma)Li^7$ | <1,000 | High | 1 | 0.2 | |

* From C. O. Muehlhause, *Nucleonics*, **14**:39 (April, 1956). † 2,5-diphenyloxazole. ‡ 1,4-di-[2-(5-phenyloxazolyl)]-benzene.

nuclear host which is the component that is effective in the primary nuclear reaction; atomic host, the component to which the charged particles transfer their energy; scintillator, the component primarily responsible for the light production; and the waveshifter, if present. Under "sensitivity" the neutron-energy region to which the detector responds is designated, and a comment is made on its gamma-ray sensitivity.

The proton-recoil process [designated as the H(n,n) nuclear reaction] is the basis for most fast-neutron detectors, while the (n,$\alpha$) reaction is widely used in thermal-neutron detection. Other reactions which have proved useful include the (n,p), (n,f), and (n,$\gamma$) processes.

The central problem in neutron counting by the use of scintillation detectors is the discrimination against gamma rays. Except for the gas scintillators, this is a much greater problem with scintillation detectors than it is with ionization chambers or proportional counters. Because of the high density, both the heavy charged particles, alphas or protons, released by the neutrons and the secondary electrons released by the gamma rays often dissipate their entire energies in the scintillators. Therefore, the scintillator outputs for the gamma rays are often at least as large as those for the neutrons. In addition, in organic scintillators the efficiency of conversion from nuclear energy to light is larger for electrons than for heavy particles. For example, in anthracene the conversion efficiency is nine times higher for electrons than for alpha particles (see Table 7–1).

An additional problem is the discrimination between fast and slow neutrons in neutron scintillators. The slow neutrons are often captured by the organic scintillators used for fast-neutron detection. The resulting captured gammas cause the registering of counts due to slow neutrons.

Various methods which have been devised to reduce the background will be discussed in the following sections. These include special scintillator designs as well as special electronic circuitry.

### 9–24. *Neutron Detection by* (n,$\alpha$) *Reaction in Scintillators*

The $Li^6$ and the $B^{10}$ (n,$\alpha$) reactions are used extensively for detection of slow neutrons. These reactions are useful because of the large energy of the alpha particles which are released and because of the high cross section and the simple energy dependence of the reaction. The $B^{10}$(n,$\alpha$) reaction was discussed in Sec. 9–3. For the $Li^6$(n,$\alpha$) reaction the energy released is 4.78 Mev, the thermal absorption cross section is 945 barns, and the energy dependence is $1/v$ in the thermal and epithermal range.

Lithium iodide crystals activated with thallium behave, in many respects, similarly to sodium iodide crystals activated with thallium; the latter is the most widely used scintillator for gamma rays. Hofstadter [40] has shown that LiI(Tl) does give scintillations with thermal neutrons. The pulse heights are proportional to the energy, and the conversion efficiencies for alpha and beta particles are equal. Therefore the neutron pulses being produced by 4.78-Mev alpha particles can be distinguished from gamma-ray or electron pulses which are generally below about 2 Mev. Schenck [38] has reported similar results with lithium iodide activated with europium.

The efficiency of the LiI crystals is quite high. If the multiple scattering of the neutrons is neglected, the efficiency is given by Eq. (1–34) as $1 - e^{-\sigma N d}$, where $d$ is the crystal thickness in centimeters, $N$ is the number of lithium atoms per cubic centimeter, and $\sigma$ is the cross section for the $(n,\alpha)$ reaction. For natural lithium, $N$ is $1.827 \times 10^{22}$ atoms/cm$^3$ and $\sigma$ is 71 barns at 0.025 ev. Consequently a 1-cm-thick crystal is 69 per cent efficient, and a 2-cm-thick crystal is 90 per cent efficient for thermal neutrons. Thus it is seen that lithium iodide detectors have a great advantage over gaseous-type counters with respect to the size required for high efficiency.

Muehlhause [34] has investigated the use of liquid organic scintillators containing borates. One satisfactory recipe employs methyl borate in terphenyl. The boron compound is found to be an inert material in the scintillator and does not affect the fluorescent process. The efficiency of this liquid scintillator for thermal neutrons is quite high, approaching 100 per cent for relatively small cells. A cell 1¾ in. thick [34] has an efficiency of about 90 per cent.

Even though the liquid scintillators are composed of elements with low atomic numbers, there is a significant response to gamma rays through the Compton effect. The pulses from gamma rays are often larger than those due to neutrons because of the small conversion efficiency of alpha particles relative to that of electrons. Thus the principal technical problem is the discrimination against gamma rays.

Bollinger [41] has described a boron-loaded liquid scintillation counter which minimizes the discriminator problems. The cell containing the scintillator is viewed by four photomultiplier tubes mounted in a circle on one side of the container. These tubes are paired by joining the anodes of those diagonally opposite, the signal from each pair being independently amplified. The electronic system which is used requires coincidence between the two amplifier outputs, thus eliminating tube-noise counts. Gamma-ray background is minimized by requiring that the sum of the amplifier outputs be in a given pulse-height range.

When a fast neutron enters the liquid scintillator containing boron, two light pulses may be produced, one by the protons scattered by the neutrons and the other upon the capture of the neutrons by the boron. The two pulses should be separated by about 0.5 $\mu$sec, the time required for the capture of the neutron in the boron. Since the individual pulses are quite short (around $5 \times 10^{-9}$ sec), they can be resolved. Thus the fast neutron can be identified by the appearance of the two pulses. By use of a delayed coincidence circuit (see Chap. 10), the fast neutrons can be separated from the gamma rays and the slow neutrons, each of which gives only a single pulse.

Mixtures of boron and lithium compounds with ZnS(Ag) phosphors form very satisfactory neutron scintillators. These as well as other mixtures are discussed in the following section.

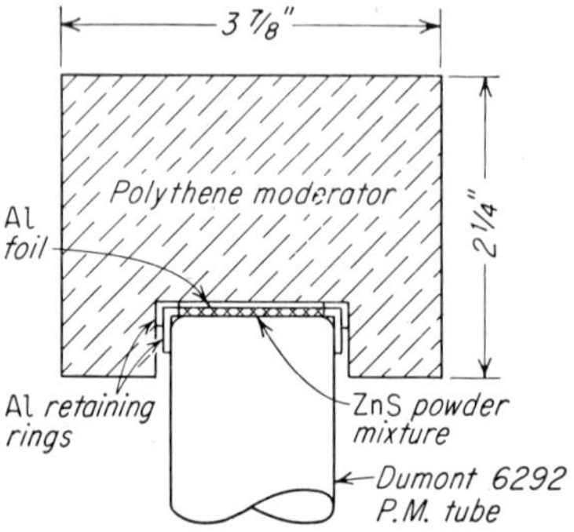

Fig. 9–19. Standard counting geometry for the study of various phosphor mixtures. [*From P. G. Koontz, G. R. Keepin, and J. E. Ashley, Rev. Sci. Instr.,* **26**:352(1955).]

### 9–25. ZnS(Ag) *Phosphor Mixtures for Neutron Counting*

Because of their relatively large alpha-beta ratio (a factor important in gamma discrimination), ZnS(Ag) phosphor mixtures have found important applications in neutron counting. Furthermore, it has been established [42] that the principal decay component of ZnS(Ag) has a decay constant of approximately 0.04 $\mu$sec, rather than the $10^{-5}$ sec which was reported earlier; consequently these mixtures offer distinct advantages even where short resolving times are required.

Using the standard counting geometry shown in Fig. 9–19, Koontz, Keepin, and Ashley [42] have studied the following mixtures:

1. ZnS(Ag) powdered phosphor
2. ZnS(Ag) + hydrogenous compounds [(n,p) scattering]
3. ZnS(Ag) + lithium compounds [$Li^6(n,\alpha)$]
4. ZnS(Ag) + uranium compounds [U(n,f)]

The results are summarized in Fig. 9–20.

Sun et al. [43] have investigated the optimization of a mixture of boron-containing plastic and ZnS(Ag) phosphor for a slow-neutron counter of high efficiency. The most satisfactory scintillator developed was a molded plastic disk consisting of two parts of ZnS(Ag) and one part of a boron plastic. The boron plastic was formed by heating a mixture of boric acid and glycerol (6:1 weight ratio). A finished scintillator of 1.2-mm thickness achieved 33 per cent efficiency for counting thermal neutrons. Ability to discriminate against gammas was fair. Figure 9–21, giving the relative count rate versus discriminator for both gammas and Po-Be neutron sources, is indicative of this characteristic.

Sun has also discussed [44] the application of this scintillator to the photographic detection of neutrons. In this application a 1-mm-thick layer of the scintillator is laid on a photographic film of high sensitivity.

This detector is quite sensitive, as an integrated flux of only 250 neutrons/mm² will produce a visible image on the film.

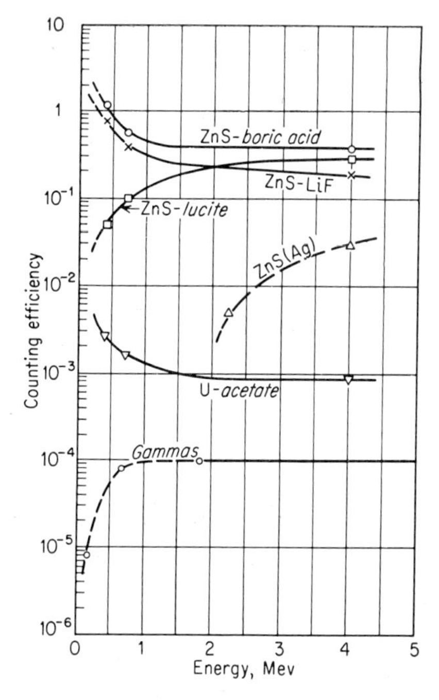


FIG. 9-20. Neutron and gamma counting efficiencies, in per cent, versus particle energy, for various optimum ZnS(Ag) mixtures. [*From P. G. Koontz, G. R. Keepin, and J. E. Ashley, Rev. Sci. Instr.*, **26**:352 (1955.).]

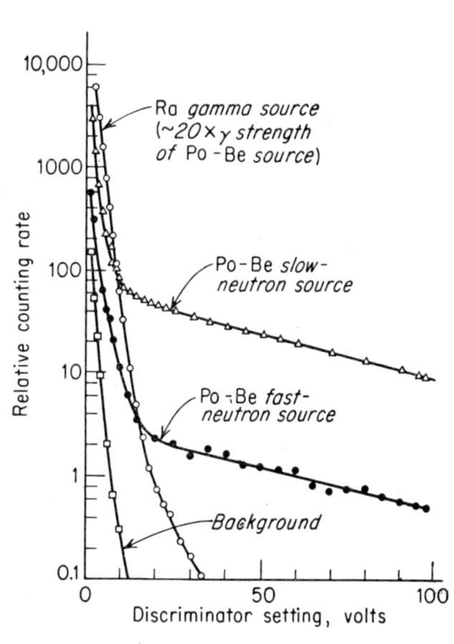


FIG. 9-21. Response of a mixture of boron plastic and ZnS(Ag) phosphor to gammas and neutrons. [*From K. H. Sun, P. R. Malmberg, and F. A. Pecjak, Nucleonics*, **14**:46 (*July*, 1956).]

## 9-26. *Neutron Scintillation Detectors Employing Proton Recoil*

A ZnS(Ag) hydrogenous mixture consisting of grains of ZnS(Ag) suspended in paraffin or in plastics such as lucite and bioplastic has proved to be [46-48] a relatively efficient fast-neutron detector with low sensitivity to gammas. The scintillator developed by Hornyak [46] consisted of 1.5 g of ZnS(Ag) in 10 g of lucite, forming a cylinder 1 in. in diameter and 5/8 in. in height. The sensitivities of these scintillators to neutrons and gammas are shown in Figs. 9-22 and 9-23, respectively. Detectors of this general type, referred to as "Hornyak buttons," are in wide-scale use for neutron dosimetry.

All organic scintillators will respond to fast neutrons through the recoil protons. However, because of the large response of these scintillators for electrons, it is impossible to count neutrons with these scintillators in the presence of large fluxes except when large energy differences exist. Falk [45], using a solution of terphenyl in xylene, has obtained maximum pulse heights of $Co^{60}$ gammas (1.2 Mev), ThC″ gammas (2.6 Mev), and 14-Mev neutrons in the ratio 1:1.4:2.4. These gamma pulses could be successfully biased out from the 14-Mev neutrons. These systems have found numerous

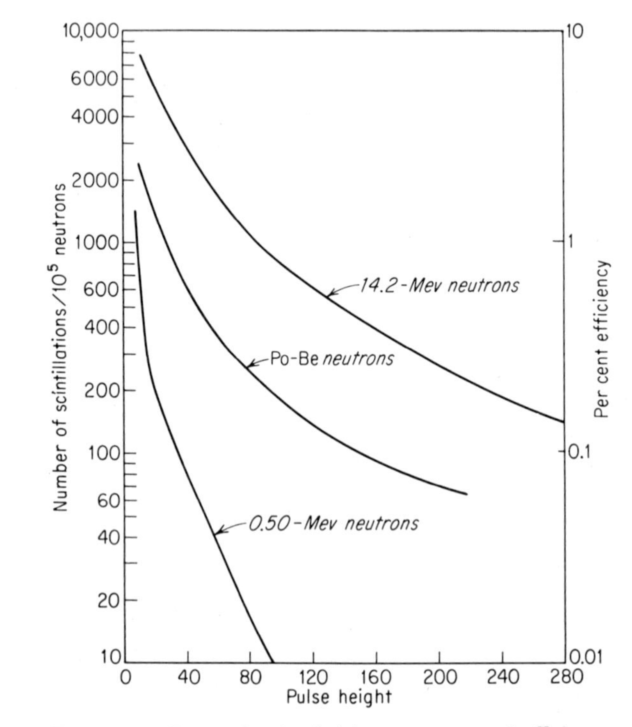


FIG. 9–22. Integral pulse-height spectrum and efficiency as a function of the discriminator setting for a "Hornyak button" with various neutron sources. Detector contains 1.5 g of ZnS (Ag) in 10 g of lucite. [*From W. F. Hornyak, Rev. Sci. Instr.*, **23**:264 (1952).]

applications in fast-neutron counting. Typical is the detector described by Christie et al. [49]; it is reported to have an efficiency of 5 per cent for counting 130-Mev neutrons.

One ingenious application of organic scintillators has resulted in the development [50] of a detector of fast neutrons which is insensitive to gamma radiation and for which the detection efficiency is strongly dependent on neutron energy. The construction of this counter is shown in Fig. 9–24. The counting medium consists of spheres of a plastic scintillator immersed in nonhydrogenous optically inert material (glass or trifluorochloroethylene liquid). The sphere diameter is chosen large enough that, for a particular neutron energy, most recoil protons dissipate their energy within the scintillator; it must be small enough, however, to prevent the pulses of maximum size caused by gamma rays from being in the same pulse-height range as those due to the neutrons. Electrons due to gamma rays are prevented from traversing more than one sphere by the non-

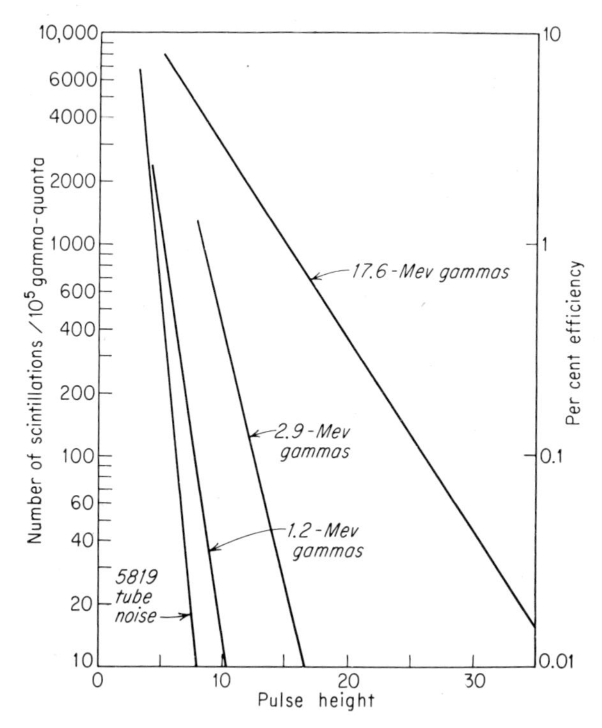


FIG. 9–23. Integral pulse-height spectrum and efficiency as a function of the discriminator setting for a "Hornyak button" with various gamma-ray sources; same conditions as in Fig. 9–22. [*From W. F. Hornyak, Rev. Sci. Instr.*, **23**:264 (1952).]

hydrogenous material separating them. Sphere diameters that have been used are 1.5, 2.5, 6, and 10 mm for neutrons having energies of 3.5, 4.5, 7.0, and 14 Mev, respectively.

### 9–27. *Neutron Scintillation Detectors Employing the* (n,$\gamma$) *Reaction*

Since the simple capture of gammas usually results in the emission of three or four gamma rays of a total energy of approximately 8 Mev, the incorporation of a high-cross-section thermal absorber in a hydrogenous scintillator seems attractive. If most of the gamma energy is dissipated in

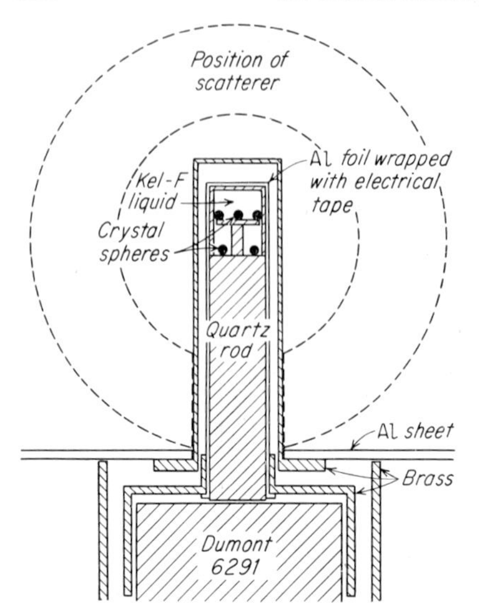


FIG. 9-24. Typical plastic- or crystal-sphere scintillation detector for fast neutrons. [*From J. H. McCrary, H. L. Taylor, and T. W. Bonner, Phys. Rev.*, **94**:808 (1954).]

the scintillator, the resulting pulses will be much larger than those from the background gammas; the latter gammas usually have an energy considerably less than 8 Mev. Therefore it may be possible to discriminate between the neutrons and the background gammas.

There are metal-organic compounds which are soluble in liquid scintillators and do but little quenching. However, their solubilities are limited to about 5 per cent, and such scintillators have relatively low efficiencies per unit thickness.

A direct approach is to place plates of absorbing material such as cadmium in the liquid scintillator. Figure 9-25 is a schematic diagram of such a counter described by Muehlhause [51]. The discrimination against background gammas is only partially effective because the partial loss of the capture-gamma energy in many cases results in a distribution in pulse size from zero to a maximum. Thus to obtain reasonable counting efficiency it may be necessary to set the lower discriminator level at a value sufficiently low to allow some of the background gammas to pass.

The experiment for the detection of the neutrino which was described in Sec. 7-35 used the (n,$\gamma$) reaction for the thermal-neutron detection.

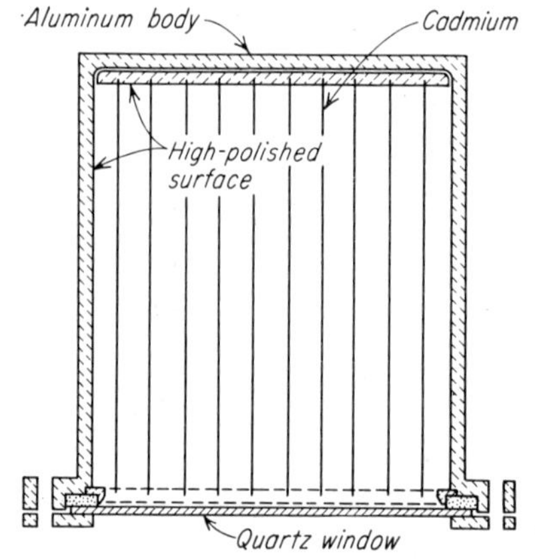


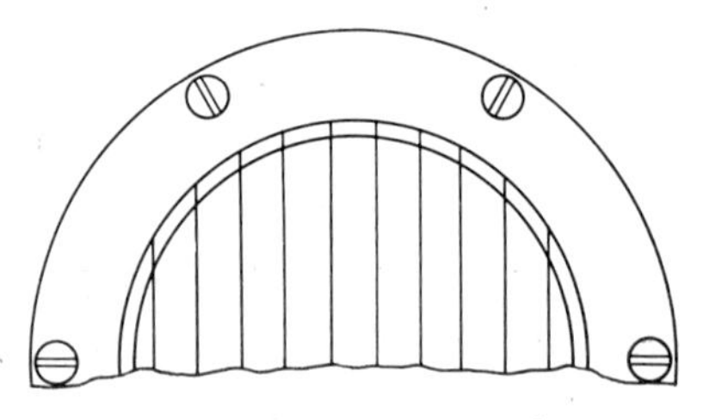

FIG. 9-25. Schematic diagram of a capture-gamma-ray neutron detector. (*From C. O. Muehlause, U.S. Atomic Energy Comm. Document BNL* 242, 1953.)

In this experiment cadmium propionate was added to an organic scintillator.

Another interesting application of the (n,$\gamma$) reaction is to a detector with sensitivity primarily to epithermal neutrons. This can be accomplished by encasing a gamma-sensitive scintillator such as an NaI(Tl) crystal in a material such as silver with a strong resonance peak for the (n,$\gamma$) reaction.

## 9–28. *Fast-neutron Scintillation Spectrometers*

The energy of fast neutrons can be measured by making use of the relationship between the neutron energy and the proton-recoil energy for a given angle, as expressed in Eq. (9–12). By use of a scintillator, the proton-recoil energy is obtained. The energy is determined by selecting for measurement only those recoil protons accompanied by neutrons which are scattered through a fixed angle. Figure 9–26 is a schematic diagram of such an arrangement. The detectors $A$ and $B$ are photomultiplier tubes with anthracene scintillators. The fast neutron whose energy is to be measured enters the detector $A$. Proton recoils within it produce pulses. If the neutron is scattered through the angle $\theta$, it may enter the scintillator $B$ and produce a pulse. The pulses produced in detector $A$ enter a coincidence circuit after being delayed by a time equal to that required for the scattered neutron to travel from detector $A$ to $B$. Consequently, pulses in the detectors $A$ and $B$ corresponding to (n,p) scattering through the angle $\theta$ will arrive at the coincidence circuit at the same time. The coincidence of the pulses is required for the passage of the pulses from the scintillator $A$ to the pulse-height analyzer. In this way the primary-neutron energy is obtained through the use of Eq. (9–12).

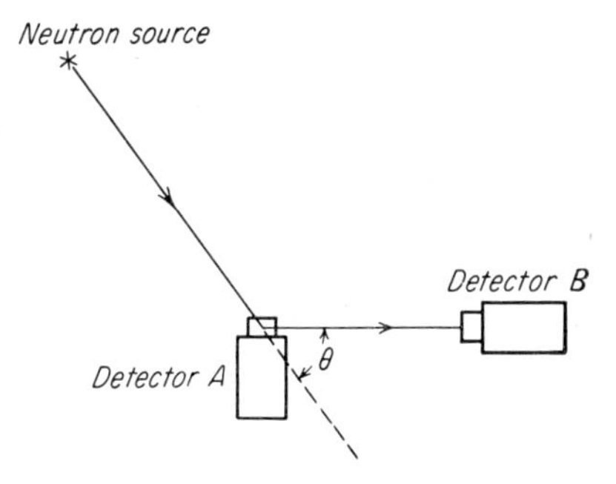


FIG. 9–26. Experimental apparatus for the determination of neutron energy.

Draper [52] has described such a detector using two stilbene crystals, each 1.9 cm by 3.2 cm in diameter mounted on type 5819 photomultiplier tubes. The angle $\theta$ was $\pi/4$, the separation between detectors $A$ and $B$ was 50 cm, and the distance from the source to detector $A$ was 28 cm. For a primary-neutron energy of 14 Mev, the coincidence counting rate was $1 \times 10^{-4}$ of the neutron-proton coincidence rate in crystal $A$ and $1 \times 10^{-8}$ of the neutron-source strength.

An alternative scheme for the measurement of neutron energies from the proton recoils is to select only those proton recoils which are accompanied by epithermal neutrons. This ensures that the recoil proton has at least 99 per cent of the incident-neutron energies. The epithermal-neutron detector described in Sec. 9–27 operates satisfactorily for this application.

The coincidence requirement in the spectrometers described above not only ensures that the correct proton recoils are being used, but it also aids in the prevention of background counts from undesirable radiation.

## NEUTRON DETECTION BY NUCLEAR EMULSIONS

### 9–29. *Neutron-energy Measurements by Nuclear Emulsions*

Nuclear emulsions have found wide use in the measurement of neutron energies and in the determination of neutron-energy spectra. Extensive reviews of this technique have been given by Rosen [53]. The fact that in an emulsion simultaneous measurements can be made of the energy and the direction of a particle makes this technique particularly attractive. Similar measurements can be made with cloud chambers. However, the nuclear emulsions require much less time from the experimental machines and the operating crews. In addition, they are much smaller and more compact than most other types of detectors. Disadvantages of nuclear emulsions for this application are the time required to analyze the necessary number of tracks in the nuclear emulsion and the limited accuracy inherent in the nuclear-emulsion techniques.

Several techniques have been developed for the measurement of neutron energy and spectra through the use of nuclear emulsions. The choice of method depends on several factors such as the degree of collimation of the neutrons, the energy region in which the measurement is required, and the facilities and time available for measuring the tracks.

The most commonly used technique is that of measuring the range of proton recoils in the emulsion within a small angle from the forward direction. This technique requires that the direction of the primary neutrons be known either through collimation or through the fact that the neutrons come from a small source placed at a sufficient distance from the plate. The emulsion is placed with its surface parallel to the direction of the incident neutron.

Through the use of range-energy relationships in the emulsion (see Fig. 8–1 and the discussion in Sec. 8–4), the energies associated with the proton recoils can be determined. The procedure for measuring the tracks consists of selecting a fixed volume in the emulsion and measuring the length of all tracks which lie within a fixed angle, usually 15°, of the direction of the incident neutron. Care is taken to ensure that the tracks do not leave the emulsion. The measurements are placed in small energy groups, and the results are expressed as the number of protons per unit energy interval.

For monoenergetic neutrons the recoil protons have a distribution in energy. This is in part because of the fact that the angle between the incident neutron and the recoil proton varies and in part because of the straggling in the range of a fixed-energy proton. Nereson and Reines [54] have found that the resolution (fractional full width at half amplitude) varies from 25 per cent for 0.24-Mev neutrons to 6 per cent for 1.5-Mev neutrons. As the energy of the neutrons increases, the relative importance of the spread due to the finite angle increases until it makes equal contributions to that of the proton straggling at 1.5 Mev.

If $N_p(E)$ represents the distribution in energy measured for the proton recoils, the corresponding distribution in energy for the incident neutron $N_n(E)$ is

$$N_n(E) \sim \frac{N_p(E)}{\sigma_p} \tag{9-45}$$

where $\sigma_p$ is the cross section for the proton-recoil process.

Nuclear emulsions have been found satisfactory for the neutron energy-distribution measurements of neutrons in the energy range from about 0.5 to 15 Mev. The lower limit arises since the track ranges become too short for accurate measurements, while the upper limit comes from a practical limit of the emulsion thickness. The detection efficiency is such that, for neutrons of 7 Mev, a neutron flux of $10^8$ neutrons/cm$^2$ will produce, in 1 mm$^2$ of a 200-$\mu$ emulsion, approximately 60 acceptable proton recoils which make an angle of less than 15° with respect to the neutron direction and come to rest within the emulsion.

Another technique suitable for use with highly collimated beams is the nuclear-plate camera. A schematic diagram of such a camera is shown in Fig. 9–27. In this arrangement the proton recoils can be measured more easily and quickly than those produced in emulsions. However, it requires that the neutrons be in a well-collimated beam of considerable intensity.

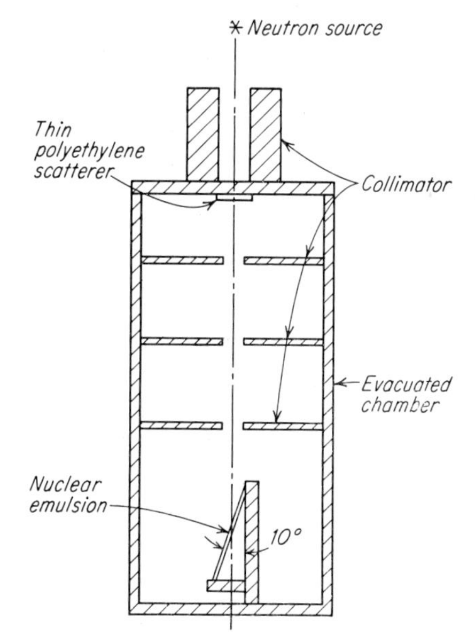


FIG. 9–27. Nuclear-plate camera for neutron-energy spectra determinations.

The neutrons enter through a collimator and strike the hydrogenous radiator, say polyethylene. The thickness of the polyethylene should be small compared with the range of the recoil protons. However, unless the neutron flux is sufficiently high, a compromise in the thickness is required to obtain sufficient proton recoils. A few milligrams per square centimeter of thickness is usually employed. The camera is evacuated to prevent the absorption of the protons. The nuclear plate is placed at an angle of 10° to the incident-neutron beam. The proton produces a track in the nuclear plate, a track length being proportional to the energy of the proton.

All proton tracks to be measured start at the surface of the plate. Consequently the tracks to be measured can be readily identified. The camera is particularly useful for the measurement of high-energy neutron spectra where thicker radiators can be used.

When the direction of the neutrons cannot be determined, it is more difficult to measure the neutron energy. One method which has been tried uses lithium-impregnated emulsions. The reaction $Li^6(n,\alpha)H^3$ leads to two tracks, one produced by the alpha particle and the other by the triton ($H^3$) particle. Through measurement of the ranges of the alpha particle and the triton along with determination of the angle between the two paths, both the energy and direction of the incident neutrons can be determined in principle.

The technique involving the $Li^6(n,\alpha)$ reaction is difficult to apply. It is hard to distinguish between the triton and alpha tracks, and in addition proton tracks can easily be confused with them. Further, it is difficult to determine precisely the point of origin of the tracks of interest. The accurate application of this method will require additional development work [55].

### 9–30. *Neutron-flux Measurements by Nuclear Emulsions*

Nuclear emulsions provide sensitive means for the measurement of neutron flux. Methods available for obtaining neutron sensitivity in the nuclear emulsions are (1) the use of the neutron-capture or scattering cross sections of the nuclides normally present in the emulsions, (2) addition to the emulsion of high-cross-section nuclides, and (3) the combination of a nuclear emulsion and an external radiator.

In the normal emulsion the $N^{14}(n,p)$ reaction has a thermal-neutron cross section of 1.76 barns. The protons which are produced by thermal-neutron capture have an energy of 0.63 Mev which gives a track of about 7 $\mu$ in the emulsion. In an emulsion of thickness $d$, the number of tracks per square centimeter of emulsion per unit neutron flux is obtained from Eq. (1–37) as

$$\text{Number tracks per cm}^2 = N\sigma_{n,p}d \qquad (9\text{–}46)$$

where $N$ is the number of nitrogen atoms per cubic centimeter and $\sigma_{n,p}$ is the cross section for the (n,p) reaction. Taking $N$ as $4.7 \times 10^{21}$ atoms/cm$^3$, a value appropriate for NTA film, and an emulsion thickness $d$ of 30 $\mu$, one obtains $2.5 \times 10^{-5}$ track/cm$^2$ per unit neutron flux. This is a convenient sensitivity for monitoring exposure of personnel to slow neutrons. The maximum permissible exposure of 1,800 slow neutrons/(cm$^2$)(sec) for a 40-hr week gives $2.6 \times 10^8$ neutrons/cm$^2$ per 40-hr week. This total dosage would lead to 6,500 tracks/cm$^2$, which is a convenient track density to count. A field of view of $2 \times 10^{-4}$ cm$^2$ would have 1.3 tracks, on an average.

A disadvantage of the $N^{14}(n,p)C^{14}$ reaction is the confusion of its proton tracks with those caused by the proton recoils of fast neutrons. The sensitivity of an emulsion to fast neutrons through the proton recoils depends to a large extent on the energy spectrum and the criterion adopted for selecting the tracks to be counted. In addition, proton recoils from the paper in which the films are wrapped add to the counts.

Cheka [56], studying the application of films to the monitoring of fast neutrons, found 2,500 tracks/cm$^2$ produced by $4.96 \times 10^6$ neutrons/cm$^2$, the maximum permissible exposure of fast neutrons from a Po-Be source in a week's time. The emulsion thickness was 30 $\mu$. This represents a sensitivity of $5.6 \times 10^{-4}$ track/cm$^2$ per unit neutron flux.

Emulsions with very high sensitivity to thermal neutrons can be obtained by the addition of high-cross-section materials to the emulsion. As an example, Kaplan and Yagoda [57] have succeeded in adding 34 mg/cm$^3$ of boron and 12 mg/cm$^3$ of lithium to Ilford emulsions. By utilizing the high cross sections of $Li^7$ and particularly of $B^{10}$, sensitivities as high as 0.94 track/cm$^2$ per unit neutron flux can be obtained in emulsions of thickness of 200 $\mu$. This corresponds to an efficiency of 0.94 track per neutron passing through the emulsion.

Electron-sensitive emulsions may be sandwiched between materials such as cadmium which have high cross sections for the $(n,\gamma)$ reaction. In these applications the over-all darkening of the film rather than the track density is used as the measure of the neutron flux.

## THERMAL EFFECTS FOR NEUTRON DETECTION

### 9-31. *Neutron-sensitive Thermopile*

At the high neutron fluxes experienced in nuclear reactors, macroscopic physical and chemical effects are available for neutron-flux measurements. Neutron dosimetry by the gas evolution from water decomposition has been discussed in Sec. 8-25. A neutron-sensitive thermopile is described in the present section.

The operation of the neutron-sensitive thermopile is based on the thermoelectric effect. When two dissimilar metals are connected as in Fig. 9-28*a* and the two junctions are held at temperatures $T_1$ and $T_2$, respectively, a potential difference $V$ which is proportional to the temperature difference appears across the thermocouple. If one junction of the thermocouple is coated so that heat is developed in it because of nuclear reactions induced by neutrons, the resulting output voltage can be taken as a measure of the neutron flux.

Both fissionable materials, such as $U^{235}$, and materials undergoing the (n,$\alpha$) reaction, such as $B^{10}$, could be applied as the coating material. The heat produced per unit neutron flux is similar for both materials. However, $U^{235}$ has the disadvantage of becoming radioactive after exposure to neutrons.

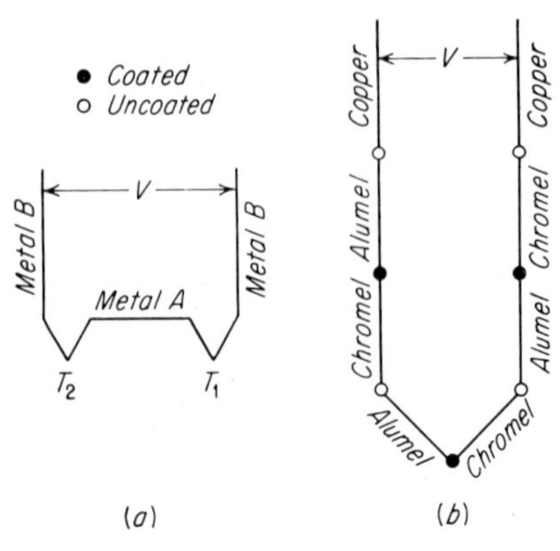


Fig. 9–28. Principles of the neutron-sensitive thermopile. (a) A single thermocouple; (b) a three-couple thermocouple.

The voltage output can be increased by placing several thermocouples in series, as shown in Fig. 9–28*b*. A thermopile consisting of *n* thermocouples in series has an output *n* times larger than a single thermocouple. Satisfactory couple materials are chromel and alumel. Since it is necessary ultimately to make connections to other materials in the measuring circuit, leads such as copper may be connected to the thermopile, as in Fig. 9–28*b*. The junctions to the copper wires are uncoated.

It is to be noted that the output of the thermopile is independent of the ambient temperature in which it is operated. However, since the separate junctions are a finite distance apart, a temperature gradient in the detector may cause an output voltage. This effect can be eliminated by careful construction. If in the plane normal to the temperature gradient there are equal numbers of hot and cold junctions, the effect of the temperature gradient is zero. In addition, the junctions of the copper leads to the thermocouple material must both be at the same temperature.

Lapsley [58] has described a compact neutron-sensitive thermopile. It consisted of the standard Brown Radiamatic Thermopile designed by the Brown Instrument Division of the Minneapolis-Honeywell Regulator Company. It was the standard light-sensitive unit so arranged that alternate thermal junctions met in the central area. The central area was coated with $B^{10}$; this was applied by mixing the boron powder in porcelain cement and placing the mixture on the central area. Fifteen milligrams of boron powder were applied as a disk 3.5 mm in diameter and 1 mm thick. The thermopile consisted of 10 chromel-constantan elements and developed a total voltage of 0.5 mv per degree Centigrade. The unit developed 1 mv at a neutron flux of $10^{11}$ neutrons/(cm$^2$)(sec). It was expected that the sensitivity of this unit would start to drop at fluxes around $10^{13}$ since the accompanying temperature difference of around 200°C would result in some heat loss by radiation.

The $B^{10}$ coating on the junction acted as a neutron sink, absorbing all neutrons which entered it. Throughout the life of the detector its sensitivity fell because of the reduction in the effective area of the junction coatings due to the burnout of the boron-10 in the surface layers. Lapsley [58] has computed, for the thermopile described above, that at a flux of $10^{12}$ burnout will decrease its sensitivity in the order of 1 per cent in 3 years.

A commercial model* of a neutron thermopile is available. It consists of a 21-element thermopile encased in an aluminum tube of 6½-in. length and ½-in. diameter. The thermoelements are made by the welding together of no. 28 chromel and alumel wire. The voltage generated by a flux of $2 \times 10^{11}$ neutrons/(cm$^2$)(sec) is about 1 mv. The response is linear from $10^7$ to $10^{12}$ neutrons/(cm$^2$)(sec). The thermopile resistance is only 4 ohms so that a relatively simple galvanometer can be used to measure the output at high fluxes. The unit is insensitive to temperature gradients, to gamma radiation fluxes encountered in present reactor designs, and to ambient temperature changes from 20 to 400°C. The response time constant for a step-function change in slow-neutron flux is in the range from 5 to 8 sec.

## ABSOLUTE NEUTRON MEASUREMENTS

### 9–32. *Introductory Considerations*

In many measurements of neutrons, relative rather than absolute values are required. These can be made quite accurately, in certain cases to a fraction of a per cent. Occasionally the necessity arises for absolute measurements of neutron fluxes and of source strength. Accuracy of these measurements is quite limited, often to several per cent.

At each laboratory conducting extensive neutron measurements it is desirable to have available methods for absolute flux measurements. This requires either the use of detection systems of known sensitivity or the availability of sources of known strength and fluxes in order that the equipment can be calibrated. An example of the need for absolute flux measurements arises in the monitoring of neutrons for health-physics purposes.

### 9–33. *Calibration of Standard Neutron Source*

Artificial neutron sources of known strength are quite useful in absolute neutron measurements. Sources employing the ($\alpha$,n) reaction, such as radium-alpha-beryllium sources, are suitable.

A concise explanation of the methods used for the calibration of neutron

* Nuclear Instrument and Chemical Corporation, model 3782.

sources has been given by Feld [59]. The calibration is usually achieved by the method of "space integration." There are many modifications of this technique. In this method the neutron source of strength $Q$ is placed in the center of a water solution containing a high-cross-section thermal absorber, such as boron. The neutrons are slowed down by collisions with hydrogen in the water solution. At equilibrium

$$Q = 4\pi N \int_0^\infty r^2\, dr \int_0^{E_{\max}} \phi(r,E)\, \sigma_a(E)\, dE \tag{9–47}$$

where $r$ = distance from source
$N$ = no. of nuclei per cm in medium
$\sigma_a(E)$ = absorption cross section for neutrons of energy $E$
$\phi(r,E)$ = neutron flux of energy $E$ per unit energy interval as function of $r$

The second integral can be written as $\Phi(r)\,\bar{\sigma}_a$, where $\Phi(r)$ is the total flux at $r$ and $\bar{\sigma}_a$ is the average cross section. Thus Eq. (9–47) becomes

$$Q = 4\pi N \int_0^\infty \Phi(r)\bar{\sigma}_a r^2\, dr \tag{9–48}$$

The quantity $\Phi(r)\bar{\sigma}_a$ can be determined by the measurement of the absolute flux versus $r$ with a detector having a cross section with the same energy dependence as the solution. As an example, if the solution contains a $1/v$ absorber such as $B^{10}$, a $1/v$ detector should be used. With a $BF_3$ counter, the counting rate $R(r)$ at position $r$ is, from Eq. (9–4),

$$R(r) = N'_T\, \Phi(r)\bar{\sigma}' \tag{9–49}$$

where $N'_T$ is the total number of $B^{10}$ atoms in the detector and $\bar{\sigma}'_a$ is the average cross section of $B^{10}$. Combining Eqs. (9–48) and (9–49), one obtains

$$Q = \frac{4\pi N \bar{\sigma}_a}{N'_T \bar{\sigma}'_a} \int_0^\infty R(r)\, r^2\, dr \tag{9–50}$$

In this example the measurement is dependent on the known efficiency of the $BF_3$ detector, as given by Eq. (9–49).

Since the $BF_3$ detectors occupy considerable space, it is difficult to determine $R(r)$ through their use. An alternative method is to use activation detectors such as indium and manganese. Walker [60] has described this technique in detail.

### 9–34. *Absolute Thermal-flux Measurements*

Through the use of a standard neutron source such as that described in the preceding section, it is possible to set up a thermal-neutron flux the value of which is known nearly as accurately as the source strength. The thermal flux is produced by placing the standard neutron source in a large block of graphite. Such an arrangement is known as a "standard pile." The relationship between the neutron-source strength and the distribution of thermal flux in the "standard pile" has been discussed by Hughes [61].

The spatial variation of the slowing-down density at the indium resonance is determined throughout the pile by the use of indium foils. Absolute values are assigned to the slowing-down density through the application of the condition that the volume integral of the slowing-down density equal the total source strength. The thermal flux is determined

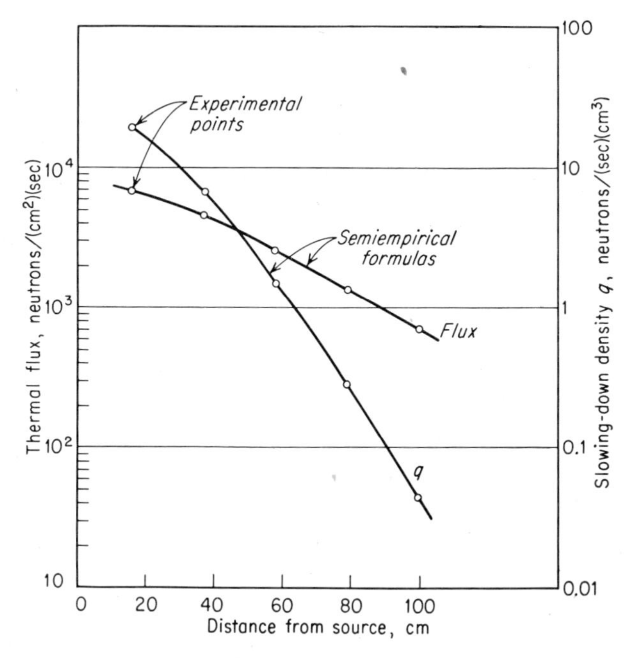


Fig. 9–29. Neutron flux and slowing-down-density distribution versus distance from the neutron source in the Argonne "standard pile." *(From D. J. Hughes, "Pile Neutron Research," by permission of Addison-Wesley Publishing Co., Reading, Mass., publishers.)*

from the slowing-down density. Figure 9–29 contains plots of both the slowing-down density and the thermal-neutron flux as a function of distance from the source for the "standard pile" at Argonne. The source strength was $(5.5 \pm 0.4) \times 10^6$ neutrons/sec.

The "standard pile" can be used to calibrate the various types of thermal-neutron detectors. Consideration must be given to perturbations which the detectors make in the flux. If the detector is calibrated in the "standard graphite pile," it can then be used to measure flux in a graphite diffusion medium without correction for perturbations.

Measurements of thermal-neutron flux versus distance from radium-alpha-beryllium sources of known strength have been made in water. The expression for thermal-neutron flux is

$$\Phi_{th} = Qf(r) \tag{9-51}$$

where $Q$ is the neutron source and $f(r)$ is a function of the distance $r$ from the source. Figure 9–30 is a plot of $f(r)$ versus $r$ made from data given by Feld [59]. If a standard Ra-$\alpha$-Be source is available, Fig. 9–30 can be used to establish known thermal-neutron fluxes.

When known neutron fluxes are not available for calibration purposes, absolute flux measurements can still be made by calculation of the sensitivities of certain neutron detectors. A boron-trifluoride-filled proportional counter for absolute flux measurements was described in Sec. 9–5. Through measurement of the absolute activities induced in foils and the relationships discussed in Sec. 9–16, absolute fluxes can be determined. Photographic emulsions with a known content of boron can also be used, as discussed in Sec. 9–30.

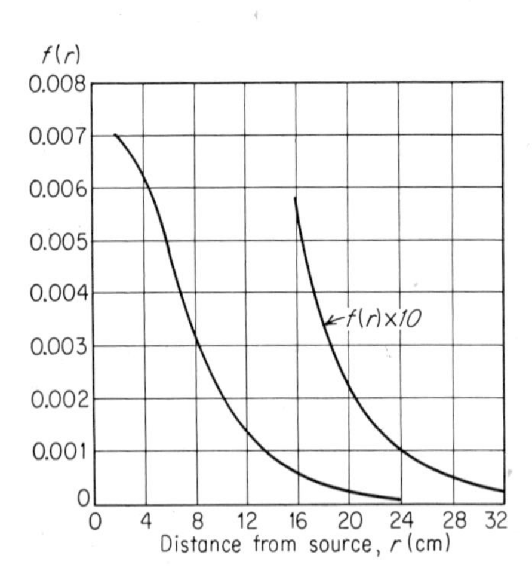


FIG. 9–30. Plot of $f(r)$ for an Ra-Be source in water. [*Data taken with permission from B. T. Feld, Article in E. Segrè (ed.), "Experimental Nuclear Physics," vol.* II, *John Wiley & Sons, Inc., New York,* 1953.]

## 9–35. *Absolute Fast-flux Measurements*

The total fast or uncollided neutron flux integrated over a surface surrounding a standard neutron source is, of course, equal to the source strength $Q$. Provided that the distribution in direction and the law for neutron absorption are known, the flux at a given distance from the source can be calculated. As an example, the flux at a distance $r$ from a point isotropic source of neutrons of source strength $Q$ is

$$\Phi(r) = \frac{Q}{4\pi r^2} \tag{9-52}$$

provided that there is no absorption of the neutrons between the source and the point in question. The relationship can be used to calibrate detectors. It should be kept in mind, however, that the calibration so obtained will be accurate only when used in a flux of the same distribution in energy.

The absolute sensitivity of some proton-recoil counters can be calculated.

As an example, the sensitivity of the counter designed by Skyrme, Tunnicliffe, and Ward (see Sec. 9–12) can be calculated to 5 per cent for neutrons in the energy range 0.1 to 1 Mev.

For the energy region above 3 Mev, the most convenient and accurate means of absolute flux determination is probably the counter telescope shown in Fig. 9–31. The device depends on the counting of the recoil protons emerging in a given solid angle from a thin hydrogenous radiator of known weight and cross section. In this instrument only those recoil protons are chosen which emerge from a thin solid radiator in a direction close to that of the incident neutrons. Recoil protons are collimated by a system of apertures of carefully measured geometry as they traverse the two proportional counters; they lose a small amount of energy in each, giving rise

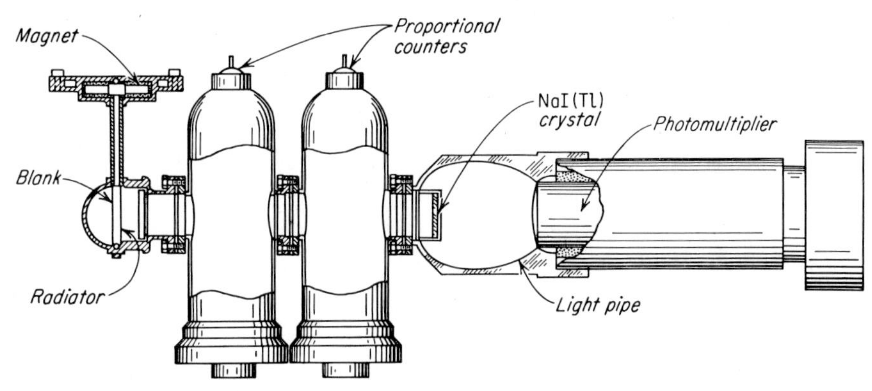


Fig. 9–31. Counter telescope for flux measurements. (*From B. C. Diven, "Proceedings of the International Conference on the Peaceful Uses of Atomic Energy," vol.* 4, *p.* 251, *United Nations, New York,* 1956.)

to pulses in these counters. Finally, most of the energy is lost in the NaI scintillator. To reduce the background, triple coincidence is required between the pulses from the two proportional counters and the scintillator, in order for a scintillator pulse to be admitted into the counting channel.

With this counter telescope, flux measurements can be made to an accuracy of about 3 per cent.

## 9–36. *Monitoring of Neutron Radiation*

The monitoring of neutron radiation for health-physics purposes is an important application of the neutron-detection methods which have been discussed in the preceding sections. The ultimate information required is the biological effect of the radiation on man or the dosage expressed in the rem (roentgen-equivalent-man) unit. The dosage in rem is related to the energy absorbed through the relative biological effectiveness. Through consideration of the mechanisms for interaction of neutron radiation with matter, the neutron flux which will result in the maximum permissible exposure in a given period of time has been determined.

The principal mechanisms for the interaction of neutron radiation with tissue are the $p(n,\gamma)H^2$ and the $N^{14}(n,p)C^{14}$ reactions for slow neutrons and proton recoil for fast neutrons. Through the use of Fig. 9–32, measurements of the neutron fluxes in the various energy regions can be expressed in terms

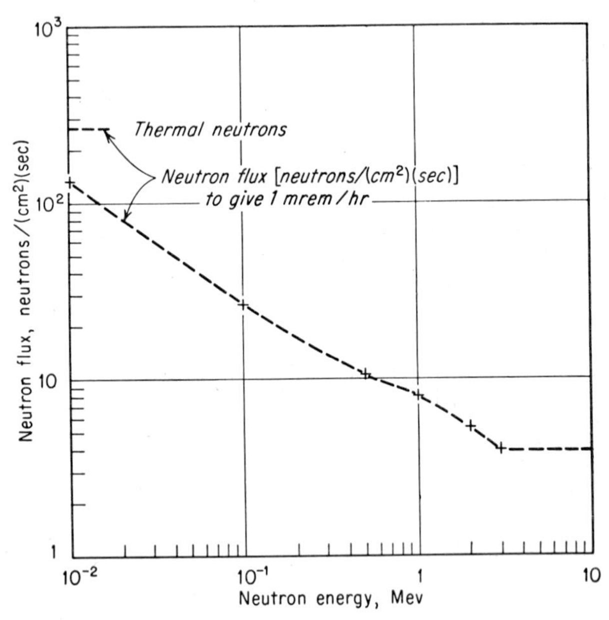


FIG. 9–32. Conversion from neutron flux to dose rate. [*From Federal Register*, **22**:19 (*Jan.* 29, 1957).]

of dosage in millirem per hour. When a distribution in energy exists for the neutron flux, the dosage rate is

$$D = \int_0^\infty \frac{\phi(E)}{F(E)}\,dE \tag{9–53}$$

where $F(E)$ is the function given in Fig. 9–32.

Several of the neutron-detection methods have proved to be particularly useful for monitoring neutron radiation and the measurement of neutron dosage. These include $BF_3$ proportional counters (see Sec. 9–5), balanced-type current ionization chambers filled with $BF_3$ (Sec. 9–7), foil activation (Sec. 9–18), and nuclear-track plates (Sec. 9–29) for slow neutrons, and proton-recoil pulse chambers of the Hurst, Ritchie, Wilson type (Sec. 9–13), balanced current ionization chambers employing proton recoil (Sec. 9–14), neutron emulsions employing proton recoil (Sec. 9–30), and Hornyak buttons (Sec. 9–26) for fast neutrons. For detailed discussions of neutron dosimetry, see the articles by Hurst [63, 64] and by Rossi [65].

## PROBLEMS

**9–1.** Estimate the maximum efficiency of a lithium-lined proportional counter used for counting thermal neutrons.

**9–2.** If a neutron detector using $B^{10}$ is employed to monitor a nuclear reactor having an average thermal flux of $10^9$ neutrons/(cm$^2$)(sec), estimate the percentage decrease in efficiency that will occur because of the neutron depletion of the $B^{10}$ in one week of operation.

**9–3.** What percentage of 0.3-ev neutrons are transmitted through 0.010 in. of cadmium? Repeat the calculation for 0.025-ev and 1.0-ev neutrons.

**9–4.** The following data are taken with a $B^{10}$-lined neutron-counter tube: the counting rate is 374 counts/min when the tube is completely surrounded with 0.040-in.-thick cadmium; the counting rate increases to 1,295 counts/min when a window of 7.5 cm$^2$ is opened in the cadmium shield. Compute the thermal-neutron flux that is incident on the window if the efficiency for counting thermal neutrons is 0.03.

**9–5.** Calculate the current per unit neutron flux for the PCP neutron chamber described in Sec. 9–7.

**9–6.** Calculate the maximum sensitivity for counting 10-Mev neutrons that could be achieved in a proportional counter containing a 0.5-mg/cm$^2$-thick polyethylene radiator with an area of 10 cm$^2$.

**9–7.** Compute the saturation activity induced in a cadmium-covered indium foil having a thickness of 100 mg/cm$^2$ and an area of 7 cm$^2$ when placed in a thermal-neutron flux of 1,800 neutrons/(cm$^2$)(sec).

**9–8.** Compare the sensitivity or the saturation activity per unit neutron flux for gold and cobalt foils, both of 100 mg/cm$^2$ thickness, when used to detect thermal neutrons.

**9–9.** The cadmium ratio for gold foils in a region containing epithermal neutrons with a $1/E$ distribution is found to be 30. If the thermal-neutron flux is found to be $10^{12}$ neutrons/(cm$^2$)(sec), what is the neutron flux per unit energy interval in the epithermal region?

**9–10.** Consider $P^{31}$ used as a threshold detector, employing the $P^{31}$(n,p)$S^{31}$ reaction. Calculate the neutron flux that exists above the threshold of the reaction if an $S^{31}$ activity of 1 curie per gram of $P^{31}$ is obtained in a 2-hr irradiation. The cross section for the $P^{31}$(n,p)$S^{31}$ reaction is approximately 75 millibarns.

**9–11.** Compute the time required for a decrease of 1 per cent in the sensitivity of a $B^{10}$-coated thermopile due to burnout of the $B^{10}$ if the unit is operated in a thermal flux of $10^{13}$ neutrons/(cm$^2$)(sec).

## REFERENCES


1. Petree, G., C. H. Johnson, and D. W. Miller: *Phys. Rev.*, **83**:1148 (1951).
2. Graves, A. C., and D. K. Froman: "Miscellaneous Physical and Chemical Techniques of the Los Alamos Project," National Nuclear Energy Series, div. V, vol. 3, McGraw-Hill Book Company, Inc., New York, 1952.
3. Lowde, R. D.: *Rev. Sci. Instr.*, **21**:835 (1950).
4. Abele, R. K., and J. Gundlach: *U.S. Atomic Energy Comm. Document* AECD-3494, 1951.
5. McCreary, H. S., Jr., and R. T. Bayard: *Rev. Sci. Instr.*, **25**:161 (1954).

6. Hanson, A. O., and J. L. McKibben: *Phys. Rev.*, **72**:673 (1947).
7. Nobles, R. A., et al.: *Rev. Sci. Instr.*, **25**:334 (1954).
8. Rossi, B. B., and H. H. Staub: "Ionization Chambers and Counters," chap. 9, National Nuclear Energy Series, div. V, vol. 2, McGraw-Hill Book Company, Inc., New York, 1949.
9. Baer, W., and R. T. Bayard: *Rev. Sci. Instr.*, **24**:138 (1953).
10. Nobles, R. G., and A. B. Smith: *Nucleonics*, **14**:60 (January, 1956).
11. Allen, W. D., and A. T. G. Ferguson: *J. Nuclear Energy*, **2**:38 (1955).
12. Wiegand, C.: *Rev. Sci. Instr.*, **19**:790 (1948).
13. Rossi, B. B., and H. H. Staub: "Ionization Chambers and Counters," chap. 7, National Nuclear Energy Series, div. V, vol. 2, McGraw-Hill Book Company, Inc., New York, 1949.
14. Skyrme, T. H. R., P. H. Tunnicliffe, and A. G. Ward: *Rev. Sci. Instr.*, **23**:204 (1952).
15. Hurst, G. S., R. H. Ritchie, and H. N. Wilson: *Rev. Sci. Instr.*, **22**:981 (1951).
16. Reddie, J. S., and G. H. Whipple: *U.S. Atomic Energy Comm. Document* HW-17561, 1950.
17. Rossi, H. H., and G. Failla: *Nucleonics*, **14**:32 (February, 1956).
18. Gamertsfelder, C. C.: *U.S. Atomic Energy Comm. Document* AECD-2173, 1948.
19. Ray, W. H.: *U.S. Atomic Energy Comm. Document* AECD-2357, 1944.
20. Hughes, D. J., and J. A. Harvey: "Neutron Cross Sections," U.S. Atomic Energy Commission Document, McGraw-Hill Book Company, Inc., New York, 1955.
21. Macklin, R. L., and H. S. Pomerance: "Proceedings of the International Conference on the Peaceful Uses of Atomic Energy," vol. 5, p. 96, United Nations, New York, 1956.
22. Hollander, J. M., I. Perlman, and G. T. Seaborg: *Revs. Mod. Phys.*, **23**:613 (1953).
23. Bothe, W.: *Z. Physik*, **120**:437 (1943).
24. Tittle, C. W.: *Nucleonics*, **9**:60 (July, 1951); **8**:5 (June, 1951).
25. Klema, E. D., and R. H. Ritchie: *Phys. Rev.*, **87**:167 (1952).
26. Koontz, R. L., and A. A. Jarrett: Paper at Second Annual Meeting, American Nuclear Society, 1956.
27. Hughes, D. J.: "Pile Neutron Research," chap. 5, Addison-Wesley Publishing Company, Reading, Mass., 1953.
28. Cohen, B. L.: *Nucleonics*, **8**:29 (February, 1951); *Phys. Rev.*, **81**:184 (1951).
29. Hurst, G. S., et al.: *Rev. Sci. Instr.*, **27**:153 (1956).
30. Uthe, P. M.: Attainment of Neutron Flux-Spectra from Foil Activations, Thesis, Air Force Institute of Technology, Wright-Patterson Air Force Base, Ohio, 1957.
31. Cowan, F. P., and J. F. O'Brien: "Proceedings of the International Conference on the Peaceful Uses of Atomic Energy," vol. 14, p. 213, United Nations, New York, 1956.
32. McKay, H. A. C.: Article in O. R. Frisch (ed.), "Progress in Nuclear Physics," vol. 1, Academic Press, Inc., New York, 1950.
33. Eggler, C., and C. M. Huddleston: *Nucleonics*, **14**:34 (April, 1956).
34. Muehlhause, C. O., and G. E. Thomas: *Nucleonics*, **11**:44 (January, 1953).
35. Reines, F., C. C. Cowan, F. B. Harrison, and P. S. Carter: *Rev. Sci. Instr.*, **25**:1061 (1954).
36. McCrary, J. H., H. L. Taylor, and T. W. Bonner: *Phys. Rev.*, **94**:908 (1954); *Nucleonics*, **13**:77 (September, 1955).
37. Buck, W. L., and R. K. Swank: *Nucleonics*, **11**:48 (November, 1953).
38. Schenck, J.: *Nature*, **171**:518 (1953).
39. Cleland, R.: *Phys. Rev.*, **89**:896A (1953).

40. Hofstadter, R., J. A. McIntyre, H. Roderick, and H. I. West, Jr.: *Phys. Rev.*, **82**:749 (1951).
41. Bollinger, L. M.: "Proceedings of the International Conference on the Peaceful Uses of Atomic Energy," vol. 4, p. 47, United Nations, New York, 1956.
42. Koontz, P. G., G. R. Keepin, and J. E. Ashley: *Rev. Sci. Instr.*, **26**:352 (1955).
43. Sun, K. H., P. R. Malmberg, and F. A. Pecjak: *Nucleonics*, **14**:46 (July, 1956).
44. Sun, K. H.: Paper at Second Annual Meeting, American Nuclear Society, 1956.
45. Falk, C. E., H. L. Poss, and L. C. L. Yuan: *Phys. Rev.*, **83**:176 (1951).
46. Hornyak, W. F.: *Rev. Sci. Instr.*, **23**:264 (1952).
47. Emmerich, W. S.: *Rev. Sci. Instr.*, **25**:69 (1954).
48. Seagondollar, L. W., K. A. Esch, and L. M. Cartwright: *Rev. Sci. Instr.*, **25**:689 (1954).
49. Christie, E. R., B. T. Feld, A. C. Odian, P. C. Stein, and A. Waltenberg: *Rev. Sci. Instr.*, **27**:127 (1956).
50. McCrary, J. H., H. L. Taylor, and T. W. Bonner: *Phys. Rev.*, **94**:808 (1954).
51. Muehlhause, C. O.: *U.S. Atomic Energy Comm. Document* BNL-242, 1953.
52. Draper, J. E.: *Rev. Sci. Instr.*, **25**:558 (1954).
53. Rosen, L.: *Nucleonics*, **11**:32 (July, 1953); **11**:38 (August, 1953); "Proceedings of the International Conference on the Peaceful Uses of Atomic Energy," vol. 4, p. 97, United Nations, New York, 1956.
54. Nereson, N., and F. Reines: *Rev. Sci. Instr.*, **21**:534 (1950).
55. Barton, D. M., G. R. Keepin, and J. H. Roberts: *U.S. Atomic Energy Comm. Document* LA-1526, Los Alamos Scientific Laboratory.
56. Cheka, J. S.: *Nucleonics*, **12**:40 (June, 1954).
57. Kaplan, N., and H. Yagoda: *Rev. Sci. Instr.*, **23**:155 (1952).
58. Lapsley, A. C.: *Nucleonics*, **11**:62 (May, 1953).
59. Feld, B. T.: Article in E. Segrè (ed.), "Experimental Nuclear Physics," vol. II, John Wiley & Sons, Inc., New York, 1953.
60. Walker, R. L.: *U.S. Atomic Energy Comm. Document* MDDC-414, 1946.
61. Hughes, D. J.: "Pile Neutron Research," chap. 3, Addison-Wesley Publishing Co., Reading, Mass., 1953.
62. Diven, B. C.: "Proceedings of the International Conference on the Peaceful Uses of Atomic Energy," vol. 4, p. 251, United Nations, New York, 1956.
63. Hurst, G. S., W. A. Mills, F. P. Conte, and A. C. Upton: *Radiation Research*, **4**:49 (1956).
64. Hurst, G. S.: *Brit. J. Radiol.*, **27**:353 (1954).
65. Rossi, H. H.: Article in G. J. Hine and G. L. Brownell (eds.), "Radiation Dosimetry," Academic Press, Inc., New York, 1956.

## CHAPTER 10

# ELECTRONICS FOR NUCLEAR-RADIATION DETECTION

The output of most of the detectors which have been described in the previous chapters is an electric signal. Therefore there exists a large variety of electronic equipment which is used as the measuring apparatus in nuclear-detection systems. For the most part, these electronic instruments have been treated only in sufficient detail to ensure an understanding of the application of the detection systems. The present chapter is a detailed treatment of this electronic apparatus. The major emphasis is on the electronic circuits for use with pulse-type detectors. Pulse-type ionization chambers, proportional counters, and scintillation detectors are treated as examples. The composite characteristics of these detectors are sufficiently broad to be illustrative of the other detector systems.

The chapter is completed with a discussion of some special circuits for current-type ionization chambers and other devices, the operation of which depends on the time average of the current. The emphasis is placed on instruments useful in nuclear-reactor controls.

Most of the electronic instruments which are discussed in this chapter are available commercially. In addition, Elmore et al. [1] have discussed the practical aspects of the construction of equipment of this type.

## PULSE SHAPING

### 10–1. *Nature of the Pulse Input Signal*

The interaction of the nuclear particle with the detector can be considered to release a charge at the input of the succeeding electronic circuit. This pulse of charge is considered to be the pulse input signal. The nature of the final signal after passage through the electronic circuit depends on both the characteristics of the pulse input signal and the electronic circuit.

A typical input circuit for use with a pulse ionization chamber or a proportional counter is shown in Fig. 10–1. Likewise, Fig. 10–2 is schematic of an input circuit for use with the photomultiplier tube of a scintillation detector. In both circuits the collector is at a high positive potential above ground, and a blocking capacitor is provided between it and the tube grid. This arrangement has the advantage that insulation from ground of the major portion of the apparatus (for example, the walls of the ionization chamber) is not required. In each case, the capacity $C_2$ represents the sum of the input capacity of the vacuum tube and all wiring and stray capacities in addition to any other capacity that may be placed at that position.

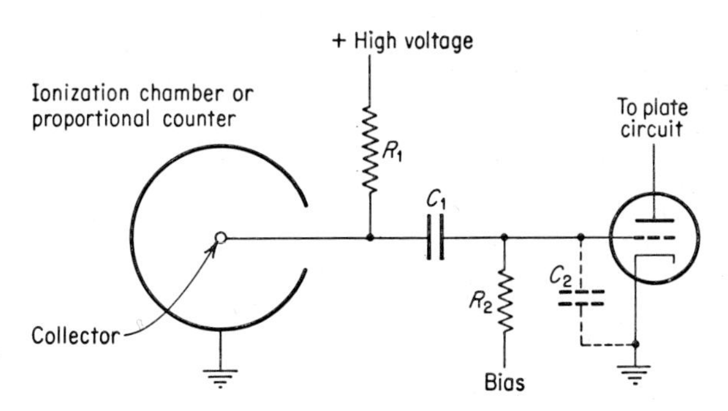


FIG. 10–1. Input circuit for use with proportional counters or pulse ionization chambers.

Figure 10–3 is a simplification representing both Figs. 10–1 and 10–2 in which d-c potentials are disregarded; $C_1$ has been replaced by a short circuit; and the photomultiplier tube, ionization chamber, or proportional counter has been replaced by a capacitor $C_3$ (the capacity of the collector to ground).

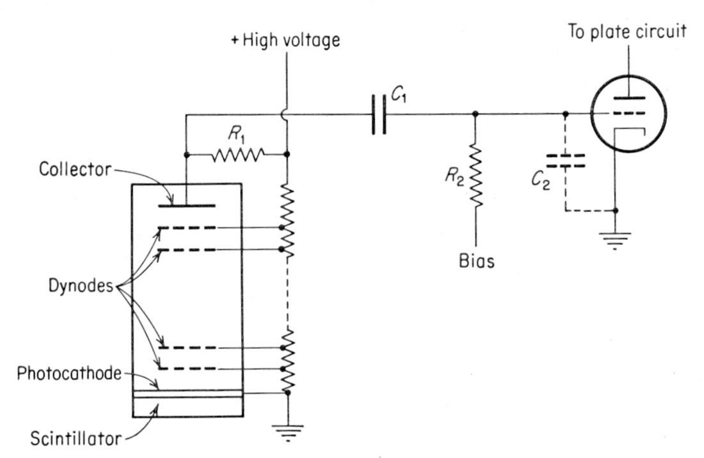


FIG. 10–2. Input circuit for use with scintillation detectors.

This representation is possible for analysis of the pulse input signal since (1) $C_1$ is much larger than $C_2$ and $C_3$ and (2) the d-c potentials merely represent constant voltages on which the input pulses are superimposed. As a further simplification, $R_1$ and $R_2$ can be replaced by the resistance $R_o$ which is equal to $R_1R_2/(R_1 + R_2)$, and the capacitances $C_2$ and $C_3$ can be

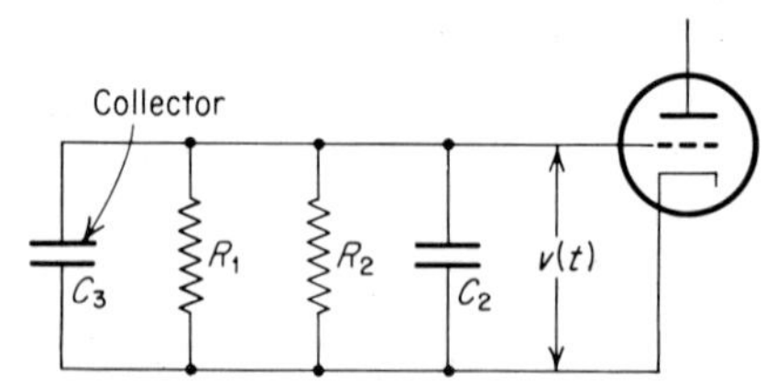


FIG. 10–3. Input circuit for use in the analysis of pulse input signals.

represented by $C_o$ which is equal to $C_2 + C_3$.

For purposes of studying the pulse input signal, consider the voltage produced at the input circuit when the time constant $R_oC_o$ is much larger than the time required for the collection of the charge. For this case the pulse shape is determined entirely by the time dependence of the charge collection. The instantaneous voltage $v(t)$ is related to the charge $q(t)$ which has been collected by the equation

$$v(t) = \frac{q(t)}{C_o} \tag{10–1}$$

The pulse shapes in parallel-plate chambers and coaxial cylindrical ionization chambers were discussed in Chap. 4. When the chamber gas was such that negative ions were not formed, the negative charge was carried by electrons. Such chambers were said to employ electron collection and were referred to as electron pulse chambers, or simply electron chambers.

Electron chambers are characterized by a rapid rise in voltage as the electrons are collected, followed by a slow rise as the positive ions are collected. As an example, Fig. 10–4*a* is the voltage produced by the formation of $N$ ion pairs midway between the plates of a parallel-plate ionization chamber. In parallel-plate chambers in which the ion pairs are produced at varying distances from the collector and in cylindrical chambers, the rise in voltage during electron collection is no longer linear; however, it still occurs in the order of a microsecond.

The pulse shape in proportional counters was discussed in Chaps. 5 and 6. The collector for these de-

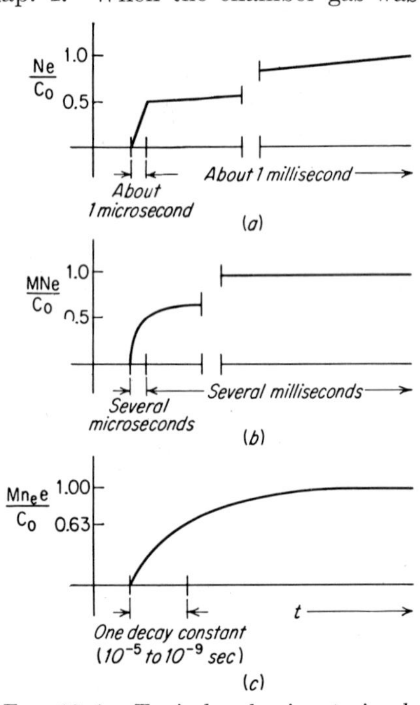


FIG. 10–4. Typical pulse input signals from various detectors (infinite time constant). (*a*) Parallel-plate ionization chamber; (*b*) proportional counter (spread in collection time neglected); (*c*) scintillation counter.

vices is the central wire. A charge of $M$ times the primary charge $Ne$ is produced in the immediate vicinity of the collector wire. The voltage as a function of time is given by the logarithmic function Eq. (5–3). This voltage rises quite quickly initially, reaching one-half of the ultimate value in about a microsecond. The complete collection of all the ions requires several milliseconds. Figure 10–4*b* represents a typical pulse input signal for a proportional counter.

**Example 10–1.** Compute the time required for the signal voltage to reach (*a*) one-half of its final value and (*b*) its final value after the passage of an ionizing particle through a proportional counter with inner and outer electrodes of $6 \times 10^{-4}$ and 1.75 cm, respectively, if the filling gas is 1 atm and the applied voltage is 500 volts. Assume that the time constant of the input circuit is large compared with the positive-ion collection time.

*Solution.* For part (*a*) the value of $v(t)$ in Eq. (5–3) is set equal to $-Ne/2C$; that is,

$$1 = \frac{\ln (2V\mu t/r_1^2 \ln r_2/r_1 + 1)}{\ln (r_2/r_1)} = \frac{\ln\left[\dfrac{(2)(500)(1{,}040)t}{(6 \times 10^{-4})^2 \ln (1.75/6 \times 10^{-4})} + 1\right]}{\ln (1.75/6 \times 10^{-4})}$$

$$= \frac{\ln (4.9 \times 10^8 t + 1)}{\ln (2.9 \times 10^3)}$$

where $\mu$ has been taken from Table 4–1. Solving the $t$ yields 5.9 $\mu$sec for the time required to reach one-half of the maximum.

By Eq. (5–4), the value $t_+$ for the collection time of positive ions is

$$t_+ = \frac{(r_2^2 - r_1^2)p}{2V\mu} \ln \frac{r_2}{r_1} = \frac{[(1.75)^2 - (6 \times 10^{-4})^2]760}{2(500)(1{,}040)} \ln(2.9 \times 10^3)$$

$$= 1.7 \times 10^{-3} \text{ sec}$$

When the primary ionization in a proportional counter is distributed perpendicular to the collector, the primary electrons which initiate the secondary ionization arrive at the center wire at times varying over a couple of microseconds. This has the effect of modifying the shape of the initial fast rise of the pulse, slowing it down somewhat and making the rise more nearly linear.

In a scintillation detector the rise of the voltage input pulse (see Fig. 10–4*c*) is controlled by the decay time of the scintillator and by the variation of the electron transit time through the photomultiplier tube. The number of photons emitted after passage of the ionizing radiation follows the exponential growth law of Eq. (7–3), with decay constants for various scintillators ranging from a few millimicroseconds to several microseconds (see Table 7–1). The contribution of the spread in electron transit time to the finite pulse-rise time has been treated by Lewis and Wells [2]. The transit time has been found to be a Gaussian function of time with a standard deviation of about $10^{-9}$ sec. When the decay constant is $10^{-8}$ sec or greater, the effect of the spread in transit time on the pulse shape is insignificant.

Each of the pulse input signals described above is characterized by an initial fast rise. In the pulsed electronic circuitry discussed in this chapter.

only the portion of the input pulses which occur in the first few microseconds are important to the final signal. Thus, in the pulsed ionization chamber, only the rapid rise during electron collection needs to be considered. For all applications except those which require the reproduction of the very fast rise of the pulses, the signal for the pulse ionization chamber can be considered as the sudden appearance of a charge at the input; the magnitude of the charge is the total induced on the collector at the end of the electron collection. Such a signal is referred to as a step input. Likewise, in scintillation detectors which employ scintillators with decay times less than 1 μsec, the pulse input signal for many applications can be taken as a step input of a charge $Mn_e e$, the total charge released by the scintillation. A similar representation can be made for a proportional counter. However, because of the longer rise time and the absence of a point in the first few microseconds at which the positive-ion collection is essentially complete, the concept is less useful.

A further characteristic of the pulse input signals is their random distribution in time. If $\bar{n}$ represents the average number of pulses per unit time, the probability of the occurrence of $k$ pulses in a time $\delta t$ is obtained from Eq. (3–17) as

$$W(k) = \frac{(\bar{n}\delta t)^k \, e^{-\bar{n}\delta t}}{k!} \tag{10–2}$$

**Example 10–2.** Compute the probability of obtaining one, two, and three counts in the time interval equal to the average time between pulses.

*Solution.* The average number of pulses in time $1/\bar{n}$ is $\bar{n}/\bar{n} = 1$. The probability of obtaining one pulse is obtained by Eq. (10–2) as

$$W(1) = \frac{(1)^1 \, e^{-1}}{1!} = \frac{1}{e} = 0.368$$

Likewise, $W(2) = 0.164$ and $W(3) = 0.061$.

If the time interval $\delta t$ is considered to begin immediately after the start of any pulse, then

$$W(1) = \bar{n}\delta t \, e^{-\bar{n}\delta t} \tag{10–3}$$

can be considered as the probability of a second pulse occurring within this interval. This expression also represents the fraction of the time that a pulse follows a previous pulse within the time $\delta t$. When this fraction is much less than 1, it can be approximated by $\bar{n}\delta t$. Thus if $\bar{n}$ is 2,000 pulses/sec, 2 per cent of the pulses are separated by less than 10 μsec.

## 10–2. *Requirements for Pulse Shaping*

The applications of pulse-type detectors can be divided into three broad groups: (1) counting measurements, (2) energy measurements, and (3) time-interval measurements or time discrimination between related pulses.

Each of these measurements requires pulse shaping within the electronic circuitry.

The shape of a pulse can be designated in terms of four characteristics, namely, the rise time, delay time, decay time, and pulse duration. These same characteristics are used to describe pulse amplifiers. In this case the characteristics of the amplifier are designated as the characteristics of the output pulse which is produced when a step-input pulse signal is applied to the amplifier. The delay time $T_D$ may be defined as the time required for the pulse to rise to one-half of its maximum value. The rise time $T_R$ is then defined as the reciprocal of the slope at this one-half maximum point. An alternative definition of the rise time, convenient for laboratory use, is the time required for the pulse to rise from 0.1 to 0.9, the maximum value. The latter form of this definition of $T_R$ is illustrated in Fig. 10–5, along with $T_D$.

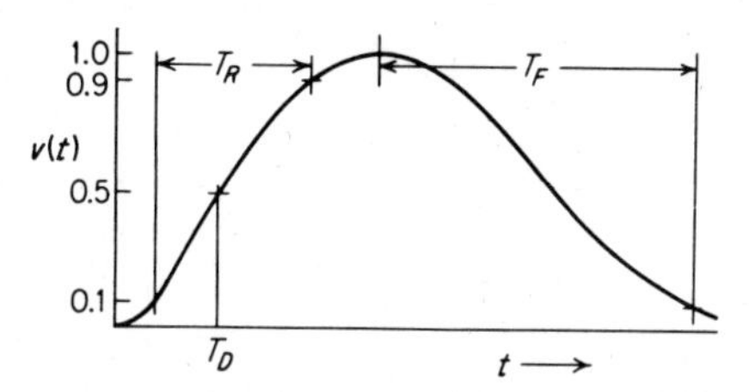


FIG. 10–5. Illustration of the concepts of the pulse rise time $T_R$, pulse delay time $T_D$, and pulse decay time $T_F$.

The decay time, or fall time $T_F$, is sometimes defined arbitrarily as the time required for the pulse to drop from the maximum to 0.1 of the maximum value. This is illustrated in Fig. 10–5 also. Often the pulse decay is determined by a single short-time constant differentiating network. In this case the time constant is used to designate the decay, and it is referred to as the clipping time of the amplifier which produced the decay.

The concept of pulse duration has an obvious meaning for rectangular-shape pulses only. Elmore [3] has given a definition of pulse duration $\tau$ applicable to shapes such as that in Fig. 10–5; it is

$$\tau^2 = \frac{2\pi \int_0^\infty (t - t_0)^2 v(t)\, dt}{\int_0^\infty v(t)\, dt} \tag{10–4}$$

where $t_0 = \int_0^\infty t v(t)\, dt \Big/ \int_0^\infty v(t)\, dt$, the centroid of the pulse. This is equivalent to defining the pulse duration as $\sqrt{2\pi}$ times the standard deviation of $v(t)$.

The basic requirements for counting apparatus are (1) the ability to count accurately, often up to high counting rates, and (2) the ability to separate the desired pulses, which are called the signal, from the unwanted pulses. These unwanted pulses may be either those originating in the detector because of other radiation types or those due to noise in the electronic circuitry.

The measuring apparatus for counting can be considered as consisting of three units for the purpose of discussing the pulse shaping.* These units are the amplifier, the discriminator, and the scaler. In the amplifier the pulses are amplified and shaped. The function of the discriminator is to pass only the desired pulses. Finally, the scaler counts the pulses passed by the discriminator.

The ability of a counter to count accurately at high rates can be referred to as its resolving power. The reciprocal of the resolving power, known as the resolving time, is the minimum time which can elapse between the start of two pulses if they are to be counted as two pulses. The fraction of the counts lost is given by Eq. (10–3). The resolving time is substituted for $\delta t$.

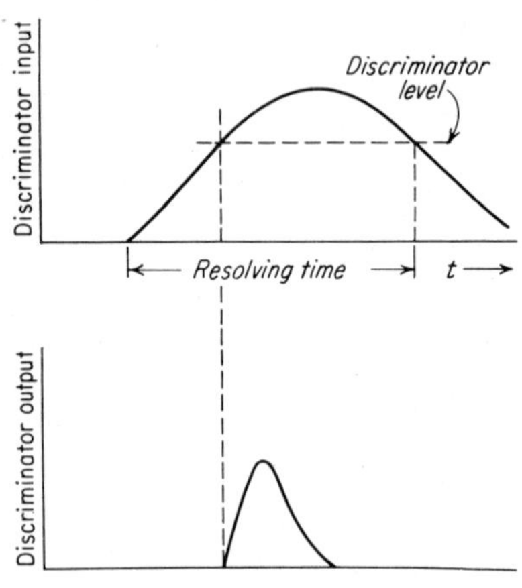


Fig. 10–6. Resolving time of a counting system through the discriminator.

The resolving time of the system is the result of the composite characteristics of all the elements in it. If the pertinent characteristics of the detector and associated electronic equipment are known, the resolving time of the system can be calculated [4], at least in certain ideal cases. Methods of measuring resolving time were discussed in Chap. 5. Equation (5–8) is the working equation for the two-source method. To see the effect of pulse shape, consider the resolving time of the system up through the discriminator. This resolving time will be that of the entire system, provided that the resolving time of the scaler unit itself is no greater. The resolving time up through the discriminator is illustrated in Fig. 10–6. From this figure it is seen that decreases in the rise time, decay time, and pulse duration all improve the resolving power. The resolving time is seen also to be a function of the pulse height for a given discriminator setting, increasing as the pulse height increases.

The effect of pulse shape on the ability of a counting system to discriminate between the desired signal and the unwanted signal comes about through the signal-noise ratio and through the pile-up of unwanted pulses. The signal-noise ratio is discussed in Sec. 10–4. The pile-up of pulses comes about when more than one pulse occurs during a time interval of the order of the pulse duration. Even though the ratio of the amplitude of the wanted to unwanted pulses is sufficiently large to allow easy discrimination

* This division into units is different from the one usually employed in the physical arrangement.

when the pulses occur singly, pile-up results in unwanted counts when the rate of occurrence of the unwanted pulses becomes sufficiently high.

Another effect of pile-up comes from the superposition of the smaller unwanted pulses on either the falling or the rising edge of the desired pulse. The small pulse properly placed will cause the single wanted pulse to be counted twice. These situations arise, for example, in counting alpha particles in the presence of a large background of gamma rays.

Gillespie [5] has discussed pile-up in a semiquantitative fashion. Qualitatively, it is clear that the effect is minimized by the reduction of the rise time, fall time, and the duration of the pulses. The shorter the time interval

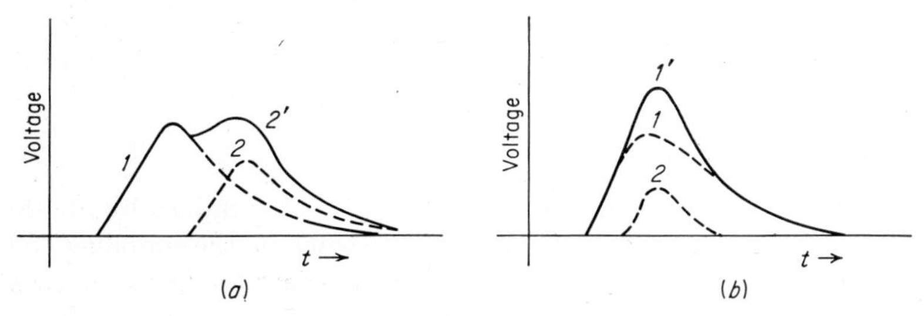


FIG. 10–7. Errors in pulse height because of pulse superposition. (*a*) Pulses 1 and 2 separated but with pulse 2 superimposed on the trailing edge of pulse 1; (*b*) pulses 1 and 2 not separated.

involved, the smaller the probability that another one or more pulses will occur to produce pile-up.

The electronic apparatus for energy measurements can be considered to consist of an amplifier and a pulse-height analyzer. The function of the amplifier is to amplify and shape the pulse input signals so that a pulse-height-distribution curve is the true-energy-distribution curve (see Sec. 2–8.) Thus the primary requirement is that the height of the pulses be proportional to the particle energy. The pile-up of pulses is important in energy measurements also but for a reason different from that in counting experiments. Two illustrations are given in Fig. 10–7. In Fig. 10–7*a* pulse 2 follows too soon after pulse 1 so that, instead of the correct height as indicated by the dotted curve 2, the incorrect height as given by the solid curve 2′ is measured. Some discriminator circuits automatically discard all pulses that are preceded by another pulse within a fixed time interval. In Fig. 10–7*b* the two pulses are not separated, and a single pulse height is measured which is the sum of those of pulses 1 and 2.

The resolving time for an amplifier for energy-distribution measurements can be defined as the minimum time which can elapse between the start of two pulses if their heights are to be proportional to the particle energy within a specified limit.

**Example 10–3.** Calculate the resolving time of an amplifier for energy-distribution measurements if the clipping time of the amplifier is 10 μsec and the error in pulse height due to superposition on the falling edge of a pulse is to be less than 1 per cent of the maximum pulse height.

*Solution.* If the rise time is neglected, the resolving time is the time required for the pulse to decay to $\frac{1}{100}$ of the maximum value. This time $t$ is given by $e^{-t/10} = 0.01$, or $t = 4.6 \times 10 = 46$ μsec.

From this example it is clear that the decay time of the pulses is an important consideration in energy measurements.

For measurements involving time of occurrence of related pulses, the pulse rise time and pulse delay time become of primary importance. For highest accuracy in these measurements, the pulse rise time should be as short as possible, while the pulse delay time should be either negligible or not variable.

## 10–3. *Methods of Pulse Shaping*

The shape of the output pulse of an amplifier is determined by the shape of the pulse input signal and the characteristics of the amplifier. The schematic diagram shown in Fig. 10–8 is an idealized amplifier representa-

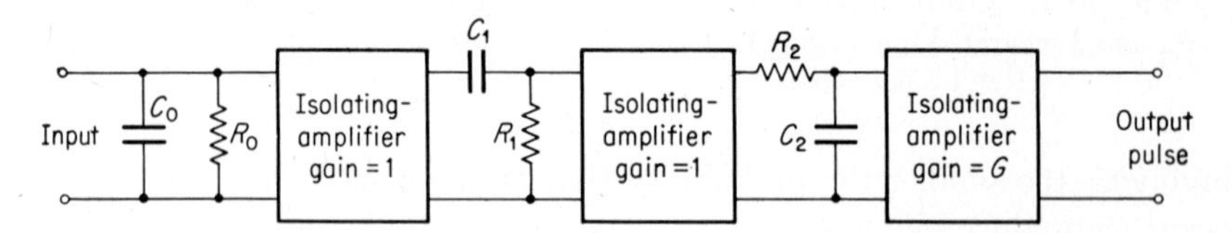


Fig. 10–8. Equivalent circuit of a pulse input circuit and pulse amplifier.

tion that is useful for discussing the pulse shaping produced. A practical amplifier in which the upper and lower cutoff frequencies are each determined by simple $RC$ circuits can be represented by this equivalent circuit. The circuit elements $R_o$ and $C_o$ represent the typical input circuit for a detector, as described in Sec. 10–1. The idealized isolating amplifiers have the characteristics of infinite input impedance, zero output impedance, and an infinite-width frequency passband with constant gain throughout; therefore the isolating amplifier has no effect on the pulse shape. The circuit consisting of $R_1$ and $C_1$, known as the differentiation network, determines the lower frequency cutoff and the clipping time of the amplifier. The time constant $R_1C_1$, designated as $\tau_1$, is known as the differentiation time constant. The circuit $R_2C_2$, an integration network with a time constant $\tau_2$ equal to $R_2C_2$, determines the upper frequency cutoff of the amplifier and affects the rise and delay times of the pulses. The lower half-power frequency, defined as the frequency at which the gain for sinusoidal signals falls to 0.707 of the mid-frequency gain, is related to the differentiation time constant $\tau_1$ by

$$f_1 = \frac{1}{2\pi\tau_1} = \frac{1}{2\pi R_1 C_1} \tag{10-5}$$

while the upper half-power frequency is given by

$$f_2 = \frac{1}{2\pi\tau_2} = \frac{1}{2\pi R_2 C_2} \tag{10-6}$$

As an example, consider the step-input signal of $V_o$. This would correspond to the pulse input signal of a charge $C_oV_o$ from a detector with a negligibly small collection time. Under these conditions, the pulse output signal is

$$\text{Output} = \frac{GV_o\tau_1}{\tau_1 - \tau_2}(e^{-t/\tau_1} - e^{-t/\tau_2}) \tag{10-7}$$

provided that the input-circuit time constant $R_oC_o$ is much greater than $\tau_1$. As a second example, consider a linear input signal, as during the electron collection in a parallel-plate ionization chamber. The output voltage is obtained as

$$\text{Output} = \frac{GV_o\tau_1}{T}(1 - e^{-t/\tau_2}) - \frac{GV_o\tau_1^2}{T(\tau_1 - \tau_2)}(e^{-t/\tau_1} - e^{-t/\tau_2}) \qquad \text{for } 0 < t < T$$

$$\text{Output} = \frac{GV_o\tau_1^2}{T(\tau_1 - \tau_2)}(e^{T/\tau_1} - 1)e^{-t/\tau_1} - \frac{GV_o\tau_1\tau_2}{T(\tau_1 - \tau_2)}(e^{T/\tau_2} - 1)e^{-t/\tau_2}$$

$$\text{for } \tau < t \tag{10-8}$$

where $T$ is the time required for the input signal to rise from zero to the maximum value $V_o$. These solutions are obtained by applying the pulse input signal to the differentiation network and then using its output signal as the input for the integration network.

These output pulses are illustrated in Fig. 10–9 for an amplifier in which $\tau_1$ equals $5\tau_2$. The cases for the time $T$ of zero, $\tau_2$, and $5\tau_2$ are included. These illustrations show that the time of rise of the pulse input signal affects the output pulse shape but little as long as the input-pulse rise time $T$ is less than the integration time constant $\tau_2$. Further, when $T$ is much greater than $\tau_2$, the rise time of the output-pulse signal is determined by the pulse input signals and not by the amplifier characteristics.

The effect of the circuit time constants on the maximum value of the output pulse is shown in Fig. 10–10. The ratio of the maximum value reached by the pulse $V_m$ to the value $GV_o$ which would be obtained with an infinite-band-width amplifier is given as a function of the ratio $\tau_1/\tau_2$. Again, the total rise time $T$ of a linear input pulse is the parameter.

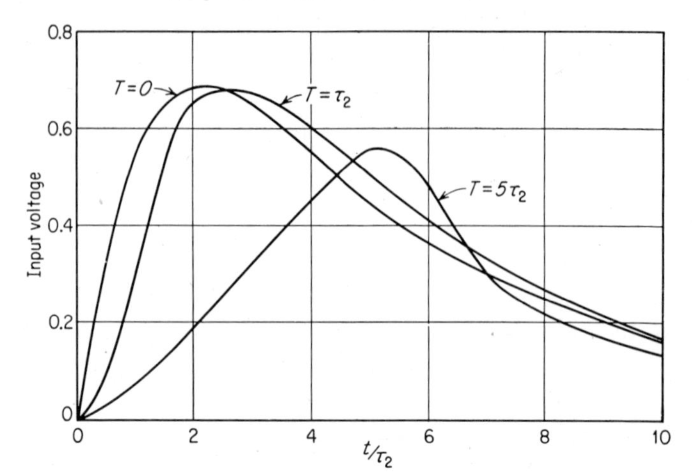


FIG. 10–9. Pulse output signals for an amplifier with a differentiation time constant $\tau_1$ equal to $5\tau_2$, where $\tau_2$ is the integration time constant. The parameter $T$ is the total rise time for a pulse input signal with a linear rise; input time constant much greater than $\tau_1$.

**Example 10–4.** Find the variation in the maximum height of an output pulse when the total rise time for a linear input pulse varies from 0.5 to 2.5 $\mu$sec in an amplifier with a clipping time of 10 $\mu$sec and an integration time constant of 0.5 $\mu$sec. Repeat for an integration time constant of 1.0 $\mu$sec.

*Solution.* By use of Fig. 10–10, the pulse sizes are in the ratio of 0.85 to 0.82 for $\tau_2 = 0.5$ $\mu$sec and 0.77 to 0.76 for $\tau_2 = 1$ $\mu$sec.

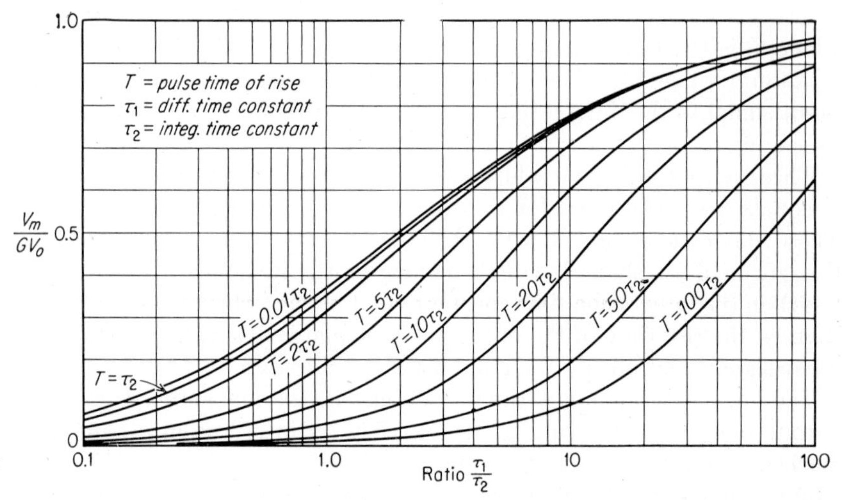


FIG. 10–10. Pulse amplitude as a function of chamber collection time and amplifier time constants. (*From A. B. Gillespie, "Signal, Noise and Resolution in Nuclear Counter Amplifiers," chap. 2, McGraw-Hill Book Company, Inc., New York, 1953.*)

The characteristics of a pulse amplifier are designated as those of the amplifier output pulse that results from a step input. For the idealized amplifier discussed above, the following characteristics can be computed [2, 3]:

$$
\begin{aligned}
\text{Rise time} &= \sqrt{2\pi} R_2 C_2 \\
\text{Delay time} &= R_2 C_2 \\
\text{Clipping time} &= R_1 C_1 \\
\text{Pulse duration} &= \sqrt{2\pi} R_2 C_2 \, (1 + \lambda^2)^{1/2} \\
\text{Maximum amplitude of pulse} &= V_o \lambda^{1/(1-\lambda)}
\end{aligned}
\qquad (10\text{–}9)
$$

where $\lambda = R_1C_1/R_2C_2$ and $V_o = Q_o/C_o$.

An alternative method of pulse shaping is by the use of delay lines [3]. This system is illustrated in Fig. 10–11 in an idealized form. The delay line has a characteristic impedance $Z_o$ and a length such that the time

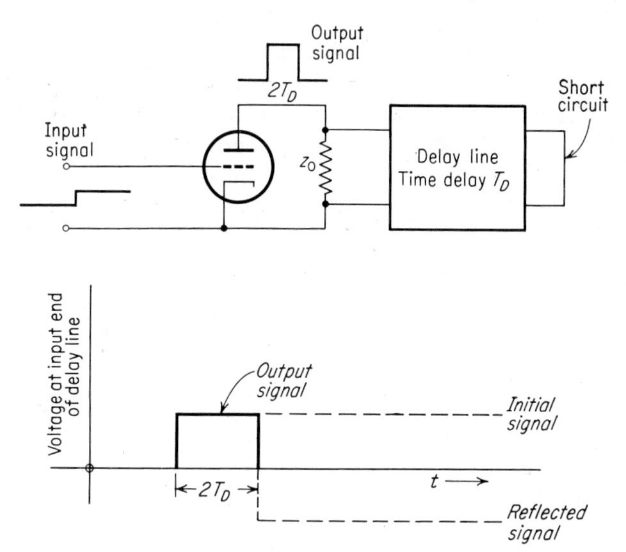


FIG. 10–11. Delay-line pulse shaping, idealized for a step-input signal and no attenuation in the line.

required for the signal to travel from the input to the termination is $T_D$. This delay line is used as the plate load of the vacuum tube. Its input is terminated with its characteristic impedance $Z_o$ while the other end of the line is short-circuited. When the step-input signal is applied to the grid of the tube, a step voltage signal travels down the delay line. At the short-circuited end it is reflected with an accompanying phase reversal. When the reflected signal arrives at the input end at time $2T_D$ after its start, it combines with the input signal to cancel the remaining portion of it, thus producing a rectangular-shape pulse of duration $2T_D$.

Delay-line pulse shaping results in a pulse with a shorter decay time than possible with differentiation of the same input pulse. It has the further advantage of a constant-width base on the pulse; for input pulses of very fast rise time, the pulses also have constant duration. In addition, the signal-noise ratio is slightly better than that for differentiation, provided that the input-pulse rise time is smaller than the amplifier rise time (see Sec. 10–4). The principal disadvantage is the lack of simplicity and ease in varying pulse shapes as compared with the differentiation method.

## LINEAR AMPLIFIERS

### 10–4. *Amplifier Noise*

Noise in an amplifier for pulse work is any signal not arising from the nuclear radiation. Part of this signal may arise from sources which can be eliminated by proper design and care in the use of the amplifier, while the remaining part of it is inherent in the principles of operation of amplifiers and therefore sets a lower limit on the level to which the noise can be reduced. The first type of sources includes extraneous transients, hum, microphonics, and noise from defective components. The latter type of sources includes resistor noise, grid-current noise, shot-effect noise, and flicker noise. In detectors employing photomultiplier tubes, additional unwanted signals arise from the phototubes. This effect was discussed in Sec. 7–24.

Flicker noise is a fluctuation in the anode current, thought to be caused by the random appearance of impurity centers on the cathode surfaces. The frequency spectrum of flicker noise is so low that its contribution is insignificant in the frequency band of interest here and will not be discussed further.

Thermal noise arises because the free electrons within a conductor are in a constant state of random motion caused by thermal agitation. These motions correspond to small fluctuations of current within the conductor and give rise to small fluctuations of voltage across the ends of the conductor, the magnitude of the fluctuation depending on the resistance of the conductor.

The shot-effect noise arises from the fact that the electron emission from a cathode is in discrete units, or electrons, and that the emission of the individual electrons is random in nature. Thus the steady plate current of a tube has superimposed upon it this random noise known as shot-effect noise.

The grid-current noise arises from statistical fluctuations in the amount of grid current, mostly positive-ion current, which flows. This fluctuation is also largely due to statistical variation in the electron emission.

These noise sources have been considered in detail by many authors, such as Gillespie [5]. Elmore [3] has presented the results in a particularly useful form for the analysis of amplifiers for use with pulse-type detectors. He expresses the results in terms of $Q_n^2$, the mean-square equivalent-noise charge at the input of an amplifier, the band width of which is determined by the two time constants $\tau_1$ and $\tau_2$. From this the root-mean-square noise output voltage is $GQ_n/C_o$, where $G$ is the gain which the amplifier would have if its band width were infinite and $C_o$ is the input capacity. Elmore's results are

$$Q_n^2 = kT \frac{\tau_1^2}{\tau_1 + \tau_2}\left(\frac{1}{R_o} + \frac{1}{R_g} + \frac{R_s C_o^2}{\tau_1 \tau_2}\right) \tag{10–10}$$

where $R_g = 4kT/2eI_g$
$R_s = \eta 2eI_p/4kTg_m^2$
$k$ = Boltzmann's constant
$T$ = absolute temperature
$I_g$ = grid current
$I_p$ = plate current
$g_m$ = transconductance of input tube
$\eta$ = factor equal to or less than 1 which takes into account suppression of shot effect by space charge

For a typical triode,

$$R_s \simeq \frac{3}{g_m} \tag{10–11}$$

while for a pentode

$$R_s \simeq \frac{I_p}{I_p + I_s}\left(\frac{2.5}{g_m} + \frac{20I_s}{g_{ms}}\right)$$

where $I_s$ and $g_{ms}$ are the current and transconductance of the screen. The grid current $I_g$ is taken as the sum of the magnitudes of the positive-ion and electron currents.

**Example 10–5.** Compute the root-mean-square equivalent noise at the input of an amplifier with the following characteristics: integration time constant, 1 $\mu$sec; clipping time, 10 $\mu$sec; total input capacity, 30 $\mu\mu$f; total input resistance, $10^8$ ohms; input tube, type 6AK5. Assume that the temperature is 27°C and that the parameters of the 6AK5 are $g_m$ and $g_{ms}$, equal to 4,000 and 1,000 $\mu$mhos, respectively, while $I_g$, $I_p$, and $I_s$ are $10^{-8}$, $5 \times 10^{-3}$, and $2 \times 10^{-3}$ amp, respectively.

*Solution.* The rms noise voltage $V_n$ is

$$V_n = \frac{Q_n}{C_o}$$

where $Q_n$ is to be calculated from Eq. (10–10) and $C_o$ is 30 $\mu\mu$f. The calculation is carried out in the mks system of units, in which $k = 1.37 \times 10^{-23}$ joule per degree Centigrade.

$$R_g = \frac{4kT}{2eI_g} = \frac{(2)(1.37 \times 10^{-23})(300)}{(1.60 \times 10^{-19})(10^{-8})} = 5.13 \times 10^6 \text{ ohms}$$

$$R_s = \frac{I_p}{I_p + I_s}\left(\frac{2.5}{g_m} + \frac{20I_s}{g_{ms}}\right) = \frac{0.005}{0.005 + 0.002}\left[\frac{2.5}{0.004} + \frac{(20)(0.002)}{0.001}\right] = 475 \text{ ohms}$$

$$Q_n^2 = 4.1 \times 10^{-21} \frac{10^2 \times 10^{-6}}{10 + 1}\left[\frac{1}{10^8} + \frac{1}{5.13 \times 10^6} + \frac{(475)(30 \times 10^{-12})^2}{10^{-6} \times 10 \times 10^{-6}}\right]$$

$$= 3.7 \times 10^{-34}\,(1 + 0.02 + 4.3) = 19.6 \times 10^{-34} \text{ coulomb}^2$$

Therefore

$$V_n = \frac{Q_n}{C_o} = \frac{4.4 \times 10^{-17}}{30 \times 10^{-12}} = 1.5\mu\text{v}$$

It is of interest to notice the relative contribution of the different types of noise. These are thermal, grid-current, and shot-effect noise in the order of appearance in Eq. (10–10).

The noise is seen to depend on the amplifier time constants $\tau_1$ and $\tau_2$ by Eq. (10–10), while the dependence of the signal amplitudes on $\tau_1$ and $\tau_2$ for a specific input signal $Q_o$ is given by Eqs. (10–9). The conditions for optimum signal-noise ratio depend on the pulse-shape requirements, as discussed by Elmore [3]. It develops that the optimum signal-noise ratio occurs when the amplifier rise time and the clipping time are about equal. Consequently, it is desirable to adjust these time constants simultaneously when changes in pulse duration are made. This adjustment is not particularly critical, however, since a ratio of $\tau_1/\tau_2$ as high as 5 only reduces the signal-noise ratio by 2 from the optimum value at $\tau_1/\tau_2$ equal to 1.

Gillespie [5] has discussed the signal-noise ratio for amplifiers employing delay-line pulse shaping. It is concluded that the signal-noise ratio is best when the delay time $T_D$ is one-half the amplifier rise time. Further, this ratio is better than that obtained when differentiated pulse shaping is employed, provided that the input-pulse rise time is considerably less than the amplifier rise time.

### 10–5. *Pulse-amplifier Requirements*

The requirements for the pulse amplifier with regard to pulse shaping were discussed in Sec. 10–2. Other important requirements include gain, polarity, stability, linearity, and physical arrangement.

The gain requirements, of course, depend on the available input signals and the desired output voltages. Typical values of rms noise voltages are around 3 $\mu$v (see Example 10–5). The occurrence of noise peaks of three times the rms value, or about 10 $\mu$v, would be rare. Therefore 10 $\mu$v is a typical lower limit for the height of the useful input pulses. For operating discriminators, as in counting applications, about 10 volts are required, giving a maximum gain requirement of $10^6$. For accurate pulse-height-analysis work, output voltages up to a maximum value of 100 volts are required. However, since one would ordinarily not require that the 10-$\mu$volt noise peak be amplified to more than one-tenth of the maximum, a maximum gain of $10^6$ would suffice here also. The amplifier must, of course, be provided with a gain control if it is to be versatile.

Because of the variety of circuit types which the amplifier is required to drive, it is desirable to have its output impedance as low as possible. Since this is not compatible with the high-voltage requirements, it is the practice to provide two output circuits, one with low output impedance and voltages and one with high output impedance and voltages. A typical arrangement provides 9 volts at 90 ohms and 100 volts at 1,000 ohms.

The pulse input signal may be either positive or negative, although the negative signals as produced by the circuits in Figs. 10–1 and 10–2 are the most common. The output pulse is usually positive so that a low-impedance cathode-follower output stage can be used. The operation of the cathode-follower circuit is discussed in Sec. 10–6.

Stability of the amplifier gain is often quite important. In energy measurements the proportionality between pulse height and particle energy must remain constant, while in counting measurements a change in gain may result in a shift in the fraction of the pulses passing the discriminator. A change of a small fraction of per cent in the output voltage for a 1 per cent change in line voltage is not an uncommon requirement. The primary methods employed for stabilization of the gain are the use of negative feedback in the amplifier section and the provision for good regulation in the power-supply section.

Linearity between pulse input signal and output signal of 0.5 per cent or better is often necessary. This is obtained by the choice of the operating points for the vacuum tubes within their linear ranges and by the use of negative feedback.

The pulse amplifier is usually divided into two parts, the preamplifier and the main amplifier. The use of the preamplifier makes it possible to provide the shortest possible leads to the detector and thereby to minimize the input capacity. The gain of the preamplifier depends on the designer, with common values varying from less than 1 to 100. Its output stage is always a cathode follower which can drive the long cable required to couple it to the main amplifier.

The gain control of a pulse amplifier is located several stages beyond the input. Often the gain control is inserted between the main amplifier and the preamplifier, particularly if the latter has a gain of around 100. The location of the gain control is determined by balancing two effects. If the gain control is placed too early in the amplifier, the signal-noise ratio will be reduced because of the introduction of noise beyond the gain control which is not reduced by the gain control proportionately to the signal. The placing of the gain control at too high a level will result in an overload of the stages immediately preceding the gain control when the latter is set for low gain.

### 10–6. *Pulse-amplifier Circuits*

The usual arrangement for linear pulse amplifiers employs resistance-capacitance coupled amplifiers with negative feedback. The decay time of the pulse is controlled by a single differentiation. It can be shown [6] that a multistage $R$-$C$ coupled amplifier produces an oscillating output for a step-input signal but that the oscillatory portion can be made vanishingly small. To accomplish this, the pulse decay is determined by a single coupling stage with time constant $\tau_1$; the time constants of all the remaining coupling networks should be at least $100\tau_1$. If desired, the differentiation network can be replaced by the delay line, as discussed in Sec. 10–3.

The position of the pulse-shaping circuit needs special consideration. When low noise level is important, the short time constant cannot be placed in the early stages, since the low resistance associated with it would make the thermal noise intolerable. This is seen from the dependence of $Q_n$ on $R_o$ in Eq. (10–10). On the other hand, the pulse shaping cannot be left to the high-level stages because of the shift in the operating points of the tubes. This shift occurs because of the pile-up of the pulses with the long decay constants. The usual position of the pulse-shaping network is after a gain of about 100, often between the preamplifier and the main amplifier. A further advantage of placing the pulse-shaping network at the intermediate level rather than at a low level is that it serves to reject the hum and other low-frequency noise generated at the low-gain levels of the amplifier.

The rise time of the resistance-capacitance coupled unfed-back amplifiers is determined by the plate circuits of the individual stages. For a given total gain, the minimum rise time is obtained when all stages have equal rise times [6]. Under these conditions, the rise time for an amplifier with $n$ stages is

$$T_R = \sqrt{2\pi n} R_2 C_2 \qquad (10\text{–}12)$$

where $R_2$ and $C_2$ are the plate resistance and distributed capacitance, respectively. An approximate expression relating the rise time of a multistage amplifier to the upper half-power frequency is [6]

$$T_R f_2 \simeq \tfrac{1}{3} \qquad (10\text{–}13)$$

The gain per stage is $g_m R_2$, where $g_m$ is the tube transconductance; therefore the total gain $G$ of an $n$-stage unfed-back amplifier is

$$G = (g_m R_2)^n \qquad (10\text{–}14)$$

The distributed capacitance $C_2$ cannot be reduced below about 10 $\mu\mu$f. From Eqs. (10–12) and (10–14) it is clear that, to obtain an amplifier with a given gain and rise time containing the minimum number of stages, tubes with high transconductance and low output and input capacitances must be used.

**Example 10–6.** Compute the rise time and the plate load resistance for an unfed-back, uncompensated resistance-capacitance coupled amplifier having the following characteristics: total gain, $10^6$; six identical stages; vacuum-tube transconductance, 0.009 mho; shunt capacity, 20 $\mu\mu$f.

*Solution.* By Eq. (10–14), the plate load resistance $R_2$ is obtained by

$$\log R_2 = \frac{\log G}{n} - \log g_m = 1 - \log 0.009 = 3.046$$

or

$$R_2 = 1{,}100 \text{ ohms}$$

The rise time is calculated by Eq. (10–12) as

$$T_R = \sqrt{2\pi n}\, R_2C_2 = \sqrt{2\pi 6}\; 1{,}100 \times 20 \times 10^{-12} = 0.13\ \mu\text{sec}$$

When a shorter rise time (say 0.1 $\mu$sec or less) is required, shunt compensation of the load resistance [6], a common practice in conventional video amplifiers, may be employed. When extremely short rise times are re-

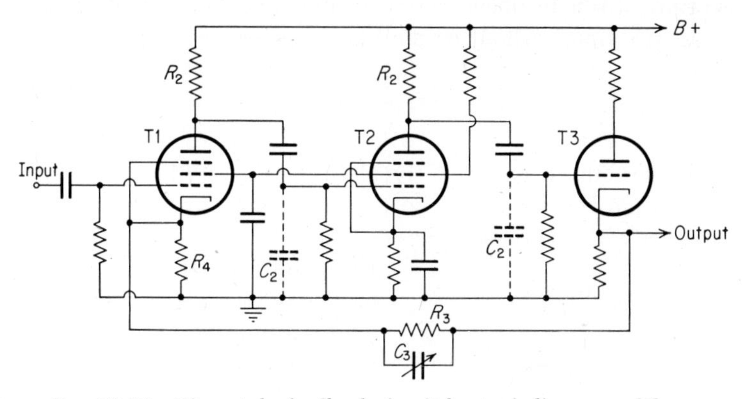


FIG. 10–12. Three-tube feedback circuit for use in linear amplifiers.

quired, such as in the reproduction of the leading edge of the pulses from organic scintillators, distributed amplification may be used [7]. Rise times of less than 2 m$\mu$sec have been reported.

By using feedback, large gains over the unfed-back amplifier performance can be made. By far the most popular type of circuit for this application is the three-tube feedback circuit shown in Fig. 10–12. This circuit consists of two resistance-capacitance coupled amplifier stages with tubes $T1$ and $T2$ followed by the cathode follower $T3$. A fraction of the output $\beta$ given by

$$\beta = \frac{R_4}{R_3 + R_4} \tag{10–15}$$

is fed back to the cathode-grid circuit of the input. The gain $G'$ of the fed-back circuit is

$$G' = \frac{G}{1 + \beta G} \tag{10–16}$$

where $G$ is the gain of the unfed-back circuit. The improvement in stability to line voltage fluctuation or change in tube characteristics can be expressed by the ratio

$$S = \frac{dG/G}{dG'/G'} = 1 + \beta G \tag{10–17}$$

Also, by Eq. (10–17) the departure in linearity is seen to be reduced by the same factor $1 + \beta G$.

For the feedback to be effective, the factor $\beta G$ must be much greater than 1. Under this condition the gain becomes

$$G' = \frac{R_3 + R_4}{R_4} \tag{10–18}$$

The rise time of this feedback circuit can be adjusted by the capacitor $C_3$. The fastest rise time without oscillatory overshoot is given by

$$T_R = \frac{\sqrt{4\pi}\, R_2 C_2}{\sqrt{1 + \beta G}} \tag{10–19}$$

where $C_2$ is the shunt capacity in the plate circuits of $T1$ and $T2$. This rise time is seen from Eq. (10–12) to be smaller than that of a two-stage unfed-back amplifier with the same values of $R_2$ and $C_2$ by the factor $(1 + \beta G)^{-1/2}$. However, when the gain of the unfed-back amplifier is reduced to that of the fed-back amplifier through the reduction of the plate resistance from $R_2$ to $R_2'$, the rise time decreases. It can be shown [6] that the rise time is the same in a three-tube feedback circuit and a two-tube unfed-back circuit when the two circuits are adjusted to have the same gain.

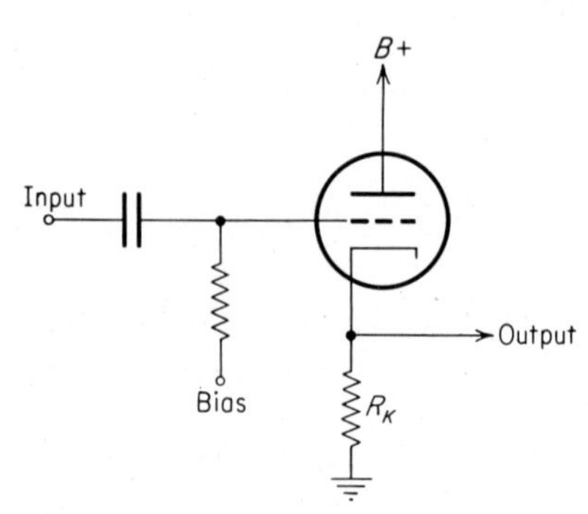

FIG. 10–13. The basic cathode-follower circuit.

The feedback resistors can be adjusted to be relatively low. Often $R_4$ can be chosen to give the correct bias for $T1$. For example, if $T1$ is a 6AC7, $R_4$ may be 100 ohms. If the gain of the three-tube circuit is to be 100, then $R_3 = 10{,}000$ ohms. For proper adjustment of the rise time, $C_3$ would be a few micromicrofarads.

The cathode-follower circuit is widely used in pulse amplifiers for nuclear detectors. The chief application is as an impedance-matching device where pulses with fast rise time must be transferred through a coaxial cable from one part of the circuit to the other. A second application is the production of high input impedances and the low input capacities required for small pulse rise time.

Figure 10–13 is the basic circuit for the cathode follower. The gain for the circuit is

$$G = \frac{g_m}{1/R_K + g_m + 1/r_p} \simeq 1 \tag{10–20}$$

where $r_p$ is the dynamic plate resistance of the tube. However, in all practical cases, $1/r_p$ is much less than $g_m$, and $1/R_K$ is often negligible compared with $g_m$. Thus the gain of the cathode follower is approximately 1. The output impedance $Z_o$ is

$$Z_o = \frac{1}{g_m + 1/R_K + 1/r_p} \simeq \frac{1}{g_m} \tag{10–21}$$

to the same approximation. The effective input impedance $Z_{in}$ between the grid and the cathode is

$$Z_{in} = Z\frac{g_m + 1/R_K + 1/r_p}{1/R_K + 1\ r_p} \simeq \frac{Zg_m r_p R_K}{R_K + r_p} \tag{10–22}$$

where $Z$ is the input impedance without the feedback through the cathode resistor.

The cathode follower is particularly well suited as the output stage where the output pulse is to be positive with a short rise time. For this application the tube is biased to just above cutoff. The application of a positive step input to the grid causes the plate current to rise quickly. This current initially goes almost entirely to charging up the capacity $C_K$ which shunts the cathode load $R_K$, thus giving a very rapid rise of output voltage. When the input pulse returns quickly to zero, the plate current is initially cut off completely because of the positive potential of the cathode. It will therefore decay initially with the time constant $R_K C_K$.

**Example 10–7.** A cathode-follower circuit having a 4,000-ohm cathode resistor drives a 5-ft coaxial cable of a capacity of 20 $\mu\mu$f/ft. If a step-input voltage causes the tube current to increase to 40 mamp, find the initial rate of rise of the output voltage; further, find the clipping time of the output pulse for the portion of the decay during which no plate current flows, following a step decrease in the voltage.

*Solution.* The initial rate of rise of the voltage is

$$\frac{dV}{dt} = \frac{I}{C_K} = \frac{40 \times 10^{-3}}{5 \times 20 \times 10^{-12}} = 400 \text{ volts}/\mu\text{sec}$$

The clipping time is $R_K C_K = 4{,}000 \times 100 \times 10^{-12} = 10^{-7}$ sec $= 10^{-1}$ $\mu$sec.

The circuit in Fig. 10–14 makes use of the decrease in input capacitance due to the cathode follower to increase the upper half-power frequency of the gain-producing stage *T*1. The total capacitance of the plate load on the tube *T*1 can be further reduced when a miniature twin triode such as a 12AX7 is used for the two tubes, since a short, direct connection can be made from the plate of *T*1 to the grid of *T*2 right on the socket.

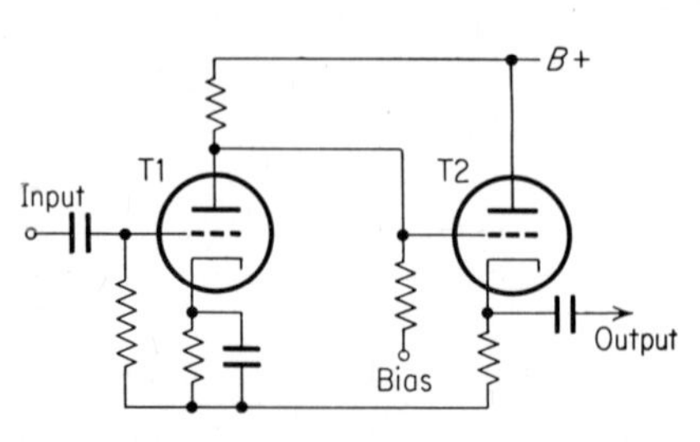


FIG. 10–14. Cathode-follower circuit for use in increasing the rise time of the pulse.

## 10–7. *A Complete Pulse Amplifier*

A schematic diagram of a general-purpose linear amplifier is shown in Figs. 10–15 and 10–16. Figure 10–15 is the preamplifier section, while Fig. 10–16 shows the amplifier along with a discriminator and the power supply. This instrument is a refined version of the linear amplifier designed by Jordan and Bell [8].

Basically, the amplifier consists of three sections, each one being a three-tube feedback circuit of the type discussed in the previous section. The first section is located in the preamplifier; its output is coupled to the main amplifier by the tube *V*4 which is operated as a cathode follower.

The pulse shaping which is accomplished by this amplifier is controlled by means of the selector switch *S*1; the switch section *S*1*a* selects the pulse decay while the section *S*1*b* controls the pulse rise time. The pulse decay is controlled by a delay line or by one of two *RC* differentiation networks. The pulse rise time is controlled by the *RC* integration networks; the three switch positions correspond to approximately 0.15, 0.7, and 4 μsec rise times.

The voltage gain of this amplifier varies from $5 \times 10^4$ to $5 \times 10^5$, increasing as the rise time increases. The preamplifier gain is only about 30, as it must be limited to avoid excessive pulse pile-up preceding differentiation. Further total amplification would not be particularly useful since it would serve only to raise the amplifier noise to a value approaching the maximum possible amplifier output voltage. The output voltage can be as high as 100 volts at the high impedance output. Good linearity can be maintained up to this level.

In some applications pulse amplifiers are driven considerably beyond their design operating region by being subjected to large amplitude pulses. The heights of the normal pulses immediately following these overload conditions are usually in error, principally because of grid-current flow which the overload produces. This grid current tends to charge coupling

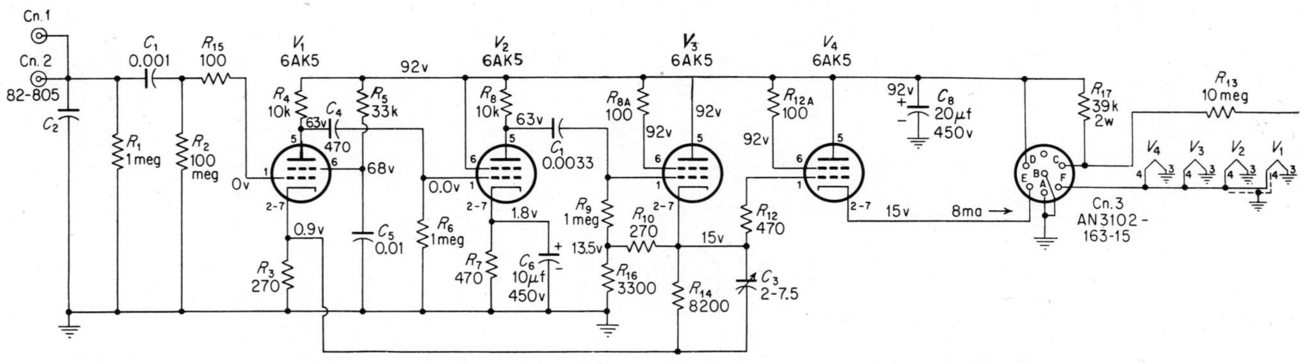


FIG. 10–15. The AID preamplifier. (Designed by Bell, Kelly, and Goss of Oak Ridge National Laboratory.)

capacitors in the high-level stages; as these capacitors discharge through the grid resistors, the base lines of the pulses are shifted and the pulse heights are in error. Chase and Higinbotham [9] have designed a pulse amplifier with good overload characteristics. It employs cathode-coupled amplifiers in a negative feedback loop. These amplifiers can accept, without drawing grid current, signals considerably larger than the quiescent bias voltages of the tubes.

## PULSE-AMPLITUDE DISCRIMINATORS

### 10–8. *Trigger Circuits*

The amplitude discriminators and the scaling stages which are discussed in this chapter usually employ trigger circuits; therefore a brief discussion of this circuit type is included at this point. More detailed treatments can be found in electronic textbooks [10].

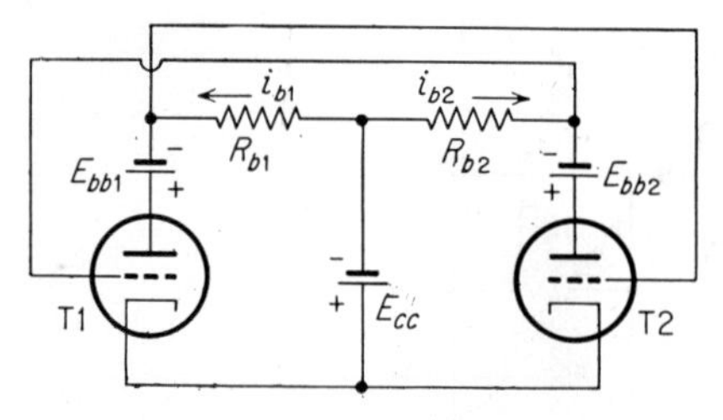


FIG. 10–17. Eccles-Jordan trigger circuit.

Figure 10–17 is a schematic diagram of the basic Eccles-Jordan [11] trigger circuit. This circuit is characterized by the fact that it has only two stable states. In one state, tube $T1$ is conducting and tube $T2$ is essentially cut off; in the other state the conduction and cutoff conditions are interchanged. By the following considerations, a sharing of the current flow by the two tubes can be seen to be unstable. Suppose that the two halves of the circuit are symmetrical with regard to their tubes and other circuit components. Assume further that equal currents flow in the two tubes. If a small fluctuation such as a momentary increase in the plate supply voltage $E_{bb1}$ causes an increase in the plate current $i_{b1}$, a regenerative condition builds up rapidly, causing the current $i_{b1}$ to increase further while the current $i_{b2}$ is decreased to a very small value. Therefore the assumed condition of equal currents is unstable.

The development of the regeneration proceeds as follows: The increase in the voltage drop across $R_{b1}$, when applied to the grid of $T2$, causes a drop in $i_{b2}$. This drop, in turn, allows the grid voltage of $T1$ to rise, thus tending to support the initial increase in $i_{b1}$. Provided that the tube transconductances and the resistances are sufficiently large, this grid-voltage increase more than supports the initial fluctuation.

The conduction can be caused to transfer from one stable state to the other by the application of suitable trigger signals. For example, a negative pulse applied to the grid of $T1$ can cause the change of the conduction from $T1$ to $T2$.

## 10–9. *Low-performance Discriminators*

Pulse-amplitude discriminators may be either simple discriminators, the function of which is to pass pulses whose amplitude exceeds a certain limit, or differential discriminators which pass pulses with amplitudes between an upper and lower limit. The differential discriminators may consist basically of combinations of simple discriminators.

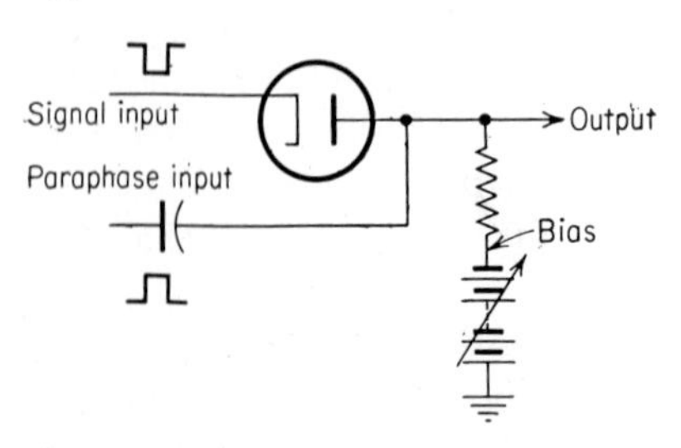


Fig. 10–18. Biased-diode discriminator.

A low-performance type of simple discriminator can be achieved by the use of a biased diode; this is illustrated in Fig. 10–18. The signal input is a negative pulse applied to the cathode of the diode. When the pulse height is high enough that the cathode is driven below the potential of the biased plate, a current flows through the diode and the resistor $R$, thus allowing the signal to pass through the discriminator. A pulse with a fast leading edge can pass through the plate-to-cathode capacitance of the diode, even though its height is not great enough to cause conduction. This signal is canceled out by the paraphase signal which is an out-of-phase signal with an amplitude equal to that of the desired signal.

A variation on the diode discriminator consists of a triode or pentode connected as an amplifier with its grid biased below cutoff. Figure 10–19

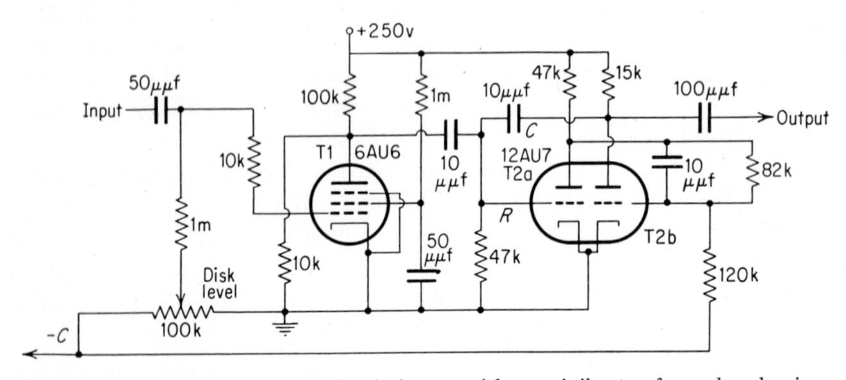


Fig. 10–19. A biased-pentode discriminator with a univibrator for pulse shaping. (*From E. Bleuler and G. J. Goldsmith, "Experimental Nucleonics," p. 22, Rinehart & Company, Inc., New York,* 1952.)

illustrates this circuit. Positive pulses are applied to the grid of the 6AU6. When the pulse height exceeds the amount by which the tube is biased below cutoff, a negative signal appears at the plate of the 6AU6.

A discriminator should produce a standard output pulse whenever a

pulse is passed. The 12AU7 tube, a twin triode, and its associated circuitry in Fig. 10–19 comprise a pulse-shaping circuit for this purpose. This circuit, known as a univibrator, is a variation of the Eccles-Jordan trigger circuit. Conduction in the tube section $T2a$ is a stable state but conduction in the other side, $T2b$, is only quasi-stable. Thus, when a negative signal appears at the grid of $T2a$ after passing the biased discriminator tube, it causes the transfer of conduction to $T2b$, dropping the voltage at the output and forming the output signal. The duration of the conduction in $T2b$ is controlled by the coupling capacitor $C$ and the grid resistor $R$. When the charging current through $C$ has dropped sufficiently, regeneration sets in and transfers the conduction back to $T2a$. Thus the output pulse has fixed height and duration.

Both the biased-diode and the biased-amplifier discriminators are limited in their abilities to discriminate between pulses of similar heights; the limitation is inherent in the logarithmic nature of the input-output characteristics near the tube cutoff points. Therefore, while these discriminators are quite adequate for applications such as counting by means of Geiger-Müller tubes, where the pulses to be passed are considerably larger than those to be rejected, they are not suitable for precision applications where continuous distributions of pulse heights are being analyzed. Circuits which are based on the Schmitt trigger circuit are commonly used for precision work.

## 10–10. *Schmitt Discriminators*

A typical diagram of a circuit based on the Schmitt trigger circuit [6] is shown in Fig. 10–20. Its operation depends on the characteristic that either $T1$ or $T2$ is conducting, depending on the potential $E_{cc1}$ of the control grid of $T1$. As $E_{cc1}$ is increased, after starting well below +100 volts, a critical voltage is reached at about +100 volts. At this point, regeneration sets in, causing a very rapid transfer of conduction from $T2$ to $T1$. As long as $E_{cc1}$ is above this critical voltage, $T1$ continues to conduct. When $E_{cc1}$ is lowered, the conduction reverses again but at a voltage a few volts below the critical voltage for rising values of $E_{cc1}$. This difference in critical voltages can be varied from a fraction of a volt to perhaps 50 volts through changes in the resistor $R_5$. However, a few volts of this hysteresis are required to prevent oscillation when the voltage $E_{cc1}$ is near the critical voltage.

When this circuit is used for pulse-amplitude discrimination, the potentiometers $P_1$ and $P_2$ can be used to adjust the discriminator level. This circuit can be used with either positive or negative pulses. For example, if it is desired to pass all positive pulses with amplitudes above 20 volts, the bias voltage for $T1$ is set 20 volts below the critical voltage for rising voltages.

The output pulses are shown in Fig. 10–21 for input voltages of two different time durations. In Fig. 10–21*a* the critical grid voltage is exceeded for a time much greater than a microsecond; on this time scale the output pulse is rectangular. In Fig. 10–21*b*, where the critical voltage is exceeded for only about a microsecond, the output voltage does not have time to reach equilibrium. The rise time of the output pulse is determined primarily by $R_5$. The circuit which is shown has a resolving time somewhat less than 5 $\mu$sec. By the use of higher $g_m$ tubes and lower plate resistors, 0.3-$\mu$sec resolving times can be achieved [6].

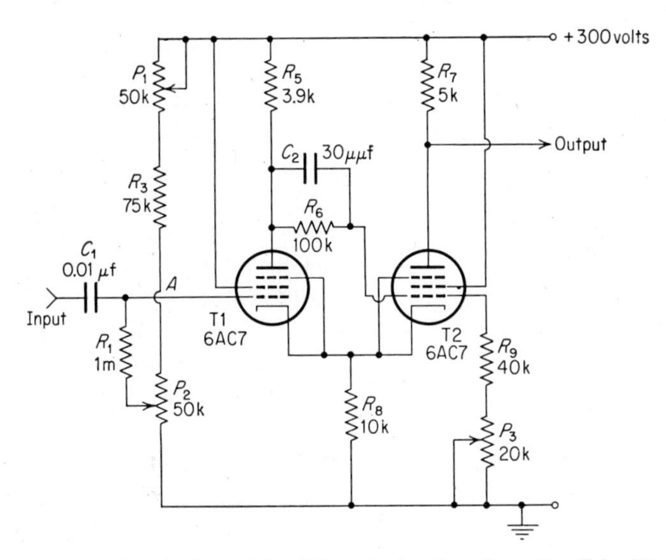


FIG. 10–20. Pulse-height discriminator based on the Schmitt trigger circuit. (*From W. C. Elmore and M. Sands, "Electronics," chap.* 4, *National Nuclear Energy Series, div.* V, *vol.* 1, *McGraw-Hill Book Company, Inc., New York,* 1949.)

The Schmitt discriminator has good overload characteristics. It is found [3] that the amplitude of the input pulse can exceed the critical voltage by 100 volts before $T1$ draws grid current, thereby shifting the bias voltage.

Uncertainty in the triggering level of a Schmitt circuit may be due to shifts in the power-supply voltages and to variations in the values of circuit components, particularly the resistors. By the use of stabilizer power supplies and wire-wound resistors, the uncertainty in the triggering level can be made as low as 0.1 volt [6].

The discriminator which is incorporated in the general-purpose amplifier shown in Fig. 10–16 consists of a Schmitt trigger circuit preceded by a gain-of-10 difference amplifier biased to the desired discrimination level. This circuit has been analyzed by Van Rennes [12]. The addition of the amplifier to the basic Schmitt discriminator permits the analysis of smaller pulses since the limitation which is set by the hysteresis of the circuit is lowered by the gain of the amplifier.

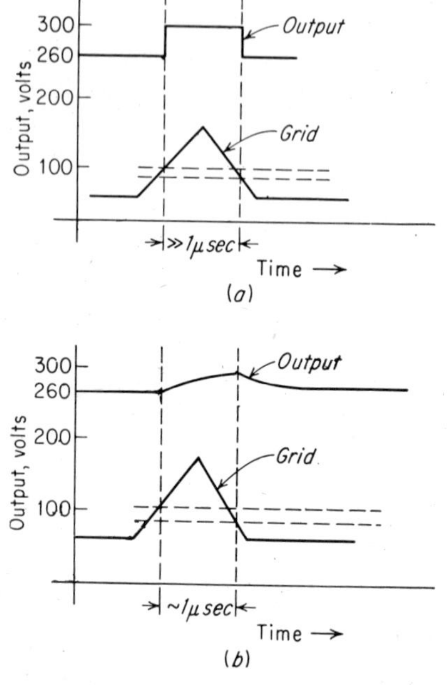


Fig. 10-21. Dependence of the output-pulse shape of a Schmitt trigger circuit on the duration of the input pulse. (*From W. C. Elmore and M. Sands, "Electronics," chap. 4, National Nuclear Energy Series, div.* V, *vol.* 1, *McGraw-Hill Book Company, Inc., New York,* 1949.)

## 10-11. *Differential Discriminators*

Applications of differential pulse-height analyzers were discussed in Sec. 2-8. In addition, a block diagram of a single-channel instrument was presented. The multichannel differential pulse-height analyzer is an extension of the single-channel instrument. Through its use, differential pulse-height curves can be obtained more rapidly because several pulse-height intervals can be analyzed simultaneously.

The multichannel analyzer can be constructed by the use of an array of simple discriminators whose biases are progressively and accurately increased. Each of the several channels is formed by a voltage increment between the levels of adjacent pairs of discriminators. A coincidence circuit is connected between each adjacent pair of discriminators in such a manner that a pulse produces a count only in the channel which separates the discriminators which are passed from those which are not.

An excellent series of review articles on pulse-height analyzers has been written by Van Rennes [12-15]. In addition, Kelley [16] has reviewed the developments which have occurred since 1952. Analyzers have been developed which are based on electromechanical and electrooptical principles as well as on straight electronic principles.

# SCALING CIRCUITS

## 10-12. *Typical Scale-of-2 Circuit*

A typical scale-of-2 circuit of the type referred to in Sec. 2-7 is shown in Fig. 10-22. This so-called "flip-flop" circuit is a direct adaptation of the basic Eccles-Jordan circuit. The sequence of operation is as follows: The opening of the reset switch ensures that tube *T2b* is conducting; also under this condition the interpolation light will not be lit. Reclosing the switch makes no further change. The input signal consists of the input voltage dropping from 300 to 250 volts or less, as shown in Fig. 10–23. This causes current flow through *T1a*, resulting in a drop in the plate voltage of *T2a* and a transfer of conduction from *T2b* to *T2a*. Because of the current drawn through *T1b*, the plate potential of *T2b* does not return to its final value until the input voltage returns to 300 volts. As the input voltage

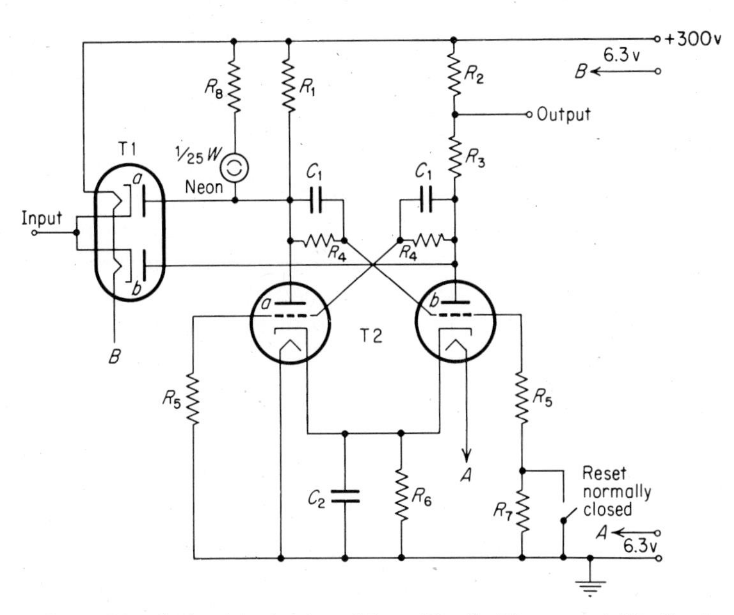


FIG. 10–22. Scale-of-2 circuit. (*From W. C. Elmore and M. Sands, "Electronics," chap. 4, National Nuclear Energy Series, div.* V, *vol.* 1, *McGraw-Hill Book Company, Inc., New York,* 1949.)

returns to 300 volts, no transfer of the conduction occurs. When the input voltage again drops, the conduction transfers from *T2a* to *T2b*. Accompanying this transfer there is a drop in the output voltage which actuates the succeeding scale-of-2 circuit. The interpolation light is lit when tube *T2a* is conducting. These lights are used to determine the counts which have entered the counting system in addition to those indicated on the mechanical register.

With the circuit components shown in Fig. 10–22, the unit has a resolving time of 3 to 5 μsec [3]. If the values in parentheses are used, including a 6SL7 tube, the unit will require less power, and the resolving time will be about 20 μsec.

## 10–13. *Fast Scale-of-2 Circuits*

The maximum rate at which the scale-of-2 circuit discussed above can operate is limited by the resistance-capacitance networks which couple the plates to the opposite grids. If the capacitance in these circuits is reduced too much, insufficient voltage is coupled to the grids; therefore the principal reduction in resolving time must be achieved by lowering the plate resistors. In this manner, resolving times as low as 1 μsec can be obtained [6]. However, these units require frequent adjustment, as their stability is not good. In addition, their requirement for plate current is quite high.

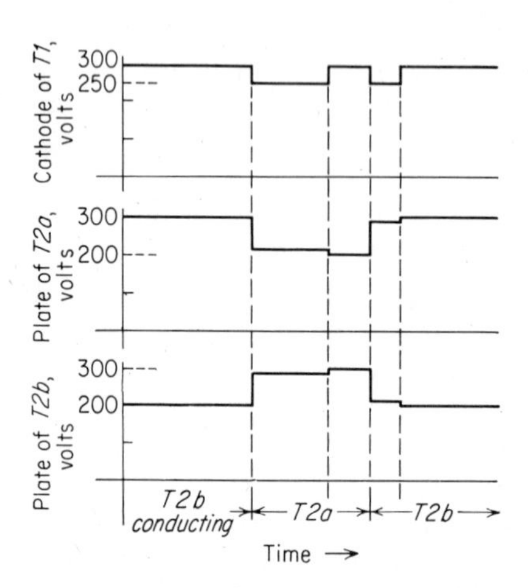


FIG. 10–23. Voltages in a scale-of-2 circuit. (*From W. C. Elmore and M. Sands, "Electronics," chap. 4, National Nuclear Energy Series, div.* V, *vol.* 1, *McGraw-Hill Book Company, Inc., New York,* 1949.)

A further improvement in the resolving power of a scale-of-2 circuit can be realized by limiting the excursions in the grid and plate voltages. In this way, the tubes are always operating in regions of high transconductance; in addition, the discharge of the resistance-capacitance coupling network is not required to be as complete. Moody et al. [17] have described a scaler of this type with a resolving time of 0.25 μsec. One such scale-of-2 unit is shown in Fig. 10–24. The pentodes *T*2 and *T*3 form the trigger pair, while *T*1 is the driver tube. The grid excursion, when triggering occurs, is between 0 and −6 volt. The upper limit is set by the occurrence of grid-current flow at zero voltage while the lower limit comes from the clamping which the dual diode *T*4 supplies. The maximum plate voltages of *T*2 and *T*3 are held at 65 volts by the crystal diodes *X*1 and *X*2. The plate voltage of *T*1 is supplied by the excess current flow through the diodes.

## 10–14. *Scale of* 10

There has been a tendency in recent years for decade-scaling circuits to replace scale-of-2 circuits for applications in which decimal recording appears to have particular advantages. A number of scale-of-10 circuits have been developed which are based on binary stages [18,19]; these circuits are used to give either 16 − 6 or 8 + 2 counts. The resulting scalers contain more tubes for a given scale factor than do the straight binary systems; in addition, they are reported to require more servicing.

Various self-contained decade counter tubes are available. These devices have 10 separate states of conduction; in addition, some types provide visible indication of the state that is occupied. The use of the decade tubes has made possible the development of reliable and compact decade-scaling units. These tubes are either of the cold-cathode gas-filled type or of the electron-beam vacuum type.

The cold-cathode tubes have the advantages of practically unlimited life, relative insensitiveness to voltage variations and temperature conditions,

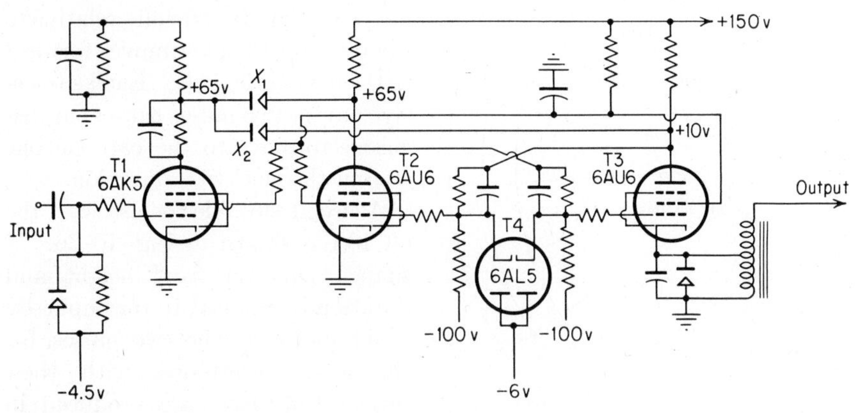


Fig. 10–24. High-speed scale-of-2 circuit. [*From N. F. Moody, W. D. Howell, W. J. Battell, and R. H. Taplin, Rev. Sci. Instr.*, **22**:439 (1951).]

and compactness. On the other hand, their resolving power is limited because the gas-ionization processes are relatively slow.

The electron-beam scaling tubes are much faster than the cold-cathode tubes. However, being filamentary tubes, their lives are limited. In addition, circuits which employ them are much more critical to adjust.

Baker and Eichholz [20] have surveyed the availability of decade tubes and of reliable circuits for them. The Dekatrons made by Ericsson Telephone Company [21,22] are examples of the cold-cathode tubes; the Dekatron GC10A is one of the most satisfactory of these. A cathode glow on one of a set of interconnected cathodes, arranged around a central common anode, is caused to transfer from one position to the next by the application of controlling voltages to intermediate electrodes or "guides." This tube is illustrated by Fig. 10–25. In addition to the anode $A$, the tube contains 30 electrodes of which 10 are cathodes, 10 are guide 1 electrodes, and 10 are guide 2 electrodes. Nine of the cathodes are connected internally, as shown in Fig. 10–25; the tenth cathode is brought out separately to provide the output signal. The 10 guide 1 electrodes, designated as $g_1$, $g_{1a}$, etc., are connected internally, as are also the 10 guide 2 electrodes.

Let it be assumed that a discharge is taking place between the anode $A$ and the cathode $k_2$ in Fig. 10–25. If a negative pulse of 120 volts is applied to the group of guide 1 electrodes which were originally at +60 volts with respect to the cathode, the glow transfers to $g_{1A}$. If, simultaneously with the restoration of $g_{1A}$ to +60 volts, a 120-volt negative pulse is applied to $g_2$, the glow moves to $g_{2a}$. When guide 2 is restored to its original potential of +60 volts relative to the cathode, the glow moves forward to the next cathode $k_3$. Each successive pair of two pulses causes the discharge to move to the cathode one step in the clockwise direction.

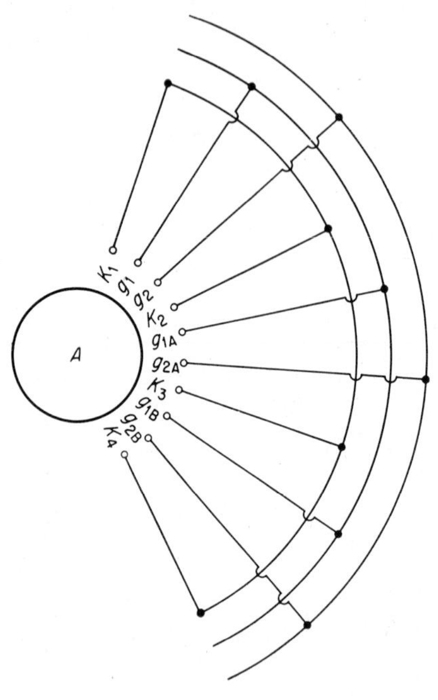


FIG. 10–25. Schematic diagram of a cold-cathode decade counting tube.

A circuit suitable for use with the GC10A is shown in Fig. 10–26. A shaped pulse of fixed height and duration is supplied to the input by a univibrator. The two pulses, for the guide electrodes, with their proper time lags, are produced in the circuits containing the double triode ($T1a$ and $T1b$), both sections of which are biased to cutoff. The delayed pulse is produced when the rising edge of the pulse at the anode of $T1a$, after differentiation, drives $T1b$ into conduction. The shapes and timing of the pulses are indicated in Fig. 10–26. When the tenth cathode in the Dekatron is reached, the output pulse occurs. This circuit is capable of counting at rates up to 2,500 counts/sec.

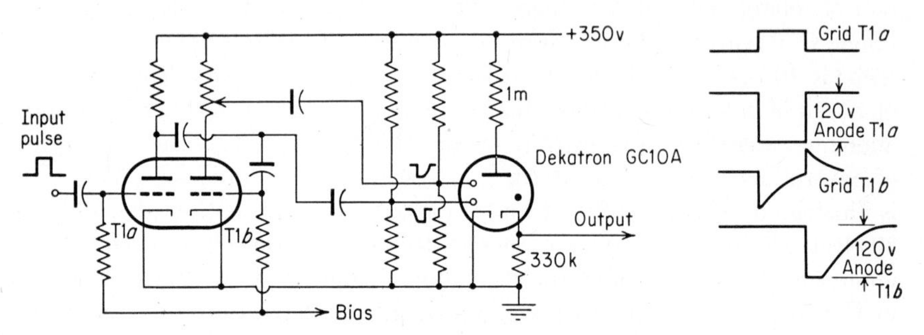


FIG. 10–26. Driver circuit for a Dekatron GC10A decade counter tube. [*From J. C. Baker and G. G. Eichholz, Nucleonics,* **12**:44 (*April,* 1954).]

The Philips tube [23], type E1T, is one of the most satisfactory electron-beam scaling tubes. In this device a beam of electrons is focused on a slotted screen which provides 10 stable beam positions. Corresponding to each position there is a numbered spot on a fluorescent screen on the inside wall of the tube; this spot lights up when hit by the beam. As the beam sweeps across the slots, the current fluctuates; it provides a particularly large pulse when it reaches the tenth, or output, position.

Several circuits have been developed [23] for driving the E1T tube. Baker and Eichholz [20] have described one which is capable of reliable counting up to $10^5$ counts/sec.

## COUNTING-RATE METERS

### 10–15. *Basic Counting-rate Circuit*

A counting-rate meter is a device which indicates the counting rate directly. It is to be distinguished from the counter, i.e., a scaler-impulse-register combination, used in conjunction with a timer. The counting-rate meter has the advantage that the counting rate can be indicated and recorded continuously. On the other hand, the counter-timer combination can attain the highest accuracy in situations in which the measuring time is limited.

Most counting-rate meters are arranged so that each input pulse feeds a known charge $q$ into a tank capacitor which is shunted by a resistor $R$. The voltage across the capacitor builds up to an equilibrium value at which the rate of loss of charge through the shunt resistor equals the rate of input of the charge by the pulses. If the charge per pulse is a constant, the equilibrium value of the voltage $v$ is

$$v = rqR \tag{10–23}$$

where $r$ is the average number of pulses per second. If a linear meter is used to measure $v$, a linear relationship exists between the meter reading and the counting rate.

The equilibrium voltage across the tank capacitor, as given by Eq. (10–23), is seen to be independent of the size of the capacitor. However, the capacity does affect the time required to reach equilibrium and the statistical accuracy, as discussed in Sec. 10–18.

The diode-pump circuit [24] which is shown in Fig. 10–27 is a satisfactory method of feeding the charge into the tank capacitor. The generator $E$ with internal resistance $R_f$ produces a rectangular pulse of duration $T$ and height $V$. The capacitor $C_f$ is charged, through the resistance $R_f$ in series with $T1$, up to nearly the pulse voltage $V$, provided that the pulse duration $T$ is greater than about five time constants or $5R_fC_f$. When the input pulse returns to zero, $C_f$ discharges through $T2$, placing a fixed charge $VC_f$ per pulse on the tank capacitor $C_t$, provided that the following conditions hold:

$$C_f \ll C_t$$
$$v \ll V$$

and

$$\frac{1}{r} - T > 5R_fC_f$$

The first two conditions ensure that negligible charge remains on $C_f$ in equilibrium, while the third condition ensures that sufficient time elapses for equilibrium to be nearly reached before the next pulse occurs.

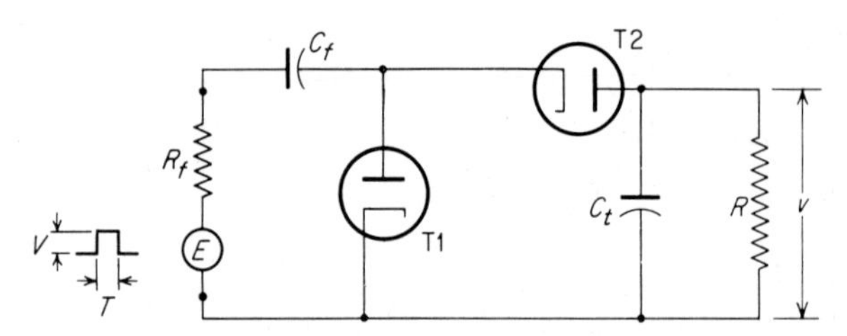


FIG. 10–27. Diode-pump circuit for a counting-rate meter. [*From E. H. Cooke-Yarborough, Proc. Inst. Elec. Engrs., (London),* **98** (*pt.* 2):191 (1951).]

If the condition $v \ll V$ is not satisfied, the charge per pulse becomes $(V - v)C_f$; therefore Eq. (10–23) leads to

$$v = \frac{VrC_fR}{1 + rC_fR} \tag{10–24}$$

This equation indicates that, by proper choice of circuit components, relationships between voltage and counting rate other than linear can be obtained.

### 10–16. *Linear Counting-rate Meter*

Several circuits for linear counting-rate meters have been described in the literature [6,24,25]. Figure 10–28 is a block diagram which represents these instruments. The requirements for and the circuits used in the amplifiers and the discriminators are the same as those described for previous pulse circuits. In some counting-rate meters, the pulse shaping is accomplished by univibrators (see Sec. 10–9); in others the output of a scale-of-2 circuit is used as the shaped pulse.

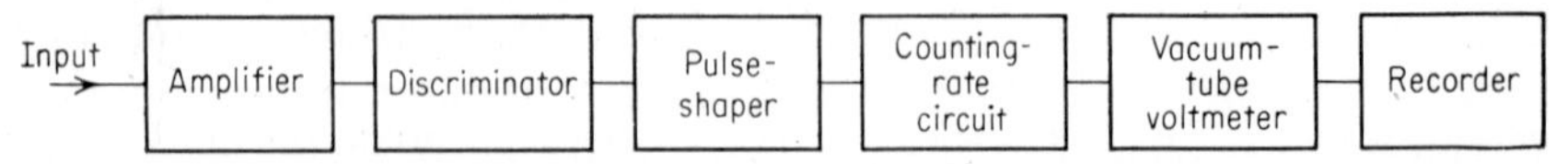


FIG. 10–28. Block diagram of a counting-rate meter.

The counting-rate circuits are all basically the diode pump. They differ in the way in which the range and time constant are varied and in the manner in which linearity is achieved. The Cooke-Yarborough circuit [24] satisfies the condition $v \ll V$ by making $C_t$ and $R$ of Fig. 10–27 the feedback elements of a fed-back d-c amplifier, as shown in Fig. 10–29. The capacitor $C_f$ discharges into $C_t$ through $T2$ as before; however, because of the feedback, practically all the resultant voltage change appears on the output terminal side of $C_t$. This is the case because the feedback in the amplifier circuit consisting of $T3$ and $T4$ keeps the potential at the grid of

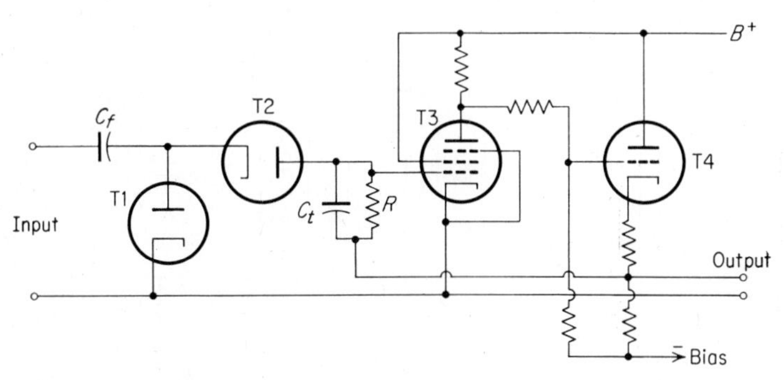


FIG. 10–29. Diode-pump circuit with a fed-back amplifier. [*From E. H. Cooke-Yarborough, Proc. Inst. Elec. Engrs. (London)*, **98** (*pt.* 2):191 (1951).]

$T3$ nearly constant. The voltage change appearing at that point is less than that across $C_t$ by the factor $G$, where $G$ is the gain of the d-c amplifier without feedback.

Figure 10–30 is the complete schematic diagram (except for the discriminator) of the Cooke-Yarborough [24] linear counting-rate meter. The pulse shaping is accomplished by the scale-of-2 circuit consisting of tubes $V7$ and $V8$ followed by the limiter tube $V9$. The remainder of the circuit is the diode pump and feedback amplifier as discussed above.

The instrument as shown has six ranges varying from 0 to 1 pulse/sec to 0 to 100,000 pulses/sec; the range is selected by the ganged switch $S5$. The switch $S6$ adjusts the tank-circuit time constant.

Both a panel-type meter and a recorder jack are provided for reading the output. The instrument, when properly adjusted and calibrated, is capable of 1 per cent full-scale accuracy and stability. Further, its resolving time is less than 5 $\mu$sec.

### 10–17. *Logarithmic Counting-rate Meters*

When wide ranges of counting rates must be covered, the linear counting-rate meter may have serious limitations. The accuracy and sensitivity at

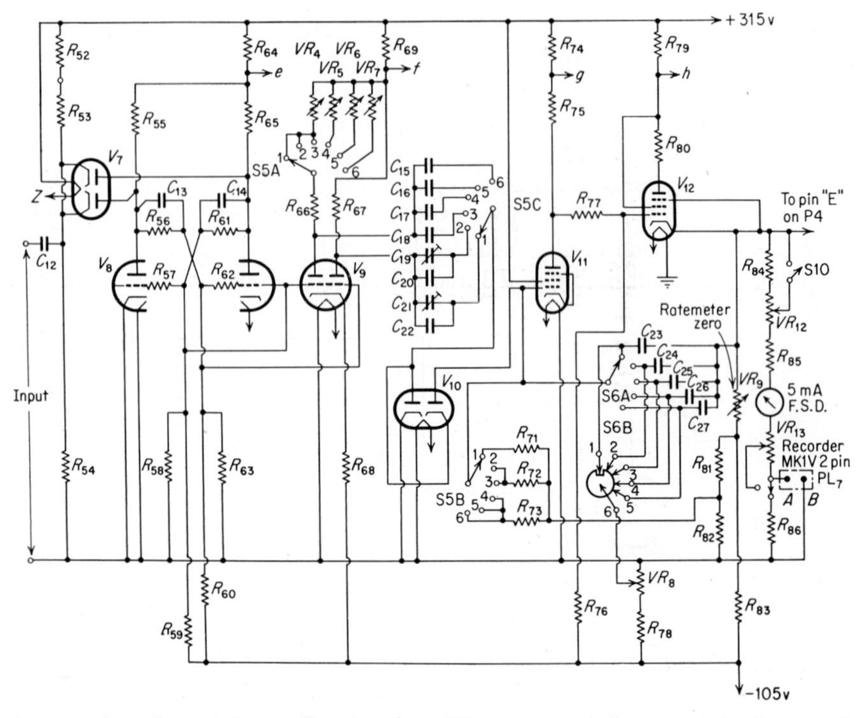


| $R_{52}$ 3.3 kΩ | $R_{64}$ 3.9 Ω | $R_{77}$ 470 kΩ | $VR_4$ 5,000 Ω | $C_{14}$ 15 μμf | $C_{26}$ 0.1 μf |
|---|---|---|---|---|---|
| $R_{53}$ 27 kΩ | $R_{65}$ 15 kΩ | $R_{78}$ 82 kΩ | $VR_5$ 5,000 Ω | $C_{15}$ 0.05 μf | $C_{27}$ 0.02 μf |
| $R_{54}$ 270 kΩ | $R_{66}$ 12 kΩ | $R_{79}$ 18 Ω | $VR_6$ 5,000 Ω | $C_{16}$ 0.005 μf | |
| $R_{55}$ 15 kΩ | $R_{67}$ 6.8 kΩ | $R_{80}$ 100 Ω | $VR_7$ 5,000 Ω | $C_{17}$ 470 μμf | $V_7$ CV140 |
| $R_{56}$ 180 kΩ | $R_{68}$ 10 kΩ | $R_{81}$ 220 kΩ | $VR_8$ 5,000 Ω | $C_{18}$ 220 μμf | $V_8$ CV858 |
| $R_{57}$ 100 Ω | $R_{69}$ 6.8 Ω | $R_{82}$ 220 kΩ | $VR_9$ 5,000 Ω | $C_{19}$ 30 μμf | $V_9$ CV858 |
| $R_{58}$ 100 kΩ | $R_{71}$ 240 kΩ | $R_{83}$ 22 kΩ | $VR_{12}$ 2,500 Ω | $C_{20}$ 47 μμf | $V_{10}$ CV140 |
| $R_{59}$ 82 kΩ | $R_{72}$ 2.4 MΩ | $R_{84}$ 6.8 kΩ | $VR_{13}$ 2,500 Ω | $C_{21}$ 30 μμf | $V_{11}$ CV138 |
| $R_{60}$ 82 kΩ | $R_{73}$ 10 MΩ | $R_{85}$ 3.3 kΩ | | $C_{22}$ 22 μμf | $V_{12}$ CV138 |
| $R_{61}$ 180 kΩ | $R_{74}$ 27 Ω | $R_{86}$ 20 Ω | $C_{12}$ 0.001 μf | $C_{23}$ 8 μf | |
| $R_{62}$ 100 Ω | $R_{75}$ 330 kΩ | | $C_{13}$ 15 μμf | $C_{24}$ 2 μf | |
| $R_{63}$ 100 kΩ | $R_{76}$ 1 MΩ | | | $C_{25}$ 0.5 μf | |

FIG. 10–30. Linear counting-rate circuit. [*From E. H. Cooke-Yarborough, Proc. Inst. Elec. Engrs. (London)*, **98** (*pt.* 2):191 (1951).]

the lower end of any range become poor. While this may be alleviated by switching ranges, this solution is not always feasible, particularly in cases where the counting rate is changing rapidly, thus requiring frequent scale shifts. Logarithmic counting-rate meters have been developed to meet the requirement for a wide-range instrument.

The logarithmic response can be introduced into the meter by the use of a logarithmic d-c vacuum-tube voltmeter to read the voltage across the tank capacitor $C_t$. Amplifiers with logarithmic response are discussed in

Sec. 10–24. Stone and Wade [26] have described a design utilizing a logarithmic-diode-type amplifier. The instrument is calibrated to read from 1 to $10^5$ counts/sec on a single scale. LeVine [27] has also described a logarithmic counting-rate meter. This is a moderate-accuracy instrument which covers five or more decades; it is specifically intended for use with a portable scintillation counter. The circuit utilizes the nearly logarithmic grid-current versus plate-current characteristic of a variable-mu tube.

Cooke-Yarborough [28] has designed a logarithmic instrument that is a very good approximation to a logarithmic law and is at the same time independent of vacuum-tube characteristics. The proper response is obtained by adding the outputs of a number of diode pumps, each of which has a response of the type given by Eq. (10–24). If all the diode pumps are driven in parallel and the time constant $RC_t$ of each one differs from that of the preceding one by a factor of 10, the sum of the outputs of the several diode pumps is shown [28] to be a logarithmic function of the counting rate $r$. The instrument which is described [28] employs six diode pumps. It is capable of operation over five decades with an accuracy better than 10 per cent over the entire range. Higher accuracy is obtained by decreasing the range.

A logarithmic counting-rate recorder with an instrument error of less than 1 per cent employs a rotating cylinder with a logarithmic spiral cut uniformly around it [29]. The recorder plots directly points which are proportional to the logarithm of the time for a predetermined number of counts. The recorder is controlled by a scaler. At the beginning of the counting period, the cylinder starts to rotate, causing the marker to advance along the logarithmic spiral. At the end of the predetermined count, the scaler actuates the marker; the displacement of the marker is proportional to the logarithm of the elapsed time.

### 10–18. *Accuracy of Counting-rate Meters*

The instantaneous value of the voltage across the tank capacitor in a counting-rate meter fluctuates even though the source of the pulses which it is counting has a constant average value. These variations are contributed to by the exponential discharge-charge characteristic of the tank circuit, as well as by the statistical nature of the radiation-detector output which the meter receives. Since this problem is essentially identical to that discussed in Sec. 3–8 for a mean-level ionization chamber, the results derived there are applicable. By Eq. (10–23), the equilibrium value of the average voltage $v$ is $rqR$. The standard deviation $\sigma$ of an instantaneous value taken at random is obtained from Eq. (3–33) as

$$\sigma_v = \left(\frac{q^2rR}{2C_t}\right)^{1/2} \tag{10–25}$$

where $R$ and $C_t$ are the resistance and capacity, respectively, of the counting-rate-meter tank circuit.

For determining the improvement in accuracy by taking the time average of the recorded output, Eq. (3–36) may be used [30].

**Example 10–8.** A linear counting-rate meter having a tank-circuit time constant of 20 sec is used to measure a detector output of about 10 counts/sec. Find the percentage standard error for a single reading and for one averaged from a recorder trace over a 2-min interval. Assume that sufficient time has elapsed for equilibrium to be established and that the instrument errors are entirely statistical. In addition, compute the time required to obtain the same accuracies with a scaler-timer combination.

*Solution.* By Eqs. (10–23) and (10–25), the percentage error of a single reading is

$$\text{Percentage error} = (r2RC_t)^{-1/2} \times 100\% = [(10)(2)(20)]^{-1/2} \times 100\% = 5\%$$

The error in the mean of a 2-min interval is, by Eq. (3–36),

$$\text{Percentage error} = \frac{\sigma_1\, 2RC_t}{T}\left(1 - \frac{RC_t}{T} + \frac{RC_t}{T}e^{-T/RC_t}\right)$$

$$= \frac{5}{3}\left(1 - \frac{1}{6} + \frac{1}{6}e^{-6}\right) = 1.4\%$$

By Eq. (3–24), the time $t$ required to obtain a given percentage error $\sigma$ by a scaler-timer combination is $t = 10^4/\sigma^2 r$. Therefore, for a 5 per cent error,

$$t = \frac{10^4}{(5)^2(10)} = 40 \text{ sec}$$

while for a 1.4 per cent error, $t = 500$ sec.

The results of this section were based on the assumption that sufficient time had elapsed for equilibrium to be established in the tank circuit. It can be shown [31] that, if the meter is subjected to a constant input, the tank circuit comes within $\sigma_1$, or one standard deviation for a single reading, of the equilibrium value in a time $t_o$ given by

$$t_o = RC_t(\tfrac{1}{2} \ln 2rRC_t + 0.394) \qquad (10\text{–}26)$$

## COINCIDENCE CIRCUITS

### 10–19. *Resolving Time in Coincidence Circuits*

A general discussion of coincidence circuits was included in Sec. 2–9. In addition, examples of the uses of coincidence circuits have been outlined in numerous places throughout this book. Detailed descriptions of applications of coincidence techniques are available in many references, including Bleuler and Goldsmith [32].

The importance of the coincidence-circuit resolving time $\tau$ was discussed in Sec. 2–9. The reduction of $\tau$ not only reduces chance coincidences as given by Eq. (2–5) but also increases the resolution in the measurement of short time intervals between pulses.

The resolving time may be determined experimentally by a method which is based on Eq. (2–5). Two independent sources are counted by two different counters. The two sources must be well shielded from each other so that no direct or scattered radiation which is in true coincidence can reach both counters. Under these conditions the coincidence counting rate $\dot{n}_c$ is caused by the chance coincidences $c_c$ due to the finite resolving time of the system and the background coincidence rate $b_c$ due to cosmic rays which actuate both counters. Thus one has

$$\dot{n}_c = c_c + b_c = 2\tau\dot{n}_1\dot{n}_2 + b_c \tag{10–27}$$

where $\dot{n}_1$ and $\dot{n}_2$ are the individual counting rates measured by the separate source-counter combinations. The quantity $2\tau$ is therefore the slope of the straight line which is obtained by plotting the measured coincidence rate $\dot{n}_c$ versus the product $\dot{n}_1\dot{n}_2$.

Alternatively, $\tau$ can be determined by the measurement of the true-coincidence counting rate as a time delay which is inserted between two pulses, otherwise in coincidence, is varied. The full width of the curve of coincidence rate versus delay time, measured at half height, is taken as the quantity $2\tau$, by definition.

The over-all resolving time in a coincidence apparatus is dependent on the input signals as well as on the coincidence circuits. It is relatively easy to build a coincidence circuit whose resolving time is limited by the performance of presently available counters. Bell [33] has reviewed the status of fast-coincidence techniques; resolving times as low as $10^{-9}$ sec have been reached with circuits employing scintillation, Cerenkov, and electron-multiplier counters.

In order to reach the lowest resolving times, it is necessary to bring the pulses into the actual coincidence circuits with a minimum amount of amplification and pulse shaping between the counter and the coincidence circuit. This fact puts a premium on coincidence circuits that will work with the small pulses that come directly from the counters.

### 10–20. *Rossi or Parallel Coincidence Circuit*

The basic circuit of the Rossi coincidence counter is illustrated in Fig. 10–31. Circuits of this type are sometimes referred to as parallel coincidence circuits because of the parallel paths for the current flow through the two tubes. In the quiescent condition, each of the tubes $T1$ and $T2$ is conducting, carrying a current $i$; this results in a voltage drop $2Ri$ across the common plate resistor. The input signals are negative pulses. A single negative pulse reduces the plate current in one tube, thereby tending to reduce the voltage drop in $R$. However, if the two inputs receive negative pulses simultaneously, a larger change in the voltage drop occurs, thus producing a larger positive output pulse. By following this circuit with a discriminator which passes the output pulses due to coincident inputs while rejecting the smaller ones due to single inputs, coincident counting is achieved.

If the resistance $R$ is large compared with the tube resistances in the quiescent state, the drop across $R$ approaches $+E$. Further, because of the anode-bend characteristic of the pentode, a single negative pulse sufficiently large to cut off the current in one tube makes but a small change in the voltage drop. On the other hand, coincident pulses cutting off both tubes simultaneously causes a large positive output pulse which the succeeding counter can easily distinguish from that due to a single input pulse.

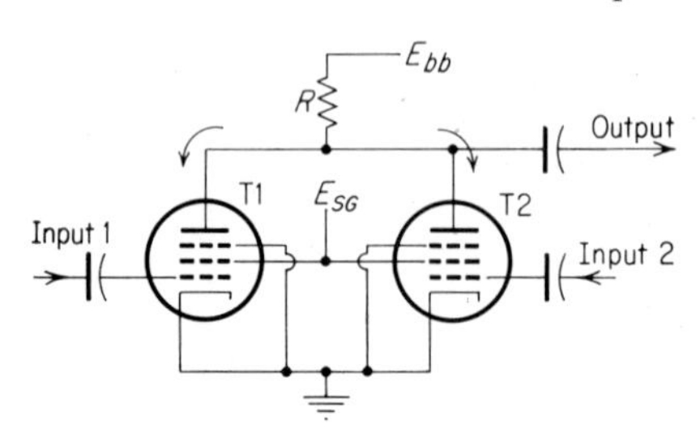


FIG. 10-31. Basic Rossi coincidence circuit.

The use of large values of resistance in the plate circuits limits the minimum resolving time achievable with this circuit. The input-pulse durations must be of the order of the time constant $RC$, where $C$ is the distributed capacity from the tube plates to ground. Thus if $R$ is 50,000 ohms and $C$ is 20 $\mu\mu$f, the time constant is 1 $\mu$sec. This limits the minimum useful pulse lengths and therefore the resolving time to the order of 1 $\mu$sec.

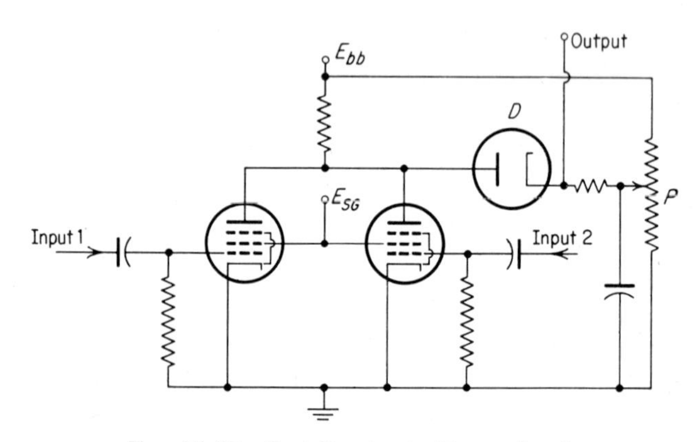


FIG. 10-32. Fast Rossi coincidence circuit.

To achieve really short resolving times with this circuit, $R$ must be quite small. If the capacity can be reduced to as small a value as 10 $\mu\mu$f, $R$ can be, at the most, 100 ohms for a time constant of $10^{-9}$ sec. The addition of the diode and potentiometer to the basic Rossi coincidence circuit, as shown in Fig. 10-32, makes it possible to discriminate between the small single and coincidence output pulses which result with the small values of

$R$. The diode $D$ is biased by means of the potentiometer to pass only the pulses produced by the coincident pulses.

Other variations of the parallel coincidence circuits have been discussed by Bell [33] and by Elmore and Sands [6].

### 10–21. *Series and Bridge Coincidence Circuits*

The series coincidence circuits [34] are equivalent to two switches in series, both of which must be closed for the current flow to occur. Positive input pulses effectively close the switches; the existence of an output current indicates the occurrence of coincident input pulses.

A series coincidence circuit developed by Fischer and Marshall [35] is shown in Fig. 10–33. The coincidence circuit proper consists only of the

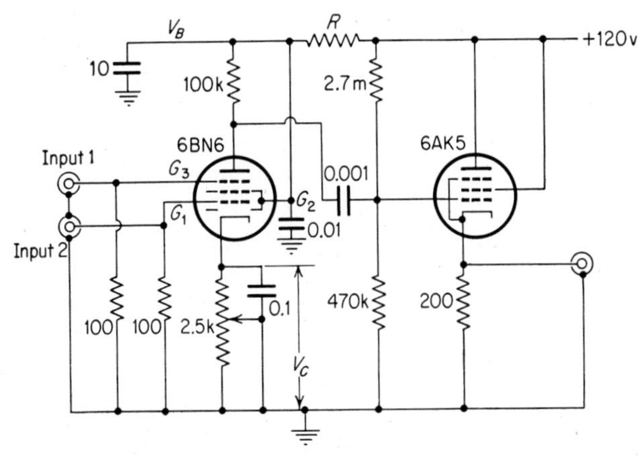


Fig. 10–33. Diagram of the 6BN6 coincidence circuit. [*From J. Fischer and J. Marshall, Rev. Sci. Instr.,* **23**:417 (1952).]

6BN6 tube. This is a gated-beam tube, having the property that either of the two grids, $G_1$ or $G_3$, can effectively cut off the plate current, independent of the voltage on the other grid. If positive pulses are applied in coincidence to $G_1$ and $G_3$, large currents flow to the plate, thus charging up the plate-to-ground capacity; this produces an output pulse which is further amplified by the 6AK5 tube. This circuit is capable of resolving times less than $10^{-9}$ sec. Further, it will operate with small-amplitude input pulses, a few volts being adequate except for the shortest-duration pulses.

Crystal diodes have been employed in coincidence circuits in various ways. Parallel coincidence circuits based on crystal diodes have been developed [36]; however, these offer little if any gain over vacuum tubes. More recently Bay and co-workers [37–40] have developed bridge-type coincidence circuits which are based on diodes. These circuits are simple and compact and will work with small input pulses. Further, they are capable of resolving times of less than $10^{-9}$ sec. Their main disadvantage lies in the difficulty of preventing large single input pulses from producing an output pulse and thus being counted as coincident events.

## SMALL-CURRENT ELECTROMETERS

### 10–22. *D-C Feedback Amplifiers*

The various types of d-c electrometers were surveyed in Chap. 4. These included mechanical electrometers which operate by electrostatic forces, vacuum-tube electrometers, and vibrating-capacitance electrometers. In the present chapter vacuum-tube electrometers employing feedback amplifiers and vibrating-capacitance amplifiers are described in detail.

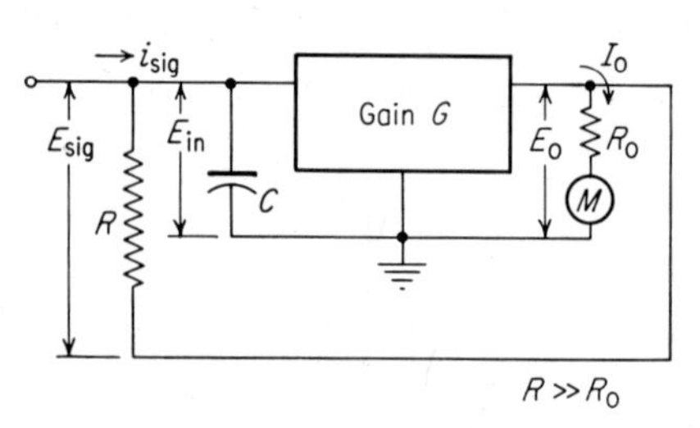


FIG. 10–34. Schematic diagram of a 100 per cent fed-back amplifier.

Vacuum-tube electrometers of the type shown in Fig. 4–8 are rather dependent on tube characteristics and power-supply voltages for their scale linearity and stability. Consequently, feedback amplifiers have been developed for electrometer applications partially to circumvent these difficulties. One hundred per cent negative feedback is usually employed. This is illustrated in Fig. 10–34. A high-gain amplifier is connected in such a way that the output signal $E_o$ is fed back in series with the input signal $E_{sig}$. Thus the voltage which appears at the amplifier input is

$$E_{in} = E_{sig} + E_o \tag{10–28}$$

Using the relationship $E_o = -GE_{in}$, one obtains the expression

$$E_o = \frac{-E_{sig}}{1 + 1/G} \tag{10–29}$$

Thus if $G \gg 1$,

$$E_o \simeq E_{sig} \qquad \text{and} \qquad \frac{I_{in}}{I_o} \simeq \frac{R_o}{R} \tag{10–30}$$

The amplifier is seen to act as a current amplifier, the gain of which is dependent only on the output and input resistors. This makes possible not only improved stability but also very good linearity in the input-output relationship.

The feedback affects the impedance between the input and ground in such a manner that the capacitance $C$ is reduced to $C/(1 + G)$. This effectively reduces the time constant of the input circuit and decreases the time required for the instrument to reach equilibrium following a change in the input signal.

A number of amplifiers using 100 per cent negative feedback have been described [6,41,42]. For example, Fig. 10–35 is a circuit diagram of a d-c electrometer which was designed by Zindler and Underwood [43]. This instrument has good stability with a full-scale sensitivity of $10^{-12}$ amp and

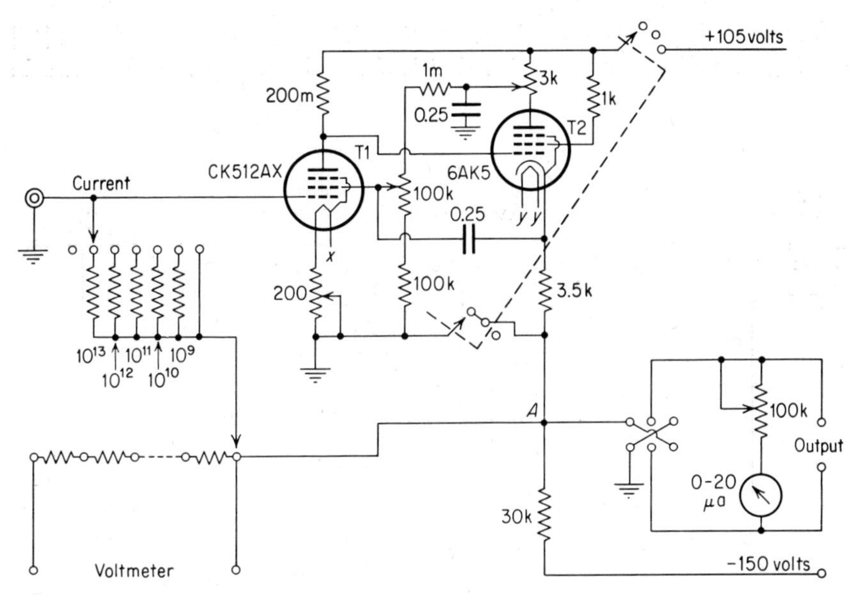


FIG. 10–35. D-C vacuum-tube electrometer employing 100 per cent negative feedback. [*From G. F. Zindler and N. Underwood, Nucleonics,* **13**:62 (*January,* 1955).]

can be used, with care, for a full-scale sensitivity of $10^{-13}$ amp. The negative feedback is applied in series with the input resistors, these being connected to the point *A* in the cathode circuit of the 6AK5. Transient negative feedback is also incorporated, by means of the 0.25-μf capacitor, from the cathode of *T*2 to the screen grid of *T*1, in order to maintain the negative-feedback characteristics under transient signal conditions.

Positive feedback is used from the plate of *T*2 to the screen grid of *T*1 in order to increase the gain of the feedback loop and thus improve the response of the system. This feedback increases the total gain in the amplifier loop by a factor of about 3.

The power supply for this electrometer is a regulated unit powered by the 110-volt–60-cycles/sec power line. This is a useful feature of a d-c electrometer since it makes it possible to operate the instrument continuously over long periods of time, thus minimizing drifts in the zero setting.

### 10–23. *Vibrating-capacitance Electrometer*

The development of the vibrating-capacitance electrometer [44] was a very important addition to the techniques of measuring small d-c currents. This instrument can be made more sensitive than the vacuum-tube electrometer by a factor of approximately 100; at the same time it provides a ready recording of the output and has a smaller zero drift than does the vacuum-tube electrometer.

The vibrating-capacitance instrument which was described by Reese [45] is a rugged and stable apparatus that is simple in concept. It is shown in

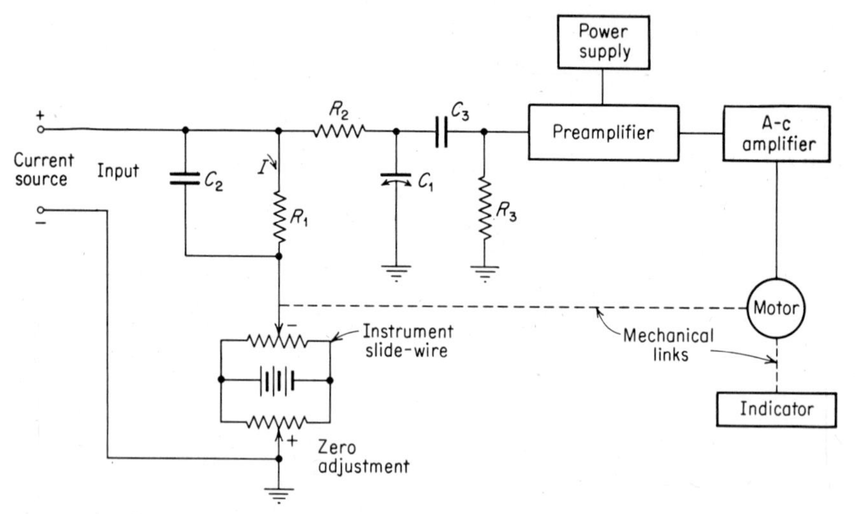


FIG. 10–36. Block diagram of a vibrating-capacitance electrometer. [*From H. Reese, Nucleonics,* **6**:40 (*March,* 1950).]

block diagram in Fig. 10–36. This electrometer is basically a null-seeking instrument in which the voltage drop due to the flow of the current $I$ through the high resistance $R_1$ is balanced out by the potentiometer indicated as the instrument slide-wire. Any error in this balance condition produces a charge $q$ on the vibrating capacitance $C_1$. The resistances $R_2$ and $R_3$ are sufficiently large that the charge on $C_1$ is essentially constant during its period of vibration, this being $\frac{1}{60}$ sec. Consequently, as $C_1$ is varied in accordance with the expression

$$C_1 = \frac{K}{D + A \sin \omega t} \tag{10–31}$$

where $D$ is the average distance between the plates and $A$ is the amplitude of the vibration, the voltage across $C_1$ follows the equation

$$v = \frac{q}{C_1} = \frac{qD}{K} + \frac{qA}{K} \sin \omega t \tag{10–32}$$

The a-c component of this error voltage is amplified by the preamplifier and the four-stage a-c amplifier.

The output of the amplifier is used to drive the two-phase balancing motor which moves the instrument slide-wire to the balance condition, thus eliminating the error signal and stopping the motor. The balancing motor also drives the indicator and the pen recorder. In fact, a Brown strip-chart recorder was used for the servo portion of this instrument as well as for the four-stage a-c amplifier.

The instrument which was described by Reese had a full-scale deflection of 10 mv on the most sensitive scale. Its zero adjust was very stable, any drifts being due primarily to variations in the contact-potential difference across the plates of the vibrating capacitor. By special design of the capacitor, this variation was kept as low as 0.5 mv over a period of months.

By employing the rate-of-drift method (see Sec. 4–11), after replacing $R_1$ by an open circuit, currents as small as $10^{-16}$ amp can be measured by the vibrating-capacitance electrometer. The lower limit on the current is set by the background currents such as those produced by mechanical stresses in the insulators which are employed in the input circuit.

The instrument which was designed by Palevsky et al. [44] is basically similar to the one just described in that it employs an a-c amplifier to amplify the signal which appears across the vibrating capacitor. However, instead of the servo system and slide-wire, it uses a phase-sensitive rectifier at the a-c amplifier output. The d-c output current operates an indicator and a recorder. The output voltage across this output circuit is fed back to the input by 100 per cent negative feedback. Since the a-c amplifier gain is large (around 1,000), the output voltage is maintained approximately equal to the input signal, as was discussed in the previous section.

Both types of vibrating-capacitance electrometers which are discussed above have the limitation that the methods of feedback which are employed do not reduce the input capacity, as was the case for the 100 per cent negative-feedback vacuum-tube electrometers. Therefore the latter-type instrument has a decided advantage with regard to speed of response. Wade and Stone [46] have described an electrometer which combines the speed of response of the d-c vacuum-tube feedback electrometer with the low zero drift of the vibrating-capacitance instrument. This electrometer contains a d-c amplifier, the output of which is fed back negatively to its input. The error voltage at its input also passes to a vibrating-capacitance amplifier. The output of this latter amplifier, after rectification and filtering, is applied to the second grid of the differentially connected input of the d-c amplifier. In effect, the vibrating-capacitance amplifier degenerates the slow drift of the d-c unit without affecting the speed of response of the system. The extremely rapid response of this instrument, combined with its good stability and low-drift characteristics, make it a useful instrument for reactor controls.

### 10–24. *Logarithmic Amplifiers*

When an instrument is required to operate over a wide range, it is often desirable that its response be logarithmic. This is particularly true if the nature of its operation makes frequent scale switching unfeasible. Logarithmic counting-rate meters were discussed in Sec. 10–17. In addition,

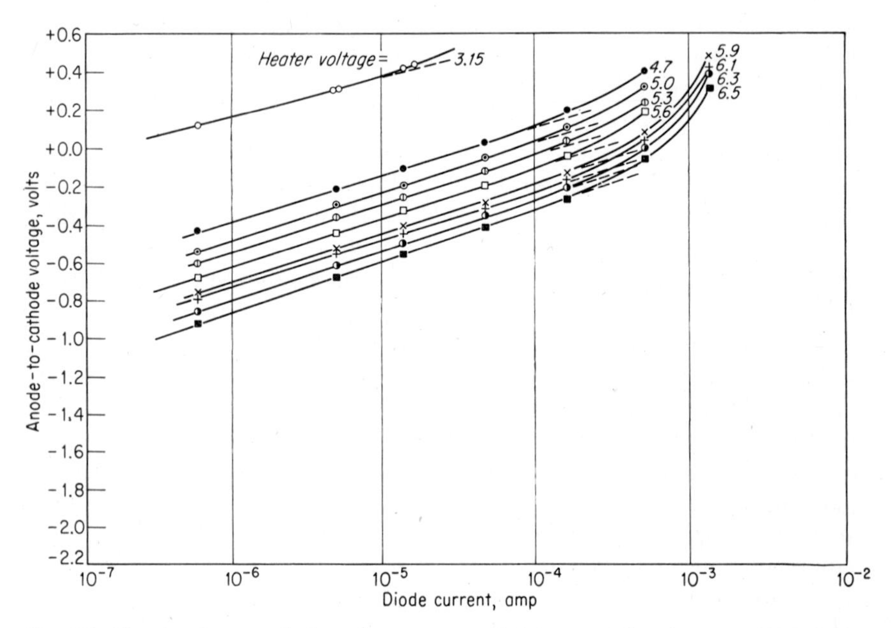


FIG. 10–37. Anode-to-cathode voltage versus diode current for the type 9004 diode; diode current range, $10^{-3}$ to $10^{-6}$ amp; heater voltages, 3.15 to 6.5 volts. (*From W. H. Jordan, H. B. Frey, and G. G. Kelley, U. S. Atomic Energy Comm. Document ORNL–110, 1948.*)

the Neher-White ionization-chamber instrument, described in Sec. 4–16, had a logarithmic response. Logarithmic instruments are particularly useful in nuclear-reactor control systems, as discussed in the next section.

The various methods of obtaining a logarithmic response were reviewed by James [47]. The methods which were considered included diodes with negative anodes, contact rectifiers, variable-mu tubes, and special slide-wires. In addition, instruments based on the nearly logarithmic relation between the voltage and gain in a photomultiplier tube have been described [48–50]. Only the diodes and the photomultiplier-tube methods are discussed in this text.

If the quantity to be measured is a current or can be transformed to a current in the range from $3 \times 10^{-14}$ to $2 \times 10^{-4}$ amp and if the current comes from a high-impedance source, an output that is proportional to the logarithm of the current can be obtained by the use of diodes with negative anodes. In Figs. 10–37 and 10–38 curves are presented [51] for the anode-to-cathode voltage versus the diode current in a type 9004 diode for various heater voltages. The currents from $10^{-6}$ to $10^{-10}$ amp are not included

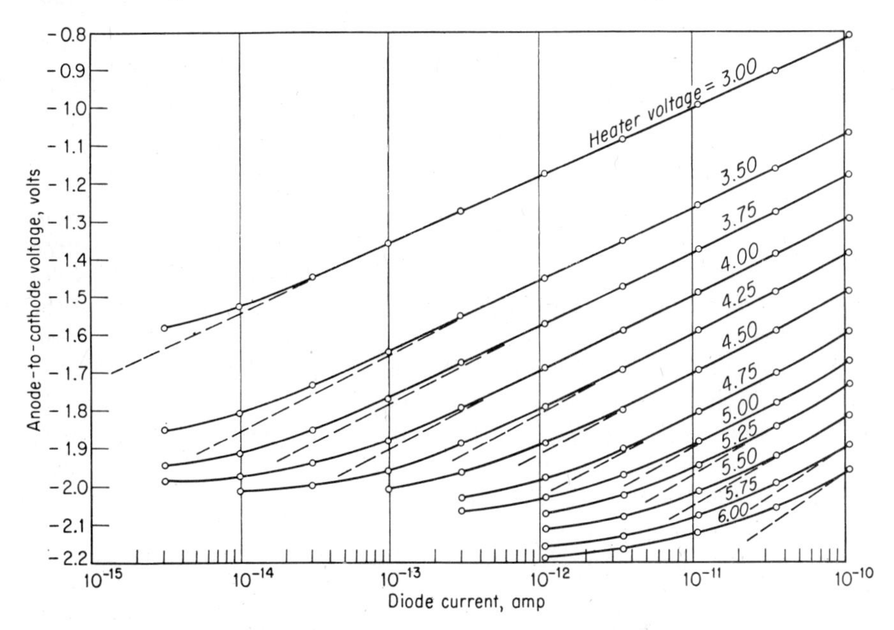


FIG. 10–38. Anode-to-cathode voltage versus diode current for the type 9004 diode; diode current range, $10^{-10}$ to $10^{-15}$ amp; heater voltages, 3.0 to 6.0 volts. (*From W. H. Jordan, H. B. Frey, and G. G. Kelley, U.S. Atomic Energy Comm. Document ORNL–110, 1948.*)

because the relationship in this range is perfectly logarithmic. The 9004, an acorn-type diode, is particularly well suited for this application since its small electrode spacing permits relatively larger anode currents, while its small internal leakage permits the measurement of small anode currents. The type 6AL5 diodes are also useful for this application, although the fraction [52] of the production tubes which have logarithmic relationships over at least six decades ($10^{-4}$ to $10^{-10}$ amp) is less than with the type 9004.

For diode currents less than $10^{-9}$ amp, the heater of the diode should be powered by direct current, and all parts of it should be below the cathode in potential. This method of operation avoids large a-c hum due to induced voltages and prevents the conduction of current directly from the heater to the plate.

An empirical equation which relates the anode-to-cathode voltage $v$ and the diode current $i$ is

$$v = A \log i + v_o \qquad (10\text{–}33)$$

For a type 9004, $A$ is 0.21 volt. The quantity $v_o$ is independent of $i$ but varies with heater voltage and also with the particular tube. Its value is about 1 volt when $i$ is expressed in amperes.

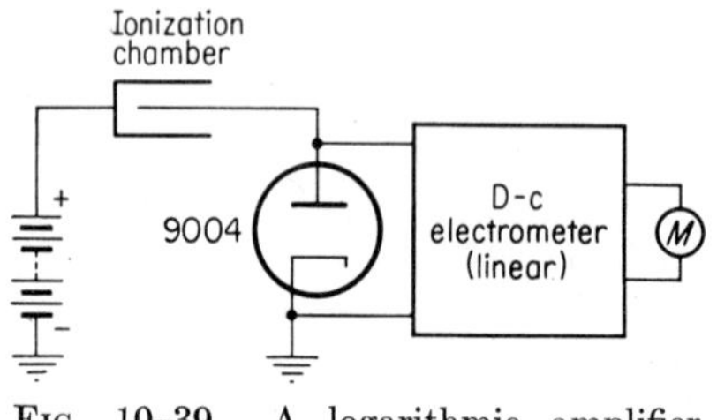


FIG. 10–39. A logarithmic amplifier using a diode.

The use of a diode in a logarithmic amplifier is illustrated in Fig. 10–39. The input current of the electrometer must be small compared with the diode current. In addition, the electrometer sensitivity must be consistent with the change in anode-to-cathode voltage, that is, 0.21 volt/decade. The zero adjustment in the electrometer may be used to adjust the output scale of the meter.

A variation of the logarithmic diode is obtained by allowing a triode grid to serve the function of the negative anode in the diode. Thus the grid voltage varies as the logarithm of the grid current. Since the triode plate current varies approximately linearly with the grid voltage, the plate current of the triode varies approximately as the logarithm of the grid current. The circuit in Fig. 4–18 illustrates this application.

Still another logarithmic amplifier [53] uses a pentode in the manner shown in Fig. 10–40. The d-c amplifier maintains the anode current of the

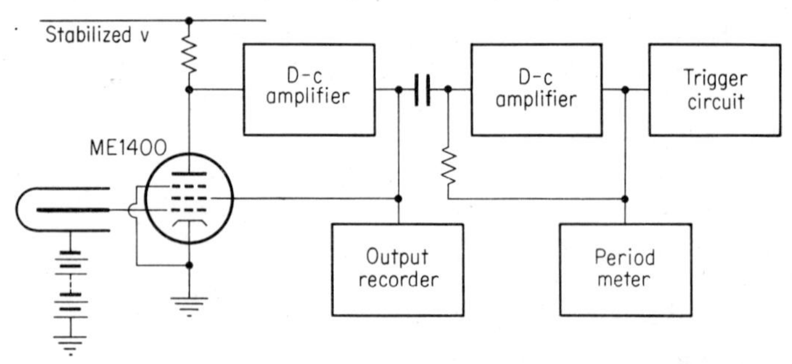


FIG. 10–40. Block diagram of a logarithmic channel for reactor instrumentation, employing a logarithmic amplifier. (*From R. J. Cox, A. B. Gillespie, and W. Abson, "Proceedings of the International Conference on the Peaceful Uses of Atomic Energy," vol. 5, p. 393, United Nations, New York,* 1956.)

amplifier constant by varying the screen-grid potential to accommodate changes in control-grid potential. The screen-grid potential varies as the logarithm of the input current, and the stability of the circuit to variations in heater supply is better than that of the single diode. With an ME.1400 (CV.432) at 200 μamp of anode current, the logarithmic characteristic extends over six decades from $5 \times 10^{-11}$ to $5 \times 10^{-5}$ amp. Alternatively, the electrometer pentode ME.1403 (CV.2348) at an anode current of 10 μamp will operate satisfactorily from $10^{-13}$ to $10^{-7}$ amp.

The relationship between the electron multiplication in a photomultiplier tube and the voltage applied to its dynodes was discussed in Chap 7. Figure 7–13 is a typical curve illustrating this function. Figure 10–41 presents the same data plotted on semilog paper. While the applied voltage is not strictly a logarithmic function of the multiplication, this is a sufficiently good approximation to be useful for these applications.

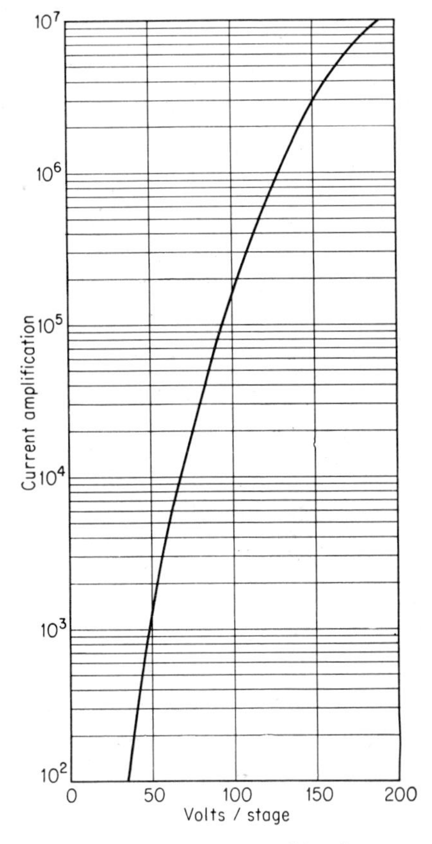


FIG. 10–41. Current amplification versus tube voltage in the Du Mont type 6292 photomultiplier tube.

A block diagram of a wide-range radiation-detection instrument [49] is shown in Fig. 10–42. The detector for this instrument is a scintillator such as an NaI crystal. The current produced in the photomultiplier by the radiation is allowed to pass through the resistor $R$ shunted by the capacitor $C$. The average value of the current is held constant by keeping the voltage drop due to it equal to the reference voltage $E_R$. Any error in the relationship energizes the servoamplifier so as to adjust the photomultiplier-tube voltage. Thus the voltage $V$ applied to the phototube is a measure of the radiation level. In this application a change of six decades in the radiation level is represented by a voltage change from 800 to 200 volts.

### 10–25. *Log n Meters and Period Meters*

The power level of a reactor varies over many orders of magnitude in passing from start-up to full power. The "log $n$ meter," so called because it measures the logarithm of the neutron density $n$, is an important component of a reactor control system which makes possible a continuous measurement of $n$ over several decades. An instrument such as that shown in the block diagram in Fig. 10–39 will serve as a log $n$ meter provided that the ionization chamber is one of the current type which is used for neutron detection, as discussed in Chap. 9. Since the ionization-chamber current $i$

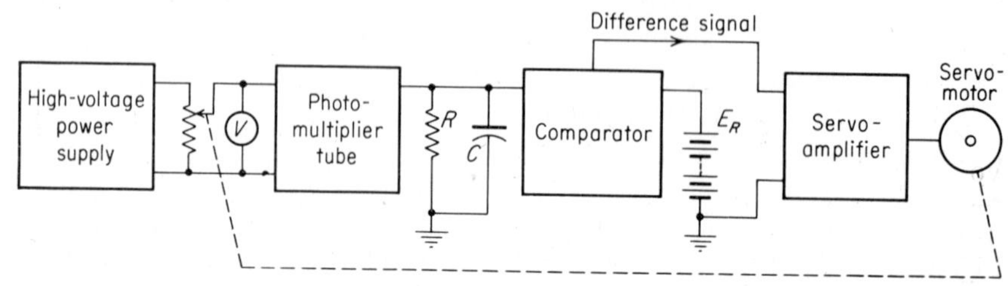


FIG. 10–42. Block diagram of a wide-range instrument employing a photomultiplier tube. [*From L. Burgwald and W. Reiffel, Nucleonics,* **11**:46 (*March,* 1953).]

is proportional to the neutron density $n$, the voltage across the diode is given by the expression

$$v = A \ln kn + v_o \tag{10–34}$$

Therefore the indication on the output meter is a logarithmic function of $n$. For very low levels, such as may occur in reactor start-up, a pulse-type neutron detector (usually a fission counter) can be employed. This detector feeding into a logarithmic counting-rate meter can function as a log $n$ meter.

An additional logarithmic instrument which is used in reactor control systems is the period meter. It measures the reactor period $T$, where $T$ is the $e$ folding time; here the reactor power is assumed to be increasing according to an exponential function of time. Since the reactor power and neutron density are proportional, the expression for $n$ is

$$n = n_o e^{t/T} \tag{10–35}$$

where $n_o$ is the neutron density at $t = 0$. If, again, a logarithmic diode is used along with a current ionization chamber, the voltage across the diode is obtained by substituting Eq. (10–35) in Eq. (10–34). This gives

$$v = \frac{At}{T} + A \ln kn_o + v_o \tag{10–36}$$

If the voltage $v$ across the diode is amplified by means of a d-c amplifier and the output $v'$ of the amplifier is applied to a differentiation network, as shown in Fig. 10–43, the current flow $i'$ through the output meter $M$ is

$$i' = C\frac{dv'}{dt} + i_o e^{-t/RC} \tag{10–37}$$

where $i_o$ is a constant, the value of which depends on the initial conditions in the output circuit. Neglecting the transient term and substituting $Gv$ for $v'$, where $G$ is the amplifier gain and $v$ is given by Eq. (10–36), one has

$$i' = \frac{GAC}{T} = \frac{k'}{T} \tag{10-38}$$

Thus the current through the output meter is inversely proportional to the period $T$, and the scale of the meter can be calibrated to read the period directly.

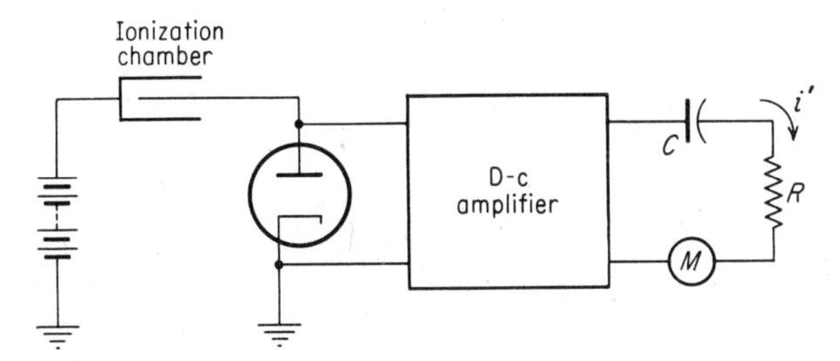


FIG. 10–43. Block diagram of a period meter.

The time constant $RC$ is an important parameter in the design [51] of a period meter. If it is too large, the transient term dies out too slowly, and the instrument does not respond quickly enough to changes in periods. On the other hand, making the time constant too small increases the relative importance of the transient current which is produced by sudden changes in output voltage. It has been shown [51] that the ratio of the current $i'$ due to a period $T$ to $i'_t$, the transient current due to a step change in power from $P_o$ to $P$, is

$$\frac{i'}{i'_t} = \frac{RC}{T \ln(P/P_o)} \tag{10-39}$$

Thus, if the time constant $RC$ is 1 sec, a jump in power level by a factor of $e$ would produce a transient signal equal to that due to a 1-sec period.

Figure 10–44 is a circuit diagram of a combination log $n$ and period meter [51] which is based on the principles that were discussed above. The logarithmic diode is a type 9004. The d-c amplifier employs three stages with negative feedback between the cathodes of the first and last stages to stabilize the gain and to improve the linearity. The quantity log $n$ may be read on the meter $M_2$ or on a 10-mv recorder connected to $J_5$.

Two derivative circuits are provided for indicating the period. The first is for measuring periods from 50 to 3 sec, the 3-sec period producing a full-scale deflection on the 100-$\mu$amp meter $M_1$ or on the recorder connected to $J_1$. The time constant $R_{17}C_1$ of this circuit is 1 sec. The second derivative circuit has a 0.1-sec time constant and produces a 100-$\mu$amp current with a 0.3-sec period. The biased diodes $V_5$ and $V_6$ are connected across each derivative circuit to protect the meters against large transients such as those produced by turning on or off the equipment.

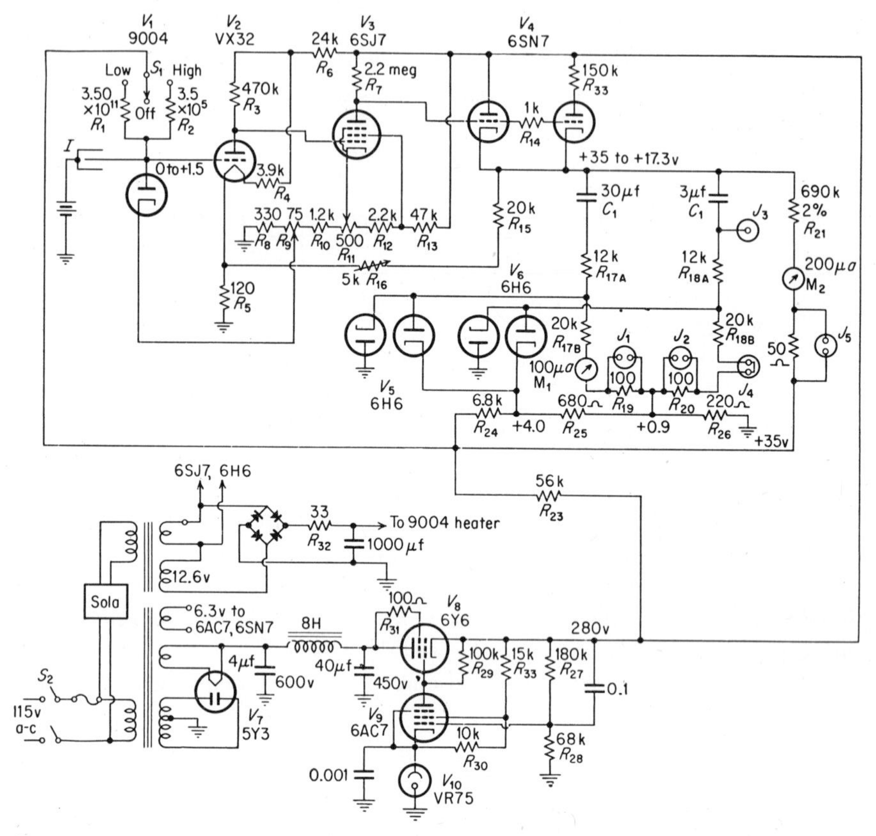


FIG. 10–44. Circuit diagram of a log-$n$–period meter. (*From W. H. Jordan, H. B. Frey, and G. G. Kelley, U.S. Atomic Energy Comm. Document ORNL*-110, 1948.)

Connor et al. [50] have described a logarithmic-level–period meter for reactor control which is based on the photomultiplier-tube logarithmic characteristics described in the last section. Either a gamma-sensitive or a neutron-sensitive scintillator may be employed with the photomultiplier tube. In this instrument, as well as in the one shown in Fig. 10–42, the voltage which is applied to the photomultiplier tube is varied so that the anode current which the nuclear radiation produces is held constant. The high voltage which is applied to the photomultiplier tube is made self-adjusting through the action of an electronic regulator circuit that is incorporated in the meter. The logarithm of the reactor level is given by a voltmeter which is connected directly across the photomultiplier-tube high-voltage circuit. The reactor period is given by differentiation circuits which are connected across the same portion of the circuit.

The photomultiplier logarithmic-level–period meter has proved to be highly satisfactory. Instrument drift in the level output information is negligible, and the stability of the period information is reported [50] to be at least an order of magnitude better than that of a logarithmic diode period meter. The increased stability of the instrument is partially due to the much larger voltage change per decade change in the input signal.

## PROBLEMS

**10–1.** A parallel-plate ionization chamber containing argon at 1 atm of pressure is used to count alpha particles. Compute the time for a pulse to reach (*a*) one-half of its final value and (*b*) its final value, if the applied voltage is 200 volts, the plate spacing is 2 cm, and the path of the alpha particles is parallel to the chamber plates.

**10–2.** Consider an idealized pulse amplifier with an integration time constant of 2 $\mu$sec and a differentiation time constant of 10 $\mu$sec. Compute the following characteristics of the amplifier: rise time, delay time, clipping time, and pulse duration.

**10–3.** A counting-rate meter with a time constant of 10 sec is used to measure an average counting rate of about 500 counts/min. Compute the standard error of an instantaneous reading and of a mean taken over a 2-min interval. In addition, estimate the time required for the instrument to reach essentially equilibrium as the tank capacitor charges up after a large increase in the counting rate.

**10–4.** Describe in detail one type of multichannel pulse-height analyzer.

**10–5.** Explain how coincidence measurements can be used to measure the absolute activity of a radioactive source (see Ref. 32). What are the requirements of the source for this method to be applicable?

**10–6.** Draw the schematic diagram in block form for a log $n$ meter employing a type 9004 diode (see Figs. 10–37 and 10–38), to read the output of a PCP neutron chamber. Specify the flux range to be covered and indicate the sensitivity that is required for the voltmeter.

## REFERENCES

1. Elmore, W. C., H. Kallman, and C. E. Mandeville: *Nucleonics*, **8**:S-3 (June, 1951).
2. Lewis, I. A. D., and F. H. Wells: "Millimicrosecond Pulse Techniques," chap. 7, McGraw-Hill Book Company, Inc., New York, 1954.
3. Elmore, W. C.: *Nucleonics*, **2**:16 (March, 1948); **2**:4 (February, 1948).
4. Damon, P. E., and P. N. Winters: *Nucleonics*, **12**:36 (December, 1954).
5. Gillespie, A. B.: "Signal, Noise and Resolution in Nuclear Counter Amplifiers," chap. 2, McGraw-Hill Book Company, Inc., New York, 1953.
6. Elmore, W. C., and M. Sands: "Electronics," chap. 4, National Nuclear Energy Series, div. V, vol. 1, McGraw-Hill Book Company, Inc., New York, 1949.
7. Lewis, I. A. D., and F. H. Wells: "Millimicrosecond Pulse Techniques," chap. 5, McGraw-Hill Book Company, Inc., New York, 1954.
8. Jordan, W. H., and P. R. Bell: *Rev. Sci. Instr.*, **18**:703 (1947).
9. Chase, R. L., and W. A. Higinbotham: *Rev. Sci. Instr.*, **23**:34 (1952).
10. Von Tersch, L. W., and A. W. Swago: "Recurrent Electrical Transients," chap. 8, Prentice-Hall, Inc., Englewood Cliffs, N.J., 1953.

11. Eccles, W. H., and F. W. Jordan: *Radio Rev.*, **1**:143 (1919).
12. Van Rennes, A. B.: *Nucleonics*, **10**:20 (July, 1952).
13. Van Rennes, A. B.: *Nucleonics*, **10**:22 (August, 1952).
14. Van Rennes, A. B.: *Nucleonics*, **10**:32 (September, 1952).
15. Van Rennes, A. B.: *Nucleonics*, **10**:50 (October, 1952).
16. Kelley, G. G.: "Proceedings of the International Conference on the Peaceful Uses of Atomic Energy," vol. 14, p. 260, United Nations, New York, 1956.
17. Moody, N. F., W. D. Howell, W. J. Battell, and R. H. Taplin: *Rev. Sci. Instr.*, **22**:439 (1951).
18. Isbin, H. S.: *Nucleonics*, **10**:10 (March, 1952); **10**:65 (June, 1952).
19. Guggenheim, E. A., and M. H. L. Pryce: *Nucleonics*, **11**:49 (February, 1953).
20. Baker, J. C., and G. G. Eichholz: *Nucleonics*, **12**:44 (April, 1954).
21. Bacon, R. C., and J. R. Pollard: *Electronic Eng.*, **22**:173 (1950).
22. Acton, J. R.: *Electronic Eng.*, **24**:48 (1952).
23. Jonkers, J. L. H., A. J. van Overbeck, and P. H. de Beurs: *Philips Research Repts.*, **7**:81 (1952).
24. Cooke-Yarborough, E. H.: *Proc. Inst. Elec. Engrs.*, (*London*), **98** (pt. 2):191 (1951).
25. Kip, A., A. Bouquet, R. Evans, and W. Tuttle: *Rev. Sci. Instr.*, **17**:323 (1946).
26. Stone, R. S., and E. J. Wade: *U.S. Atomic Energy Comm. Document* KAPL-1237, 1954.
27. LeVine, H.: *Nucleonics*, **12**:36 (February, 1954).
28. Cooke-Yarborough, E. H.: *Proc. Inst. Elec. Engrs.* (*London*), **98** (pt. 2):196 (1951).
29. Shaw, D., and R. N. Weltmann: *Rev. Sci. Instr.*, **23**:528 (1952).
30. Burgess, R. E.: *Rev. Sci. Instr.*, **20**:964 (1949).
31. Schiff, L. I., and R. D. Evans: *Rev. Sci. Instr.*, **7**:456 (1936).
32. Bleuler, E., and G. J. Goldsmith: "Experimental Nucleonics," chaps. 22–24, Rinehart & Company, Inc., New York, 1952.
33. Bell, R. E.: *Ann. Rev. Nuclear Sci.*, **4**:93 (1954).
34. Bothe, W.: *Z. Physik*, **59**:1 (1930).
35. Fischer, J., and J. Marshall: *Rev. Sci. Instr.*, **23**:417 (1952).
36. Chen, T. C.: *Proc. IRE*, **38**:511 (1950).
37. Bay, Z.: *Rev. Sci. Instr.*, **22**:397 (1951).
38. Bay, Z.: *Phys. Rev.*, **83**:242 (1951).
39. Bay, Z., H. R. Meijer, and G. Papp: *Nucleonics*, **10**:39 (March, 1952).
40. Bay, Z., M. R. Cleland, and F. McLernon: *Phys. Rev.*, **87**:90 (1952).
41. Roberts, S.: *Rev. Sci. Instr.*, **10**:181 (1939).
42. Dowben, R. M.: *Rev. Sci. Instr.*, **23**:506 (1952).
43. Zindler, G. F., and N. Underwood: *Nucleonics*, **13**:62 (January, 1955).
44. Palevsky, H., R. K. Swank, and R. Crenchik: *Rev. Sci. Instr.*, **18**:298 (1947).
45. Reese, H.: *Nucleonics*, **6**:40 (March, 1950).
46. Wade, E. J., and R. S. Stone: *Nucleonics*, **13**:28 (April, 1955).
47. James, W. G.: *U.S. Atomic Energy Comm. Document* ORNL-413, 1949.
48. Sweet, M. H.: *Electronics*, **19**:105 (November, 1946); *Nucleonics*, **11**:68 (August, 1953).
49. Burgwald, L., and W. Reiffel: *Nucleonics*, **11**:46 (March, 1953).
50. Connor, J. C., R. G. Durnal, and V. G. Shaw: *Nucleonics*, **11**:71 (November, 1953).
51. Jordan, W. H., H. B. Frey, and G. G. Kelley: *U.S. Atomic Energy Comm. Document* ORNL-110, 1948.
52. Johnstone, C. W.: *U.S. Atomic Energy Comm. Document* AECU-363, 1949.
53. Cox, R. J., A. B. Gillespie, and W. Abson: "Proceedings of the International Conference on the Peaceful Uses of Atomic Energy," vol. 5, p. 393, United Nations, New York, 1956.

# INDEX